Microsoft Exam Objectives
Exam 70-216: Implementing and Administering a Microsoft Windows 2000 Network Infrastructure

Installing, Configuring, Managing, Monitoring, and Troubleshooting DNS in a Windows 2000 Network Infrastructure	Chapter
Install, configure, and troubleshoot DNS.	6
Install the DNS Server service.	6
Configure a root name server, zones, a caching-only server, and zones for dynamic updates.	7
Configure a DNS client	6
Test the DNS Server service.	6
Implement a delegated zone for DNS.	7
Manually create DNS resource records.	7
Manage and monitor DNS.	6

Installing, Configuring, Managing, Monitoring, and Troubleshooting DHCP in a Windows 2000 Network Infrastructure	Chapter
Install, configure, and troubleshoot DHCP.	5
Install the DHCP Server service.	5
Create and manage DHCP scopes, superscopes, and multicast scopes.	5
Configure DHCP for DNS integration.	5
Authorize a DHCP server in Active Directory.	5
Manage and monitor DHCP.	5

Configuring, Managing, Monitoring, and Troubleshooting Remote Access in a Windows 2000 Network Infrastructure	Chapter
Configure and troubleshoot remote access.	11
Configure inbound connections and create a remote access policy.	11
Configure a remote access profile, a virtual private network (VPN), multilink connections, Routing and Remote Access for DHCP Integration, remote access security, authentication protocols, and encryption protocols.	11
Manage and monitor remote access.	11

Installing, Configuring, Managing, Monitoring, and Troubleshooting Network Protocols in a Windows 2000 Network Infrastructure	Chapter(s)
Install, configure, and troubleshoot network protocols.	4
Install and configure TCP/IP.	4
Install the NWLink protocol.	4
Configure network bindings and TCP/IP packet filters.	4
Configure and troubleshoot network protocol security and IPSec.	4
Manage and monitor network traffic and IPSec.	4
Enable IPSec and configure IPSec for transport mode and tunnel mode.	4, 5
Customize IPSec policies and rules.	4

Installing, Configuring, Managing, Monitoring, and Troubleshooting WINS in a Windows 2000 Network Infrastructure	Chapter
Install, configure, and troubleshoot WINS.	8
Configure WINS replication and Configure NetBIOS name resolution.	8
Manage and monitor WINS.	8

Installing, Configuring, Managing, Monitoring, and Troubleshooting IP Routing in a Windows 2000 Network Infrastructure	Chapter
Install, configure, and troubleshoot IP routing protocols.	9
Update a Windows 2000-based routing table by means of static routes.	9
Implement Demand-Dial Routing.	9
Manage and monitor IP routing, border routing, internal routing, and IP routing protocols.	9
Installing, Configuring, and Troubleshooting Network Address Translation (NAT)	10
Install Internet Connection Sharing and NAT.	10
Configure NAT properties and NAT interfaces.	10

Installing, Configuring, Managing, Monitoring, and Troubleshooting Certificate Services	Chapter
Install and configure Certificate Authority (CA).	13
Issue and revoke certificates.	13
Remove the Encrypting File System (EFS) recovery keys.	13

MCSE™
Windows® 2000
Network

Tammy Smith
Sandra Smeeton

MCSE™ Windows® 2000 Network Exam Prep

Limits of Liability and Disclaimer of Warranty

The author and publisher of this book have used their best efforts in preparing the book and the programs contained in it. These efforts include the development, research, and testing of the theories and programs to determine their effectiveness. The author and publisher make no warranty of any kind, expressed or implied, with regard to these programs or the documentation contained in this book.

The author and publisher shall not be liable in the event of incidental or consequential damages in connection with, or arising out of, the furnishing, performance, or use of the programs, associated instructions, and/or claims of productivity gains.

Trademarks

Trademarked names appear throughout this book. Rather than list the names and entities that own the trademarks or insert a trademark symbol with each mention of the trademarked name, the publisher states that it is using the names for editorial purposes only and to the benefit of the trademark owner, with no intention of infringing upon that trademark.

The Coriolis Group, LLC
14455 N. Hayden Road, Suite 220
Scottsdale, Arizona 85260

(480)483-0192
FAX (480)483-0193
www.coriolis.com

Library of Congress Cataloging-in-Publication Data
Smith, Tammy.
    MCSE Windows 2000 network exam prep / by Tammy Smith and Sandra Smeeton.
        p.   cm.
    ISBN 1-57610-643-8
    1. Electronic data processing personnel--Certification.   2. Computer networks--Examinations--Study guides.   3. Microsoft Windows (Computer file)   I. Smeeton, Sandra.   II. Title.

QA76.3 .S62 2000
005.7'13769--dc21
                                                    00-060295
                                                    CIP

President and CEO
Keith Weiskamp

Publisher
Steve Sayre

Acquisitions Editor
Shari Jo Hehr

Development Editor
Deborah Doorley

Product Marketing Manager
Brett Woolley

Project Editor
Tom Lamoureux

Technical Reviewer
George Sparks

Production Coordinator
Todd Halvorsen

Cover Designer
Jesse Dunn

Layout Designer
April Nielsen

CD-ROM Developer
Michelle McConnell

Printed in the United States of America
10 9 8 7 6 5 4 3 2 1

The Coriolis Group, LLC • 14455 North Hayden Road, Suite 220 • Scottsdale, Arizona 85260

ExamCram.com Connects You to the Ultimate Study Center!

Our goal has always been to provide you with the best study tools on the planet to help you achieve your certification in record time. Time is so valuable these days that none of us can afford to waste a second of it, especially when it comes to exam preparation.

Over the past few years, we've created an extensive line of *Exam Cram* and *Exam Prep* study guides, practice exams, and interactive training. To help you study even better, we have now created an e-learning and certification destination called **ExamCram.com**. (You can access the site at **www.examcram.com**.) Now, with every study product you purchase from us, you'll be connected to a large community of people like yourself who are actively studying for their certifications, developing their careers, seeking advice, and sharing their insights and stories.

I believe that the future is all about collaborative learning. Our **ExamCram.com** destination is our approach to creating a highly interactive, easily accessible collaborative environment, where you can take practice exams and discuss your experiences with others, sign up for features like "Questions of the Day," plan your certifications using our interactive planners, create your own personal study pages, and keep up with all of the latest study tips and techniques.

I hope that whatever study products you purchase from us—*Exam Cram* or *Exam Prep* study guides, *Personal Trainers*, *Personal Test Centers*, or one of our interactive Web courses—will make your studying fun and productive. Our commitment is to build the kind of learning tools that will allow you to study the way you want to, whenever you want to.

Help us continue to provide the very best certification study materials possible. Write us or email us at **learn@examcram.com** and let us know how our study products have helped you study. Tell us about new features that you'd like us to add. Send us a story about how we've helped you. We're listening!

Visit *ExamCram.com* now to enhance your study program.

Good luck with your certification exam and your career. Thank you for allowing us to help you achieve your goals.

Keith Weiskamp

Keith Weiskamp
President and CEO

Look for these other products from The Coriolis Group:

MCSE Windows 2000 Accelerated Exam Prep
By Lance Cockcroft, Erik Eckel, and Ron Kauffman

MCSE Windows 2000 Server Exam Prep
By David Johnson and Dawn Rader

MCSE Windows 2000 Professional Exam Prep
By Michael D. Stewart, James Bloomingdale, and Neall Alcott

MCSE Windows 2000 Directory Services Exam Prep
By David V. Watts, Will Willis, and Tillman Strahan

MCSE Windows 2000 Security Design Exam Prep
By Richard Alan McMahon and Glen Bicking

MCSE Windows 2000 Network Design Exam Prep
By Geoffrey Alexander, Anoop Jalan, and Joseph Alexander

MCSE Windows 2000 Directory Services Design Exam Prep
By J. Peter Bruzzese and Wayne Dipchan

MCSE Migrating from NT 4 to Windows 2000 Exam Prep
By Glen Bergen, Graham Leach, and David Baldwin

MCSE Windows 2000 Core Four Exam Prep Pack

MCSE Windows 2000 Network Exam Cram
By Hank Carbeck, Derek Melber, and Richard Taylor

MCSE Windows 2000 Server Exam Cram
By Natasha Knight

MCSE Windows 2000 Professional Exam Cram
By Dan Balter, Dan Holme, Todd Logan, and Laurie Salmon

MCSE Windows 2000 Directory Services Exam Cram
By Will Willis, David V. Watts, and J. Peter Bruzzese

MCSE Windows 2000 Security Design Exam Cram
By Phillip G. Schein

MCSE Windows 2000 Network Design Exam Cram
By Kim Simmons, Jarret W. Buse, and Todd B. Halpin

MCSE Windows 2000 Directory Services Design Exam Cram
By Dennis Scheil and Diana Bartley

MCSE Windows 2000 Core Four Exam Cram Pack

and...

MCSE Windows 2000 Foundations
By James Michael Stewart and Lee Scales

This book is dedicated to James Fisher, our subject matter expert (SME),
without whom this book would not have been possible
and with gratitude and appreciation to those friends from whom we have learned so much
with the hope that others may learn a little from us.
—Tammy Smith and Sandra Smeeton

❧

Loving thanks and appreciation to my family, Rick, Becky, Adam and Samantha
for allowing me the opportunity to write this book
and for their continued support and understanding of my pursuit for technical knowledge.
—Tammy Smith

❧

I would like to dedicate this book to the memory of my father.
Without his love and encouragement I would not have had the courage to take on such an endeavor.
I would also like to dedicate this book to my mother, sister and stepfather
for their support and encouragement of my career.
—Sandra Smeeton

❧

About the Authors

Tammy Smith lives in the village of Whitney Point, NY with her husband Richard and three children. She is currently employed as a Technical Trainer at Ridley-Lowell Business and Technical Institute, a Microsoft Certified Solution Provider (MCSP) and a Microsoft Certified Technical Education Center (CTEC). Tammy is a Microsoft Certified Professional (MCP), a Microsoft Certified Systems Engineer (MCSE), and a Microsoft Certified Trainer (MCT). She is Network + certified, and recently became a Certified Internet Webmaster Certified Instructor (CIWCI). Tammy earned a Bachelor of Science (Computer Science) degree in August 1997 from Binghamton University where she is currently pursuing her Masters in Computer Science. Tammy is a member of ACM and Upsilon Pi Epsilon (Computer Science Honor Society) and while she was employed as a Senior Associate Software Engineer at Lockheed Martin, she completed a Silicon University training program. Tammy holds a New York State teaching permit in Networking, Operating Systems, Internet and Programming.

Sandra Smeeton lives in Binghamton, NY and is employed at Ridley-Lowell Business and Technical Institute, a Microsoft Certified Solution Provider (MCSP) and a Microsoft Certified Technical Education Center (CTEC). Sandra is the Administrator of the Networking and Technical Support Specialist Program as well as a CTEC Administrator. Sandra received her A+ Certification in April of 2000. She graduated from Bloomsburg University in 1995 with a Bachelors of Science in Business Education, and a minor in Office Administration and Data Processing. Sandi has provided technical training for over five years. Sandra holds a New York State teaching permit in Hardware, Operating Systems, Internet and Applications.

Acknowledgments

Special thanks to Diane Bates for her guidance and inspiration in starting this book and her technical assistance with DNS, to Lesha Camille Haight for her hard work and dedication in writing review questions, and to David Hiner for his research and development of case studies.

—*Tammy Smith and Sandra Smeeton*

Contents at a Glance

Table of Contents

Chapter 3
Network Protocols 89

Chapter 4
Dynamic Host Configuration Protocol 123

Chapter 5
Domain Name System (DNS) 157

Chapter 8
IP Routing 275

Chapter 9
Multicasting and Network Address Translation 303

Chapter 11
Security 351

Chapter 13
File, Web, and Print Services 401

Chapter 14
Troubleshooting 425

Exam Insights

Welcome to *MCSE Windows 2000 Network Exam Prep!* This book aims to help you get ready to take—and pass—Microsoft certification Exam 70-216, titled "Implementing and Administering a Microsoft Windows 2000 Network Infrastructure." This Exam Insights section discusses exam preparation resources, the testing situation, Microsoft's certification programs in general, and how this book can help you prepare for Microsoft's Windows 2000 certification exams.

Exam Prep study guides help you understand and appreciate the subjects and materials you need to pass Microsoft certification exams. We've worked from Microsoft's curriculum objectives to ensure that all key topics are clearly explained. Our aim is to bring together as much information as possible about Microsoft certification exams.

Nevertheless, to completely prepare yourself for any Microsoft test, we recommend that you begin by taking the Self-Assessment included in this book immediately following this Exam Insights section. This tool will help you evaluate your knowledge base against the requirements for an MCSE under both ideal and real circumstances.

Based on what you learn from that exercise, you might decide to begin your studies with some classroom training or some background reading. You might decide to read The Coriolis Group's *Exam Prep* book that you have in hand first, or you might decide to start with another study approach. You may also want to refer to one of a number of study guides available from Microsoft or third-party vendors. We also recommend that you supplement your study program with visits to **ExamCram.com** to receive additional practice questions, get advice, and track the Windows 2000 MCSE program.

We also strongly recommend that you install, configure, and fool around with the software that you'll be tested on, because nothing beats hands-on experience and familiarity when it comes to understanding the questions you're likely to encounter on a certification test. Book learning is essential, but hands-on experience is the best teacher of all!

How to Prepare for an Exam

Preparing for any Windows 2000 Server-related test (including "Implementing and Administering a Microsoft Windows 2000 Network Infrastructure") requires that you obtain and study materials designed to provide comprehensive information about the product and its capabilities that will appear on the specific exam for which you are preparing. The following list of materials will help you study and prepare:

➤ The Windows 2000 Server product CD includes comprehensive online documentation and related materials; it should be a primary resource when you are preparing for the test.

➤ The exam preparation materials, practice tests, and self-assessment exams on the Microsoft Training & Services page at **www.microsoft.com/ trainingandservices/default.asp?PageID=mcp**. The Testing Innovations link offers samples of the new question types found on the Windows 2000 MCSE exams. Find the materials, download them, and use them!

➤ The exam preparation advice, practice tests, questions of the day, and discussion groups on the **ExamCram.com** e-learning and certification destination Web site (**www.examcram.com**).

In addition, you'll probably find any or all of the following materials useful in your quest for Windows 2000 Network Infrastructure expertise:

➤ *Microsoft training kits*—Microsoft Press offers training kits that specifically target the exams. For more information, visit: **http://mspress.microsoft.com/ findabook/list/series_ak.htm**. This training kit contains information that you will find useful in preparing for the test.

➤ *Microsoft TechNet CD*—This monthly CD-based publication delivers numerous electronic titles that include coverage of Windows 2000 Network Infrastructure and related topics on the Technical Information (TechNet) CD. Its offerings include product facts, technical notes, tools and utilities, and information on how to access the Seminars Online training materials for Windows 2000 Network Infrastructure. A subscription to TechNet costs $299 per year, but it is well worth the price. Visit **www.microsoft.com/technet/** and check out the information under the "TechNet Subscription" menu entry for more details.

➤ *Study guides*—Several publishers—including The Coriolis Group—offer Windows 2000 titles. The Coriolis Group series includes the following:

  ➤ *The Exam Cram series*—These books give you information about the material you need to know to pass the tests.

➤ *The Exam Prep series*—These books provide a greater level of detail than the *Exam Cram* books and are designed to teach you everything you need to know from an exam perspective. Each book comes with a CD that contains interactive practice exams in a variety of testing formats.

Together, the two series make a perfect pair.

➤ *Multimedia*—These Coriolis Group materials are designed to support learners of all types—whether you learn best by reading or doing:

➤ *The Exam Cram Personal Trainer*—Offers a unique, personalized self-paced training course based on the exam.

➤ *The Exam Cram Personal Test Center*—Features multiple test options that simulate the actual exam, including Fixed-Length, Random, Review, and Test All. Explanations of correct and incorrect answers reinforce concepts learned.

➤ *Classroom training*—CTECs, online partners, and third-party training companies (like Wave Technologies, Learning Tree, Data-Tech, and others) all offer classroom training on TCP/IP. These companies aim to help you prepare to pass the TCP/IP test. Although such training runs upwards of $350 per day in class, most of the individuals lucky enough to partake find them to be quite worthwhile.

➤ *Other publications*—There's no shortage of materials available about Windows 2000 Network Infrastructure. The complete resource section in the back of the book should give you an idea of where we think you should look for further discussion.

By far, this set of required and recommended materials represents a nonpareil collection of sources and resources for Windows 2000 Network Infrastructure and related topics. We anticipate that you'll find that this book belongs in this company.

Taking a Certification Exam

Once you've prepared for your exam, you need to register with a testing center. Each computer-based MCP exam costs $100, and if you don't pass, you may retest for an additional $100 for each additional try. In the United States and Canada, tests are administered by Prometric (formerly Sylvan Prometric), and by Virtual University Enterprises (VUE). Here's how you can contact them:

➤ *Prometric*—You can sign up for a test through the company's Web site at **www.prometric.com**. Or, you can register by phone at 800-755-3926 (within the United States or Canada) or at 410-843-8000 (outside the United States and Canada).

➤ *Virtual University Enterprises*—You can sign up for a test or get the phone numbers for local testing centers through the Web page at **www.vue.com/ms/**.

To sign up for a test, you must possess a valid credit card, or contact either company for mailing instructions to send them a check (in the U.S.). Only when payment is verified, or a check has cleared, can you actually register for a test.

To schedule an exam, call the number or visit either of the Web pages at least one day in advance. To cancel or reschedule an exam, you must call before 7 P.M. pacific standard time the day before the scheduled test time (or you may be charged, even if you don't appear to take the test). When you want to schedule a test, have the following information ready:

➤ Your name, organization, and mailing address.

➤ Your Microsoft Test ID. (Inside the United States, this means your Social Security number; citizens of other nations should call ahead to find out what type of identification number is required to register for a test.)

➤ The name and number of the exam you wish to take.

➤ A method of payment. (As we've already mentioned, a credit card is the most convenient method, but alternate means can be arranged in advance, if necessary.)

Once you sign up for a test, you'll be informed as to when and where the test is scheduled. Try to arrive at least 15 minutes early.

The Exam Situation

When you arrive at the testing center where you scheduled your exam, you'll need to sign in with an exam coordinator. He or she will ask you to show two forms of identification, one of which must be a photo ID. After you've signed in and your time slot arrives, you'll be asked to deposit any books, bags, or other items you brought with you. Then, you'll be escorted into a closed room.

All exams are completely closed book. In fact, you will not be permitted to take anything with you into the testing area, but you will be furnished with a blank sheet of paper and a pen or, in some cases, an erasable plastic sheet and an erasable pen. Before the exam, you should memorize as much of the important material as you can, so you can write that information on the blank sheet as soon as you are seated in front of the computer. You can refer to this piece of paper anytime you like during the test, but you'll have to surrender the sheet when you leave the room. You will have some time to compose yourself and record this information before you begin the exam.

Typically, the room will be furnished with anywhere from one to half a dozen computers, and each workstation will be separated from the others by dividers designed to keep you from seeing what's happening on someone else's computer.

Most test rooms feature a wall with a large picture window. This permits the exam coordinator to monitor the room, to prevent exam-takers from talking to one another, and to observe anything out of the ordinary that might go on. The exam coordinator will have preloaded the appropriate Microsoft certification exam—for this book, that's Exam 70-216—and you'll be permitted to start as soon as you're seated in front of the computer.

All Microsoft certification exams allow a certain maximum amount of time in which to complete your work (this time is indicated on the exam by an on-screen counter/clock, so you can check the time remaining whenever you like). All Microsoft certification exams are computer generated. In addition to multiple choice, you'll encounter select and place (drag and drop), create a tree (categorization and prioritization), drag and connect, and build list and reorder (list prioritization) on most exams. Although this may sound quite simple, the questions are constructed not only to check your mastery of basic facts and figures about Windows 2000 Network Infrastructure, but they also require you to evaluate one or more sets of circumstances or requirements. Often, you'll be asked to give more than one answer to a question. Likewise, you might be asked to select the best or most effective solution to a problem from a range of choices, all of which technically are correct. Taking the exam is quite an adventure, and it involves real thinking. This book shows you what to expect and how to deal with the potential problems, puzzles, and predicaments.

When you complete a Microsoft certification exam, the software will tell you whether you've passed or failed. If you need to retake an exam, you'll have to schedule a new test with Prometric or VUE and pay another $100.

Note: *The first time you fail a test, you can retake the test the next day. However, if you fail a second time, you must wait 14 days before retaking that test. The 14-day waiting period remains in effect for all retakes after the second failure.*

In the next section, you'll learn more about how Microsoft test questions look and how they must be answered.

Exam Layout and Design

The format of Microsoft's Windows 2000 exams is different from that of its previous exams. For the design exams (70-219, 70-220, 70-221), each exam consists entirely of a series of case studies, and the questions can be of six types. For the Core Four exams (70-210, 70-215, 70-216, 70-217), the same six types of questions can appear, but you are not likely to encounter complex multiquestion case studies.

For design exams, each case study or "testlet" presents a detailed problem that you must read and analyze. Figure 1 shows an example of what a case study looks like. You must select the different tabs in the case study to view the entire case.

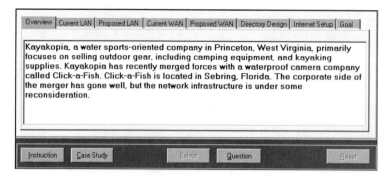

Figure 1   This is how case studies appear.

Following each case study is a set of questions related to the case study; these questions can be one of six types (which are discussed next). Careful attention to details provided in the case study is the key to success. Be prepared to toggle frequently between the case study and the questions as you work. Some of the case studies also include diagrams, which are called *exhibits*, that you'll need to examine closely to understand how to answer the questions.

Once you complete a case study, you can review all the questions and your answers. However, once you move on to the next case study, you may not be able to return to the previous case study and make any changes.

The six types of question formats are:

➤ Multiple choice, single answer

➤ Multiple choice, multiple answers

➤ Build list and reorder (list prioritization)

➤ Create a tree

➤ Drag and connect

➤ Select and place (drag and drop)

Note: *Exam formats may vary by test center location. You may want to call the test center or visit **ExamCram.com** to see if you can find out which type of test you'll encounter.*

Multiple-Choice Question Format

Some exam questions require you to select a single answer, whereas others ask you to select multiple correct answers. The following multiple-choice question requires you to select a single correct answer. Following the question is a brief summary of each potential answer and why it is either right or wrong.

Question 1

A request is sent to an SNMP-managed device, but no response is obtained. Assume that the community name is correct, the OID is correct, and a request with other OIDs does elicit a response. What could be the problem?

○ a. The network is unstable.

○ b. The request is a **set** request.

○ c. There is no alarm condition.

○ d. This is not a manageable device.

The correct answer is b because a **set** request does not require a response. Answer a is not plausible because other OIDs do elicit responses. If an alarm condition existed, a trap would be sent. Therefore, answer c is incorrect. Answer d is incorrect because the first condition of the question is that the device is manageable.

This sample question format corresponds closely to the Microsoft certification exam format—the only difference on the exam is that questions are not followed by answer keys. To select an answer, you would position the cursor over the radio button next to the answer. Then, click the mouse button to select the answer.

Let's examine a question where one or more answers are possible. This type of question provides checkboxes rather than radio buttons for marking all appropriate selections.

Question 2

Which of the following describe a router? [Check all correct answers]

❑ a. A gateway

❑ b. An information service

❑ c. A specialized standalone device

❑ d. Software used to exchange email

Answers a and c are correct. A router can be a gateway or a standalone device. A router is not an information service. Therefore, answer b is incorrect. And, although they may sometimes be described this way, email exchange programs are generally gateways, not routers. Therefore, answer d is incorrect.

For this particular question, two answers are required. Microsoft sometimes gives partial credit for partially correct answers. For Question 2, you have to check the boxes next to items a and c to obtain credit for a correct answer. Notice that picking the right answers also means knowing why the other answers are wrong!

Build-List-and-Reorder Question Format

Questions in the build-list-and-reorder format present two lists of items—one on the left and one on the right. To answer the question, you must move items from the list on the right to the list on the left. The final list must then be reordered into a specific order.

These questions can best be characterized as "From the following list of choices, pick the choices that answer the question. Arrange the list in a certain order." To give you practice with this type of question, some questions of this type are included in this study guide. Here's an example of how they appear in this book; for a sample of how they appear on the test, see Figure 2.

Question 3

From the following list of famous people, pick those that have been elected President of the United States. Arrange the list in the order that they served.

Thomas Jefferson

Ben Franklin

Abe Lincoln

George Washington

Andrew Jackson

Paul Revere

The correct answer is:

George Washington

Thomas Jefferson

Andrew Jackson

Abe Lincoln

On an actual exam, the entire list of famous people would initially appear in the list on the right. You would move the four correct answers to the list on the left, and then reorder the list on the left. Notice that the answer to the question did not include all items from the initial list. However, this may not always be the case.

To move an item from the right list to the left list, first select the item by clicking on it, and then click on the Add button (left arrow). Once you move an item from one list to the other, you can move the item back by first selecting the item and then clicking on the appropriate button (either the Add button or the Remove button). Once items have been moved to the left list, you can reorder an item by selecting the item and clicking on the up or down button.

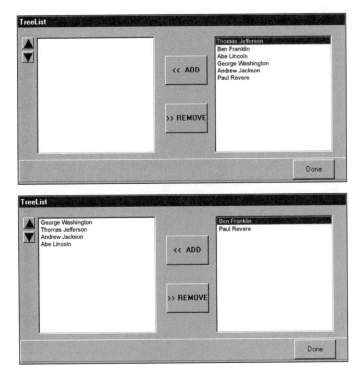

Figure 2   This is how build-list-and-reorder questions appear.

Create-a-Tree Question Format

Questions in the create-a-tree format also present two lists—one on the left side of the screen and one on the right side of the screen. The list on the right consists of individual items, and the list on the left consists of nodes in a tree. To answer the question, you must move items from the list on the right to the appropriate node in the tree.

These questions can best be characterized as simply a matching exercise. Items from the list on the right are placed under the appropriate category in the list on the left. Here's an example of how they appear in this book; for a sample of how they appear on the test, see Figure 3.

Question 4

The calendar year is divided into four seasons:

Winter

Spring

Summer

Fall

Identify the season when each of the following holidays occurs:

Christmas

Fourth of July

Labor Day

Flag Day

Memorial Day

Washington's Birthday

Thanksgiving

Easter

The correct answer is:

Winter
  Christmas
  Washington's Birthday

Spring
    Flag Day
    Memorial Day
    Easter
Summer
    Fourth of July
    Labor Day
Fall
    Thanksgiving

In this case, all the items in the list were used. However, this may not always be the case.

To move an item from the right list to its appropriate location in the tree, you must first select the appropriate tree node by clicking on it. Then, you select the item to be moved and click on the Add button. If one or more items have been added to a tree node, the node will be displayed with a "+" icon to the left of the node name. You can click on this icon to expand the node and view the item(s) that have been added. If any item has been added to the wrong tree node, you can remove it by selecting it and clicking on the Remove button.

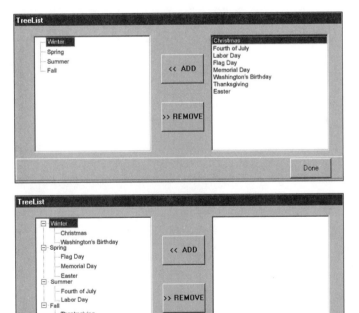

Figure 3   This is how create-a-tree questions appear.

Drag-and-Connect Question Format

Questions in the drag-and-connect format present a group of objects and a list of "connections." To answer the question, you must move the appropriate connections between the objects.

This type of question is best described using graphics. Here's an example.

Question 5

The following objects represent the different states of water:

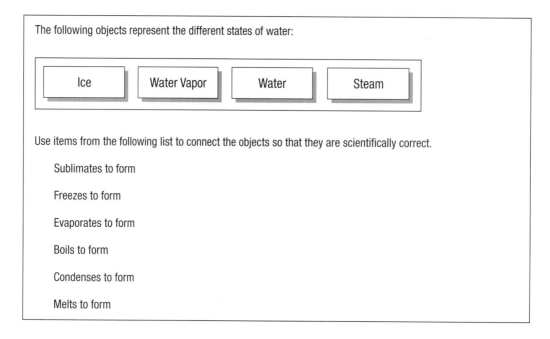

| Ice | Water Vapor | Water | Steam |

Use items from the following list to connect the objects so that they are scientifically correct.

Sublimates to form

Freezes to form

Evaporates to form

Boils to form

Condenses to form

Melts to form

The correct answer is:

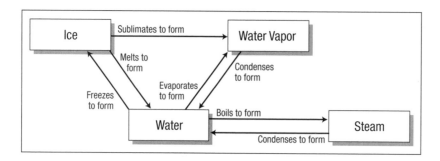

For this type of question, it's not necessary to use every object, and each connection can be used multiple times.

Select-and-Place Question Format

Questions in the select-and-place (drag-and-drop) format present a diagram with blank boxes, and a list of labels that need to be dragged to correctly fill in the blank boxes. To answer the question, you must move the labels to their appropriate positions on the diagram.

This type of question is best described using graphics. Here's an example.

Question 6

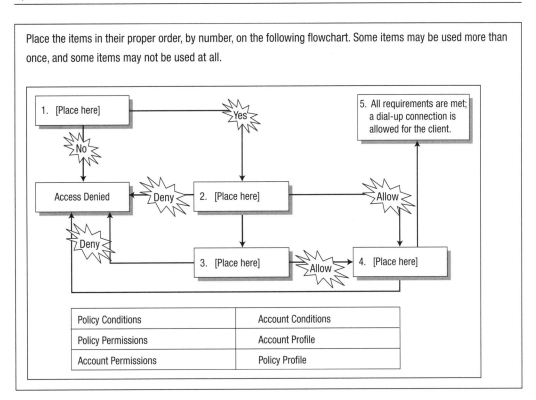

Place the items in their proper order, by number, on the following flowchart. Some items may be used more than once, and some items may not be used at all.

Policy Conditions	Account Conditions
Policy Permissions	Account Profile
Account Permissions	Policy Profile

The correct answer is:

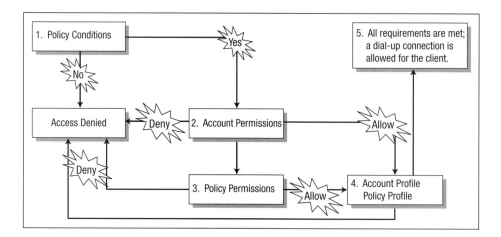

Microsoft's Testing Formats

Currently, Microsoft uses four different testing formats:

➤ Case study

➤ Fixed length

➤ Adaptive

➤ Short form

As we mentioned earlier, the case study approach is used with Microsoft's design exams. These exams consist of a set of case studies that you must analyze to enable you to answer questions related to the case studies. Such exams include one or more case studies (tabbed topic areas), each of which is followed by 4 to 10 questions. The question types for design exams and for Core Four Windows 2000 exams are multiple choice, build list and reorder, create a tree, drag and connect, and select and place. Depending on the test topic, some exams are totally case-based, whereas others are not.

Other Microsoft exams employ advanced testing capabilities that might not be immediately apparent. Although the questions that appear are primarily multiple choice, the logic that drives them is more complex than older Microsoft tests, which use a fixed sequence of questions, called a *fixed-length test*. Some questions employ a sophisticated user interface, which Microsoft calls a *simulation*, to test your knowledge of the software and systems under consideration in a more or less "live" environment that behaves just like the original. The Testing Innovations link at **www.microsoft.com/trainingandservices/default.asp?PageID=mcp** includes a downloadable practice simulation.

For some exams, Microsoft has turned to a well-known technique, called *adaptive testing*, to establish a test-taker's level of knowledge and product competence. Adaptive exams look the same as fixed-length exams, but they discover the level of difficulty at which an individual test-taker can correctly answer questions. Test-takers with differing levels of knowledge or ability therefore see different sets of questions; individuals with high levels of knowledge or ability are presented with a smaller set of more difficult questions, whereas individuals with lower levels of knowledge are presented with a larger set of easier questions. Two individuals may answer the same percentage of questions correctly, but the test-taker with a higher knowledge or ability level will score higher because his or her questions are worth more.

Also, the lower-level test-taker will probably answer more questions than his or her more-knowledgeable colleague. This explains why adaptive tests use ranges of values to define the number of questions and the amount of time it takes to complete the test.

Adaptive tests work by evaluating the test-taker's most recent answer. A correct answer leads to a more difficult question (and the test software's estimate of the test-taker's knowledge and ability level is raised). An incorrect answer leads to a less difficult question (and the test software's estimate of the test-taker's knowledge and ability level is lowered). This process continues until the test targets the test-taker's true ability level. The exam ends when the test-taker's level of accuracy meets a statistically acceptable value (in other words, when his or her performance demonstrates an acceptable level of knowledge and ability), or when the maximum number of items has been presented (in which case, the test-taker is almost certain to fail).

Microsoft also introduced a short-form test for its most popular tests. This test delivers 25 to 30 questions to its takers, giving them exactly 60 minutes to complete the exam. This type of exam is similar to a fixed-length test, in that it allows readers to jump ahead or return to earlier questions, and to cycle through the questions until the test is done. Microsoft does not use adaptive logic in this test, but claims that statistical analysis of the question pool is such that the 25 to 30 questions delivered during a short-form exam conclusively measure a test-taker's knowledge of the subject matter in much the same way as an adaptive test. You can think of the short-form test as a kind of "greatest hits exam" (that is, the most important questions are covered) version of an adaptive exam on the same topic.

Note: Several test-takers have reported that some of the Microsoft exams can appear as a combination of adaptive and fixed-length questions.

Microsoft tests can come in any one of these forms. Whatever you encounter, you must take the test in whichever form it appears; you can't choose one form over another. If anything, it pays more to prepare thoroughly for an adaptive exam than for a fixed-length or a short-form exam: The penalties for answering incorrectly are built into the test itself on an adaptive exam, whereas the layout remains the same for a fixed-length or short-form test, no matter how many questions you answer incorrectly.

Tip: The biggest difference between an adaptive test and a fixed-length or short-form test is that on a fixed-length or short-form test, you can revisit questions after you've read them over one or more times. On an adaptive test, you must answer the question when it's presented and will have no opportunities to revisit that question thereafter.

Strategies for Different Testing Formats

Before you choose a test-taking strategy, you must know if your test is case study based, fixed length, short form, or adaptive. When you begin your exam, you'll know right away if the test is based on case studies. The interface will consist of a tabbed Window that allows you to easily navigate through the sections of the case.

If you are taking a test that is not based on case studies, the software will tell you that the test is adaptive, if in fact the version you're taking is an adaptive test. If your introductory materials fail to mention this, you're probably taking a fixed-length test (50 to 70 questions). If the total number of questions involved is 25 to 30, you're taking a short-form test. Some tests announce themselves by indicating that they will start with a set of adaptive questions, followed by fixed-length questions.

Tip: You'll be able to tell for sure if you are taking an adaptive, fixed-length, or short-form test by the first question. If it includes a checkbox that lets you mark the question for later review, you're taking a fixed-length or short-form test. If the total number of questions is 25 to 30, it's a short-form test; if more than 30, it's a fixed-length test. Adaptive test questions can be visited (and answered) only once, and they include no such checkbox.

The Case Study Exam Strategy

Most test-takers find that the case study type of test used for the design exams (70-219, 70-220, and 70-221) is the most difficult to master. When it comes to studying for a case study test, your best bet is to approach each case study as a standalone test. The biggest challenge you'll encounter is that you'll feel that you won't have enough time to get through all of the cases that are presented.

Tip: Each case provides a lot of material that you'll need to read and study before you can effectively answer the questions that follow. The trick to taking a case study exam is to first scan the case study to get the highlights. Make sure you read the overview section of the case so that you understand the context of the problem at hand. Then, quickly move on and scan the questions.

As you are scanning the questions, make mental notes to yourself so that you'll remember which sections of the case study you should focus on. Some case studies may provide a fair amount of extra information that you don't really need to answer the questions. The goal with this scanning approach is to avoid having to study and analyze material that is not completely relevant.

When studying a case, carefully read the tabbed information. It is important to answer each and every question. You will be able to toggle back and forth from case to questions, and from question to question within a case testlet. However, once you leave the case and move on, you may not be able to return to it. You may want to take notes while reading useful information so you can refer to them when you tackle the test questions. It's hard to go wrong with this strategy when taking any kind of Microsoft certification test.

The Fixed-Length and Short-Form Exam Strategy

A well-known principle when taking fixed-length or short-form exams is to first read over the entire exam from start to finish while answering only those questions you feel absolutely sure of. On subsequent passes, you can dive into more complex questions more deeply, knowing how many such questions you have left.

Fortunately, the Microsoft exam software for fixed-length and short-form tests makes the multiple-visit approach easy to implement. At the top-left corner of each question is a checkbox that permits you to mark that question for a later visit.

Note: Marking questions makes review easier, but you can return to any question by clicking the Forward or Back button repeatedly.

As you read each question, if you answer only those you're sure of and mark for review those that you're not sure of, you can keep working through a decreasing list of questions as you answer the trickier ones in order.

Tip: There's at least one potential benefit to reading the exam over completely before answering the trickier questions: Sometimes, information supplied in later questions sheds more light on earlier questions. At other times, information you read in later questions might jog your memory about Windows 2000 Network Infrastructure facts, figures, or behavior that helps you answer earlier questions. Either way, you'll come out ahead if you defer those questions about which you're not absolutely sure.

Here are some question-handling strategies that apply to fixed-length and short-form tests. Use them if you have the chance:

➤ When returning to a question after your initial read-through, read every word again—otherwise, your mind can fall quickly into a rut. Sometimes, revisiting a question after turning your attention elsewhere lets you see something you missed, but the strong tendency is to see what you've seen before. Try to avoid that tendency at all costs.

➤ If you return to a question more than twice, try to articulate to yourself what you don't understand about the question, why answers don't appear to make sense, or what appears to be missing. If you chew on the subject awhile, your subconscious might provide the details you lack, or you might notice a "trick" that points to the right answer.

As you work your way through the exam, another counter that Microsoft provides will come in handy—the number of questions completed and questions outstanding. For fixed-length and short-form tests, it's wise to budget your time by making sure that you've completed one-quarter of the questions one-quarter of the way through the exam period, and three-quarters of the questions three-quarters of the way through.

If you're not finished when only five minutes remain, use that time to guess your way through any remaining questions. Remember, guessing is potentially more valuable than not answering, because blank answers are always wrong, but a guess may turn out to be right. If you don't have a clue about any of the remaining questions, pick answers at random, or choose all a's, b's, and so on. The important thing is to submit an exam for scoring that has an answer for every question.

Tip: At the very end of your exam period, you're better off guessing than leaving questions unanswered.

The Adaptive Exam Strategy

If there's one principle that applies to taking an adaptive test, it could be summed up as "Get it right the first time." You cannot elect to skip a question and move on to the next one when taking an adaptive test, because the testing software uses your answer to the current question to select whatever question it plans to present next. Nor can you return to a question once you've moved on, because the software gives you only one chance to answer the question. You can, however, take notes, because sometimes information supplied in earlier questions will shed more light on later questions.

Also, when you answer a question correctly, you are presented with a more difficult question next, to help the software gauge your level of skill and ability. When you answer a question incorrectly, you are presented with a less difficult question, and the software lowers its current estimate of your skill and ability. This continues until the program settles into a reasonably accurate estimate of what you know and can do, and takes you on average through somewhere between 15 and 30 questions as you complete the test.

The good news is that if you know your stuff, you'll probably finish most adaptive tests in 30 minutes or so. The bad news is that you must really, really know your stuff to do your best on an adaptive test. That's because some questions are so convoluted, complex, or hard to follow that you're bound to miss one or two, at a minimum, even if you do know your stuff. So the more you know, the better you'll do on an adaptive test, even accounting for the occasionally weird or unfathomable questions that appear on these exams.

Tip: Because you can't always tell in advance if a test is fixed length, short form, or adaptive, you will be best served by preparing for the exam as if it were adaptive. That way, you should be prepared to pass no matter what kind of test you take. But if you do take a fixed-length or short-form test, remember the tips from the preceding section. They should help you improve on what you could do on an adaptive test.

If you encounter a question on an adaptive test that you can't answer, you must guess an answer immediately. Because of how the software works, you may suffer for your guess on the next question if you guess right, because you'll get a more difficult question next!

Question-Handling Strategies

Based on exams we have taken, some interesting trends have become apparent. For those questions that take only a single answer, usually two or three of the answers will be obviously incorrect, and two of the answers will be plausible—of course, only one can be correct. Unless the answer leaps out at you (if it does, reread the question to look for a trick; sometimes those are the ones you're most likely to get wrong), begin the process of answering by eliminating those answers that are most obviously wrong.

Almost always, at least one answer out of the possible choices for a question can be eliminated immediately because it matches one of these conditions:

➤ The answer does not apply to the situation.

➤ The answer describes a nonexistent issue, an invalid option, or an imaginary state.

After you eliminate all answers that are obviously wrong, you can apply your retained knowledge to eliminate further answers. Look for items that sound correct but refer to actions, commands, or features that are not present or not available in the situation that the question describes.

If you're still faced with a blind guess among two or more potentially correct answers, reread the question. Try to picture how each of the possible remaining answers would alter the situation. Be especially sensitive to terminology; sometimes the choice of words ("remove" instead of "disable") can make the difference between a right answer and a wrong one.

Only when you've exhausted your ability to eliminate answers, but remain unclear about which of the remaining possibilities is correct, should you guess at an answer. An unanswered question offers you no points, but guessing gives you at least some chance of getting a question right; just don't be too hasty when making a blind guess.

Note: If you're taking a fixed-length or a short-form test, you can wait until the last round of reviewing marked questions (just as you're about to run out of time, or out of unanswered questions) before you start making guesses. You will have the same option within each case study testlet (but once you leave a testlet, you may not be allowed to return to it). If you're taking an adaptive test, you'll have to guess to move on to the next question if you can't figure out an answer some other way. Either way, guessing should be your technique of last resort!

Numerous questions assume that the default behavior of a particular utility is in effect. If you know the defaults and understand what they mean, this knowledge will help you cut through many Gordian knots.

Mastering the Inner Game

In the final analysis, knowledge breeds confidence, and confidence breeds success. If you study the materials in this book carefully and review all the practice questions at the end of each chapter, you should become aware of those areas where additional learning and study are required.

After you've worked your way through the book, take the practice exam in the back of the book and the practice exams on the CD-ROM. Be sure to click on the Update button in our CD-ROM's testing engine to download additional free questions from **ExamCram.com**! Taking tests will provide a reality check and help you identify areas to study further. Make sure you follow up and review materials related to the questions you miss on the practice exams before scheduling a real exam. Only when you've covered that ground and feel comfortable with the whole scope of the practice exams should you set an exam appointment. Only if you score 85 percent or better should you proceed to the real thing (otherwise, obtain some additional practice tests so you can keep trying until you hit this magic number).

Tip: If you take a practice exam and don't score at least 85 percent correct, you'll want to practice further. Microsoft provides links to practice exam providers and also offers self-assessment exams at **www.microsoft.com/trainingandservices/**). You should also check out **ExamCram.com** for downloadable practice questions.

Armed with the information in this book and with the determination to augment your knowledge, you should be able to pass the certification exam. However, you need to work at it, or you'll spend the exam fee more than once before you finally pass. If you prepare seriously, you should do well. We are confident that you can do it!

The next section covers the exam requirements for the various Microsoft certifications.

The Microsoft Certified Professional (MCP) Program

The MCP Program currently includes the following separate tracks, each of which boasts its own special acronym (as a certification candidate, you need to have a high tolerance for alphabet soup of all kinds):

➤ *MCP (Microsoft Certified Professional)*—This is the least prestigious of all the certification tracks from Microsoft. Passing one of the major Microsoft exams qualifies an individual for the MCP credential. Individuals can demonstrate proficiency with additional Microsoft products by passing additional certification exams.

➤ *MCP+SB (Microsoft Certified Professional + Site Building)*—This certification program is designed for individuals who are planning, building, managing, and maintaining Web sites. Individuals with the MCP+SB credential will have demonstrated the ability to develop Web sites that include multimedia and searchable content and Web sites that connect to and communicate with a back-end database. It requires one MCP exam, plus two of these three exams: "70-055: Designing and Implementing Web Sites with Microsoft FrontPage 98," "70-057: Designing and Implementing Commerce Solutions with Microsoft Site Server 3.0, Commerce Edition," and "70-152: Designing and Implementing Web Solutions with Microsoft Visual InterDev 6.0."

➤ *MCSE (Microsoft Certified Systems Engineer)*—Anyone who has a current MCSE is warranted to possess a high level of networking expertise with Microsoft operating systems and products. This credential is designed to prepare individuals to plan, implement, maintain, and support information systems, networks, and internetworks built around Microsoft Windows 2000 and its BackOffice family of products.

To obtain an MCSE, an individual must pass four core operating system exams, one core option exam, and two elective exams. The operating system exams require individuals to prove their competence with desktop and server operating systems and networking/internetworking components.

For Windows NT 4 MCSEs, the Accelerated exam, "70-240: Microsoft Windows 2000 Accelerated Exam for MCPs Certified on Microsoft Windows NT 4.0," is an option. This free exam covers all of the material tested in the Core Four exams. The hitch in this plan is that you can take the test only once. If you fail, you must take all four core exams to recertify. The Core Four exams are: "70-210: Installing, Configuring and Administering Microsoft Windows 2000 Professional," "70-215: Installing, Configuring and Administering Microsoft Windows 2000 Server," "70-216: Implementing and Administering a Microsoft Windows 2000 Network Infrastructure," and "70-217: Implementing and Administering a Microsoft Windows 2000 Directory Services Infrastructure."

To fulfill the fifth core exam requirement, you can choose from three design exams: "70-219: Designing a Microsoft Windows 2000 Directory Services Infrastructure," "70-220: Designing Security for a Microsoft Windows 2000 Network," or "70-221: Designing a Microsoft Windows 2000 Network Infrastructure." You are also required to take two elective exams. An elective exam can fall in any number of subject or product areas, primarily BackOffice Server 2000 components. The two design exams that you don't select as your fifth core exam also qualify as electives. If you are on your way to becoming an MCSE and have already taken some exams, visit **www.microsoft.com/trainingandservices/** for information about how to complete your MCSE certification.

In September 1999, Microsoft announced its Windows 2000 track for MCSE and also announced retirement of Windows NT 4.0 MCSE core exams on 12/31/2000. Individuals who wish to remain certified MCSEs after 12/31/2001 must "upgrade" their certifications on or before 12/31/2001. For more detailed information than is included here, visit **www.microsoft.com/trainingandservices/**.

New MCSE candidates must pass seven tests to meet the MCSE requirements. It's not uncommon for the entire process to take a year or so, and many individuals find that they must take a test more than once to pass. The primary goal of *Exam Prep* and *Exam Cram* test preparation books is to make it possible, given proper study and preparation, to pass all Microsoft certification tests on the first try. Table 1 shows the required and elective exams for the Windows 2000 MCSE certification.

➤ *MCSD (Microsoft Certified Solution Developer)*—The MCSD credential reflects the skills required to create multitier, distributed, and COM-based solutions, in addition to desktop and Internet applications, using new technologies. To obtain an MCSD, an individual must demonstrate the ability to analyze and interpret user requirements; select and integrate products, platforms, tools, and technologies; design and implement code, and customize applications; and perform necessary software tests and quality assurance operations.

To become an MCSD, you must pass a total of four exams: three core exams and one elective exam. Each candidate must choose one of these three desktop application exams—"70-016: Designing and Implementing Desktop Applications with Microsoft Visual C++ 6.0," "70-156: Designing and Implementing Desktop Applications with Microsoft Visual FoxPro 6.0," or "70-176: Designing and Implementing Desktop Applications with Microsoft Visual Basic 6.0"— *plus* one of these three distributed application exams—"70-015: Designing and Implementing Distributed Applications with Microsoft Visual C++ 6.0," "70-155: Designing and Implementing Distributed Applications with Microsoft Visual FoxPro 6.0," or "70-175: Designing and Implementing Distributed

Table 1 MCSE Windows 2000 Requirements

Core

If you have not passed these 3 Windows NT 4 exams	
Exam 70-067	Implementing and Supporting Microsoft Windows NT Server 4.0
Exam 70-068	Implementing and Supporting Microsoft Windows NT Server 4.0 in the Enterprise
Exam 70-073	Microsoft Windows NT Workstation 4.0
then you must take these 4 exams	
Exam 70-210	Installing, Configuring and Administering Microsoft Windows 2000 Professional
Exam 70-215	Installing, Configuring and Administering Microsoft Windows 2000 Server
Exam 70-216	Implementing and Administering a Microsoft Windows 2000 Network Infrastructure
Exam 70-217	Implementing and Administering a Microsoft Windows 2000 Directory Services Infrastructure
If you have already passed exams 70-067, 70-068, and 70-073, you may take this exam	
Exam 70-240	Microsoft Windows 2000 Accelerated Exam for MCPs Certified on Microsoft Windows NT 4.0

5th Core Option

Choose 1 from this group	
Exam 70-219*	Designing a Microsoft Windows 2000 Directory Services Infrastructure
Exam 70-220*	Designing Security for a Microsoft Windows 2000 Network
Exam 70-221*	Designing a Microsoft Windows 2000 Network Infrastructure

Elective

Choose 2 from this group	
Exam 70-019	Designing and Implementing Data Warehouse with Microsoft SQL Server 7.0
Exam 70-219*	Designing a Microsoft Windows 2000 Directory Services Infrastructure
Exam 70-220*	Designing Security for a Microsoft Windows 2000 Network
Exam 70-221*	Designing a Microsoft Windows 2000 Network Infrastructure
Exam 70-222	Migrating from Microsoft Windows NT 4.0 to Microsoft Windows 2000
Exam 70-028	Administering Microsoft SQL Server 7.0
Exam 70-029	Designing and Implementing Databases on Microsoft SQL Server 7.0
Exam 70-080	Implementing and Supporting Microsoft Internet Explorer 5.0 by Using the Internet Explorer Administration Kit
Exam 70-081	Implementing and Supporting Microsoft Exchange Server 5.5
Exam 70-085	Implementing and Supporting Microsoft SNA Server 4.0
Exam 70-086	Implementing and Supporting Microsoft Systems Management Server 2.0
Exam 70-088	Implementing and Supporting Microsoft Proxy Server 2.0

This is not a complete listing—you can still be tested on some earlier versions of these products. However, we have included mainly the most recent versions so that you may test on these versions and thus be certified longer. We have not included any tests that are scheduled to be retired.

* The 5th Core Option exam does not double as an elective.

Applications with Microsoft Visual Basic 6.0." The third core exam is "70-100: Analyzing Requirements and Defining Solution Architectures." Elective exams cover specific Microsoft applications and languages, including Visual Basic, C++, the Microsoft Foundation Classes, Access, SQL Server, Excel, and more.

➤ *MCDBA (Microsoft Certified Database Administrator)*—The MCDBA credential reflects the skills required to implement and administer Microsoft SQL Server databases. To obtain an MCDBA, an individual must demonstrate the ability to derive physical database designs, develop logical data models, create physical databases, create data services by using Transact-SQL, manage and maintain databases, configure and manage security, monitor and optimize databases, and install and configure Microsoft SQL Server.

To become an MCDBA, you must pass a total of three core exams and one elective exam. The required core exams are "70-028: Administering Microsoft SQL Server 7.0," "70-029: Designing and Implementing Databases with Microsoft SQL Server 7.0," and "70-215: Installing, Configuring and Administering Microsoft Windows 2000 Server."

The elective exams that you can choose from cover specific uses of SQL Server and include "70-015: Designing and Implementing Distributed Applications with Microsoft Visual C++ 6.0," "70-019: Designing and Implementing Data Warehouses with Microsoft SQL Server 7.0," "70-155: Designing and Implementing Distributed Applications with Microsoft Visual FoxPro 6.0," "70-175: Designing and Implementing Distributed Applications with Microsoft Visual Basic 6.0," and two exams that relate to Windows 2000: "70-216: Implementing and Administering a Microsoft Windows 2000 Network Infrastructure," and "70-087: Implementing and Supporting Microsoft Internet Information Server 4.0."

If you have taken the three core Windows NT 4 exams on your path to becoming an MCSE, you qualify for the Accelerated exam (it replaces the Network Infrastructure exam requirement). The Accelerated exam covers the objectives of all four of the Windows 2000 core exams. In addition to taking the Accelerated exam, you must take only the two SQL exams—Administering and Database Design.

Note that the exam covered by this book is an elective for the MCDBA certification. Table 2 shows the requirements for the MCDBA certification.

➤ *MCT (Microsoft Certified Trainer)*—Microsoft Certified Trainers are deemed able to deliver elements of the official Microsoft curriculum, based on technical knowledge and instructional ability. Thus, it is necessary for an individual seeking MCT credentials (which are granted on a course-by-course basis) to pass the related certification exam for a course and complete the official Microsoft training in the subject area, and to demonstrate an ability to teach.

This teaching skill criterion may be satisfied by proving that one has already attained training certification from Novell, Banyan, Lotus, the Santa Cruz Operation, or Cisco, or by taking a Microsoft-sanctioned workshop on instruction. Microsoft makes it clear that MCTs are important cogs in the Microsoft

Table 2   MCDBA Requirements

Core

If you have not passed these 3 Windows NT 4 exams	
Exam 70-067	Implementing and Supporting Microsoft Windows NT Server 4.0
Exam 70-068	Implementing and Supporting Microsoft Windows NT Server 4.0 in the Enterprise
Exam 70-073	Microsoft Windows NT Workstation 4.0
you must take this exam	
Exam 70-215	Installing, Configuring and Administering Microsoft Windows 2000 Server
plus these 2 exams	
Exam 70-028	Administering Microsoft SQL Server 7.0
Exam 70-029	Designing and Implementing Databases with Microsoft SQL Server 7.0

Elective

Choose 1 of the following exams	
Exam 70-015	Designing and Implementing Distributed Applications with Microsoft Visual C++ 6.0
Exam 70-019	Designing and Implementing Data Warehouses with Microsoft SQL Server 7.0
Exam 70-087	Implementing and Supporting Microsoft Internet Information Server 4.0
Exam 70-155	Designing and Implementing Distributed Applications with Microsoft Visual FoxPro 6.0
Exam 70-175	Designing and Implementing Distributed Applications with Microsoft Visual Basic 6.0
▶ Exam 70-216	Implementing and Administering a Microsoft Windows 2000 Network Infrastructure

OR

If you have already passed exams 70-067, 70-068, and 70-073, you may take this exam	
Exam 70-240	Microsoft Windows 2000 Accelerated Exam for MCPs Certified on Microsoft Windows NT 4.0
plus these 2 exams	
Exam 70-028	Administering Microsoft SQL Server 7.0
Exam 70-029	Designing and Implementing Databases with Microsoft SQL Server 7.0

training channels. Instructors must be MCTs before Microsoft will allow them to teach in any of its official training channels, including Microsoft's affiliated Certified Technical Education Centers (CTECs) and its online training partner network. As of January 1, 2001, MCT candidates must also possess a current MCSE.

Microsoft has announced that the MCP+I and MCSE+I credentials will not be continued when the MCSE exams for Windows 2000 are in full swing because the skill set for the Internet portion of the program has been included in the new MCSE program. Therefore, details on these tracks are not provided here; go to **www.microsoft.com/trainingandservices/** if you need more information.

Once a Microsoft product becomes obsolete, MCPs typically have to recertify on current versions. (If individuals do not recertify, their certifications become invalid.) Because technology keeps changing and new products continually supplant old ones, this should come as no surprise. This explains why Microsoft has announced that MCSEs have 12 months past the scheduled retirement date for the Windows NT 4 exams to recertify on Windows 2000 topics. (Note that this means taking at least two exams, if not more.)

The best place to keep tabs on the MCP Program and its related certifications is on the Web. The URL for the MCP program is **www.microsoft.com/mcp/**. But Microsoft's Web site changes often, so if this URL doesn't work, try using the Search tool on Microsoft's site with either "MCP" or the quoted phrase "Microsoft Certified Professional Program" as a search string. This will help you find the latest and most accurate information about Microsoft's certification programs.

Tracking MCP Status

As soon as you pass any Microsoft exam (except Networking Essentials), you'll attain Microsoft Certified Professional (MCP) status. Microsoft also generates transcripts that indicate which exams you have passed. You can view a copy of your transcript at any time by going to the MCP secured site and selecting Transcript Tool. This tool will allow you to print a copy of your current transcript and confirm your certification status.

Once you pass the necessary set of exams, you'll be certified. Official certification normally takes anywhere from six to eight weeks, so don't expect to get your credentials overnight. When the package for a qualified certification arrives, it includes a Welcome Kit that contains a number of elements (see Microsoft's Web site for other benefits of specific certifications):

➤ A certificate suitable for framing, along with a wallet card and a lapel pin.

➤ A license to use the MCP logo, thereby allowing you to use the logo in advertisements, promotions, and documents, and on letterhead, business cards, and so on. Along with the license comes an MCP logo sheet, which includes camera-ready artwork. (Note: Before using any of the artwork, individuals must sign and return a licensing agreement that indicates they'll abide by its terms and conditions.)

➤ A subscription to *Microsoft Certified Professional Magazine*, which provides ongoing data about testing and certification activities, requirements, and changes to the program.

Many people believe that the benefits of MCP certification go well beyond the perks that Microsoft provides to newly anointed members of this elite group. We're starting to see more job listings that request or require applicants to have an MCP, MCSE, and so on, and many individuals who complete the program can qualify for increases in pay and/or responsibility. As an official recognition of hard work and broad knowledge, one of the MCP credentials is a badge of honor in many IT organizations.

About the Book

Career opportunities abound for well-prepared Windows 2000 administrators. This book is designed as your doorway into Network Infrastructure. If you are new to Windows 2000 administration, this is your ticket to an exciting future. Others who have prior experience with Windows 2000 will find that the book adds depth and breadth to that experience. Also, the book provides the knowledge you need to prepare for Microsoft's certification exam 70-216, "Implementing and Administering a Microsoft Windows 2000 Network Infrastructure." The exam is one of the core four requirements, so it is a crucial step in becoming a Microsoft Certified Systems Engineer.

Windows 2000 Server is marvelously scalable and fits into both large and small organizations. It provides the cornerstone on which to implement and administer a Windows 2000 Network Infrastructure, while protecting your network from the outside world. The success of Windows 2000 Server is reflected in the huge number of software vendors and developers who develop in this environment or who have switched from other environments to Windows 2000 Server.

When you complete this book, you will be at the threshold of a career that can be very fulfilling and challenging. This is a rapidly advancing field that offers ample opportunity for personal growth and for making a contribution to your business or organization. The book is intended to provide you with knowledge that you can apply right away and a sound basis for understanding the changes that you will encounter in the future. It also is intended to give you the hands-on skills you need to be a valued professional in your organization.

The book is filled with real-world projects that are designed to make what you learn come alive through actually performing the tasks. Also, every chapter includes a range of practice questions to help prepare you for the Microsoft certification exam. All of these features are offered to reinforce your learning, so you'll feel confident in the knowledge you have gained from each chapter.

Features

To aid you in fully understanding Network Infrastructure concepts, there are many features in this book designed to improve its value:

➤ *Chapter objectives*—Each chapter in this book begins with a detailed list of the topics to be mastered within that chapter. This list provides you with a quick reference to the contents of that chapter, as well as a useful study aid.

➤ *Illustrations and tables*—Numerous illustrations of screenshots and components aid you in the visualization of common setup steps, theories, and concepts. In addition, many tables provide details and comparisons of both practical and theoretical information.

➤ *Notes, tips, and warnings*—Notes present additional helpful material related to the subject being described. Tips from the author's experience provide extra information about how to attack a problem, or what to do in certain real-world situations. Warnings are included to help you anticipate potential mistakes or problems so you can prevent them from happening.

➤ *Chapter summaries*—Each chapter's text is followed by a summary of the concepts it has introduced. These summaries provide a helpful way to recap and revisit the ideas covered in each chapter.

➤ *Review questions*—End-of-chapter assessment begins with a set of review questions that reinforce the ideas introduced in each chapter. These questions not only ensure that you have mastered the concepts, but are written to help prepare you for the Microsoft certification examination. Answers to these questions are found in Appendix A.

➤ *Real-world projects*—Although it is important to understand the theory behind networking technology, nothing can improve upon real-world experience. To this end, along with theoretical explanations, each chapter provides numerous hands-on projects aimed at providing you with real-world implementation experience.

➤ *Sample tests*—Use the sample test and answer key in Chapters 15 and 16 to test yourself. Then, move on to the interactive practice exams found on the CD-ROM. The testing engine offers a variety of testing formats to choose from.

Where Should You Start?

This book is intended to be read in sequence, from beginning to end. Each chapter builds upon those that precede it. After completing the chapters, you may find it useful to go back through the book and use the review questions and projects to prepare for the Microsoft certification test for "Implementing and Administering a Microsoft Windows 2000 Network Infrastructure" (Exam 70-216). Readers are also encouraged to investigate the many pointers to online and printed sources of additional information that are cited throughout this book.

Please share your feedback on the book with us, especially if you have ideas about how we can improve it for future readers. We'll consider everything you say carefully, and we'll respond to all suggestions. Send your questions or comments to us at **learn@examcram.com**. Please remember to include the title of the book in your message; otherwise, we'll be forced to guess which book you're writing about. And we don't like to guess—we want to *know*! Also, be sure to check out the Web pages at **www.examcram.com**, where you'll find information updates, commentary, and certification information. Thanks, and enjoy the book!

Self-Assessment

The reason we included a Self-Assessment in this *Exam Prep* book is to help you evaluate your readiness to tackle MCSE certification. It should also help you understand what you need to know to master the topic of this book—namely, Exam 70-216, "Implementing and Administering a Microsoft Windows 2000 Network Infrastructure." But before you tackle this Self-Assessment, let's talk about concerns you may face when pursuing an MCSE for Windows 2000, and what an ideal MCSE candidate might look like.

MCSEs in the Real World

In the next section, we describe an ideal MCSE candidate, knowing full well that only a few real candidates will meet this ideal. In fact, our description of that ideal candidate might seem downright scary, especially with the changes that have been made to the program to support Windows 2000. But take heart: Although the requirements to obtain an MCSE may seem formidable, they are by no means impossible to meet. However, be keenly aware that it does take time, involves some expense, and requires real effort to get through the process.

Increasing numbers of people are attaining Microsoft certifications, so the goal is within reach. You can get all the real-world motivation you need from knowing that many others have gone before, so you will be able to follow in their footsteps. If you're willing to tackle the process seriously and do what it takes to obtain the necessary experience and knowledge, you can take—and pass—all the certification tests involved in obtaining an MCSE. In fact, we've designed *Exam Preps*, the companion *Exam Crams*, *Exam Cram Personal Trainers*, and *Exam Cram Personal Test Centers* to make it as easy on you as possible to prepare for these exams. We've also greatly expanded our Web site, **www.examcram.com**, to provide a host of resources to help you prepare for the complexities of Windows 2000.

Besides MCSE, other Microsoft certifications include:

➤ MCSD, which is aimed at software developers and requires one specific exam, two more exams on client and distributed topics, plus a fourth elective exam drawn from a different, but limited, pool of options.

➤ Other Microsoft certifications, whose requirements range from one test (MCP) to several tests (MCP+SB, MCDBA).

The Ideal Windows 2000 MCSE Candidate

Just to give you some idea of what an ideal MCSE candidate is like, here are some relevant statistics about the background and experience such an individual might have. Don't worry if you don't meet these qualifications, or don't come that close— this is a far from ideal world, and where you fall short is simply where you'll have more work to do.

➤ Academic or professional training in network theory, concepts, and operations. This includes everything from networking media and transmission techniques through network operating systems, services, and applications.

➤ Three-plus years of professional networking experience, including experience with Ethernet, token ring, modems, and other networking media. This must include installation, configuration, upgrade, and troubleshooting experience.

Note: The Windows 2000 MCSE program is much more rigorous than the previous NT MCSE program; therefore, you'll really need some hands-on experience. Some of the exams require you to solve real-world case studies and network design issues, so the more hands-on experience you have, the better.

➤ Two-plus years in a networked environment that includes hands-on experience with Windows 2000 Server, Windows 2000 Professional, Windows NT Server, Windows NT Workstation, and Windows 95 or Windows 98. A solid understanding of each system's architecture, installation, configuration, maintenance, and troubleshooting is also essential.

➤ Knowledge of the various methods for installing Windows 2000, including manual and unattended installations.

➤ A thorough understanding of key networking protocols, addressing, and name resolution, including TCP/IP, IPX/SPX, and NetBEUI.

➤ A thorough understanding of NetBIOS naming, browsing, and file and print services.

➤ Familiarity with key Windows 2000-based TCP/IP-based services, including HTTP (Web servers), DHCP, WINS, DNS, plus familiarity with one or more of the following: Internet Information Server (IIS), Index Server, and Proxy Server.

➤ An understanding of how to implement security for key network data in a Windows 2000 environment.

➤ Working knowledge of NetWare 3.x and 4.x, including IPX/SPX frame formats, NetWare file, print, and directory services, and both Novell and Microsoft client software. Working knowledge of Microsoft's Client Service For NetWare (CSNW), Gateway Service For NetWare (GSNW), the NetWare Migration Tool (NWCONV), and the NetWare Client For Windows (NT, 95, and 98) is essential.

➤ A good working understanding of Active Directory. The more you work with Windows 2000, the more you'll realize that this new operating system is quite different than Windows NT. New technologies like Active Directory have really changed the way that Windows is configured and used. We recommend that you find out as much as you can about Active Directory and acquire as much experience using this technology as possible. The time you take learning about Active Directory will be time very well spent!

Fundamentally, this boils down to a bachelor's degree in computer science, plus three years' experience working in a position involving network design, installation, configuration, and maintenance. We believe that well under half of all certification candidates meet these requirements, and that, in fact, most meet less than half of these requirements—at least, when they begin the certification process. But because all the people who already have been certified have survived this ordeal, you can survive it too—especially if you heed what our Self-Assessment can tell you about what you already know and what you need to learn.

Put Yourself to the Test

The following series of questions and observations is designed to help you figure out how much work you must do to pursue Microsoft certification and what kinds of resources you may consult on your quest. Be absolutely honest in your answers, or you'll end up wasting money on exams you're not yet ready to take. There are no right or wrong answers, only steps along the path to certification. Only you can decide where you really belong in the broad spectrum of aspiring candidates.

Two things should be clear from the outset, however:

➤ Even a modest background in computer science will be helpful.

➤ Hands-on experience with Microsoft products and technologies is an essential ingredient to certification success.

Educational Background

1. Have you ever taken any computer-related classes? [Yes or No]

    If Yes, proceed to question 2; if No, proceed to question 4.

2. Have you taken any classes on computer operating systems? [Yes or No]

   If Yes, you will probably be able to handle Microsoft's architecture and system component discussions. If you're rusty, brush up on basic operating system concepts, especially virtual memory, multitasking regimes, user mode versus kernel mode operation, and general computer security topics.

   If No, consider some basic reading in this area. We strongly recommend a good general operating systems book, such as *Operating System Concepts, 5th Edition*, by Abraham Silberschatz and Peter Baer Galvin (John Wiley & Sons, 1998, ISBN 0-471-36414-2). If this title doesn't appeal to you, check out reviews for other, similar titles at your favorite online bookstore.

3. Have you taken any networking concepts or technologies classes? [Yes or No]

   If Yes, you will probably be able to handle Microsoft's networking terminology, concepts, and technologies (brace yourself for frequent departures from normal usage). If you're rusty, brush up on basic networking concepts and terminology, especially networking media, transmission types, the OSI Reference Model, and networking technologies such as Ethernet, token ring, FDDI, and WAN links.

   If No, you might want to read one or two books in this topic area. The two best books that we know of are *Computer Networks, 3rd Edition*, by Andrew S. Tanenbaum (Prentice-Hall, 1996, ISBN 0-13-349945-6) and *Computer Networks and Internets, 2nd Edition*, by Douglas E. Comer (Prentice-Hall, 1998, ISBN 0-130-83617-6).

   Skip to the next section, "Hands-on Experience."

4. Have you done any reading on operating systems or networks? [Yes or No]

   If Yes, review the requirements stated in the first paragraphs after questions 2 and 3. If you meet those requirements, move on to the next section. If No, consult the recommended reading for both topics. A strong background will help you prepare for the Microsoft exams better than just about anything else.

Hands-on Experience

The most important key to success on all of the Microsoft tests is hands-on experience, especially with Windows 2000 Server and Professional, plus the many add-on services and BackOffice components around which so many of the Microsoft certification exams revolve. If we leave you with only one realization after taking this Self-Assessment, it should be that there's no substitute for time spent installing, configuring, and using the various Microsoft products upon which you'll be tested repeatedly and in depth.

5. Have you installed, configured, and worked with:

> ➤ Windows 2000 Server? [Yes or No]

If Yes, make sure you understand basic concepts as covered in Exam 70-215. You should also study the TCP/IP interfaces, utilities, and services for Exam 70-216, plus implementing security features for Exam 70-220.

Tip: You can download objectives, practice exams, and other data about Microsoft exams from the Training and Certification page at **www.microsoft.com/trainingandservices/default.asp?PageID=mcp/**. Use the "Exams" link to obtain specific exam information.

If you haven't worked with Windows 2000 Server, you must obtain one or two machines and a copy of Windows 2000 Server. Then, learn the operating system and whatever other software components on which you'll also be tested.

In fact, we recommend that you obtain two computers, each with a network interface, and set up a two-node network on which to practice. With decent Windows 2000-capable computers selling for about $500 to $600 apiece these days, this shouldn't be too much of a financial hardship. You may have to scrounge to come up with the necessary software, but if you scour the Microsoft Web site you can usually find low-cost options to obtain evaluation copies of most of the software that you'll need.

> ➤ Windows 2000 Professional? [Yes or No]

If Yes, make sure you understand the concepts covered in Exam 70-210.

If No, you will want to obtain a copy of Windows 2000 Professional and learn how to install, configure, and maintain it. You can use *MCSE Windows 2000 Professional Exam Cram* to guide your activities and studies, or work straight from Microsoft's test objectives if you prefer.

Tip: For any and all of these Microsoft exams, the Resource Kits for the topics involved are a good study resource. You can purchase softcover Resource Kits from Microsoft Press (search for them at **http://mspress.microsoft.com/**), but they also appear on the TechNet CDs (**www.microsoft.com/technet**). Along with *Exam Crams* and *Exam Preps*, we believe that Resource Kits are among the best tools you can use to prepare for Microsoft exams.

---

6. For any specific Microsoft product that is not itself an operating system (for example, SQL Server), have you installed, configured, used, and upgraded this software? [Yes or No]

If the answer is Yes, skip to the next section. If it's No, you must get some experience. Read on for suggestions on how to do this.

Experience is a must with any Microsoft product exam, be it something as simple as FrontPage 2000 or as challenging as SQL Server 7.0. For trial copies of other software, search Microsoft's Web site using the name of the product as your search term. Also, search for bundles like "BackOffice" or "Small Business Server."

Tip: If you have the funds, or your employer will pay your way, consider taking a class at a Certified Training and Education Center (CTEC) or at an Authorized Academic Training Partner (AATP). In addition to classroom exposure to the topic of your choice, you get a copy of the software that is the focus of your course, along with a trial version of whatever operating system it needs, with the training materials for that class.

Before you even think about taking any Microsoft exam, make sure you've spent enough time with the related software to understand how it may be installed and configured, how to maintain such an installation, and how to troubleshoot that software when things go wrong. This will help you in the exam, and in real life!

Testing Your Exam-Readiness

Whether you attend a formal class on a specific topic to get ready for an exam or use written materials to study on your own, some preparation for the Microsoft certification exams is essential. At $100 a try, pass or fail, you want to do everything you can to pass on your first try. That's where studying comes in.

We have included a practice exam in this book, so if you don't score that well on the test, you can study more and then tackle the test again. We also have exams that you can take online through the **ExamCram.com** Web site at **www.examcram.com**. If you still don't hit a score of at least 70 percent after these tests, you'll want to investigate the other practice test resources we mention in this section.

For any given subject, consider taking a class if you've tackled self-study materials, taken the test, and failed anyway. The opportunity to interact with an instructor and fellow students can make all the difference in the world, if you can afford that privilege. For information about Microsoft classes, visit the Training and Certification page at **www.microsoft.com/education/partners/ctec.asp** for Microsoft Certified Education Centers or **www.microsoft.com/aatp/default.htm** for Microsoft Authorized Training Providers.

If you can't afford to take a class, visit the Training and Certification page anyway, because it also includes pointers to free practice exams and to Microsoft Certified Professional Approved Study Guides and other self-study tools. And even if you can't afford to spend much at all, you should still invest in some low-cost practice exams from commercial vendors.

7. Have you taken a practice exam on your chosen test subject? [Yes or No]

If Yes, and you scored 70 percent or better, you're probably ready to tackle the real thing. If your score isn't above that threshold, keep at it until you break that barrier.

If No, obtain all the free and low-budget practice tests you can find and get to work. Keep at it until you can break the passing threshold comfortably.

Tip: When it comes to assessing your test readiness, there is no better way than to take a good-quality practice exam and pass with a score of 70 percent or better. When we're preparing ourselves, we shoot for 80-plus percent, just to leave room for the "weirdness factor" that sometimes shows up on Microsoft exams.

Assessing Readiness for Exam 70-216

In addition to the general exam-readiness information in the previous section, there are several things you can do to prepare for the Implementing and Administering a Microsoft Windows 2000 Network Infrastructure exam. As you're getting ready for Exam 70-216, visit the Exam Cram Windows 2000 Resource Center at **www.examcram.com/studyresource/w2kresource/**. Another valuable resource is the Exam Cram Insider newsletter. Sign up at **www.examcram.com** or send a blank email message to **subscribe-ec@mars.coriolis.com**. We also suggest that you join an active MCSE mailing list. One of the better ones is managed by Sunbelt Software. Sign up at **www.sunbelt-software.com** (look for the Subscribe button).

You can also cruise the Web looking for "braindumps" (recollections of test topics and experiences recorded by others) to help you anticipate topics you're likely to encounter on the test. The MCSE mailing list is a good place to ask where the useful braindumps are, or you can check Shawn Gamble's list at **www.commandcentral.com**.

Tip: You can't be sure that a braindump's author can provide correct answers. Thus, use the questions to guide your studies, but don't rely on the answers in a braindump to lead you to the truth. Double-check everything you find in any braindump.

Microsoft exam mavens also recommend checking the Microsoft Knowledge Base (available on its own CD as part of the TechNet collection, or on the Microsoft Web site at **http://support.microsoft.com/support/**) for "meaningful technical support issues" that relate to your exam's topics. Although we're not sure exactly what the quoted phrase means, we have also noticed some overlap between technical support questions on particular products and troubleshooting questions on the exams for those products.

Onward, through the Fog!

Once you've assessed your readiness, undertaken the right background studies, obtained the hands-on experience that will help you understand the products and technologies at work, and reviewed the many sources of information to help you prepare for a test, you'll be ready to take a round of practice tests. When your scores come back positive enough to get you through the exam, you're ready to go after the real thing. If you follow our assessment regime, you'll not only know what you need to study, but when you're ready to make a test date at Prometric or VUE. Good luck!

CHAPTER ONE

Introduction to Windows 2000

After completing this chapter, you will be able to:

✓ Describe the new features and enhancements of Windows 2000 Server and Advanced Server

✓ Install Windows 2000 Server and Advanced Server

✓ Describe the system requirements of Windows 2000 Server and Advanced Server

✓ Define a solution for either an install or upgrade

✓ Configure a dual-boot system

✓ Understand the differences in Windows 2000 file systems

✓ Decide which components you want to install

✓ Understand the differences between workgroups and domains

✓ Understand what disk mirroring is

This chapter discusses the new features and enhancements that Windows 2000 Server and Advanced Server have to offer both small business and large corporate network environments. It addresses the preparations needed for an effective migration to Windows 2000, as well as whether to upgrade or make a fresh installation. You will gain insightful information on what licensing mode is and if a dual-boot system is right for you, as well as instruction on how to do it. An overview of the different file systems employed by Windows will also help in understanding the installation process. Windows 2000 offers the ability to choose components during installation. We will discuss what these components are. To ensure familiarity, we will provide a brief overview of the differences in workgroups and domains, and we will explain disk mirroring. Please keep in mind the scalable nature of Windows 2000 during installation or upgrade, so you can add the features you desire or only those you need. With that said, let's take a look at those new features.

New Features and Enhancements

Windows 2000 Server and Advanced Server have many new features and enhancements. Most are updates of older standards; some are new technologies that integrate several key features of Windows NT. Some of the newer features first appeared in Windows NT, but now with advances in hardware and LAN technologies, they can be fully implemented using Windows 2000. For example, the Windows 2000 environment can make full use of high-speed network hardware for faster data throughput and has the ability to offer smart-card technology for security authentication.

The Windows 2000 operating system has a lot to offer networks of all sizes and allows for the scaling of needs for future growth. In these next sections we will look at the new enhancements and features available for Windows 2000 Server and Advanced Server separately. Keep in mind, though, that Advanced Server has all the features of the Server version, but Server does not have all the features of Advanced Server.

Windows 2000 Server

Both Windows 2000 Server and Advanced Server build on the strengths of Windows NT technology. They integrate standards-based directory, Internet, application, communications, file, and print services with high reliability, efficiency, management, and support for the latest innovations in networking hardware technologies—the intention being to provide the infrastructure for integrating a business with the Internet. Windows 2000 Server is a perfect entry-level solution for running reliable and manageable file, print, intranet, communications, and infrastructure servers.

Internet Information Services 5.0

Integrated Web services let users host and manage Web sites to share information; create Web-based business applications; and extend file, print, media, and communications services to the Web. In Internet Information Services (IIS) 5.0, Internet technologies are integrated with other services at the operating-system level to let organizations efficiently share information using the Internet, as well as create Web-based business applications.

Active Server Pages Programming Environment

Active Server Pages (ASP) is an open-compile free application environment. It integrates HTML page scripting and ActiveX server components for creating powerful Web-based business solutions. ASP is consistently the easiest, highest-performance-rated Web server-scripting environment available. ASP allows Visual Basic programmers to create high-performance Internet solutions with the tools they are already familiar with. Web page processing is faster because of the scalability of ASP processing, its improved flow control, and ASP Fast Path for scriptless files.

XML Parser

Extensible Markup Language (XML) is specifically designed for Web documents. A markup language is a method of identifying structures in a document, where XML defines a standard for adding markup to Web documents. When designing a Web document with content having structured information such as footnotes, table headings, figure captions, and/or headers, you will most likely want to use XML. *Parsing* generally is a way to split data or data types for processing. An XML parser lets users create applications that enable the Web server to exchange XML-formatted data with Microsoft Internet Explorer and any server that supports XML parsing.

Windows DNA 2000

The Distributed Internet Architecture (DNA) development model for the Windows platform offers the ability to build secure, reliable, and scalable solutions. These solutions help ease the integration of mixed systems, network environments, and applications.

Component Object Model

With the Component Object Model (COM), you can create and use components. It makes software easier to write and reuse, while providing a wide selection of tools, services, languages, and applications. COM offers off-the-shelf third-party products that include server controls, tools, and components. You can use the services and design techniques of COM in a standard way with programming languages that have integrated development tools offering flexible security and multiple network transports. COM+ includes Transaction Services and Message

Queuing Services for distributed applications. Windows 2000 Server includes COM and COM+ for application services needed to build integrated, component-based Web-aware applications faster and more efficiently. Features for Application Programming Interfaces (APIs), Message Queuing, and support for ASPs can make application development easier as well.

Multimedia Platform

Windows Media Services lets users configure and manage high-quality digital media content across the Internet and intranets, thus delivering live and on-demand content to the maximum number of users. With Windows Media Services, organizations can integrate streaming multimedia into applications, corporate communications, customer and sales support, news and entertainment services, and product promotions.

Directory-Enabled Applications

Developers can use several standard interfaces to write applications that employ information about users, other applications, and devices, stored in the Active Directory service. This enables rich, dynamic applications that are easier to develop and manage. All Active Directory functions are available through the Lightweight Directory Access Protocol (LDAP), Active Directory Services Interface (ADSI), and Mail API (MAPI) for extending and integrating with other applications, directories, and devices. Directory services are an essential and inseparable part of the Windows 2000 network architecture. They are specifically designed for distributed networking environments.

Web Folders and Internet Printing

By using Web Document Authoring and Versioning (WebDAV) to enable drag-and-drop Web publishing, Web Folders bring the richness of Windows to the Web. Users can also send print jobs across the Internet to an URL.

Terminal Services

In Windows 2000, Terminal Services are up to 20 percent more scalable and have dramatically improved performance for both high- and low-bandwidth connections. Terminal Services is a technology that lets you remotely execute applications on a Windows 2000-based server from a wide range of devices over virtually any type of network connection. With the integration of Terminal Services into the core server operating system, you can choose to deploy the latest Windows-based applications in a fully server-centric mode, where applications run entirely on the server. When Terminal Services is enabled on Windows 2000 Server, administrators do not have to install 32-bit applications on each desktop computer. Instead, the application is installed once on the server, and the clients automatically have access to the new or upgraded software package through Terminal Services Client software.

Multisite Hosting

IIS 5.0 adds the ability to host thousands of small Web sites per server with a high degree of performance. The multisite hosting feature can also scale to large numbers of Web sites across several servers. This is of great significance for Internet Service Providers (ISPs) who do a large amount of virtual site hosting for businesses that need a cost-effective Web-site solution. IIS also can help a company save time and money by allowing it to have Web sites on a single server instead of managing several servers at a time.

IIS CPU Throttling

IIS 5.0 can limit the amount of CPU time a Web application or Web sites can use during predefined time intervals. Administrators can therefore ensure that processor time and better performance are available for non-Web applications and other mission-critical Web sites.

High Throughput and Bandwidth Utilization

Windows 2000 Server delivers high-performance processing on high-performance networks, with support for up to 1GB networks. Increased throughput increases performance without increasing network bandwidth.

Support for the Latest Security Standards

Windows 2000 Distributed Security has many new features to simplify domain administration, improve performance, and integrate Internet security technology based on public-key cryptography. One highlight of the Windows 2000 Distributed Security Services is integration with Windows 2000 Active Directory services to provide scalable, flexible account management for large domains with fine-grain access control and delegation of administration. Kerberos V.5 authentication protocol is implemented as the default protocol for network authentication. Another highlight is strong authentication using public-key certificates, secure channels based on Secure Sockets Layer (SSL) 3.0, and CryptoAPI to deliver industry-standard protocols for data integrity and privacy across public networks.

Active Directory Integration

The integration of Active Directory with an underlying security infrastructure provides a focal point for security management of users, computers, and devices, thus making Windows 2000 easier to manage.

Using Active Directory, organizations can efficiently share and manage information about network resources and users. It acts as the central authority for network security, letting the operating system readily verify a user's identity and control his or her access to network resources. Active Directory also acts as an integration point for bringing systems together and centralizing management tasks. Likewise, the Meta-directory service allows Active Directory to manage identity information that applications and network services store in places other than a directory, and synchronization services allow Active Directory to share information with other directory services.

Kerberos Authentication

Full support for Kerberos V.5 provides fast, single sign-on to Windows resources and other environments that support it. With Kerberos V.5 support, users can access Windows 2000 Server-based enterprise resources, as well as other environments that support this protocol. Support for Kerberos V.5 includes additional benefits, such as mutual authentication and delegated authentication.

Public Key Infrastructure

The Certificate Server is a critical part of a public key infrastructure (PKI) that enables customers to issue their own X.509 certificates to their users for PKI functionality, such as certificate-based authentication, Internet Protocol Security (IPSec), secure email, and so forth. Integration with Active Directory simplifies user enrollment.

Smart-Card Support

Windows 2000 supports logon via smart cards "out-of-the-box" for strong authentication to sensitive resources. A smart card is a credit card-sized device that can be used to securely store public and private keys, passwords, and other personal information. Smart cards can enable certificate-based authentication and single sign-on for an enterprise. For smart cards to be used with Windows 2000, a smart-card reader must be attached to the computer.

Encrypting File System

Encrypting File System increases the security of the hard disk by encrypting the data on it. The data remains encrypted even when backed up or archived.

Secure Network Communications

Secure network communications are end-to-end encrypted communications across your company network using the IPSec standard. This is important for protecting sensitive internal communications from intentional or accidental viewing. Active Directory provides central policy control for its use to make it deployable.

Windows 2000 offers enhanced security and policy controls while still increasing performance and simplifying system setup, management, and use. The operating system integrates complete network services to let organizations affordably set up and manage networks, connect remote employees, connect branch offices, and set up partner extranets. Windows 2000 Server adheres to standards-based protocols on an open platform, which can take advantage of new technologies as they are developed.

Routing and Remote Access Service

Routing and Remote Access Service allows the connection of remote workers, telecommuters, and branch offices to the corporate network through dial-up, leased line, and Internet links.

Virtual Private Networking

Virtual Private Networking (VPN) is a full-featured gateway that encrypts communications to connect remote users and satellite offices securely over the Internet.

High System Uptime

Several features help keep high system uptime:

➤ *Kernel-Mode Write Protection*—Helps prevent errant code from interfering with system operations.

➤ *Windows File Protection*—Prevents new software installations from replacing essential system files.

➤ *Driver Certification*—Identifies device drivers that have passed the Windows Hardware Quality Labs test and warns users if they are about to install an uncertified driver.

➤ *IIS Application Protection*—Keeps Web applications running separately from the Web server, preventing an application from crashing the Web server.

Increased Server and Network Availability

When combined, several new features have increased server and network availability:

➤ *Job Object API*—Has the ability to set up processor affinity, establish time limits, control process priorities, and limit memory utilization for a group of related processes. This allows an application to manage and control dependent system resources. This level of control means the Job Object API can prevent an application from negatively affecting overall system scalability.

➤ *Application Certification and DLL Protection*—Certified to run on Windows 2000 Server and tested by Microsoft to ensure high quality and reliability. These applications protect DLLs from conflicts that can cause application failure.

➤ *Multimaster Replication*—Used by Active Directory to ensure high scalability and availability in distributed network configurations. *Multimaster* means that each directory replica in the network is a peer of all other replicas; changes made to one replica will be reflected across all of them.

➤ *Distributed File System (DFS)*—Allows users to build a single, hierarchical view of multiple file servers and file server shares on a network. DFS makes it easier for users to locate files, and increases their availability by maintaining multiple copies across distributed servers. To address traditional and Internet-based data requirements, the Windows 2000 Server operating system provides a united file and print infrastructure for securely sharing, storing, and publishing data. Organizations can use Windows 2000 Server to improve storage management, help users locate and access information, and extend the usefulness of shared printers.

➤ *Disk Quotas*—Set limits on disk-space usage per user and per volume to provide increased availability of disk space.

➤ *Hierarchical Storage Management*—Automatically migrates data that has not been recently accessed to less expensive storage media, thereby maximizing disk space for the most heavily accessed data on the disk.

Dynamic System Configuration

The following features allow for increased drive performance, troubleshooting methods, and information management:

➤ *Dynamic Volume Management*—Lets administrators add new volumes, extend existing volumes, break or add a mirror, or repair a RAID 5, while the server is online, without affecting the end user.

➤ *Disk Defragmentation*—Reverses the process that has occurred because of fragmentation. Over time, fragmentation can have a severe impact on the performance of a busy file or Web server. Disk Defragmentation increases disk availability and performance.

➤ *Safe Mode Boot*—Allows for system troubleshooting during startup by enabling users to change the default settings or remove a newly installed program that is causing a problem.

➤ *Backup and Recovery*—Makes backing up and recovering data easier in the event of a hard-disk failure. Backups can be to both hard disk and tape media.

➤ *Automatic*—Allows administrators to configure services across the operating system, including IIS, to restart automatically if they fail.

➤ *Kill Process Tree*—Lets administrators stop all processes related to a failed process or application without rebooting the system.

Easy to Deploy, Configure, and Use

With the features discussed in this section, administrators can easily deploy and configure Windows 2000 Server.

➤ *Configuration Wizard*—Automatically sets up file, print, Web, communications, networking, Active Directory, and Domain Name System (DNS) services.

➤ *System Preparation Tool*—Saves deployment time by using SysPrep to create an image of a computer's hard drive that then can be used to duplicate onto other computers.

➤ *Windows Installer*—Supervises application installations and cleanly performs uninstall/removal tasks.

➤ *Plug and Play*—Automatically detects and recognizes newly installed hardware components, simplifying network system configuration and reducing service downtime.

➤ *Service Pack Slipstreaming*—Simplifies operating system updates by maintaining one master image of the operating system on the network.

➤ *Dynamic DNS service*—Simplifies object naming and location through Internet protocols, and improves scalability, performance, and interoperability. Systems that receive addresses from a Dynamic Host Configuration Protocol (DHCP) server are automatically registered in DNS. Replication options with legacy DNS systems and through Active Directory can simplify and strengthen name replication infrastructure.

➤ *Microsoft Connection Manager Administration Kit and Connection Point Services*—Wizard-driven tools that let administrators centrally configure and deploy customized remote access dialers that can integrate automatic-update phonebooks, custom connect actions, driver updates, and more.

➤ *Internet Connection Sharing*—Enables multiple users within small business or workgroups to share a single Internet connection, making connection to the Internet easier and less costly.

➤ *Search for and Connect to Printers*—Allows users to locate and connect to printers based on criteria such as location, ability to print color, and speed.

Centralized Management for Lower Total Cost of Ownership

Features that allow Windows 2000 to be managed centrally at a lower cost of ownership include:

➤ *Cluster Administration*—Remotely controls multiple clusters from a single location. Run Cluster Administrator from any Windows NT or Windows 2000 system.

➤ *Integrated Directory Services*—Allows Active Directory to administer Windows-based clients and servers centrally through a single management interface, thereby reducing costs.

➤ *Windows Management Instrumentation*—A uniform model that allows all management data from any source to be controlled. Windows Management Instrumentation (WMI) provides this for software, and WMI extensions for the Windows Driver Model (WDM) provide the same benefit for hardware or hardware device drivers.

➤ *Delegated Administration*—The administrator's ability to delegate a selected set of administrative privileges to designated individuals within the organization. Delegation reduces the number of domains a company needs to support a large organization over multiple geographic locations.

➤ *Microsoft Management Console (MMC)*—Unifies and simplifies system management tasks through a central console, allowing control, monitoring, and administration of widespread network resources. All management functions in Windows 2000 are available through MMC.

➤ *Remote Management with Terminal Services*—Safely enables Terminal Services for remote administration purposes. There can be two concurrent sessions before performance or application compatibility is affected.

➤ *Windows Script Host*—Allows for server administration and task automation via the command line instead of graphical user interface tools with scripts.

➤ *Group Policy*—Allows central management of groups of users, computers, applications, and network resources instead of managing networked resources and connections on a one-by-one basis.

➤ *Centralized Desktop Management*—Allows for administrators to manage users' desktop resources by applying policies created to fulfill business needs and location of users.

➤ *Security Configuration Toolset*—Reduces the costs associated with security configuration and analysis of Windows-based networks. In Windows 2000, the administrators can use Group Policy to set and periodically update security configurations of computers. PKI Group Policy Management is used to centralize the management of domainwide PKI policies, specify which Certificate Authorities a client will trust, distribute new root certificates, adjust IPSec policy, or determine if a user will be required to use smart cards to log onto a particular system.

➤ *Directory Interoperability*—A Meta-directory technology that enables companies to use Active Directory to manage identity information stored in heterogeneous directory services. Directory synchronization tools maintain and synchronize data between Active Directory and Microsoft Exchange and Novell Directory Services (NDS).

Leverage Existing IT Investments

The Microsoft interoperability strategy is based on a four-layer framework that covers network, data, applications, and management integration. By supporting key standards, Microsoft is ensuring that Windows 2000 Server can interoperate with existing platforms and technologies. High interoperability with client computers allows for the support of Windows NT Workstation, Windows 9x, Windows 3.x, Macintosh, and Unix operating systems. Active Directory can interoperate data with other directory services using LDAP, Meta-directory technologies, Microsoft Directory Service Synchronization, or Active Directory Connector. This allows for integration with existing management applications and framework via Windows Management Services.

Server and Mainframe interoperability uses Message Queuing to enable the exchange of information between applications running on mainframe platforms. Kerberos authentication protocol support is an industry-standard authentication protocol that enables interoperability with other systems. Services for NetWare are an add-on product that increases interoperability between NetWare servers and clients and Windows-based servers and clients. Services for Unix are an add-on product that makes it easier to integrate Windows NT 4 and Windows 2000 into a Unix environment.

Best for New Drivers

Windows 2000 Server works with networking devices that support a variety of the latest networking technologies, including Plug and Play, digital subscriber line (DSL), VPN, routing, Network Address Translation (NAT), DHCP, Quality of Services (QoS) switches and routers, Directory-Enabled Networking devices, IPSec, SSL, and Asynchronous Transfer Mode (ATM). It also works with the newest peripherals, such as storage management hardware, Universal Serial Bus (USB) printers, network adapters, keyboards, and mouse devices. Windows 2000 Server delivers advanced printer driver support.

Windows 2000 Advanced Server

Windows 2000 Advanced Server includes all the new features of Windows 2000 Server, as well as enhanced memory support, support for additional processors, and clustering. Enhanced memory and processor support enables your server applications to run faster, providing better response for users on the network.

Windows Clustering includes multiple clustering technologies, such as network load balancing clusters and server clusters. You can set up these clustering technologies to work together to provide scalability and high availability for network applications.

Network load balancing clusters provide high scalability and availability for TCP/IP-based services and applications by combining up to 32 servers running Windows 2000 Advanced Server into a single cluster. The Network Load Balancing service provides a foundation for network load balancing clusters.

Server clusters provide high availability for applications through the failover of resources on servers running Windows 2000 Advanced Server. *Failover* is the process of taking one resource offline on one node and bringing it online on another node in a predefined order. The Cluster service provides a foundation for server clusters.

Active Directory

Active Directory provides a wide range of features and capabilities. Using Active Directory, you can build hierarchical information structures that make it easier for you to control administrative privileges and other security settings, and to make it easier for users to locate network resources.

You can use local policies to define permissible functions and settings for users and computers. In contrast with local policy, you can use Group Policy to set policies that apply to a larger area such as a site, domain, or organizational unit in Active Directory. Flexible and secure authentication and authorization services provide protection for information, while reducing barriers to doing business over the Internet. Active Directory supports multiple authentication protocols, such as the Kerberos V.5 protocol, SSL 3.0, and Transport Layer Security using X.509v3 certificates. Directory consolidation lets administrators organize and simplify the management of users, computers, applications, and devices, and makes it easier for users to find the information they need.

You can take advantage of synchronization support through LDAP-based interfaces, and you can work with directory consolidation requirements specific to your applications. Active Directory also simplifies configuration and management of applications and other directory-embedded network components. It can scale to millions of objects on a domain and use advanced replication techniques and indexing technology to increase performance. With Active Directory, users can access the Internet through LDAP and DNS-based namespace. Active Directory provides a powerful development environment through the ADSI.

Security Features

Windows 2000 includes a variety of features for creating a strong, flexible security system, including file encryption and the security features built into Active Directory.

The Encrypting File System in Windows 2000 complements existing access controls and adds a new level of protection for your data. The Encrypting File System runs as an integrated system service, making it easy for administrators to manage, difficult for outside users to attack, and transparent to the authorized user. You can use IPSec to secure internal communications, while creating secure VPN solutions over the Internet.

Application Support

Windows 2000 Advanced Server provides customers with a wide range of turn-key independent software vendor (ISV) solutions and a comprehensive set of Internet application services for rapid development of custom applications. More than 3,800 applications are written for Windows NT Server today, and hundreds of new server applications are scheduled to be available within months of the Windows 2000 Advanced Server release. Programmers can use the integrated Web, component management, transaction processing, and message queuing services in Windows 2000, and can rapidly develop and deploy scalable, component-based applications.

Integrated components include transaction services and message queuing. The integrated transaction services provide simple building blocks that can reliably and efficiently execute complex transactions across widespread distributed networks. The integrated message queuing functionality helps developers build and deploy applications that run more reliably over networks, including the Internet. These applications can operate with applications running on non-Microsoft platforms.

Component Services is a set of services based on extensions of the COM and on Microsoft Transaction Server. These services provide improved threading and security, transaction management, object pooling, queued components, the In-Memory Database (IMDB), and application administration and packaging.

Windows 2000 Advanced Server contains an extension to the process model called a *job*. Job objects can be named, secured, and shared, and they control attributes of their associated processes. A job object's basic function is to allow groups of processes to be managed and manipulated as one. Windows 2000 Advanced Server provides an excellent platform for running database applications by including native support for Open Database Connectivity (ODBC), Oracle, and Microsoft SQL Server.

Authentication and Smart-Card Support

Windows 2000 Advanced Server provides technologies for using smart cards. That includes full support for the Kerberos V.5 protocol, a fast, single logon process that gives users the access they need for Windows 2000 Advanced Server-based enterprise resources and other environments that support this protocol. Additional benefits of this protocol are mutual authentication (both client and server must authenticate) and delegated authentication (the user's credential is tracked end to end).

Using Certificate Services and the certificate management tools in Windows 2000, you can organize your own PKI (the laws, policies, standards, and software that regulate or manipulate certificates and public and private keys). With a PKI, you can implement standards-based technologies, including smart-card logon capabilities, client authentication, secure email, digital signatures, and secure connectivity. With Certificate Services, you can set up and manage certification authorities (CAs) that issue and revoke X.509v3 certificates.

VPN lets users remotely access the network easily and securely. By connecting through a local ISP, connect-time charges are reduced. Several new, more secure protocols for creating VPNs include Layer 2 Tunneling Protocol (L2TP), which is a more secure version of Point-to-Point Tunneling Protocol (PPTP), and IPSec. L2TP is used for tunneling, address assignment, and authentication. IPSec is a standards-based protocol that provides the highest levels of VPN security. With IPSec, virtually everything above the networking layer can be encrypted.

Routing and Remote Access is a single integrated service that terminates connections from either dial-up or VPN clients, provides routing, or both. With Routing and Remote Access service, your Windows 2000 server can operate as a remote access server, a VPN server, a gateway, or a branch-office router.

When providing remote access, Routing and Remote Access supports Point-to-Point Protocol (PPP) and Extensible Authentication Protocol (EAP) to enable vendor-provided authentication methods for remote clients.

When working as a router, Routing and Remote Access supports both local and remote routing. In addition to physical dial-up, frame relay, Integrated Services Digital Network (ISDN), or X.25 connections, the connection can be direct to the corporate network or a point-to-point, branch-office VPN connection through the Internet.

Internet Authentication Service (IAS) provides you with a central point for managing authentication, authorization, accounting, and auditing of dial-up or VPN users. IAS uses the Internet Engineering Task Force (IETF) protocol called Remote Authentication Dial-In User Service (RADIUS). RADIUS is a security authentication protocol widely used by ISPs on non-Microsoft servers and is based on clients and servers on non-Microsoft remote servers. RADIUS is the most popular means of authenticating and authorizing dial-up and tunneled network users today.

Development Support

Developers writing server-based applications can work with the powerful tools available in Microsoft Visual Studio, as well as other development tools. The system architecture in Windows 2000 lets developers design applications that are easily translated and modified into local versions. Visual Studio 6.0 is designed to address the major requirements of organizations, thus creating modern enterprise solutions. The design themes for Visual Studio 6.0 include a complete suite of tools for component-based development, enhanced life-cycle productivity, enterprise database tools, enhanced support for teams, and integration with application services. Multilanguage technology allows applications to be translated and modified into local versions in hundreds of languages.

Disk and File Management Features

Enhancements to disk, volume, and file management make Windows 2000 Advanced Server a powerful and flexible file server, and make locating and accessing information easier for users. You can use disk quotas on volumes formatted with the NT File System (NTFS) to administer the amount of disk space available to individual users. With the Distributed File System (DFS), you can create a single directory tree that includes multiple file servers and file shares in a group, division, or enterprise. This lets users easily find files or folders distributed across the network. DFS shares can also be published as Volume Objects in Active Directory.

Using Distributed Link Tracking and NTFS, you can enable applications to track linked sources that have been moved. Using Distributed Authoring and Versioning, remote authors can manipulate files, file properties, directories, and directory properties on your server over an HTTP connection. You can use Indexing Service to search for information locally or on the network. Users can use powerful queries to search contents of files in different formats and languages, either through the Start menu or through HTML pages they view in a browser.

Removable Storage simplifies tracking your removable storage media and managing the hardware libraries that contain them. *Remote* Storage uses criteria you specify to copy files automatically to removable media. If hard-disk space drops below specified levels, Remote Storage removes the cached file content from the disk. If the file is needed later, the content is automatically recalled from storage. Because removable optical discs and tapes are less expensive per megabyte than hard disks, Removable Storage and Remote Storage can decrease your costs.

Disk Management is a graphical tool for managing disk storage; it offers many new features including support for new dynamic volumes that work outside the restriction of four partitions per disk, online disk management, local and remote drive administration, and Volume Mount Points. Volume Mount Points are used to connect, or mount, a local drive at any empty folder on a local NTFS-formatted volume.

IntelliMirror Features

To help reduce costs, administrators have asked for the highest levels of control over portable and desktop systems. IntelliMirror provides this control on systems running Windows 2000 Professional. You can use IntelliMirror to define policies based on the user's business roles, group memberships, and locations. Using these policies, Windows 2000 Professional desktops are automatically reconfigured to meet a specific user's requirements each time that user logs onto the network, regardless of the machine.

At the core of IntelliMirror are three features: user data management, software installation and maintenance, and user settings management. You can use these IntelliMirror features either independently or together, depending on the requirements of the environment. This gives you the ability to provide users with consistency and reliability no matter what computer they work on.

Internationalization Features

Windows 2000 Advanced Server now provides multilanguage support on a single system. Because of the system architecture in Windows 2000, the operating system, utilities, and properly written applications can be translated and modified into local versions for hundreds of languages; therefore, local administrators do not need to be fluent in technical English.

Internet Information Services Features

A variety of powerful Internet capabilities are available in Windows 2000 Advanced Server.

➤ *Internet Information Services (IIS)*—Simplifies sharing documents and information across a company intranet or the Internet. You can also deploy scalable and reliable Web-based applications and bring existing data and applications to the Web. IIS includes several other features as well.

➤ *Active Server Pages (ASP)*—A server-side scripting environment for creating powerful, interactive Web server applications. With ASP, developers can combine HTML pages, script commands, and COM components as needed to create these applications.

➤ *Windows Media Services*—Delivers high-quality streaming multimedia to users on the Internet and intranets.

➤ *Distributed Authoring and Versioning*—Lets remote authors manipulate files, file properties, directories, and directory properties on the server over an HTTP connection.

Management and Deployment of Applications

Along with directory consolidation in Active Directory, directory-enabled applications, and infrastructure in Active Directory and IntelliMirror, the following features help you simplify the deployment of applications on desktop and portable systems:

➤ *Web-Based Enterprise Management (WBEM)*—Provides consistent access to management information. WBEM is a Distributed Management Task Force (DMTF) initiative developed to gain widespread adoption of the industry-standard Common Information Model (CIM) designed by DMTF. CIM is an extensible object-oriented schema for administering systems, networks, applications, databases, and devices.

➤ *Windows Management Instrumentation (WMI), sometimes called CIM for Windows*—The Microsoft implementation of this technology. It is WBEM compliant. Using WMI, you can administer system events that are related to software applications, hardware components, and networks. WMI significantly extends the CIM schema for the Win32 System environment and Microsoft applications. You can use the CIM schema to map data from different sources in an organized way and to establish a correlation and association between management data.

With WMI, system administrators and management application developers can use one interface for local and remote access to Win32, System Monitor, WMI for WDM, registry, event logs, Desktop Management Interface (DMI), Simple

Network Management Protocol (SNMP), and any other data WMI generates. Administrators and developers, therefore, do not have to learn multiple APIs to write powerful administrative tools. WMI provides the infrastructure for system monitoring, event consolidation, CIM query-based event thresholds, and filtering. You can use this infrastructure for any management data WMI produces. This provides a single framework for monitoring previously miscellaneous events, including free disk space dropping below a preset threshold, TCP/IP service stopping, SNMP Link down trap being received from the default router for this computer, and the server load increasing past a specified threshold. WMI includes the CIM Object Manager (CIMOM) and supports provider architecture that generates a greater quantity of information in a related schema. Other software vendors can extend the schema and build added value on the already established CIM Win32 classes by using WMI.

The WMI interfaces work with Component Services (formerly known as COM+) and scripting languages including Visual Basic, Visual Basic Scripting Edition, JScript, and Per. This enables rapid development of scripts and sophisticated applications written in C++. The Windows Script Host object model for Windows 2000 is extended by the CIM object model, allowing you to build simple but powerful command-line or Web page scripts.

System and application management adaptation is available from WMI for numerous management solutions. Computer Associates' (CA) Real World Interface for Windows 2000 is a powerful administrative application based on CA's Unicenter TNG Framework. It provides easy access to management data by automatically discovering WMI resources, storing information about them, and displaying them through its 2D and 3D Windows or Java browser interfaces. You can find this application in the Valueadd folder on the Windows 2000 CD-ROM.

Multimedia Support

Windows 2000 Advanced Server includes a variety of features to expand the possibilities for multimedia on your server.

➤ *Windows Media Services*—Delivers high-quality streaming multimedia to users on the Internet and intranets.

➤ *Windows Quality of Service (QoS)*—Lets you control how network bandwidth is distributed to applications. Important applications can be given more bandwidth, less important applications less bandwidth. QoS-based services and protocols provide a guaranteed, end-to-end, express delivery system for information across the network.

➤ *Resource Reservation Protocol (RSVP)*—Used with multimedia and other applications that require consistent bandwidth or response levels on the network.

Using RSVP, these applications can acquire the necessary service quality from the network, and you can administer the impact that these applications have on network resources. RSVP is a request/grant type of service where client reservations are granted or denied based upon policy and network resource availability.

➤ *Asynchronous Transfer Mode (ATM)*—A high-speed connection-oriented protocol designed to transport multiple types of traffic across a network. It is applicable to both LANs and WANs. Using ATM, your network can concurrently transport a wide variety of network traffic including voice, data, image, and video.

Network Protocols and Technologies

Windows 2000 Advanced Server includes a variety of network protocols and technologies to extend the capabilities of your server, including DHCP, Internet Connection Sharing, NAT, VPN, Routing and Remote Access, ATM, and Fibre Channel.

Performance and Tuning Features

New features in Windows 2000 Advanced Server provide for better performance and the ability to tune your server to your needs and environment:

➤ *I2O (also called Intelligent Input/Output) architecture*—Allows for higher input/output performance on your servers by shifting certain I/O operations to a secondary processor. Using the job object, you can limit the amount of CPU time used by a Web application or site.

➤ *Process Accounting*—Gathers information about how Web sites use CPU resources, which can be crucial for making decisions about modifying hardware or applications and problems with scripts or applications.

➤ *HTTP compression*—Reduces used bandwidth and provides faster transmission of pages between the Web server and compression-enabled clients.

➤ *Windows QoS*—Allows you to control how applications are allotted network bandwidth.

➤ *RSVP*—Used with multimedia and other applications that require consistent bandwidth or response levels on the network.

➤ *Network Load Balancing (previously known as WLBS)*—Disburses incoming TCP/IP traffic between multiple servers.

Printer and Protocol Support

Windows 2000 Advanced Server provides a variety of new features for print servers.

➤ *Improved user interface*—Allows users to quickly search for and locate the most convenient printing resources. They can choose from among more than 2,500 different printers.

➤ *Plug and Play*—Lets the server recognize and adapt to hardware configuration changes automatically, without any intervention or restarting.

➤ *Internet Printing Protocol (IPP)*—Lets users print directly to an URL over an intranet or the Internet, as well as automatically generate print-job information in HTML format, so users can view it in their browsers.

➤ *System Monitor*—Provides the ability to monitor the operation of local and remote printers with a variety of criteria set, including Bytes Printed/Second, Job Errors, and Total Pages Printed.

➤ *Microsoft Management Console (MMC)*—Allows for remotely administering a Windows 2000 print server from anywhere on the network. You no longer have to install a printer driver on a Windows 2000 client computer for it to use a printer. The driver is downloaded automatically when the client connects to a Windows 2000 print server.

Remote Management

Windows 2000 includes a number of improvements for remote system management, including new delegation of administration support, Terminal Services, MMC, and more:

➤ *Terminal Services*—Lets you remotely administer Windows 2000 systems from anywhere on your network, instead of being limited to working locally on a server. The only limitation is that the network connection needed for this is a 28.8Kbps (or faster).

➤ *MMC*—Used to arrange the administrative tools and processes you need within a single interface. You preconfigure MMCs to delegate tasks to specific users and provide the user with the tools you select.

➤ *Windows Script Host (WSH)*—Lets you automate actions including creating a shortcut and connecting to and disconnecting from a network server. WSH is language independent. You can write scripts in common scripting languages such as Visual Basic Scripting Edition and JScript.

➤ *Remote Installation Services*—Allows remote installation of Windows 2000 Professional on any client computer that can be accessed and started remotely. This makes installation of multiple clients much simpler.

Server Reliability

Increased reliability is the most critical design goal of the Windows 2000 Advanced Server release. The system offers you a variety of capabilities that help provide increased levels of reliability, including improved memory management, more robust system architecture, better diagnostic tools, safe mode start, Recovery Console, Windows File Protection, Enhanced Backup utility, and Disk Defragmenter.

Server Scalability

The Windows 2000 Server family scales from small workgroups to enterprise data center deployments. It includes products that support up to 32 processors and advanced I/O. It also integrates network load balancing and new multiprocessor optimizations for business applications.

With Enterprise Memory Architecture, you can run applications that take advantage of large amounts of physical memory on Windows 2000 Advanced Server. Using applications written with the Address Windowing Extensions API, you can map more physical memory into the applications' virtual address memory space for improved performance.

The Windows 2000 Server family makes it possible to take advantage of the growing number of competitively priced 2-, 4-, 16-, and 32-way multiprocessor computers, using ever-faster Alpha and Intel technology.

Support for Existing Systems

Microsoft designed features for Windows 2000 that ensure it is compatible with as many systems and applications as possible. The features include support of industry standards, support for existing applications including BackOffice applications, and integration with existing operating systems.

Windows 2000 Advanced Server supports Unix, Novell NetWare, Windows NT Server 4, and Macintosh interoperability, allowing you to integrate Windows 2000 Advanced Server into an existing environment. You can introduce Windows 2000 Advanced Server gradually into a network environment because it provides migration paths from any number of existing systems, devices, and applications.

Terminal Services Features

The Windows 2000 Server family is the only server operating system that integrates terminal emulation services. With Terminal Services, a user can access programs running on the server from older devices on the network. Terminal Services provides this capability for both Windows and non-Windows-based client devices. Non-Windows devices require add-on software by Citrix Systems. Terminal Services provide several advantages, including centralized application access, remote access to applications, and single application access.

Installing Windows 2000 Server and Advanced Server

In this section we will provide an overview of the different system requirements of Windows 2000 Server and Advanced Server. Then we will discuss the preparations necessary for installation, as well as how to install the operating systems. We will address the question of whether to upgrade or install and will look at the different licensing modes, what a dual-boot system is, and the different Windows file systems. Additionally, we will cover the different optional components that you can choose from during installation, as well as the differences between workgroups and domains. The last topic we will discuss is how to install and configure disk mirroring. We will begin with Windows 2000 Server and then go into Advanced Server. Please keep in mind their similarities as discussed in previous sections.

System Requirements

Windows 2000 Server and Windows 2000 Advanced Server have fairly similar system requirements. They, like hardware, tend to operate better with the more you throw at them. Keep in mind that what may appear as excessive with Windows 2000 can only benefit you. The Windows 2000 environment runs remarkably well on systems with the bare requirements, but if you're going to be upgrading to this operating system, consider replacing or upgrading the hardware as well for optimum performance.

Windows 2000 Server

The hardware requirements for Windows 2000 Server are: a 133MHz or greater Pentium-compatible CPU, 256MB of RAM recommended (128MB is the minimum that is supported; 4GB is the maximum), and 2GB hard disk with a minimum 1GB of free space. Additional free hard disk space is required if you are installing over a network. Windows 2000 Server can support up to four CPUs on one machine. Users should also check Microsoft's Hardware Compatability List for the information about the current supported hardware.

Windows 2000 Advanced Server

The hardware requirements for Windows 2000 Advanced Server are: a 133-MHz or greater Pentium-compatible CPU, 256MB of RAM is recommended (128MB is the minimum supported; 8GB is the maximum), and 2GB hard disk with a minimum 1GB of free space. Additional free hard-disk space is required if you are installing over a network. Windows 2000 Advanced Server supports up to eight CPUs on one machine.

Installation Preparation

You must address several items before installing Windows 2000 Server or Advanced Server.

1. Check system requirements.

2. Decide if a full installation is needed or if you can upgrade.

3. Decide whether to use per seat or per server licensing mode.

4. Decide if you want to create a dual-boot machine so you can choose operating systems each time you boot.

5. Determine whether to use NTFS, FAT, or FAT32.

6. Determine which partition you will install in or if you should create a new one.

7. Decide what components need to be installed.

8. Determine how to handle networking, including IP addresses and TCP/IP name resolution.

9. Decide if you are going to use domains or workgroups.

10. Decide if you need to back up existing files, and if so, how you are going to do it.

11. Uncompress any DriveSpace or DoubleSpace volumes.

12. Disable disk mirroring.

13. Disconnect UPS devices.

14. Start Setup and follow the instructions provided.

This checklist in itself raises new questions. Here are some of those questions, along with their answers.

Do I Upgrade or Install?

Before you run Windows 2000 Server Setup, you need to decide whether to upgrade or to perform a new installation. *Upgrading will replace a version of Windows NT with Windows 2000 Server. Installing means you will wipe out the previous operating system or put Windows 2000 Server on a disk or disk partition with no previous operating system.* Do not upgrade to or install Windows 2000 on a compressed drive unless the drive was compressed with the NTFS compression utility. Uncompress a DriveSpace or DoubleSpace volume before running Windows 2000 Setup on it.

Domains are an important feature of both Windows NT Server and Windows 2000 Server. *A domain is a grouping of accounts and network resources under a single domain name and security boundary.* You must have one or more domains if you want to use domain-based user accounts and other domain security features in Windows 2000

Server. With Windows 2000, servers can have one of three roles: domain controllers, member servers, or standalone servers.

All domains must have at least one domain controller. A domain should have multiple domain controllers to support logon requests and directory updates. It is recommended that you plan the roles that your servers will have within domains in Windows 2000 before running Setup, but administrators can adjust these roles after Setup. Here are several important points to remember about upgrading an existing Windows NT domain to run with Windows 2000:

➤ You can upgrade member servers before or after upgrading domain controllers. When you upgrade the domain controllers in a Windows NT domain to Windows 2000, however, you must upgrade the primary domain controller first.

➤ When you begin upgrading domain controllers and you have a remote access server that is a member server, you should upgrade it before the last domain controller is upgraded.

➤ In Windows 2000 Server the roles of the servers in a domain are named somewhat differently from Windows NT Server. With Windows NT Server, the possible roles are primary domain controller (limited to one per domain), backup domain controller, member server, or standalone server. Windows 2000 has only one kind of domain controller (without a "primary" or "backup" designation) and includes the roles of member server and standalone server.

What Is Meant by Licensing Mode?

Windows 2000 supports two types of licensing modes: per seat and per server. Using per seat mode, each computer that accesses a Windows 2000 server requires a separate Client Access License (CAL). Per server licensing means that each concurrent connection to this server requires a separate CAL. Thus, at any one time, the Windows 2000 server can support a designated number of connections.

For example, if you selected the per server client licensing mode and five concurrent connections, the Windows 2000 server could have five computers (clients) connected at any one time. Those computers would not need any additional licenses.

If you are unsure which mode to use, choose per server, because you can change once from per server to per seat at no cost.

What Are the Different File Systems and What Do They Mean for Me?

You can choose between three file systems for disk partitions on a computer running Windows 2000 Server: NTFS, FAT, and FAT32. NTFS is the recommended system. It works most easily with large disks. FAT and FAT32 are similar to each other, except that FAT32 is designed for larger disks than FAT.

NTFS is an advanced file system designed for use specifically within the Windows 2000 operating system. It supports file system recovery, extremely large storage media, long file names, and various features for the Portable Operating System Interface for Unix (POSIX) subsystem. It also supports object-oriented applications by treating all files as objects with user-defined and system-defined attributes.

FAT is a table or list maintained by some operating systems to keep track of the status of various segments of disk space used for file storage. FAT is also called *file allocation table*.

FAT32 is a derivative of the file allocation table file system. FAT32 supports smaller cluster sizes than FAT, which results in more efficient space allocation on FAT32 drives.

NTFS is a more powerful file system than FAT and FAT32. Windows 2000 Server includes a new version of NTFS, which supports a variety of features including Active Directory, which is needed for domains, user accounts, and other important security features.

What Is a Dual-Boot Machine, and Would I Want to Create One?

A computer with more than one operating system is called a dual-boot or multiboot system. Windows 2000 supports dual booting with MS-DOS, Windows 3.x, Windows 95 and 98, and Windows NT 3.51 and 4.0. If you plan to use another operating system not listed here, please check the Microsoft Web site or that operating system's manufacturer. If you plan on using Linux, note that some versions come with third-party disk partitioning software; before using a disk partitioning package, check with Microsoft to verify that it is compatible with Windows 2000.

Each operating system must be installed in its volume or partition so it can retain its own files and configuration information. In addition, each volume or partition must be formatted with the correct file system. In this scenario Windows NT 4 and Windows 2000 support FAT16, FAT32 (not supported by Windows NT), and NTFS, whereas Windows 95 and 98 support only FAT16 and FAT32. MS-DOS only supports FAT16. Using the correct file system is key if you want to use files across both operating systems, but keep in mind that combinations of file systems can exist in separate partitions, especially if file compatibility is not an issue. For example, if you choose to dual boot Windows 2000 with Windows 98, for file sharing to occur, then FAT32 or FAT16 will have to be formatted for both volumes because Windows 98 does not support NTFS.

The drawbacks of a dual-boot system revolve around downgrading from NTFS to a different file system. NTFS offers better security than other file systems, and only Windows 2000 can use the dynamic disk format feature. A dual-boot system also uses more disk space with every software application you install. For example,

Microsoft Office has to be done twice, once for each operating system. Another potential problem is the complexity that is introduced. Compatibility issues could arise that may not be reversible, leading to the choice of one operating system over the other.

If, however, you need to use applications periodically that are not supported by Windows 2000, dual booting is a viable option. This scenario is a reality for companies that have custom-built applications that are not yet compatible with Windows 2000. Another situation where something is not supported is legacy hardware on a network segment that is being slowly migrated or upgraded to Windows 2000 Professional, and is using proprietary or custom-built client/server applications that are not compatible with Windows 2000. When deciding whether or not to use a dual boot a system, you should consider certain issues, listed in the next section, during installation preparation.

Preparing for Installation

To prepare for a dual-boot system, keep the following points in mind:

➤ Microsoft does not support installing multiple operating systems to the same volume. Therefore, you must create a separate volume or partition to install Windows 2000.

➤ If you have only one volume on a hard drive, then you must repartition and reformat it before you begin installation.

➤ To dual boot with Windows NT 4, Service Pack 4 or higher must be installed as well. Windows 2000 will automatically upgrade any NTFS partition it finds to NTFS 5, and for Windows NT 4 to use NTFS 5, it needs Service Pack 4.

➤ When installing with MS-DOS or Windows 95, you must install them first to prevent them from overwriting the Windows 2000 boot sector and startup files.

➤ Do not install Windows 2000 onto a compressed drive that has not been compressed with the NTFS compression utility.

➤ Different computer names must be given if each operating system is on a Windows 2000 secure domain.

➤ When formatting partitions, use FAT16 for partitions under 2GB if using Windows 2000 with MS-DOS, Windows 3.x, Windows 95 and 98, or Windows NT.

➤ When formatting partitions, use FAT32 for partitions over 2GB but less than 32GB. Windows 2000 will format hard drives over 2GB automatically to FAT32.

➤ If a partition is going to be more than 32GB in size, then it should be partitioned using NTFS.

Dual Booting with MS-DOS, Windows 95 or 98, and Windows 2000

You will experience less difficulty if MS-DOS or Windows 95 or 98 is installed prior to Windows 2000. Be sure you have also partitioned and formatted the target drive into separate volumes. To make the appropriate partitions, use the FDISK command from a Windows or DOS boot disk and follow the instructions. If you need help, type FDISK /? at the command prompt. You will have to restart your computer afterward, then format your partitions.

1. Install MS-DOS, Windows 95, or Windows 98 on the C: drive.

2. Install Windows 2000 on the D: drive.

If Windows 98 or 95 is not updated automatically, go into the MS-DOS.SYS file and edit the line that reads bootmulti=0, so as to read bootmulti=1. This will let Windows 95 or 98 know it is in a dual-boot system. This should not be necessary, but keep it in mind.

Dual Booting with Windows NT 4 and Windows 2000

To set up the installations for these two operating systems, make sure that if NTFS partitions already exist on a hard drive, Windows NT 4 has at least Service Pack 4 installed. This is not a long-term solution. The purpose of the update for NTFS on Service Pack 4 is so Windows 2000 can be evaluated.

Make sure each Windows installation has a different computer name if it is a part of either a Windows NT or Windows 2000 domain.

Set up separate partitions (a C: and D: drive) with the appropriate file system (NTFS). Using a Windows NT boot disk, follow the instructions on the screen, and then format them to the file system you have chosen. Install Windows NT first, then install Windows 2000. With the Windows 2000 installation, just follow the on-screen instructions. When prompted where to install Windows 2000, select the unused NTFS partition, which should be the D: drive.

Setting Up the Default Startup Operating System

In order to have a choice of which operating system to use, you used to have to edit the boot.ini file to get the boot loader in Windows NT to show you your choices. You may want to try doing it through the control panel instead. If you do, just follow these instructions after Windows 2000 is loaded:

1. Point to Start.

2. Point to Settings.

3. Click on Control Panel.

4. Double-click on System.

5. On the Advanced tab, click on Startup And Recovery.

6. Under System Startup, in the Default Operating System list, click on the operating system you want to start if it is not already selected from the list displayed during startup.

7. In the Display List Of Operating Systems For box, type the number of seconds the list should be displayed before the default operating system automatically starts.

In the event that you have never installed any version of Windows, the Microsoft Web site has some instructions. Otherwise, you can follow the literature that accompanies the operating system. In general, Windows 95 and 98 use the command setup in the directory win95 or win98, where Windows NT and Windows 2000 put it under the directory i386 command winnt. Note there are a couple different ways to do these installations. The nicest is to copy the Windows CAB files to the hard drive and then run the installation directly from the hard drive. It takes up more room but also means you do not have to look for the CD when you make a change or go looking for the correct network drive.

What Components Can I Choose from for Installation?

Windows 2000 Server includes a variety of core components that Setup installs automatically. You can also choose from a number of optional components that extend the functionality of Windows 2000 Server. These components can be installed during setup, or you can add them later if you determine you need them.

The following is a list of components you can add:

➤ Accessories and Utilities

➤ Certificate Services

➤ Indexing Service

➤ Internet Information Services (IIS)

➤ Management and Monitoring Tools

➤ Message Queuing

➤ Networking Services

➤ Other Network File and Print Services

➤ Remote Installation Services

➤ Remote Storage

➤ Script Debugger

➤ Terminal Services

➤ Terminal Services Licensing

➤ Windows Media Services

What Is the Difference between a Workgroup and a Domain?

A domain is a grouping of accounts and network resources under a single domain name and security boundary. A workgroup is a more basic grouping, intended only to help users find objects such as printers and shared folders within that group. Domains are the recommended choice for all networks except very small ones with few users.

In a workgroup, users might have to enter multiple passwords, one for each network resource. In a domain, passwords and permissions are simpler to administer because a domain has a single, centralized database of user accounts, permissions, and other network details.

What Is Disk Mirroring?

Disk Mirroring is a set of software processes that maintains a backup copy of a volume at all times. Each mirror of a volume resides on a different disk; ideally, each disk has its own controller. If one member of the mirror set becomes unavailable, you can use the other mirror to gain access to the volume's data.

Step-by-Step Installation of Windows 2000 Server and Windows 2000 Advanced Server

When installing Windows 2000 Server and Windows 2000 Advanced Server, you can choose several methods to begin the Setup program. The directions for each are listed here.

To start setup from the CD-ROM on a computer running Windows:

1. Insert the CD-ROM in the drive.

2. For a computer running any version of Windows other than Windows 3.x, wait for Setup to display a dialog box.

3. For a computer running Windows 3.x, use File Manager to change to the CD-ROM drive and the i386 directory. Then double-click on winnt.exe.

To start setup from a network:

1. On a network server, share the installation files, either by inserting the CD-ROM and sharing the CD-ROM drive or by copying the files from the i386 folder on the CD-ROM to a shared folder.

2. On the computer on which you want to install Windows 2000, connect to the shared Setup files:

   ➤ If you are sharing the CD-ROM drive, connect to the shared drive and change to the I386 folder.

   ➤ If you are sharing a folder, connect to that folder.

1

3. Find and run the appropriate file on the i386 directory of the CD-ROM or in the shared folder:

   ➤ From a computer running MS-DOS or Windows 3.x, run winnt.exe.

   ➤ From a computer running Windows 95, Windows 98, Windows NT 3.51, Windows NT 4, or a version of Windows 2000, run winnt32.exe.

4. Follow the Setup instructions.

To start setup from the CD-ROM on a computer running MS-DOS:

1. Insert the CD-ROM in the drive.

2. At the command prompt, type: d:, where d is the drive letter of the CD-ROM drive (it could be different for your system) and then press Enter.

3. Type cd i386 and then press Enter.

4. Type winnt and then press Enter.

5. Follow the Setup instructions.

To start setup for a new installation by starting the computer from the CD-ROM:

1. Determine whether the computer on which you want to start Setup can be started from the CD-ROM drive, and whether you want to perform a new installation. Continue only if both are true.

2. With the computer turned off, insert the CD-ROM in the drive.

3. Start the computer and wait for Setup to display a dialog box.

4. Follow the Setup instructions.

Note: *Some systems can be booted from the CD-ROM drive if the computer's CMOS setup is altered to reflect that ability.*

To start setup for a new installation by starting the computer from floppy disks:

1. Determine whether you want to perform a new installation or an upgrade. Continue only if you want to perform a new installation.

2. Locate both the Windows 2000 Setup floppy disks and the Windows 2000 CD-ROM.

3. With your computer turned off, insert the first Setup disk into drive A:.

4. Turn on your computer.

5. Follow the Setup instructions

To start setup and provide a mass storage driver or a HAL file:

1. Determine whether you need to supply Setup with a special file—a mass storage driver or a Hardware Abstraction Layer (HAL) file—supplied by your hardware manufacturer. If you have a mass storage controller for your hard disk, make sure the controller is on the Hardware Compatibility List (HCL) released with the software (hcl.txt in the Support folder on the Windows 2000 Server CD-ROM). This file lists only the devices for which drivers are included on the Windows 2000 Server CD-ROM. If your controller is not listed in the HCL, check to see if the manufacturer has supplied a separate driver file for use with Windows 2000.

   If you have a highly specialized computer system, review your hardware documentation to see if your computer manufacturer supplies a custom HAL file.

2. If you determine that you need a driver or HAL file supplied by your hardware manufacturer, before beginning Setup, locate the floppy disk containing the file.

3. During the early part of Setup, watch the bottom of the screen for a line that prompts you to press F6. Press the appropriate key as follows:

   ➤ To supply the driver for a mass storage controller to Setup, press F6 as instructed.

   ➤ To supply a HAL file to Setup, press F5.

4. Follow further prompts for guidance in supplying the driver file to Setup so that it can gain access to the mass storage controller.

To set up remaining settings:

1. During Setup, in the Regional Settings dialog box, follow the instructions for customizing language, locale, and accessibility settings. You can set up Windows 2000 to use multiple languages and regional options.

2. In the Personalize Your Software dialog box, type your name and, optionally, your organization.

3. In the Licensing Modes dialog box, select your client-licensing mode, either per seat or per server.

4. Enter a computer name. The recommended name length for most languages is 15 characters or less. For languages that require more storage space per character, such as Chinese, Japanese, and Korean, the recommended length is seven characters or less.

5. During Setup, in Administrator Password, type a password of up to 127 characters. For the strongest system security, use a password of at least seven characters, with a mixture of uppercase and lowercase letters, numbers, and other characters such as *, ?, or $.

6. In Confirm Password, type the password again.

7. In the Windows 2000 Components dialog box, select the components you need.

8. During Setup, in the Date and Time Settings dialog box, set the date, time, and time zone.

9. If you want the system to adjust automatically for daylight savings time, select the Automatically Adjust Clock For Daylight Saving Changes checkbox.

10. To allow Setup to assign or obtain an IP address, during setup, in the Networking Settings dialog box, click Typical Settings.

11. To set a static IP address and information needed for WINS and DNS, during Setup, in the Networking Settings dialog box, click on Custom Settings.

12. In the Networking Components dialog box, click on Internet Protocol (TCP/IP), and then click on Properties.

13. In the Internet Protocol (TCP/IP) Properties dialog box, click on Use The Following IP Address.

14. In IP Address And Subnet Mask, type the appropriate numbers. (If appropriate, specify the Default gateway as well.)

15. Under Use The Following DNS Server Addresses, type the address of a preferred DNS server and, optionally, an alternative DNS server. If the local server is the preferred or alternate DNS server, type the same IP address as assigned in the previous step.

16. If you will use a WINS server, click on Advanced. On the WINS tab, click on Add to add the IP address of one or more WINS servers. If the local server is a WINS server, type the IP address assigned in Step 5.

17. Click on OK in each dialog box, and continue with Setup.

18. During Setup, choose whether your server will be in a workgroup or a domain.

19. Specify the workgroup or domain name.

When the Setup wizard completes the installation of Windows 2000, the computer will restart. Setup has now performed the basic installation. The Configure Your Server program will appear on the screen when you log on as the computer's administrator. This makes further configuration easy. At this point you can register your copy of Windows 2000 Server and configure your server.

Chapter Summary

Windows 2000 Server and Advanced Server have many new features and enhancements. The Windows 2000 Server family builds on the strengths of Windows NT technology.

Windows 2000 Server integrates Internet technologies across all services, from file and print to advanced line-of-business application services, because Internet Information Server 5.0 (IIS) is completely integrated at the operating system level. Windows 2000 Server lets organizations share information more efficiently using the Web, create Web-based business applications, and bring Windows 2000 Server operating system functionality to the Internet.

Windows 2000 Server includes COM and COM+ for application services needed to build integrated component-based Web-aware applications faster and more efficiently.

Windows 2000 Server delivers high-performance processing on high-performance networks. Windows File Protection prevents new software installations from replacing essential system files, and IIS Application Protection keeps Web applications running separately from the Web server itself to prevent an application from crashing the Web server.

Distributed File System (DFS) lets users build a single, hierarchical view of multiple file servers and file-server shares on a network.

The Integrated Directory Service for Windows 2000 allows Active Directory to administer Windows-based clients and servers centrally through a single management interface in a way that reduces costs.

High interoperability with client computers allows for the support of Windows NT Workstation, Windows 9x, Windows 3.x, Macintosh, and Unix operating systems. This allows for integration with existing management applications and framework via Windows Management Services.

Windows Clustering includes clustering technologies such as network load balancing clusters and server clusters. Server clusters provide high availability for applications through the failover of resources on Windows 2000 Advanced Server. Network load balancing clusters provide high scalability and availability for TCP/IP-based services and applications.

With the Routing and Remote Access service, a Windows 2000 server can be configured to operate as a remote access server, a VPN server, a gateway, or a branch-office router.

Active Server Pages (ASP) is a server-side scripting environment for creating powerful, interactive Web server applications.

Windows Quality of Service (QoS) allows for the control of how applications are allocated network bandwidth as well as how applications are allotted network bandwidth. Network bandwidth is the amount of information that can be transmitted over a network cable at a given time.

Windows 2000 Advanced Server supports Unix, Novell NetWare, Windows NT Server 4, and Macintosh interoperability, allowing you to integrate Windows 2000 Advanced Server into a preexisting multiprotocol network environment.

Domains are an important feature of both Windows NT Server and Windows 2000 Server. With Windows 2000, servers can have one of three roles: domain controllers, member servers, or standalone servers. The roles of servers in a domain are named somewhat differently with Windows 2000 Server as compared with Windows NT Server.

Windows 2000 Server includes a variety of core components that Setup installs automatically, such as the following:

➤ Certificate Services

➤ Indexing Service

➤ Internet Information Services (IIS)

➤ Networking Services

➤ Other Network File and Print Services

➤ Remote Installation Services

➤ Terminal Services

➤ Terminal Services Licensing

➤ Windows Media Services

You can build secure, reliable, scalable solutions that ease the integration of mixed systems and applications using the Windows Distributed Internet Applications Architecture, which is the development model of the Windows platform.

Windows Media Services allows multimedia streaming into applications, corporate communications, customer and sales support, news and entertainment services, and product promotions. It assists organizations in creating dynamic and interactive content in their daily communications and documents.

Using Active Directory, organizations can efficiently share and manage information about network resources and users. Likewise, the Meta-directory service lets Active Directory manage identity information that applications and network services store in places other than a directory, and synchronization services let Active Directory share information with services.

The Windows 2000 Server operating system provides a united file and print infrastructure for securely sharing, storing, and publishing data. Organizations can use Windows 2000 Server to improve storage management, help users locate and access information, and extend the usefulness of shared printers.

Windows 2000 Server lets you choose from three file systems for disk partitions: NTFS, FAT, and FAT32. NTFS, the recommended file system, is designed for use specifically with Windows 2000. It supports object-oriented applications by treating all files as objects with user- and system-defined attributes.

Review Questions

1. Windows 2000 Server builds on the strengths of what technology?

   a. Windows 95

   b. DOS

   c. Windows NT 4

   d. Windows 98

2. Which of the following is specifically designed for Web documents?

   a. Windows Media Services

   b. Active Server Pages

   c. Component Object Model+ (COM+)

   d. XML Parser

3. In Windows 2000, Terminal Services are what percentage more scalable and have dramatically improved performance for both high- and low-bandwidth connections?

   a. 10

   b. 5

   c. 20

   d. 25

4. What allows users to configure and manage high-quality media content across the Internet and intranets, thus delivering live and on-demand content to the maximum number of users?

   a. WebDAV

   b. Windows Media Services

   c. Terminal Services

   d. XML Parser

5. Windows 2000 Server delivers high-performance processing on high-performance networks with support for up to what size networks?

 a. 850MB

 b. 500MB

 c. 2GB

 d. 1GB

6. What allows the connection of remote workers, telecommuters, and branch offices to the corporate network through dial-up, leased line, and Internet links?

 a. Routing and Remote Access

 b. Virtual Private Networking (VPN)

 c. Encrypting File System

 d. Certificate Server

7. Kill Process Tree allows administrators to do which of the following?

 a. Reverse the process that has occurred as a result of fragmentation

 b. Troubleshoot the system during startup by changing the default settings or removing a newly installed program that is causing a problem

 c. Configure services across the operating system, including IIS, to restart automatically if they fail

 d. Stop all processes related to a failed process or application without rebooting the system

8. Which of the following saves deployment time by using SysPrep to create an image of a computer's hard drive that can be used to duplicate onto other computers?

 a. System Preparation Tool

 b. Configuration Wizard

 c. Service Pack Slipstreaming

 d. Internet Connection Sharing

9. Which statement is true about Dynamic DNS Service?

 a. Simplifies operating system updates by mirroring one master image of the operating system on the network

 b. Allows the operating system to automatically detect and recognize newly installed hardware components, simplifying network system configuration and reducing service downtime

 c. Simplifies object naming and location through Internet protocols and improves scalability, performance, and interoperability

 d. Allows users to locate and connect to printers based on criteria such as location, ability to print color, or speed

10. Which of the following provides server administration and task automation via the command line instead of graphical user interface tools with scripts?

    a. Group Policy

    b. Centralized Desktop Management

    c. Integrated Directory Services

    d. Cluster Administration

11. Network load balancing clusters provide high scalability and availability for TCP/IP-based services and applications by combining up to what maximum number of servers running Windows 2000 Advanced Server into single clusters?

    a. 12

    b. 40

    c. 32

    d. 100

12. With Routing and Remote Access Service, your Windows 2000 server can operate as which of the following?

    a. Remote access server

    b. VPN server

    c. A gateway

    d. All of the above

13. Which of the following makes it easier to track your removable storage media and to manage the hardware libraries that contain them?

    a. Disk Management

    b. Volume Mount Points

    c. Distributed Authoring and Versioning

    d. Removable Storage

14. IntelliMirror provides the highest levels of control over portable desktop systems on systems running which operating system?

    a. Windows 2000 Professional

    b. Windows 2000 Server

    c. Windows 98

    d. Windows 2000 Advanced Server

15. What is used to connect, or mount, a local drive at any empty folder on an NTFS-formatted volume?

    a. Online Disk Management

    b. Local and Remote Drive Administration

    c. Volume Mount Points

    d. None of the above

16. Using Distributed Authoring and Versioning, remote authors can manipulate files, file properties, directories, and directory properties on your server over what type of connection?

    a. Dial-up

    b. HTTP

    c. FTP

    d. SMTP

17. Which of the following is an extensible object-oriented schema for administering systems, networks, applications, databases, and devices?

    a. CIM

    b. WBEM

    c. ASP

    d. DMTF

18. Which of the following is a high-speed connection-oriented protocol designed to transport multiple types of traffic across a network?

    a. ATM

    b. TCP/IP

    c. IPX/SPX

    d. NetBIOS

19. Which of the following is an advanced file system designed for use specifically within the Windows 2000 operating system?

    a. FAT

    b. FAT32

    c. NTFS

    d. All the above

20. Which operating system can you use to integrate Windows 2000 Advanced Server into a preexisting environment?

    a. Unix

    b. Novell NetWare

    c. Windows NT Server

    d. All the above

Real-World Projects

Lesha Camille, a network analyst for the Red Family Law Firm, wants to propose a solution as to whether or not the law firm should upgrade its five servers to Windows 2000. Each server runs Windows NT 4 with varied configurations; one of these systems runs a customized accounting and client tracking system that is not compatible with Windows 2000.

Camille is uncertain whether or not to upgrade or make fresh installations. She is also considering a dual-boot system because the accounting and client tracking system is updated only once a week but is still a mission-critical system. Because compatibility is an issue, she wants to take an inventory of all the servers' hardware and compare it with the minimum/recommended system requirements for Windows 2000 Server. She also wants to check the Hardware Compatibility List (HCL) on the Microsoft Web site.

Based on Camille's proposal, with the firm's IT budget notwithstanding, the Red Family Law Firm has decided to hire you as a network consultant to do the legwork for them, with Camille providing any assistance you may need along the way. The two of you are going to decide whether to upgrade or do fresh installations. You will also do any upgrading if necessary and then migrate the systems to Windows 2000.

Project 1.1

To analyze whether to upgrade or install Windows 2000 Server, perform the following steps:

1. Upgrading will replace a preexisting version of Windows NT with Windows 2000 Server. This will retain current settings so the servers will need only minimal configurations afterward.

2. Installing Windows 2000 Server will wipe out any previous operating system installation on the server, including data and programs. The servers will need to be configured from scratch.

1

3. When either upgrading or installing, make sure to first back up any data that should be saved or you want to save.

4. When either upgrading or installing, make sure that you do the primary domain controller first to avoid any conflicts. Windows 2000 Server will not allow two domain controllers in a single domain. Also, keep in mind that in Windows 2000, servers are called *domain controllers, member servers,* and *standalone servers,* unlike in Windows NT where they are called *primary domain controllers, backup domain controllers, member servers,* and *standalone servers.*

Doing an upgrade to a server will ensure minimal configuration and, overall, make the migration easier and less time consuming. Doing a full installation will take longer and the servers will need to be reconfigured. Doing the domain controller first will ensure there will be no conflict with another domain controller. You will know if a conflict occurs, because Windows 2000 will tell you, and it will not configure the server as a domain controller.

Project 1.2

To complete an upgrade on a network with four servers, all running Windows NT 4 with varied configurations, perform the following steps:

1. Insert the CD into the CD-ROM drive.

2. Wait for the dialog box to appear.

3. Follow the screens as they come up. When asked if you want to install or upgrade, choose the upgrade option.

The process is simple. Just follow the setup wizard and everything should go smoothly. If you are worried that your original configuration will not carry over, then print it out or write it down. After the upgrade is complete, doing the domain controller first, double-check each server and make any necessary changes.

Project 1.3

To set up one of the servers as a dual-boot system, perform the following steps:

1. Separate the volume into two separate NTFS partitions using the Windows NT setup disks.

2. Create each partition as the C: drive and the D: drive.

3. Install Windows NT first into the C: drive partition, giving it a unique computer name.

4. Then install Windows 2000 into the D: drive partition, giving it a unique computer name.

If the Boot Loader does not update automatically, instead of altering the Windows NT boot.ini file, from within Windows 2000 follow these steps:

1. Point to Start.

2. Point to Settings.

3. Click on Control Panel.

4. Double-click on System.

5. On the Advanced tab, click on Startup and Recovery.

6. Under System Startup, in the Default Operating List, click on the operating system you want to start.

This will allow for a temporary solution when waiting for upgrades for software packages that are not yet compatible with Windows 2000. In addition, you will be able to get a little more life out of older software packages no longer supported by their vendors.

CHAPTER TWO

Network Architecture

After completing this chapter, you will be able to:

✓ Understand Windows 2000 networking

✓ Identify a small business network

✓ Understand a growing business network

✓ Understand what an enterprise-ready infrastructure is

✓ Understand networking architecture

✓ Identify the different LAN and WAN topologies employed

✓ Understand what both Internet and intranet structures are

✓ Understand what a Virtual Private Network is

✓ Identify and plan for a network architecture

✓ Identify simple and hybrid LAN topologies

✓ Identify enterprise-wide topologies

✓ Identify WAN topologies

✓ Understand network optimization

✓ Use network analysis and monitoring tools

✓ Install Network Monitor and the Network Monitor driver

✓ Monitor network performance

✓ Use System Monitor

✓ Evaluate monitoring results

✓ Use network management tools

✓ Understand data monitoring archiving

✓ Understand network troubleshooting tools

To be an effective administrator, you must first understand how networks are designed and set up. Administrators also need to understand how to monitor and analyze network performance and be familiar with troubleshooting and the tools available in Windows 2000. In this chapter we will present an overview of small business networks, growing business networks, and the enterprise-ready infrastructure. We will cover the structure of the Internet, Virtual Private Networks (VPNs), and the various topologies for local area networks (LANs) and wide area networks (WANs). We won't cover metropolitan area networks (MANs). We will take you through network analysis tools, network monitoring tools, monitoring network performance, network management tools, and troubleshooting a network—the basis of this being Windows 2000 networks and tools. Be prepared if you have never been down the network road before; this chapter does assume a little knowledge of basic networks. For others, this may be review.

Windows 2000 Networking Overview

Traditional networks provide for the fast access of information, improve information management, and increase the productivity of employees with easier internal communications. Networks connected to the Internet let businesses streamline their business-to-business communications and transactions, as well as connect with their customers. Any business can benefit from a network operating system (NOS) that makes creating networks and Internet connections simple, fast, secure, and reliable.

With Windows 2000, an organization will be able to build an internal network quickly and easily. Windows 2000 is an open, standards-based, networking platform giving organizations the ability to build electronic-business solutions that will interoperate with other network operating systems. Windows 2000 offers small business networks, growing business networks, and the enterprise-ready infrastructure the ability to use network LAN and WAN technologies so that businesses can connect to the Internet faster, combine networks with different vendor systems, and keep pace with concurrent business changes. The Windows 2000 network in this way is dynamic; it can scale to the specific network needs regardless of the size of the organization's network.

Small Business Networks

Most small businesses use peer-to-peer networks and share Internet connections. Small businesses generally don't have IT departments with help desks and truckloads of network technicians at their beck and call. Nor do they have network-savvy personnel who set up, configure, and do major installations, as well as perform network maintenance. A lot of small businesses outsource their network needs to consultants and other independent contractors. The idea of Windows 2000 networking is to enable small businesses to create fast, secure, and reliable networks and Internet connections, without having to be technical experts.

2

Windows 2000 gives nontechnical personnel the ability to set up a small network with plug-and-play technologies that automatically detect and install the appropriate software for hundreds of network modems and network interface cards (NICs) from industry-leading vendors. Also, because Universal Serial Bus (USB) development has increased and made a USB connection a standard port connection on PCs, small businesses can benefit by having USB network connections that are plug-in ready. This gives small businesses the ability to add network functionality to their computers without ever cracking open a computer's case to install a network card. Most everything that a small business network using Windows 2000 will need can be bought off the shelf at local retail and wholesale stores.

For small businesses, off-the-shelf networks are normal. With Windows 2000, setting up these networks consists mainly of plugging in connections to hubs and computers. The New Connections wizard walks you through configuring Internet connections and connections to other computers within a workgroup. You can do most of the setup simply with a login name, password, and telephone number (if you are using a dial-up Internet connection), without having to answer tedious technical questions. For small business networks, the ease of setup, configuration, and use is key; speed is generally secondary. As you will see in the next section, the needs of small business networks are different from those of growing business networks that have expansion issues to address.

Growing Business Networks

Growing business networks need greater power and flexibility than small business networks. Growing businesses need network features designed for medium-sized and larger organizations. Their networks need to connect and support hundreds to thousands of users with complex configurations and applications. The scalability of Windows 2000 Server allows for this kind of support, letting a growing business dynamically add to its network over time.

Among the needs of growing business networks are support for full-featured Internet standards for address naming and management. To achieve this, growing business networks need access to such technologies as the Dynamic Host Configuration Protocol (DHCP) and Domain Name System (DNS), as well as legacy support for the Windows Internet Naming Service (WINS), NetBEUI, IPX/SPX, and AppleTalk. Combining these technologies means that TCP/IP networking can share files, printers, and network and Internet connections with existing network technologies, such as Windows NT 4, Novell NetWare, and Apple Macintosh's AppleTalk protocol. Integrating several network technologies is a major aim for an organization that is expanding and that may merge with other companies that do not use the same NOS.

Growing business networks need communication services if they have remote users, as well as telephony services to provide traveling users with remote access to the company network resources. Such services also help remote users, such as sales and marketing reps, keep at their fingertips vital information they will need to present to clients. Using telephony services means that organizations can integrate voice-mail and email, and create video-conferencing systems over their networks. It also lets the organization integrate video conferencing into its Web pages. The main focus here is using telephone lines, leased lines, and the Internet to connect multimedia capabilities securely and easily, as well as to allow for remote access, giving growing businesses similar solutions to the enterprise-ready infrastructures of larger organizations.

Enterprise-Ready Infrastructure

Enterprise-class organizations have large geographically disbursed networks that are complex in nature and require scalability and centralized management. Enterprise-class organizations need full-featured DHCP capabilities to centrally configure more than just Internet addresses; they also need to integrate dynamic DNS services, WINS, and the Active Directory service. Because of the enormous size of these networks, they need load balancing, fault tolerance, failover NIC support, fault-tolerant clusters, fast network connections, and 24-hour runtime with the ability to transfer 2 Gbps or more on a single system.

They also need IP Security (IPSec) services with hardware-encryption offload support to protect large volumes of sensitive data transmissions over complex network segments. With public-key support, smart cards, and Remote Authentication Dial-in User Service (RADIUS)-based authentication and authorization for sharing information, securing communications with remote and mobile users, business partners, and their customers is easier. The key to lowering the cost of growing and managing these kinds of sophisticated networks is network access policies and system administration from any location with centralized control.

In addition to the need for integrating several voice, data, and video-streaming technologies into mission-critical systems and applications, more will be desired, especially in e-commerce forums. The enterprise-ready infrastructure will also need telephony standards, multicasting support, and end-to-end Quality of Services (QoS) for controlling traffic prioritization and network congestion. As already noted, the enterprise-ready infrastructure is complex, incorporating many types of networking technologies; it will likely have several types of topologies and network architectures.

Networking Architecture

The two most common networks are LANs and WANs. A LAN spans a relatively small area. Most LANs are confined to a single building or group of buildings. One LAN can be connected to other LANs over any distance via telephone lines and radio waves. A system of LANs connected in this way is a WAN. WANs are expansive and can connect LANs in other states or countries.

LANs

Most LANs connect workstations and personal computers. Each node or individual computer on a LAN has its own CPU with which it executes programs. It is also able to access data and devices anywhere on the LAN. This prevents businesses from having to purchase each employee his or her own devices, such as laser printers, and it allows users to share data. Users can also communicate with each other over the LAN, by sending email or engaging in chat sessions.

There are many different types of LANs—Ethernet is the most common for PCs. Most Apple Macintosh networks are based on Apple's AppleTalk network system, which is built into Macintosh computers. All LANs are different and can be separated by their topologies, protocols, and the media used for physical connectivity. The following characteristics differentiate one LAN from another:

➤ *Topology*—The geometric arrangement of devices on the network. For example, devices can be arranged in a ring or in a straight line.

➤ *Protocol*—The rules and encoding specifications for sending data. The protocol also determines whether the network uses peer-to-peer or client/server architecture.

➤ *Media*—Twisted-pair wire, coaxial cables, or fiber-optic cables can connect devices. Some networks function without physically connecting media, communicating instead using radio waves and infrared.

LANs are capable of transmitting data much faster than over telephone lines; but the distances are limited, as is the number of computers that can be attached to a single LAN, depending on the topology. We will discuss the various topologies in detail later in the chapter.

WANs

A WAN is a computer network that spans a relatively large geographical area employing both LAN and enterprise-wide topologies as buildings blocks. Typically, a WAN consists of two or more LANs connected by media not owned by the company, usually telephone lines or radio waves. They can also be connected through leased lines, such as T1 or T3 connections or satellites. Many large corporations use WANs because they have satellite offices in different states and even in different countries. A WAN in this regard will appear to users as being seamless and similar to using the network in their offices. The largest WAN is the Internet, which is made up of thousands of LANs spanning the world.

The Internet

The Internet is a global network connecting millions of computers around the world. As of 1999, the Internet had more than 200 million users worldwide, and that number is growing rapidly. More than 100 countries are linked to exchange data, news, and opinions.

Unlike company-owned online services that are centrally controlled, the Internet is decentralized by design. Each Internet computer, called a *host*, is independent of the other servers on the network. Its operators can choose which Internet services to use and which local services to make available to the global Internet community. This chaotic design works exceedingly well.

People can access the Internet in a variety of ways. Most online services, such as America Online (AOL), offer access to some Internet services. Users can also gain access through commercial Internet service providers (ISPs), often provided through local phone companies.

Intranet

An intranet is a network based on TCP/IP, belonging to an organization, usually a corporation, and accessible only by the organization's authorized members, employees, or customers and vendors. An intranet's Web site looks and acts the same as any other Web site, but a firewall surrounding an intranet fends off unauthorized access.

A firewall prevents unauthorized access to or from a private network. Firewalls can be implemented in both hardware and/or software. All messages entering or leaving the intranet pass through the firewall, where they are examined. Those that do not meet the specified security criteria are blocked.

Several types of firewall techniques are listed here:

➤ *Packet filter*—Looks at each packet entering or leaving the network and accepts or rejects it based on user-defined rules. Packet filtering is fairly effective and transparent to users, but difficult to configure. In addition, it is susceptible to IP spoofing.

➤ *Application gateway*—Applies security mechanisms to specific applications, such as FTP and Telnet servers. This is very effective, but can impose performance degradation.

➤ *Circuit-level gateway*—Applies security mechanisms when a TCP or User Datagram Protocol (UDP) connection is established. Once the connection has been made, packets can flow between the hosts without further checking.

➤ *Proxy server*—Intercepts all messages entering and leaving the network. The proxy server effectively hides the true network addresses.

In practice, many firewalls use two or more of these techniques in concert. A firewall is considered a first line of defense in protecting private information.

Like the Internet itself, intranets are used to share information. Secure intranets are now the fastest-growing segment of the Internet because they are much less expensive to build and manage than private networks based on proprietary protocols.

Virtual Private Network

A VPN connects the components of one network over another network. VPNs accomplish this by allowing the user to tunnel through the Internet or another public network in a manner that provides the same security and features in a private network.

With a VPN, users working at home or on the road can connect securely to a remote corporate server using the routing infrastructure provided by a public internetwork (such as the Internet). From the user's perspective, the VPN is a point-to-point connection between the user's computer and a corporate server. The nature of the intermediate internetwork is irrelevant to the user because the data appears as though it is being sent over a dedicated private link.

VPN technology also allows a corporation to connect to branch offices or to other companies over a public internetwork, while maintaining secure communications. The VPN connection across the Internet logically operates as a WAN link between the sites and appears to the user as a private network communication, even though this communication occurs over a public internetwork. VPN technology is designed to address issues surrounding the business trend toward telecommuting and widely distributed global operations, where workers must be able to connect to central resources and communicate with each other.

Identifying and Planning a Network Architecture

A topology is the shape of a LAN or other communication system. Topologies fall into three categories: simple LAN, hybrid LAN, and enterprise-wide. Simple LAN topologies use three basic physical layouts that can be made into more complex hybrid LAN topologies. Enterprise-wide topologies employ even more complex structures and technologies.

Simple LAN Topologies

The three principal topologies used in LANs are bus, ring, and star. Each is described in detail in the following sections.

Bus Topology

With a bus network, a single cable connects all of the computers and, as a result, can support only one channel. Therefore, every computer on the network shares the bus's total capacity.

Bus topology is considered a peer-to-peer network because all devices on the network share the responsibility of getting data from one location to another. The more computers or nodes on the network, the slower the system. When one computer on the network gets ready to send data, it releases an alert informing the system of its intentions. The receiving computer picks up this transmission, and all other nodes ignore it. Because the alert has to be sent to every computer on the line until it reaches its destination, a bus network of 200 computers would not be advisable. Each end of the bus line must have a 50-ohm resistor called a *terminator*. Terminators stop a signal that has reached the destination device. Without terminators on the line, the signal would continue to travel, endlessly creating a signal bounce and preventing new signals from accessing the network.

Networks based on the bus topology are inexpensive, but they do not scale well, are hard to troubleshoot, and are not fault tolerant. As more nodes are added, system performance degrades. Once a node sends data on, it does not remember the data; therefore, if a corruption of data occurs during transmission, determining which node is doing it is difficult. One break in the line of communication, and the whole network is down. Figure 2.1 shows an example of this topology.

Ring Topology

Ring topology gets its name from the setup of the cables attaching the computers together. Each computer is connected to the computer closest to it, and that one to the next one closest, and so one. The result is a loop or circular effect connecting all the computers. A ring network does not require terminators because, with its circular shape, the cable has no end.

One method of transmitting data on a ring is token passing. A *token* is a three-byte packet transmitted to each node, one at a time. If the computer needs to transmit

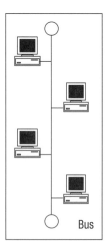

Figure 2.1   An example of bus topology.

data, it picks up the packet, adds control and data information, plus the destination address. This transforms the packet into a *data frame*, which it then passes on. The frame then circulates on the network until it reaches its destination. Figure 2.2 shows an example of this topology.

Star Topology

Star topology consists of multiple point-to-point links connected to a central device that controls data throughput. Star networks are relatively easy to install and manage, but bottlenecks can occur because all data must pass through the central device. This is usually a hub, but can also be a multiport repeater, a concentrator, or a switch. Figure 2.3 shows an example of this topology.

Star topology is used with polling media-access methods where data must flow through the central polling device or hub before reaching its destination on the network. Logically, the data in a star topology would flow in a star shape from one node to the central device or from a hub to its destination node.

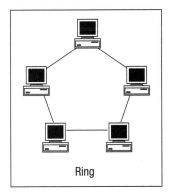

Figure 2.2   An example of ring topology.

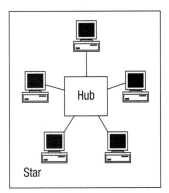

Figure 2.3   An example of star topology.

Star topology is not limited by the media it can use. Typically, it uses Ethernet technologies, but it can also use fiber-optic cabling and unbounded connections, such as microwave, radio, laser, and infrared. Ethernet uses a media-access method known as Carrier Sense, Multiple Access with Collision Detection (CSMA/CD). This method can introduce into the network bottleneck problems when multiple data collisions occur, slowing the network.

The three LAN topologies can also be mixed. For example, a bus-star network consists of a high-bandwidth bus, called the *backbone,* which connects a collection of slower-bandwidth star segments. Figure 2.4 shows an example of mixed topology.

Hybrid LAN Topologies

Very few networks follow a strict bus, ring, or star topology. Alone, these topologies can be restrictive, especially for LANs with large numbers of users. For this reason, companies often use hybrid topologies, which put simple network topologies together in more complex ways to break down restrictions and offer better fault tolerance. Examples of hybrid topologies are the star-wired ring, star-wired bus, and daisy chain.

Star-Wired Ring

A star-wired ring combines star topology with token-ring topology. A star-wired ring network benefits from the fault tolerance of the star topology and the reliability of the token ring. Data flows logically through the network as though it were a ring, but with a star topology physical layout. This topology is more likely to be found in modern token-ring networks. Figure 2.5 illustrates a star-wired ring topology.

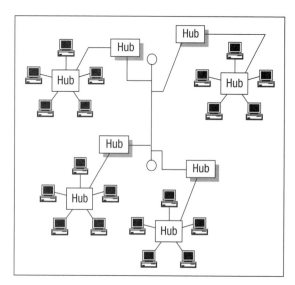

Figure 2.4   An example of mixed topology.

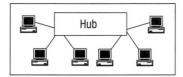

Figure 2.5 An example of a star-wired ring network.

Star-Wired Bus

In a star-wired bus topology, workstations are star-connected to a hub and then networked into a single bus. Figure 2.6 illustrates a star-wired bus.

This design is good over long distances and easily interconnected. It is also good for isolating different network segments. Its main drawback is that it is more expensive than other topologies. This type of network commonly forms the basis for Ethernet and Fast Ethernet networks.

Daisy-Chain Topology

Star-wired ring and bus topologies are too simplistic to represent a typical medium-sized LAN. Often, companies use the same hubs to form a daisy-chain topology, a series of linked devices that allow for easy expansion at a low cost. Figure 2.7 illustrates a daisy-chain topology.

The daisy-chain topology can present hazards because industry standards specify the number of hubs that can be connected in a sequence and still maintain signal integrity. Using too many hubs can affect the functionality of the LAN.

Hierarchical

None of the topologies discussed so far distinguishes between the functions or the priorities of the various workgroups. To increase the priority of a server, the company may choose to connect it directly to the backbone of the network to help ensure that it does not lose network connectivity. Machines with lower

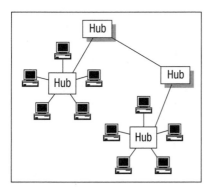

Figure 2.6 An example of star-wired bus topology.

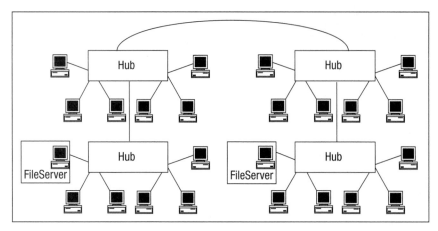

Figure 2.7   An example of daisy-chain topology.

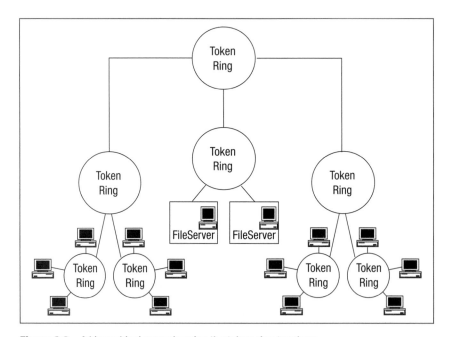

Figure 2.8   A hierarchical example using the token-ring topology.

priority can be connected to the LAN via a less expensive hub. Figure 2.8 shows a hierarchical example using the token-ring topology.

Enterprise-Wide Topologies

The term *enterprise* refers to an entire organization—all local and remote offices, computer systems, and departments. Enterprise-wide computing must take into account the diversity of computer needs in the company. The following types of topologies expand on the simple and hybrid topologies already discussed.

Backbone Networks

The backbone of a network is the cabling that connects the hubs, switches, and routers used by the network. The cabling layout for a backbone generally has more throughput than the cabling used to connect a workstation to a hub. The main types of backbones are serial, distributed, collapsed, and parallel.

➤ *Serial backbone*—The simplest type of backbone, consisting of two or more hubs connected by a single cable. Serial backbones are not suitable for large networks.

➤ *Distributed backbone*—Consists of a number of hubs connected to a series of centralized hubs. This backbone allows for singular expansion and limited capital outlay. Figure 2.9 illustrates a distributed backbone topology. Distributed LANs can add another level of complexity by connecting LAN segments or multiple LANs using routers.

➤ *Collapsed backbone*—Uses a router or a switch as the single central connection point for multiple subnetworks. The danger of using this setup is that failure at the router level results in failure for the whole network.

➤ *Parallel backbone*—The most robust enterprise-wide topology, consisting of more than one connection from the central router or switch. Figure 2.10 illustrates an example of a parallel backbone.

Mesh Network

A mesh network uses routers to interconnect other routers. At least two pathways connect each router to another on the network. This is the most complex network and generally consists of several types of backbones. Although a simple LAN can be considered a mesh network, this is more often employed for enterprise-wide networks and WANs.

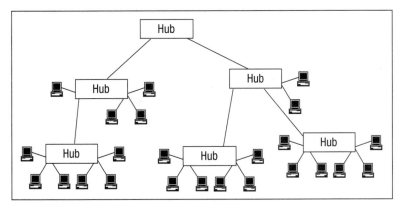

Figure 2.9 An example of a distributed backbone topology.

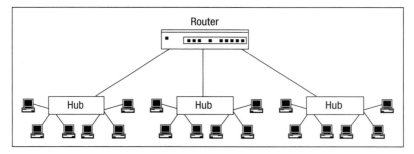

Figure 2.10 An example of a parallel backbone.

WAN Topologies

A WAN connects geographically distant areas that may or may not be part of the same organization. WAN services depend on the bandwidth required, budget, speed, and type of interface of the connecting LAN.

Price Structure

WAN providers offer a range of services, from unlimited usage to limited usage billed by the minute. The two main types of unlimited usage options are dial-up and Integrated Services Digital Network (ISDN). These two services are charged a monthly flat fee for usage. Examples of limited usage options are dedicated lines, leased lines, and frame-relay circuits.

On typical medium-sized networks, the cost of connecting to the WAN is approximately one-third of the cost of the network. Unlike LAN costs, which can vary month to month depending on upgrades and new software, WAN costs are relatively stable because they accrue monthly. That is not to say that providers do not occasionally pass the cost of upgrading hardware or software onto the customers, thereby creating a temporary increase in charges. WAN costs are related to several factors—transmission speed, technology, and geographic location. In many areas, you can purchase a low-speed dial-up connection for less than $30 per month. From Chicago to New York, a 56/64Kbps fractional DS-0 dedicated line can cost up to $1,000 a month, whereas a similar dedicated DS-0 line from New York to London can cost up to $10,000 a month, depending on the service provider.

There are both direct and indirect costs that make the actual cost of installing and maintaining a WAN complex. You should think about the following cost-related elements when considering a WAN:

➤ Monthly service charges

➤ LAN connectivity equipment

➤ User training and support

➤ Network staff training

➤ Network support and troubleshooting

➤ Lost work time when a connection is down

➤ Periodic equipment upgrade costs

Large WAN providers offer customers a Service Level Agreement (SLA) that guarantees a minimum level of service. Typically, an SLA would include level of availability, maximum delay over time, mean time to repair, throughput, and reimbursement if the SLA were breached.

Bandwidth Considerations

Bandwidth usage depends on the applications and the type of bandwidth available from the provider. Generally, WAN providers in the same service area have consistent pricing, whereas others offer "bandwidth on demand," which means that bandwidth expands or contracts to meet the required needs of the user. The cost of this type of service is based on the actual bandwidth the customer uses. Many providers offer dedicated bandwidth at speeds ranging from 56Kbps to 155Mbps, thereby giving customers strategic options for service. Also, providers offer different billing options so that even small companies or home users can take advantage of these high access speeds. Geographic location is a large factor in the type of bandwidth available. For example, rural areas are often limited to local telephone systems and, in some areas, satellite WAN services. Other locations have T1 and T3 services available to customers, and some metropolitan areas are getting new high-speed optical services.

The choice of service providers depends on the SLA offered and the amount of bandwidth needed. Large providers offer more sophisticated services than do small to medium-sized providers. An example would be a meshed architecture with multiple alternate pathways. The carrier automatically reroutes to one of these pathways if an area of the network becomes inaccessible. Smaller providers offer slow-speed connections and limit the number of hops to two.

Vendor and Customer Equipment

WAN vendor equipment varies from dial-up modems to a combination of channel banks and router interfaces. The size of the vendor determines the equipment used. Vendors should store their equipment at more than one location to prevent service loss resulting from an environmental hazard. Customers should investigate where the equipment is stored to ensure that the service provider is not running the equipment out of a basement or other unprotected area where equipment reliability can be compromised.

Some providers use their equipment on the customer site, whereas others require customers to buy their own equipment. Service providers will also build customized equipment that includes modems and other adapters for WAN communication for both servers and workstations.

Network Optimization

To keep your network running smoothly at optimal levels, you will need to use network analysis tools, as well as network monitoring tools for watching over performance. Baselining a network for performance is key to understanding where in the network performance issues are arising.

Network Analysis Tools

Event Viewer is the single most important tool for analyzing network performance problems. The log files in Event Viewer contain information on applications, the system, and security issues that could cause performance problems in a network. Event Viewer in most scenarios is an all-purpose tool for troubleshooting failures at many levels.

Event Viewer

Using the event logs in Event Viewer, you can gather information about hardware, software, and system problems, and you can monitor Windows 2000 security events. Windows 2000 records events in three kinds of logs: application, system, and security.

The application log contains events logged by applications or programs. For example, a database program might record a file error in the application log. The program developer decides which events to record.

The system log contains events logged by the Windows 2000 system components. For example, the failure of a driver or other system component to load during startup is recorded in the system log. Windows 2000 predetermines the event types logged by system components.

Event Viewer displays the following types of events in the security log:

➤ *Error*—Considered to be a significant problem, such as loss of data or loss of functionality. For example, if a service fails to load during startup, an error is logged.

➤ *Warning*—An event that is not necessarily significant, but may indicate a possible future problem. For example, when disk space is low, a warning is logged.

➤ *Information*—Any event that describes the successful operation of an application, driver, or service. For example, when a network driver loads successfully, an Information event is logged.

➤ *Success Audit*—An audited security access attempt that succeeds. For example, a user's successful attempt to log on the system is logged as a Success Audit event.

➤ *Failure Audit*—An audited security access attempt that fails. For example, if a user tries to access a network drive and fails, the attempt is logged as a Failure Audit event.

The EventLog service starts automatically when you start Windows 2000. All users can view application and system logs. Only administrators can access security logs. By default, security logging is turned off. You can use Group Policy to enable security logging. The administrator can also set auditing policies in the Registry that cause the system to halt when the security log is full. To display Event Viewer, complete the following steps:

1. Click on the Start menu.

2. Click on Run.

3. Type "eventvwr".

4. Click on OK. Event Viewer displays the screen shown in Figure 2.11.

Note: Event Viewer can also be displayed through the control panel under Administrative Tools.

Exporting the Event List

You may want to export the event list to Microsoft Excel, so you can save and analyze the data. Figure 2.12 illustrates the Save As dialog box.

To export the list, complete the following steps:

1. On the Event Viewer Action menu, click on Export List. A Save As window displays.

2. Save the file with an .xls extension.

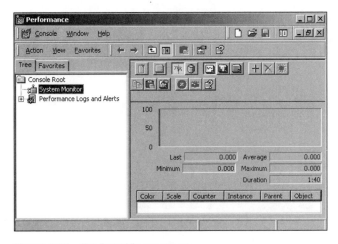

Figure 2.11   The Event Viewer screen.

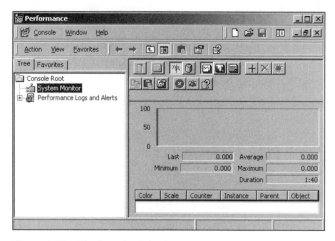

Figure 2.12 The Save As dialog box.

Sorting Events

You can sort events to review and analyze the data more easily. Figure 2.13 illustrates the Options menu.

To specify sort order, complete the following steps:

1. On the View menu, click Newest First or Oldest First. The default is from newest to oldest.

2. (Optional) On the Options menu, check the Save Settings On Exit box to use the current sort order the next time you start Event Viewer.

Note: When a log is archived, the sort order affects files that you save in text format or comma-delimited text format. The sort order does not affect event records you save in log-file format.

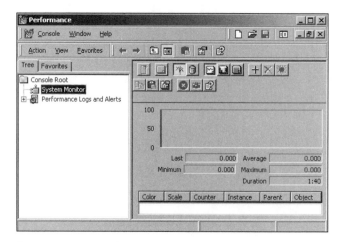

Figure 2.13 The Options menu.

Network Monitoring Tools

Before we go into detail about monitoring networks, we are going to review key concepts and explain how to install Network Monitor and the Network Monitor driver.

Reviewing Key Concepts

You use Network Monitor to capture and display the *frames* (also called *packets*) a Windows 2000 Server receives from a LAN. Network administrators can use Network Monitor to detect and troubleshoot networking problems the local computer might experience. For example, a network administrator might use Network Monitor to diagnose hardware and software problems when the server computer cannot communicate with other computers. Frames captured by Network Monitor can be saved to a file and then sent to professional network analysts or support organizations. Network application developers can use Network Monitor for monitoring and debugging network applications as they are developed.

Installing Network Monitor

To install Network Monitor, complete the following steps:

1. Open Add/Remove Programs.

2. In Add/Remove Programs, click on Add/Remove Windows Components.

3. In the Windows Components wizard, select Management and Monitoring Tools, and then click on Details.

4. In the Management and Monitoring Tools window, select the Network Monitor checkbox, and then click on OK.

5. If you are prompted for additional files, insert your Windows 2000 Server CD or type a path to the location of the files on the network.

Installing the Network Monitor Driver

The Network Monitor driver lets Network Monitor receive frames from a network adapter. It also lets users of the version of Network Monitor provided with Microsoft Systems Management Server (Systems Management Server Network Monitor) capture and display frames from remote computers, including those with dial-up network connections. When the user of a computer running Systems Management Server Network Monitor connects remotely to a computer on which the Network Monitor driver has been installed, and that user initiates a capture, statistics from the capture are transferred over the network to the managing computer. The Network Monitor driver can be installed only on computers running Microsoft Windows 2000 Professional or Windows 2000 Server.

To install the Network Monitor driver, complete the following steps:

1. Open Network and Dial-up Connections.

2. In Network and Dial-up Connections, click on Local Area Connection, click on the File menu, and then click on Properties.

3. In the Local Area Connection Properties dialog box, click on Install.

4. In the Select Network Component Type dialog box, click on Protocol, and then click on Add.

5. In the Select Network Protocol dialog box, click on Network Monitor Driver, and then click on OK.

6. If you are prompted for additional files, insert your Windows 2000 CD or type a path to the location of the files on the network.

Network Monitor Advice

The best practices for running Network Monitor are as follows:

➤ *Run Network Monitor during low-usage times*—Running Network Monitor at low-usage times or for short periods of time will decrease its effect on system performance.

➤ *Capture a minimum amount of network statistics*—Capturing only as many statistics as you need for evaluation will prevent you from capturing too much information to make a reasonably quick diagnosis of the problem.

Network Monitoring Checklist

Before using the network monitoring tools for Windows 2000 Server, you will want to keep the following checklist in mind as a starting point for monitoring any network:

1. *Confirm you are a member of the Administrators group.* The built-in groups in Windows 2000 are created automatically when you install it. Belonging to a group gives a user rights and abilities to perform various tasks on the computer. The following are the default groups:

   ➤ *Administrators*—Members of the Administrators group have full control over the computer. It is the only built-in group that is automatically granted every built-in right and ability in the system.

   ➤ *Backup Operators*—Members of the Backup Operators group can back up and restore files on the computer, regardless of any permissions that protect those files. They can also log onto the computer and shut it down, but they cannot change security settings.

➤ *Power Users*—Members of the Power Users group can create user accounts, but can modify and delete only those accounts they create. They can create local groups and remove users from local groups they have created. They can also remove users from the Power Users, Users, and Guests groups. They cannot modify the Administrators or Backup Operators groups, nor can they take ownership of files, back up or restore directories, load or unload device drivers, or manage the security and auditing logs.

➤ *Users*—Members of the Users group can perform most common tasks, such as running applications, using local and network printers, and shutting down and locking the workstation. Users can create local groups, but can modify only the local groups they create. Users cannot share directories or create local printers.

➤ *Guests*—The Guests group allows occasional or one-time users to log on to a workstation's built-in Guest account and be granted limited abilities. Members of the Guests group can also shut down the system.

➤ *Replicator*—The Replicator group supports directory replication functions. The only member of the Replicator group should be a domain user account used to log on to the Replicator services of the DC. Do not add the user accounts of actual users to this group.

2. *Create a capture filter.* A capture filter functions as a database query—use it to specify the types of network information you want to monitor. For example, to see only a specific subset of computers or protocols, you can create an address database, use the database to add addresses to your filter, and then save the filter to a file. By filtering frames, you save both buffer resources and time. Later, if necessary, you can load the capture filter file and use the filter again

3. *Create a display filter.* To design a capture filter, specify decision statements in the Capture Filter dialog box. This dialog box displays the filter's decision tree, which is a graphical representation of a filter's logic. When you include or exclude information from your capture specifications, the decision tree reflects these specifications.

4. *Interpret results.* The last step in the checklist is to interpret the results from Event Viewer and Network Monitor.

Monitoring Network Performance

Windows 2000 provides System Monitor, Performance Logs and Alerts, and Task Manager for monitoring resource usage on your computer. Monitoring system performance is an important part of maintaining and administering your Windows 2000 installation. You use performance data to do the following:

➤ Understand your workload and the corresponding effect on your system's resources.

➤ Observe changes and trends in workloads and resource usage so you can plan for upgrades.

➤ Test configuration changes or other tuning efforts by monitoring the results.

➤ Diagnose problems and target components or processes for optimization.

Both System Monitor and Performance Logs and Alerts provide detailed data about the resources used by the components of the operating system and by server programs that have been designed to collect performance data. Graphs provide a display for performance-monitoring data; logs provide recording capabilities for the data; alerts notify users with the Messenger service when a counter value reaches, rises above, or falls below a defined threshold.

Microsoft technical support often uses the results of performance monitoring in problem diagnosis. Therefore, Microsoft recommends that you monitor system performance as part of your administrative routine. Task Manager provides information about programs and processes running on your computer. It displays the most commonly used performance measures for processes. Administrators use Task Manager to monitor key indicators of computer performance. They can quickly see the status of the programs that are running and end programs that have stopped responding. They can also assess the activity of running processes using as many as 15 parameters, and they can see graphs and data on CPU and memory usage.

System Monitor

With System Monitor, you can measure the performance of your own computer or other computers on a network through the following tasks:

➤ Collect and view realtime performance data on a local computer or from several remote computers.

➤ View data collected either currently or previously in a counter log.

➤ Present data in a printable graph, histogram, or report view.

➤ Incorporate System Monitor functionality into Microsoft Word or other applications in the Microsoft Office suite by means of automation.

➤ Create HTML pages from performance views.

➤ Create reusable monitoring configurations that can be installed on other computers using Microsoft Management Console (MMC).

System Monitor also lets you collect and view extensive data about the usage of hardware resources and the activity of system services on computers you administer. You can define the data you want the graph to collect in the following ways:

➤ *Type of data*—To select the data to be collected, you specify performance objects, performance counters, and object instances. Some objects provide data on system resources, such as memory, and others provide data on the operation of applications.

➤ *Source of data*—System Monitor can collect data from your local computer or from other computers on the network where you have permission. (By default, administrative permission is required.) In addition, you can include realtime data or data collected previously using counter logs.

➤ *Sampling parameters*—System Monitor supports manual, on-demand sampling or automatic sampling based on a time interval you specify. When viewing logged data, you can also choose starting and stopping times so that you can view data spanning a specific time range.

In addition to options for defining data content, you have considerable flexibility in designing the appearance of your System Monitor views:

➤ *Type of display*—System Monitor supports graph, histogram, and report views. The graph view is the default; it offers the widest variety of optional settings.

➤ *Display characteristics*—For any of the views, you can define the colors and fonts for the display. In graph and histogram views, you can select from different options when you view performance data:

➤ Provide a title for your graph or histogram and label the vertical axis.

➤ Set the range of values depicted in your graph or histogram.

➤ Adjust the characteristics of lines or bars plotted to indicate counter values, including color, width, style, and so on.

You can extend the use of System Monitor by incorporating its functionality into Microsoft Word or other Microsoft applications by means of automation.

System Monitor Interface

When you open Performance, the graph view and a toolbar appear by default; the graph area is blank. When you have added counters to the graph, after a short delay, depending on the time you select for the update interval, System Monitor will begin charting counter values in this graph area. Figure 2.14 illustrates the System Monitor interface.

The names and associated information for the counters you have selected are shown in the columns beneath the graph. This is called the *legend*. The legend shows the following information:

➤ Computer on which System Monitor is running

➤ Performance object

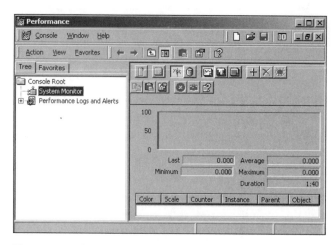

Figure 2.14   System Monitor interface.

➤ Performance counter

➤ Performance object instance

➤ Graphical properties of each counter

Note: To match a line in a graph with the counter for which it is charting values, double-click on a position in the line. The counter will be selected in the legend. If chart lines are close together, try to find a point in the graph where they diverge. Otherwise, System Monitor may not be able to pinpoint the value you are interested in.

Above the columns is the value bar, where you see the last, minimum, maximum, and average values for the selected counter. These values are calculated over the time period and number of samples displayed in the graph that is reflected by the Duration value, not over the time that has elapsed since monitoring was started. The Duration value in the value bar indicates the total elapsed time displayed in the graph and is based on the update interval. The movement of the timer bar across the graph indicates the passing of each update interval. Regardless of the update interval, the view will show up to 100 samples. System Monitor compresses log data as necessary to fit it in the display.

You can define the attributes of the graph, including: type of display, with options for graph, histogram, or report; background color of the detail pane and of the data-display area; size, type, and style of font used to show text in the display; and color, width, and style of line used to chart data.

Figure 2.15   Highlighting button.

To draw attention to a particular counter's data, use the highlighting feature. To do so, press Ctrl+H or click on the button shown in Figure 2.15. When highlighting is in effect, the bar or line representing data for the selected counter changes color to white for most background colors (including the default color) or black for white or light-colored backgrounds.

Note: Default key settings in Microsoft Word may conflict with the Ctrl+H combination used for System Monitor highlighting. You may need to change these to support highlighting when the System Monitor control (Sysmon.ocx in the system_root\System32 folder) is used in Microsoft Word.

Performance Logs and Alerts

With Performance Logs and Alerts, you can collect performance data automatically from local or remote computers. You can view logged counter data using System Monitor or export the data to spreadsheet programs or databases for analysis and report generation. Performance Logs and Alerts offers the following capabilities:

➤ It collects data in a comma-separated or tab-separated format for easy import to spreadsheet programs. A binary log-file format is also provided for circular logging or for logging instances, such as threads or processes that may begin after the log starts collecting data. (Circular logging continuously logs data to a single file, overwriting previous data with new data.)

➤ Counter data collected by Performance Logs and Alerts can be viewed during collection, as well as after collection has stopped.

➤ Because logging runs as a service, data collection occurs regardless of whether any user is logged on to the computer being monitored.

➤ You can define start and stop times, file names, file sizes, and other parameters for automatic log generation.

➤ You can manage multiple logging sessions from a single console window.

➤ You can set an alert on a counter, thereby defining that a message be sent, a program be run, or a log be started when the selected counter's value exceeds or falls below a specified setting.

Similar to System Monitor, Performance Logs and Alerts supports defining performance objects, performance counters, and object instances, and setting sampling intervals for monitoring data about hardware resources and system services. Performance Logs and Alerts also offers options related to recording performance data, such as:

➤ Starting and stopping logging either manually on demand or automatically based on a user-defined schedule.

➤ Configuring additional settings for automatic logging, such as automatic file renaming, and setting parameters for stopping and starting a log based on the elapsed time or the file size.

➤ Creating trace logs. Using the default system data provider or another provider, trace logs record data when certain activities, such as a disk I/O operation or a page fault, occur. When the event occurs, the provider sends the data to the Performance Logs and Alerts service. This differs from the operation of counter logs. When counter logs are in use, the service obtains data from the system when the update interval has elapsed, rather than waiting for a specific event. A parsing tool is required to interpret the trace log output. Developers can create such a tool using application programming interfaces (APIs) provided on the Microsoft Web site.

➤ Defining a program that runs when a log is stopped.

Note: *If you want to export log data to Microsoft Excel, the Performance Logs and Alerts service must be stopped, because Microsoft Excel requires exclusive access to the log file. Other programs are not known to require this exclusive access; therefore, in general you can work with data from a log file while the service is collecting data to that file.*

Advice for Monitoring a Network

The best practices for setting and monitoring a system include:

➤ *Setting up a monitoring configuration*—Configure Performance Logs and Alerts to report data for the recommended counters at regular intervals, such as every 10 to 15 minutes. Retain logs over extended periods of time, store data in a database, and query the data to report on and analyze it as needed for overall performance assessment, trend analysis, and capacity planning. For best results, complete the following steps before starting System Monitor or Performance Logs and Alerts on the computer you want to monitor for diagnostic purposes:

1. Stop screensaver programs.

2. Turn off services that are not essential or relevant to monitoring.

3. Increase the paging file to physical memory size plus 100MB.

4. Using Registry Editor, view the settings for the following and make note of all keys that have nonzero values:

```
HKEY_LOCAL_MACHINE\SYSTEM\CurrentControlSet\Control\SessionManager\
    Memory Management
HKEY_LOCAL_MACHINE\SYSTEM\CurrentControlSet\Services\LanmanServer\
    Parameters
```

5. If the server in question has halted or is not responding, run System Monitor from another computer.

2

➤ *Keeping monitoring overhead low*—In general, the performance tools are designed for minimal overhead. You may find, however, that the overhead increases under each of the following conditions:

1. You are running System Monitor in graph view.

2. You have selected an option other than the default (current value) for a report view.

3. You are sampling at very frequent intervals (less than three seconds apart).

4. Many different objects and counters are selected.

Other aspects of performance tool operation that affect performance are file size and the amount of disk space taken up by log files. To reduce file size and related disk space usage, extend the update interval. Also, log to a disk other than the one you are monitoring. Remember frequent logging puts a lot of demand on disk I/O.

If monitoring overhead is a concern, run only the Performance Logs and Alerts service and do not use a System Monitor graph.

During remote logging, frequent updating can slow performance as a result of network transport. In this case, you should log continuously on remote computers, but upload logs infrequently.

➤ *Analyzing performance results and establishing a performance baseline*—Review logged data by graphing it using the System Monitor display or exporting it for printing. Set your baseline according to the level of performance you consider satisfactory for your typical workload.

➤ *Setting alerts*—Set alerts according to the counter values that are unacceptable, as defined by baseline evaluation.

➤ *Planning*—Monitor trends for capacity planning and add or upgrade components as needed. Maintain logged data in a database and observe changes to identify changes in resource requirements. After you observe changes in activity or resource demand, you can identify where you may require additional resources.

➤ *Performance tuning*—Tune system settings and workload to improve performance and repeat monitoring to examine tuning results. Analysis of your monitoring data may reveal problems, such as excessive demand on certain resources resulting in bottlenecks. These are some of the common causes for bottlenecks, along with recommended strategies for tuning and testing:

➤ Resources are insufficient. Additional or upgraded components are required.

➤ Resources are not sharing workloads evenly. They need to be balanced.

➤ A resource is malfunctioning. It needs to be replaced.

➤ A program is monopolizing a particular resource. It may require substituting another program, rewriting the program, adding or upgrading resources, or running the program during periods of low demand.

➤ A resource is incorrectly configured. Configuration settings should be changed.

Table 2.1 lists the threshold values used to isolate performance problems by resource.

Lack of memory is the most common cause of serious performance problems in computer systems. If you suspect other problems, check memory counters to rule out a memory shortage. Poor response time on a workstation is most likely to result from memory and processor problems; servers are more susceptible to disk and network problems.

Recommendations for Tuning

Before you start tuning, consider the following recommendations:

➤ *Make one change at a time*—In some cases, a problem that appears to relate to a single component may be the result of bottlenecks involving multiple components. Therefore, addressing problems individually is important. Making multiple changes simultaneously may make assessing the impact of each individual change impossible.

➤ *Repeat monitoring after every change*—This is important for understanding the effect of the change and to determine whether additional changes are required. Proceed methodically, making one change at a time to the identified resource and then testing the effects of the changes on performance. Because tuning changes can affect other resources, it's important to keep records of the changes you make and to remonitor after you make a change.

➤ *In addition to monitoring, review event logs*—Some performance problems generate output you can display in Event Viewer.

➤ *Compare the performance of programs that run over the network with locally run programs*—This lets you see whether network components are playing a part in performance problems.

The following is a list of tuning tips for resources you are monitoring.

Memory:

1. Increase physical memory above the minimum required.

2. Create multiple paging files.

3. Determine the correct size for the paging file.

4. Ensure that memory settings are properly configured.

5. Run memory-intensive programs on your highest-performing computers or when system workload is light.

Table 2.1   Threshold values for performance problems.

Resource	Object\Counter	Suggested Threshold	Comments
Disk	PhysicalDisk\% Disk Time	90%	
Disk	PhysicalDisk\Disk Reads/sec, PhysicalDisk\Disk Writes/sec	Depends on manufacturer's specifications	Check the specified transfer rate for your disks to verify that this rate doesn't exceed the specifications. In general, Ultra Wide SCSI disks can handle 50 I/O operations per second.
Disk	Physical Disk\ Current Disk Queue Length	Number of spindles plus 2.	This is an instantaneous counter; observe its value over several intervals. For an average over time, see Physical Disk\Avg. Disk Queue Length.
Memory	Memory\Available Bytes	Less than 4MB	Research memory usage and add memory if needed.
Memory	Memory\Pages/sec	20	Research paging activity.
Network	Network Segment\ % Net Utilization	Depends on type of network	You must determine the threshold based on the type of network you are running. For Ethernet networks, for example, 30 percent is the recommended threshold.
Paging File	Paging File\% Usage	99%	Review this value in conjunction with Available Bytes and Pages/sec to understand paging activity on your computer.
Processor	Processor\% Processor Time	85%	Find the process that is using a high percentage of processor time. Upgrade to a faster processor or install an additional processor.
Processor	Processor\Interrupts/sec	Depends on processor.	A dramatic increase in this counter value without a corresponding increase in system activity indicates a hardware problem. Identify the network adapter causing the interrupts.
Server	Server\Bytes Total/sec		If the sum of Bytes Total/sec for all servers is roughly equal to the maximum transfer rates of your network, you may need to segment the network.
Server	Server\ Work Item Shortages	3	If the value reaches this threshold, consider tuning InitWorkItems or MaxWorkItems in the registry (under HKEY_LOCAL_MACHINE\ SYSTEM\CurrentControlSet\Services\ LanmanServer).
Server	Server\Pool Paged Peak	Amount of physical RAM	This value is an indicator of the maximum paging file size and the amount of physical memory.
Server	Server Work Queues\ Queue Length	4	If the value reaches this threshold, there may be a processor bottleneck. This is an instantaneous counter; observe its value over several intervals.
Multiple Processors	System\Processor Queue Length	2	This is an instantaneous counter; observe its value over several intervals.

Disk:

1. Upgrade to a higher-speed disk, or add disks. When you do this, upgrade the disk controller and the bus.

2. On servers, use Disk Management to create striped volumes on multiple physical disks. This solution increases throughput because I/O commands can be issued concurrently.

3. Distribute programs among servers. Distributed File System (DFS) can be used to balance workload.

4. Isolate tasks that heavily use disk I/O on separate physical disks or disk controllers.

5. Use Disk Defragmenter to optimize disk space.

6. If you want to improve the efficiency of disk access, consider installing the latest driver software for your host adapters. Contact your adapter manufacturer for information.

Processor:

1. Add a processor (especially for multithreaded programs), or upgrade to a faster processor.

2. On multiprocessor computers, manage the processor affinity with respect to process threads and interrupts.

Network:

1. Configure your network so that systems shared by the same group of people are on the same subnet.

2. Unbind infrequently used network adapters.

3. If you are using more than one protocol, you can set the order in which the workstation and NetBIOS software bind to each protocol. See Network and Dial-up Connections Help for more information. Reasons for changing the list order include:

   ➤ If the protocol you use most frequently is first in the binding list, average connection time decreases.

   ➤ Some protocols are faster than others for certain network topologies. If you are optimizing a client computer, putting the faster protocol first in the bindings list improves performance. Because the server accepts incoming connections using the protocol chosen by the client computer, there is no reason to reorder server computer bindings.

2

4. Install a high-performance network adapter in the server. If your server uses a 16-bit adapter, you can significantly increase performance by replacing it with a high-performance 32-bit adapter.

5. Use multiple network adapters. Windows 2000 supports multiple adapters for a given protocol and multiple protocols for a given adapter. Although this configuration can create distinct networks that cannot communicate with one another, it is a way to increase file-sharing throughput.

Permissions

You'll need to ensure that you have appropriate permissions on the computer you want to monitor. Setting up a monitoring configuration is the first step in evaluating your system's performance. To monitor your Windows 2000 installation, you can choose to view data in a graph or collect the data in log files for use in other applications.

Graphs are useful for short-term, realtime monitoring of a local or remote computer. Choose the update interval to capture the type of activity you are interested in. Logs are useful for record keeping and extended monitoring, especially of a remote computer. You can export logged data for report generation, and present the data as graphs or histograms using System Monitor. Logging is the most practical way to monitor multiple computers.

For routine monitoring, start by logging activity over 15-minute intervals. If you are monitoring for a specific problem, you might want to vary the interval. If you are monitoring activity of a specific process at a specific time, set a frequent update interval; however, if you are monitoring a problem that manifests itself slowly, such as a memory leak, use a longer interval.

Another consideration is the overall length of time you want to monitor when choosing this interval. Updating every 15 seconds is reasonable if you'll be monitoring for no more than four hours. If you'll be monitoring a system for eight hours or more, do not set an interval shorter than 300 seconds (5 minutes). Setting the update interval to a frequent rate can cause the system to generate a large amount of data, which can be difficult to work with and can increase the overhead of running Performance Logs and Alerts.

Monitoring a large number of objects and counters can also generate large amounts of data and consume disk space. Try to strike a balance between the number of objects you monitor and the sampling frequency to keep log file size within manageable limits.

Choosing what data to monitor can be difficult. Start by monitoring the activity of the following components in order:

1. Memory

2. Processors

3. Disks

4. Network

Table 2.2 lists the minimum counters recommended for server monitoring.

If some of the counters listed in Table 2.2 are not available on your computer, verify that you have installed the necessary services or activated the counters. You must install the Network Monitor driver to collect performance data using the Network Segment object counters.

Table 2.2   Counters recommended for server monitoring.

Component	Performance Aspect Being Monitored	Counters to Monitor
Disk	Usage	Physical Disk\Disk Reads/sec Physical Disk\Disk Writes/sec LogicalDisk\% Free Space Interpret the % Disk Time counter carefully. Because the _Total instance of this counter may not accurately reflect utilization on multiple-disk systems, it is important to use the % Idle Time counter as well. Note that these counters cannot display a value exceeding 100 percent.
Disk	Bottlenecks	Physical Disk\Avg. Disk Queue Length (all instances)
Memory	Usage	Memory\Available Bytes Memory\Cache Bytes
Memory	Bottlenecks or Leaks	Memory\Pages/sec Memory\Page Reads/sec Memory\Transition Faults/sec Memory\Pool Paged Bytes Memory\Pool Nonpaged Bytes Although not specifically Memory object counters, the following are also useful for memory analysis: Paging File\% Usage object (all instances) Cache\Data Map Hits % Server\Pool Paged Bytes and Server\Pool Nonpaged Bytes
Network	Usage	Network Segment\ % Net Utilization Note that you must install the Network Monitor driver before you can use this counter.
Network	Throughput	Protocol transmission counters (varies with networking protocol); for TCP/IP: Network Interface\Bytes total/sec Network Interface\Packets/sec Server\Bytes Total/sec or Server\Bytes Transmitted/sec and Server\ Bytes Received/sec
Processor	Usage	Processor\% Processor Time (all instances)
Processor	Bottlenecks	System\Processor Queue Length (all instances) Processor\Interrupts/sec System\Context switches/sec

Note: Unlike physical-disk counter data, logical-disk counter data is not collected by the operating system by default. To obtain performance counter data for logical drives or storage volumes, you must type diskperf -yv at the command prompt. This causes the disk performance statistics driver used for collecting disk performance data to report data for logical drives or storage volumes. By default, the operating system uses the diskperf -yd command to obtain physical drive data. For more information about using the diskperf command, type diskperf -? at the command prompt.

When monitoring computers remotely, your options for collecting data include running performance logging on the administrator's computer or drawing data continuously from each remote computer. You could also have each computer running the service to collect data and, at regular intervals, run a batch program to transfer the data to the administrator's computer for analysis and archiving.

Centralized data collection is simple to implement because only one logging service is running. You can collect data from multiple systems into a single log file. This does cause additional network traffic and may be restricted by available memory on the administrator's computer. To do centralized data collection, use the Add Counters dialog box to select a remote computer while running System Monitor on your local computer.

Distributed data collection occurs on the remote computers you are monitoring and does not incur the memory and network traffic problems of centralized collection. It does, however, result in delayed availability of the data, requiring that the collected data be transferred to the administrator's computer for review. To do distributed data collection, use Computer Management on a local computer to select a remote computer on which to collect data.

When monitoring remote computers, note that the remote computer will allow access only to user accounts that have permission to access it. To monitor remote systems from your computer, you must start the Performance Logs and Alerts service using an account that has permission to access the remote computers you want to monitor. By default, the service is started under the local computer's "system" account, which generally has permission only to access services and resources on the local computer. To start this under a different account, use Services under Computer Management and update the properties of the Performance Logs and Alerts service.

After configuring the performance tools with the counters, update intervals, and other settings you want, save those settings on your local computer or for export to another computer. If you save the settings under the name Perfmon.msc, you are permanently changing the configuration of the tools on the computer; for that reason, you should save the file under another name.

Evaluating Your Monitoring Results

Analyzing your monitoring data consists of examining counter values that are reported while your system is performing various operations. Analyzing performance data includes determining acceptable values for counters and understanding variations in performance data. You should determine which processes are most active and if any programs or threads are monopolizing a resource. Using this type of performance-data analysis, you can understand how your system is responding to workload demands. As a result of this analysis, you may find that your system performs satisfactorily at some times and unsatisfactorily at others. Depending on the causes of these variations and the degree of difference, you may choose to take corrective action or to accept these variations and delay tuning or upgrading resources to a later time.

The level of system performance that you consider acceptable when your system is handling a typical workload and running all required services is its *baseline*. The baseline performance is a subjective standard that the administrator determines based on the work environment. It may correspond to a range of counter values, including some that are temporarily unacceptable, but that generally indicate the best possible performance under the administrator's specific conditions. The baseline can be the measure used for setting performance expectations of your users and can be included in any service agreements put in place.

Archiving Data and Monitoring Trends

The data you accumulate through daily monitoring provides the information you need for trend analysis and capacity planning. You should archive this data and use the archives to monitor trends. Even if your computer is operating satisfactorily today, you should plan for changes in demand caused by users you may add or by technologies and programs you may deploy. Unanticipated network growth can result in overused resources and poor levels of network service. By characterizing system performance over time, you can justify the need for new resources before the need becomes critical.

Using the data collected from the counters, observe how the values for each component change over time. These changes may indicate a need to increase or upgrade components.

During the monitoring process, administrators use the data gathered to determine what steps need to be taken to properly manage and maintain the system.

Network Management Tools

Windows Management Instrumentation (WMI) is the Microsoft implementation of Web-Based Enterprise Management (WBEM), an initiative to establish standards for accessing and sharing management information over an enterprise network.

WMI is WBEM-compliant and provides integrated support for the Common Information Model (CIM), which is the data model that describes the objects that exist in a management environment.

WMI includes a CIM-compliant object repository and the CIM Object Manager. The CIM-compliant object repository is the database of object definitions. The CIM Object Manager handles the collection and manipulation of objects in the repository and gathers information from the WMI providers, which act as intermediaries between components of the operating system and applications.

In Windows 2000, several management tools have been WMI-enabled, including Logical Drives, System Properties, System Information, and the Dependencies component of Services. These are explained in the following sections. Also, Windows 2000 provides a tool called WMI Control that can be used to modify WMI configuration settings.

WMI Control

WMI Control lets you perform Windows Management configuration tasks, such as setting permissions for authorized users or groups, backing up the object repository, and turning error logging on or off.

To Open WMI Control, complete the following steps:

1. Click on Start.

2. Click on Run.

3. Type "wmimgmt.msc".

4. Click on OK.

A screen similar to the one shown in Figure 2.16 will appear.

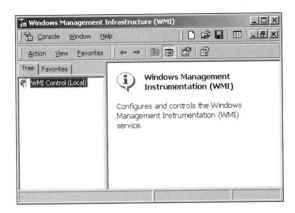

Figure 2.16 WMI Control window.

Computer Management

Administrators use Computer Management to manage local or remote computers using a single, consolidated desktop tool. It combines several Windows 2000 administration utilities into a single console tree, providing easy access to a specific computer's administrative properties and tools. Computer Management can be used to do the following:

➤ Monitor system events, such as logon times and application errors.

➤ Create and manage shares.

➤ View a list of users connected to a local or remote computer.

➤ Start and stop system services, such as the Task Scheduler and the Spooler.

➤ Set properties for storage devices.

➤ View device configurations and add new device drivers.

➤ Manage server applications and services, such as the DNS service or the DHCP service.

To Start Computer Management, complete the following steps:

1. Click on Start.

2. Point to Programs.

3. Point to Administrative Tools.

4. Click on Computer Management.

A screen similar to the one shown in Figure 2.17 will appear.

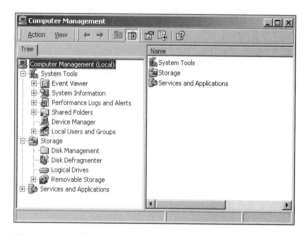

Figure 2.17   Computer Management window.

Computer Management uses a two-pane view similar to Windows Explorer. The console tree contains the administrative tools, storage devices, and server applications and services available on the local or remote computer. The three nodes in this tree are System Tools, Storage, and Services and Applications. You must be a member of the Administrators group to take full advantage of Computer Management. If you are not a member of the Administrators group, you won't have access rights to view or modify administrative properties, and you won't have permission to perform administrative tasks.

Logical Drives

Logical Drives lets you manage mapped drives and local drives on a remote computer or a local computer. You can view drive properties, change drive labels, and configure security settings for drives. WMI lets you manage an enterprise through the Internet or an intranet, thereby reducing the total cost of ownership of your enterprise.

To manage Logical Drives properties, complete the following steps:

1. Open Computer Management.

2. In the console tree, click on Logical Drives.

3. In the details pane, right-click on the appropriate drive.

4. Click on Properties.

System Properties

System Properties lets administrators view and change system properties on a local or remote computer. They can restart a remote computer to apply settings changes or detect new hardware, view the computer name and domain information for other computers on the network, or change the settings for the virtual memory paging file on a computer that might run programs requiring a lot of memory.

System Information

System Information collects and displays configuration information about your system. This is especially useful when troubleshooting the system with a support technician.

Service Dependencies

Services help you manage the services on your computer. Service dependencies identify the services upon which the current service is dependent and the services that are dependent upon it.

Windows Load Balancing Services

Network Load Balancing assembles several computers running server programs using TCP/IP. This service can be used with a group of Terminal servers to scale the performance of a single Terminal server by distributing its client requests across multiple servers.

There are limitations when using load balancing with Terminal servers. Because individual users can be connected to different Terminal servers within a group, user sessions might become broken when redistributed to another Terminal server. To use Terminal Services with load balancing, you must ensure that user information and preferences remain accessible to users.

Network Load Balancing can be used either with or without *client affinity*, the method used to associate client requests with cluster hosts. When no affinity is specified, all network requests are load-balanced across the cluster without regard to their source. Affinity is implemented by directing all client requests from the same IP address to the same cluster host.

For Terminal Services, client affinity should be used so that Network Load Balancing directs multiple requests from the same client IP address to the same Terminal server. As long as the client connects with the same IP address, the client will always connect to the same Terminal server where user data and preferences are accessible. IP addresses do not always remain the same, however. When using DHCP to distribute IP addresses as clients log on, clients get different IP addresses each time they connect. Also, if clients need to connect from multiple locations, using client affinity does not work because the IP addresses are different. You can use Network Load Balancing without client affinity, but to do so, you should set the option that automatically ends a session whenever the connection is broken or disconnected. When a session ends, it is deleted from the Terminal server and cannot be reconnected.

Therefore, by setting this option, users cannot have disconnected sessions running on different servers within the group. Ending sessions automatically can result in loss of data at the client, so this method is useful only when running applications that do not require saving current work, such as making queries on a database. In situations where users might end up connected to a different Terminal server because of a change in IP address, the storage of user data and preferences can be redirected to another location, such as a file server dedicated to storing files. This makes data and preferences accessible to the user regardless of which Terminal server supports the connection. Normally when using Terminal Services, individual user files and preferences are automatically stored on the Terminal server to which the user is currently connected. To redirect user information and preferences to a different location, configure Terminal Services user profiles to store any user data at the specified storage location.

2

Even when user data and preferences are redirected to an alternative file server, a session in which a file was created retains the open file, thereby consuming valuable system resources. The state of a session is specific to the Terminal Services computer on which the session was created and cannot be shared across Terminal servers.

Network Troubleshooting Tools

The Windows 2000 troubleshooters help users diagnose and solve technical problems. When a troubleshooter is started, users must answer a series of questions about the problem. These answers will help Windows 2000 find a solution. Table 2.3 lists the troubleshooters available in Windows 2000.

Chapter Summary

Windows 2000 networking helps small businesses create networks for internal communications, growing businesses do more with their existing networks, and enterprise businesses maximize the potential of their network and the Internet. Enterprise-class organizations will appreciate the rich network services included with Windows 2000 Server and Windows 2000 Advanced Server.

Table 2.3   Troubleshooters for Windows 2000.

Troubleshooter	Identifies and Resolves Problems Related to:
Client Service for NetWare	Client Service for NetWare, including accessing NetWare servers and Novell Directory Services (NDS) objects, printing to NetWare printers, using NetWare login scripts, and logging onto an NDS tree.
Display	Video cards and display adapters, including your computer screen, outdated or incompatible video drivers, and incorrect settings for your video hardware.
Hardware	Cameras, CD-ROM drives, game controllers, hard drives, keyboards, mouse devices, network adapter cards, and scanners. If you are having problems with a sound card, a modem, or a display or video adapter card, this troubleshooter may help you, but you can also see the individual troubleshooters for those devices.
Internet connections	Connecting and logging on to your Internet service provider (ISP).
Modem	Modem connections, setup, configuration, and detection.
MS-DOS programs	Running MS-DOS programs on Windows 2000.
Multimedia and games	Installing and configuring DirectX drivers and games.
Networking	Internet and intranet connections that use TCP/IP on a computer running Windows 2000 Professional.
Print	Network or local printers and plotters, including outdated or corrupted printer drivers, network and local printer connections, and printer configuration.
Remote access	Network and dial-up connections that use a telephone to connect your computer to another computer.
Sound	Sound cards and speakers.
System setup	Installing and setting up Windows 2000.
Windows 3.x programs	Running 16-bit Windows programs on Windows 2000. If you are having problems running an MS-DOS program, see the MS-DOS troubleshooter.

The two most common networks are LANs and WANs. A LAN spans a relatively small area. A WAN is composed of interconnected LANs that span a large geographic area.

The Internet is a global network connecting millions of computers around the world. A VPN connects the components of one network over another network. The more computers or nodes on the network, the slower the system is.

The application log contains events logged by applications or programs. The system log contains events logged by the Windows 2000 system components. Windows 2000 predetermines the event types logged by system components.

Network administrators can use Network Monitor to detect and troubleshoot networking problems the local computer might experience. For example, a network administrator might use Network Monitor to diagnose hardware and software problems when the server computer cannot communicate with other computers. Network application developers can use Network Monitor for monitoring and debugging network applications as they are developed.

The Network Monitor driver enables Network Monitor to receive frames from a network adapter, and allows users of the version of Network Monitor provided with Microsoft Systems Management Server (Systems Management Server Network Monitor) to capture and display frames from a remote computer, including those with dial-up network connections. When the user of a computer running the Systems Management Server Network Monitor connects remotely to a computer on which the Network Monitor driver has been installed, and that user initiates a capture, statistics from the capture are transferred over the network to the managing computer. The Network Monitor driver can be installed only on computers running Microsoft Windows 2000 Professional or Windows 2000 Server.

Windows 2000 provides System Monitor, Performance Logs and Alerts, and Task Manager for monitoring resource usage on your computer. System Monitor and Performance Logs and Alerts provide detailed data about the resources used by the components of the operating system and by server programs designed to collect performance data. The graphs provide a display for performance-monitoring data; logs provide recording capabilities for the data. With Performance Logs and Alerts, you can collect performance data automatically from local or remote computers.

When monitoring computers remotely, your options for collecting data include running performance logging on the administrator's computer or drawing data continuously from each remote computer. You can collect data from multiple systems into a single log file.

Administrators use Computer Management to manage local or remote computers with a single, consolidated desktop tool. It combines several Windows 2000 administration utilities into a single console tree, providing easy access to a specific computer's administrative properties and tools. Computer Management can be used to monitor system events, such as logon times and application errors; create and manage shares; view a list of users connected to a local or remote computer; start and stop system services, such as the Task Scheduler and the Spooler; set properties for storage devices; view device configurations and add new device drivers; and manage server applications and services, such as the DNS service or the DHCP service.

Network Load Balancing assembles several computers running server programs using TCP/IP. This service can be used with a group of Terminal servers to scale the performance of a single Terminal server by distributing its client requests across multiple servers. There are limitations when using load balancing with Terminal servers. Individual users can be connected to different Terminal servers within a group, so user sessions might become broken when redistributed to another Terminal server. To use Terminal Services with load balancing, you must ensure that user information and preferences remain accessible to users.

Review Questions

1. Most small businesses use what type of network to share Internet connections?

   a. Peer-to-peer

   b. Client-server

   c. Server-server

   d. Peer-to-client

2. Which of the following characteristics does not differentiate one LAN from another?

   a. Topology

   b. Protocols

   c. CPU

   d. Media

3. What term is given to each Internet computer that is independent of the other servers on the network?

   a. Node

   b. Host

   c. Client

   d. Server

4. What network protocol is commonly used on an intranet belonging to an organization, usually a corporation, accessible only by the organization's authorized members, employees, or customers and vendors?

   a. TCP/IP

   b. AppleTalk

   c. IPX/SPX

   d. NetBIOS

5. Which of the following intercepts all messages entering and leaving the network?

   a. Circuit-level gateway

   b. Packet filter

   c. Application gateway

   d. Proxy server

6. Which of the following is not a principal topology used for LANs?

   a. Bus

   b. Ring

   c. Star

   d. Square

7. Which topology gets its name from the setup of the cables attaching computers together, in which each computer is attached to the computer closest to it, and that one to the next one closest, and so on?

   a. Ring

   b. Bus

   c. Star

   d. Square

8. Which of the following is a list of cost-related elements that should be considered when you examine WAN costs?

   a. Monthly service charge

   b. LAN connectivity equipment

   c. User training and support

   d. All of the above

2

9. Members of what group can perform most common tasks, such as running applications, using local and network printers, and shutting down and locking the workstation?

    a. Administrators

    b. Backup operators

    c. Users

    d. Guests

10. Which group supports directory replication functions?

    a. Replicator

    b. Users

    c. Power users

    d. Guests

11. What tool or utility provides information about programs and processes running on your computer?

    a. System Monitor

    b. Performance Logs and Alerts

    c. Task Manager

    d. Event Viewer

12. What tool or utility is used to collect performance data automatically from local or remote computers?

    a. System Monitor

    b. Performance Logs and Alerts

    c. Task Manager

    d. Event Viewer

13. What is the correct interval to start logging activity for routine monitoring?

    a. 10 minutes

    b. 20 minutes

    c. 12 minutes

    d. 15 minutes

14. What is WBEM-compliant with and provides integrated support for the CIM, which is the data model that describes the objects that exist in a management environment?

    a. WMI

    b. CIM

    c. ASP

    d. Server

15. Logical Drives lets you manage mapped drives and local drives on a remote computer or what other type of computer?

    a. Server

    b. Mainframe

    c. Local

    d. None of the above

16. Network Load Balancing assembles several computers running server programs using which of the following protocols?

    a. IPX/SPX

    b. TCP/IP

    c. NetBIOS

    d. AppleTalk

17. Which of the following methods is used to associate client requests with cluster hosts?

    a. Client affinity

    b. Network Load Balancing

    c. Terminal Services

    d. System Information

18. What is considered a first line of defense in protecting information?

    a. Password

    b. Network

    c. Firewall

    d. VPN

19. Networks based on which of the following topologies are inexpensive, but do not scale well, are hard to troubleshoot, and are not fault tolerant?

    a. Bus

    b. Ring

    c. Star

    d. None of the above

20. Which of the following topologies are hybrid topologies?

    a. Star-wired ring

    b. Star-wired bus

    c. Daisy chain

    d. All of the above

Real-World Projects

Lesha Camille, the IT director of Red National Bank, wants to upgrade the bank's 13 computers, currently configured as a Windows 98 peer-to-peer linear bus network using 10Base2 cabling, to a physical and logical star network using 100BaseT Ethernet technology for a higher degree of security and centralized administration. She has asked you, the private network consultant, to help her meet the project's deadline.

You agree to help her, of course, because the bank has only 13 computers on its network. Six are for tellers, two for loan officers, one for the receptionist, one for accounting, and three for management staff. This setup is a mixed-up peer-to-peer network hobbled together using Windows 95 with no central point of access.

You have decided to set up the network in a client/server model by upgrading the computers to Windows 2000 Professional and Windows 2000 Server. You plan to use a single domain for the network, while being mindful of future expansion. The DC for this network is the accounting computer, because that department has limited amounts of work to accomplish and needs something to fill time. Accounting will be responsible for server and network performance reports.

Camille is unfamiliar with Windows 2000 and wants to be able to check on problems that occur during normal network operations. You have decided to show her how to display Event Viewer so that she can view the event logs generated during the normal use of the computer. You explain to her that the log pertains to the computer it is on for troubleshooting purposes.

Camille would also like to monitor the traffic on the network to see what is going on during normal operation. So you decide to show her how to install Network Monitor, included with Windows 2000 Server. You explain to her that it is not installed, by default, during the installation process.

Project 2.1

To implement a star-network with 12 Windows 2000 Professional clients and a Windows 2000 Server, perform the following steps:

To upgrade a computer to a 100BaseT PCI Ethernet card, follow these steps:

1. Open the computer case, making sure that it is unplugged.

2. Find an empty PCI expansion slot; seat the card into the slot.

3. Close the case.

To upgrade the computers to Windows 2000 Professional or Windows 2000 Server, follow these steps:

1. Turn the computer on and cancel out of the hardware setup for the card.

2. Put the Windows 2000 Professional or Windows 2000 Server CD into the CD drive and reboot.

3. Follow the setup instructions.

Mindful of future expansion, you decide to use a 24-port 100BaseT Ethernet hub as the central point of the star topology. Then you connect each computer to the hub with the proper cabling.

To connect the computers to the hub using category 5 shielded twisted-pair cabling, make sure of the following:

1. Label each cable end with an appropriate label that identifies which computer it is connected to.

2. Each cable is a minimum length of 3 feet and a maximum of 328 feet.

3. Each cable has an RJ-45 connector on each end.

4. Test each cable if possible to see if they are good.

5. Plug the cabling into the hub starting at port 1 and work your way from there, doing one cable at a time.

Note: The uplink port on the hub is for linking the hub to another hub.

Because the Red National Bank has the budget for this project, the result of its upgrade is a network structure that can handle some future growth and will have a relatively small amount of fault tolerance. This means that should an individual computer workstation go offline for any reason, it won't affect the rest of the network. This topology does, however, introduce what is known as a single point of failure for the network. The single point of failure here is the hub; if the hub fails, then the workstations cannot communicate with themselves or the server. This could be a problem when users want to log on to the system in the morning and find out they can't.

Project 2.2

To display Event Viewer on a Windows 2000 Professional computer or Windows 2000 server, perform the following steps:

1. Point to Start.

2. Click on Run.

3. In the dialog box, type "eventvwr".

4. Click on OK.

Or follow these instructions for doing it the long way:

1. Point to Start.

2. Point to Settings.

3. Click on Control Panel.

4. Double-click on Administrative Tools.

5. Click on Event Viewer.

Event Viewer logs every event that occurs on a workstation or server, whether it is a success or failure of a program or process.

The result of viewing event logs on a workstation or server will allow Red National Bank to troubleshoot its computer-related problems more easily. For example, problems with applications can be viewed in the application log.

Project 2.3

To install Network Monitor, follow these instructions:

1. Point to Start.

2. Point to Settings.

3. Click on Control Panel.

4. Double-click on Add/Remove Programs.

5. In the Windows Component wizard, select Management and Monitoring Tools.

6. Click on Details.

7. In the Management and Monitoring Tools window, select the Network Monitor checkbox.

8. Click on OK.

9. If prompted for the Windows 2000 CD, insert it into the CD-ROM drive and click on OK.

After Network Monitor has been installed, Lesha Camille will be able to trouble-shoot Red National Bank's network and some of its connections. The log files it generates can be sent to a network analyst or support organization that can tell what all the information means, so that the problem can be narrowed down. Having this capability will keep the network up and running, because problems can be "seen" as they occur and in some cases before they occur. One of the problems that can be seen with Network Monitor is a broadcast storm, which can be caused by a faulty network adapter. In this scenario, the network would be saturated by packets from the faulty card that would suck up available bandwidth that would slow the network.

CHAPTER THREE

Network Protocols

After completing this chapter, you will be able to:

✓ List network protocols

✓ Install network protocols

✓ Bind network protocols

✓ Configure network protocols

✓ Monitor network activities

✓ Monitor network activities by protocol

✓ Configure network management and optimizations

Without network protocols, the computer world as we know it today would not exist. Protocols are what allow computers around the world to communicate. This chapter discusses the most common network protocols used with Windows 2000, their components, and functions. This chapter also discusses how to install, bind, and configure protocols. Understanding protocols is important for ensuring that network segments and the PCs on the network can communicate with each other.

What Are Network Protocols?

Protocols are the common languages that computers use to communicate across a network. They are portable and can be adapted to different cabling types. For two computers to communicate, they must have the same protocol installed; more than one protocol can be bound to a network card. Some protocols, such as TCP/IP, work with IP addresses, whereas others, such as NetBEUI, work with the media access control (MAC) address, which is a 12-digit hexadecimal number burned into the network interface card (NIC) by the manufacturer. The MAC address is also referred to as the *hardware address*.

You need to consider several factors when choosing what protocol to use on a network. The two main considerations are cost and bandwidth—how efficiently the protocol sends data across the network lines.

The Open System Interconnection (OSI) model was designed to separate the networking process into understandable layers. The layers are:

1. Applications

2. Presentation

3. Transport

4. Network

5. Data link

6. Physical

Network protocols do not fall neatly into the layers of the OSI model; rather, they generally overlap two layers. Table 3.1 lists network protocols, their acronyms, descriptions, uses, and configuration options.

Installation is the first step in making a protocol work. After installation, you will learn to bind the protocol to the NIC and services. To save time, install and bind only those protocols that are used by the system, because Windows attempts to use protocols in the order they appear in the protocol listing until it finds the correct one.

Table 3.1   Network protocols.

Name	Acronym	Description, Use, and Configuration Options
Transmission Control Protocol/Internet Protocol	TCP/IP	Suite of small, specialized protocols: TCP, IP, UDP, ARP, ICMP, and others.
Internetwork Packet Exchange/Sequenced Packet Exchange	IPX/SPX	Required to ensure the interoperability of LANs running NetWare version 3.2 and lower and on LANs running higher versions of NetWare's OS.
Network Basic Input Output Systems	NetBIOS	Designed to provide Transport and Session Layer services to applications running on small homogeneous networks.
NetBIOS Enhanced User Interface	Net BEUI	Fast, efficient protocol that consumes few network resources, provides error correction, and requires little configuration.
AppleTalk	N/A	Protocol suite used to interconnect Macintosh computers. Originally designed to support peer-to-peer networking.

TCP/IP

TCP/IP is the basis for the Internet. The Internet Engineering Task Force (IETF) controls its development. By continually testing proposed changes to the protocol, IETF prevents drastic overnight changes from occurring, and the Internet remains secure.

TCP/IP has several core protocols:

➤ Address Resolution Protocol (ARP)

➤ Internet Protocol (IP)

➤ Internet Control Message Protocol (ICMP)

➤ Internet Group Management Protocol (IGMP)

➤ User Datagram Protocol (UDP)

➤ Transmission Control Protocol (TCP)

ARP

ARP is a required TCP/IP standard defined in Microsoft's Request for Comments (RFC) 826. ARP resolves IP addresses used by TCP/IP-based software to MAC addresses used by LAN hardware. ARP provides the following services to hosts located on the same physical network:

➤ A broadcast message, such as "What is the media access control address for a device that is configured with the enclosed IP address?", is sent to obtain MAC addresses.

➤ When an ARP request is answered, both the sender and the requester record for future reference each other's IP address and MAC address as an entry in a local table called the ARP cache.

Hardware Addressing

Hardware built for use on LANs must contain a unique address programmed into the device by the manufacturer. For Ethernet and Token Ring LAN hardware, this is the MAC address. Each MAC address identifies the device within its own physical network with a six-byte number programmed into ROM on the physical hardware device. The Institute of Electrical and Electronics Engineers (IEEE) oversees authority and registration of MAC addresses. The IEEE registers and assigns to individual manufacturers unique numbers for the first three bytes of the MAC address. Each manufacturer can then assign the last three bytes to individual devices.

How ARP Resolves MAC Addresses for Local Traffic

Figure 3.1 shows how ARP resolves IP addresses to hardware addresses for hosts on the same local network. In this example, two TCP/IP hosts, A and B, are located on the same physical network, where Host A is assigned the IP address of 10.0.0.99 and Host B is assigned the IP address of 10.0.0.100.

When Host A tries to communicate with Host B, the following steps resolve Host B's software-assigned address (10.0.0.100) to Host B's hardware-assigned MAC address:

1. Based on the contents of the routing table on Host A, IP determines that the forwarding IP address to be used to reach Host B is 10.0.0.100. Then Host A checks its own local ARP cache for a matching hardware address for Host B.

2. If Host A does not find a mapping in the cache, it broadcasts an ARP request frame to all hosts on the network.

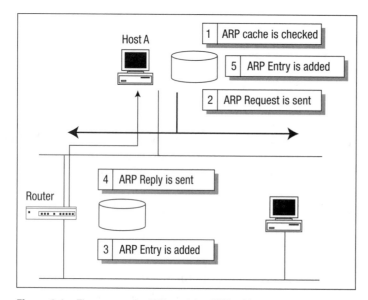

Figure 3.1   The process for ARP resolving MAC addresses.

3. Each host on the network receives the ARP request and checks for a match to its own IP address. If its address does not match the request, it discards the ARP request.

4. If Host B determines that the IP address in the ARP request matches its own, it adds a hardware/software address mapping for Host A to its local ARP cache.

5. Host B sends an ARP reply message containing its hardware address back to Host A.

6. When Host A receives the ARP reply message from Host B, it updates its ARP cache with a hardware/software address mapping for Host B.

How ARP Resolves MAC Addresses for Remote Traffic

ARP is also used to forward IP datagrams to local routers for destinations that are not on the local network. In this situation, ARP resolves the MAC address of a router interface on the local network.

The following example shows how ARP resolves IP addresses to hardware addresses for two hosts on different physical networks connected by a common router. Host A is assigned an IP address of 10.0.0.99, and Host B uses an IP address of 192.168.0.99. Router Interface 1 is on the same physical network as Host A and uses the IP address 10.0.0.1. Router Interface 2 is on the same physical network as Host B and uses the IP address 192.168.0.1.

When Host A tries to communicate with Host B, the following steps resolve Router Interface 1's software-assigned address (10.0.0.1) to its hardware-assigned MAC address:

1. Based on the contents of the routing table on Host A, IP determines that the forwarding IP address to be used to reach Host B is 10.0.0.1, the IP address of its default gateway. Host A then checks its own local ARP cache for a matching hardware address for 10.0.0.1.

2. If Host A finds no mapping in the cache, it broadcasts an ARP request frame to all hosts on the local network with the question, "What is the hardware address for 10.0.0.1?" Both hardware and software addresses for the source, Host A, are included in the ARP request.

3. Each host on the local network receives the ARP request and checks for a match to its own IP address. If a host does not find a match, it discards the ARP request.

4. The router determines that the IP address in the ARP request matches its own IP address and adds a hardware/software address mapping for Host A to its local ARP cache.

5. The router then sends an ARP reply message containing its hardware address directly back to Host A.

6. When Host A receives the ARP reply message from the router, it updates its ARP cache with a hardware/software address mapping for 10.0.0.1.

The ARP Cache

ARP maintains a cache of IP-address-to-MAC-address mappings for future use, to minimize the number of broadcasts. The ARP cache can contain dynamic and static entries. Dynamic entries are added and removed automatically over time; however, static entries remain in the cache until the computer is restarted. Each dynamic ARP cache entry has a potential lifetime of 10 minutes. If new entries added to the cache are not reused within two minutes of being time stamped, it expires and is removed from the ARP cache. If an entry is used, it receives two more minutes of lifetime. If an entry keeps getting used, it receives an additional two minutes of lifetime up to a maximum lifetime of 10 minutes.

You can view the ARP cache by using the arp command. To view the ARP cache on a computer running Windows 2000, type "arp -a" at a Windows 2000 command prompt. To view arp command-line options, type "arp /?" at a command prompt.

IP

RFC 791 specifies IP as the standard Internet protocol required for a TCP/IP network. IP is a connectionless, unreliable datagram protocol primarily responsible for addressing and routing packets between hosts. Connectionless is defined as a session not being established before exchanging data. It is unreliable because delivery is not guaranteed. IP makes a best effort to deliver a packet, which means IP packets might be lost, delivered out of sequence, duplicated, or delayed. IP does not attempt to recover from any types of errors. The acknowledgment of packets delivered and the recovery of lost packets is the responsibility of a higher-layer protocol, such as TCP.

An IP packet, also known as an *IP datagram*, consists of an IP header and an IP payload. The IP header contains the following fields for addressing and routing:

➤ *Source IP address*—The IP address of the original source of the IP datagram.

➤ *Destination IP address*—The IP address of the final destination of the IP datagram.

➤ *Time-to-Live (TTL)*—The number of network segments (or hops) on which the datagram is allowed to travel before being discarded by a router. The TTL is set by the sending host and is used to prevent packets from endlessly circulating on an IP internetwork. When forwarding an IP packet, routers are required to decrease the TTL by at least one segment (or hop).

ICMP

ICMP is also a required TCP/IP standard. With ICMP, hosts and routers that use IP communication can report errors and exchange limited control and status information. ICMP messages are usually sent automatically in one of the following situations:

➤ An IP datagram cannot reach its destination.

➤ An IP router or gateway cannot forward datagrams at the current rate of transmission.

➤ An IP router redirects the sending host to use a better route to its destination.

ICMP messages are sent within IP datagrams. ICMP headers identify the different types of ICMP messages. Users should not assume, however, that because ICMP messages are carried in IP datagrams, they are unreliable.

Users can use the ping command to send ICMP echo request messages and record the receipt of ICMP echo reply messages. These messages let users detect network or host communication failures and troubleshoot common TCP/IP connectivity problems.

IGMP

IGMP is a protocol to exchange and update information about host membership in specific multicast groups.

What Is IP Multicasting?

Multicast IP traffic is sent to a single address but is processed by multiple hosts. IP multicasting occurs when only host computers that belong to the multicast group receive and process IP traffic sent to the group's reserved IP address. The set of hosts listening on a specific IP multicast address is called a *multicast group*.

Other important aspects of IP multicasting include the following:

➤ Group membership is dynamic, allowing hosts to join and leave the group at any time.

➤ Hosts can join multicast groups by sending IGMP messages.

➤ Groups are not limited by size, and members can be spread out across multiple IP networks (if connecting routers support the propagation of IP multicast traffic and group membership information).

➤ A host can send IP traffic to the group's IP address without belonging to the corresponding group.

A single IP address within the Class D reserved range identifies each multicast group. (The Internet has five address classes—A, B, C, D, and E—defined later in the chapter.) All host members of the group who listen and receive any IP messages sent to the group's IP address share each group's reserved IP address. IP multicast addresses are mapped to a reserved set of MAC multicast addresses.

UDP

Some programs use UDP instead of TCP for fast, lightweight, unreliable transportation of data between TCP/IP hosts. UDP provides a connectionless datagram service that offers best-effort delivery. This means that UDP does not guarantee delivery or verify sequencing for any datagrams. A source host that needs reliable communication must use either TCP or a program that provides its own sequencing and acknowledgment services.

UDP Ports

UDP ports provide a location for sending and receiving UDP messages. A UDP port functions as a single message queue for receiving datagrams intended for the program specified by each protocol port number. This means UDP-based programs can receive more than one message at a time. The server side of each program that uses UDP listens for messages arriving on their well-known port number. UDP server port numbers less than 1,024 are reserved and registered by the Internet Assigned Numbers Authority (IANA). A reserved or well-known port number identifies each UDP server port. Table 3.2 shows a partial list of well-known UDP server port numbers that are used by standard UDP-based programs.

TCP

TCP is a required TCP/IP standard that provides a reliable, connection-oriented packet delivery service. TCP does the following:

➤ Guarantees delivery of IP datagrams.

➤ Performs segmentation and reassembly of large blocks of data sent by programs.

➤ Ensures proper sequencing and ordered delivery of segmented data.

Table 3.2   UDP server port numbers.

UDP Port Number	Description
53	DNS name queries
69	Trivial File Transfer Protocol (TFTP)
137	NetBIOS name service
138	NetBIOS datagram service
161	Simple Network Management Protocol (SNMP)
520	Routing Information Protocol (RIP)

➤ Performs checks on the integrity of transmitted data by using checksum calculations.

➤ Sends positive messages if data was received successfully; by using selective acknowledgments, negative acknowledgments for data not received are also sent.

➤ Offers a preferred method of transport for programs that must use reliable session-based data transmission, such as client/server database and email programs.

3

How TCP Works

TCP is based on point-to-point communication between two network hosts. It receives data from programs and processes this data as a stream of bytes. Bytes are grouped into segments that TCP then numbers and sequences for delivery. Before TCP hosts can exchange data, they first establish a session with each other. A TCP session is initialized through a process called a *three-way handshake*. This process synchronizes sequence numbers and provides control information needed to establish a connection between both hosts. Once the initial three-way handshake is complete, segments are sent and acknowledged in a sequential manner between the hosts. A similar handshake process is used by TCP before closing a connection to ensure that both hosts are finished sending and receiving all data.

TCP Ports

TCP ports are more complex than UDP ports, and they operate differently. Whereas a UDP port operates as a single message queue and the network endpoint for UDP-based communication, the final endpoint for all TCP communication is a unique connection. Each TCP connection is uniquely identified by dual endpoints. Each TCP server port is capable of offering shared access to multiple connections because two pairs of IP address and TCP ports uniquely identify all TCP connections. TCP programs use reserved port numbers. The server on each end listens for messages arriving on each reserved port. Like UDP ports, all TCP server port numbers less than 1,024 are reserved and registered by the IANA. Table 3.3 is a partial list of some well-known TCP server ports used by standard TCP-based programs.

Table 3.3   TCP server ports.

TCP Port Number	Description
20	FTP server (data channel)
21	FTP server (control channel)
23	Telnet server
53	DNS zone transfers
80	Web server (HTTP)
139	NetBIOS session service

IP Addressing

Each TCP/IP host is identified by a unique, logical IP address. Each 32-bit IP address identifies a location of a host system on the network in the same way that a street address identifies a house on a city street. Like a street address with two parts (a street name and a house number), IP addresses are separated internally into two parts: a network ID and a host ID. The network ID identifies a network segment within a larger TCP/IP internetwork. All the systems that attach and share access to the same network have a common network ID within their full IP address. The host ID identifies a workstation, server, router, or other TCP/IP device within each network, which are generally referred to as nodes on the network. The host ID for each device identifies a single system uniquely within its own network.

IP Address Classes

The Internet community has defined five address classes. Class A, B, and C addresses are used for assignment to TCP/IP nodes. (Class D addresses are used for multicasting, and Class E are experimental.) The address class defines which bits are used for the network and host ID parts of each address. The address class also defines how many networks and hosts per network can be supported. Table 3.4 uses *w.x.y.z* to designate the four octet values in any given IP address.

Subnet Masks

Network IDs and host IDs within an IP address are distinguished by using a subnet mask. Typically, default subnet mask values, as shown in Table 3.5, are acceptable for most networks with no special requirements and where each IP network segment corresponds to a single physical network. In some cases, you can use customized subnet masks to implement IP subnetting. With IP subnetting, you can subdivide the default host ID portion of an IP address to specify subnets, which are subdivisions of the original class-based network ID. By customizing the subnet mask length, you can reduce the number of bits used for the actual host ID. Table 3.5 lists subnet masks for the Internet address classes.

Table 3.4   IP addressing octets.

Class	Value of *w*	Network ID	Host ID	Number of Networks	Number of Hosts per Network
A	1–126	*w*	*x.y.z*	126	16,777,214
B	128–191	*w.x*	*y.z*	16,384	65,534
C	192–223	*w.x.y*	*z*	2,097,152	254
D	224–239	Reserved for multicast addressing	N/A	N/A	N/A
E	240–254	Reserved for experimental use	N/A	N/A	N/A

Table 3.5   Subnet classes.

Address Class	Subnet Mask
Class A	255.0.0.0
Class B	255.255.0.0
Class C	255.255.255.0

3

IP Routing

In general terms, routing is the forwarding of packets between connected networks. For TCP/IP-based networks, routing is part of the IP and is used with other network protocol services to provide forwarding between hosts located on separate network segments within a larger TCP/IP-based network.

Routing is the primary function of IP. IP datagrams are exchanged and processed on each host at the Internet layer. Above the IP layer, transport services on the source host pass data in the form of TCP segments or UDP messages to the IP layer. The IP layer assembles the datagrams with source and destination information used to route data through the network. The IP layer then passes datagrams down to the network interface layer. At this layer, data-link services convert the datagrams into frames for transmission over the network.

This process happens in reverse order on the destination host. IP layer services on each host examine the destination address of each datagram and compare this address with a locally maintained routing table. It then decides what further forwarding action it should take. IP routers are attached to two or more IP network segments that are enabled to forward packets between them.

Routing Tables

TCP/IP hosts use routing tables for information about other IP networks and IP hosts. An IP address and subnet mask identify networks and hosts. Routing tables are also important because they provide information on communicating with remote networks and hosts. For each computer on an IP network, you could maintain a routing table with an entry for every other computer or network that communicates with the local computer; this is not practical, however, so a default gateway is used instead.

When a computer prepares to send an IP datagram, it inserts the source IP address and the destination IP address of the recipient into the IP header. The computer then examines the destination IP address, compares it with a locally maintained routing table, and performs one of three tasks:

➤ It passes the datagram to a protocol layer above IP on the local host.

➤ It forwards the datagram through one of its attached network interfaces.

➤ It discards the datagram.

Name Resolution

IP is designed to work with the IP addresses of the source and the destination hosts, but people often do not know the IP addresses of the computers with which they want to communicate. They are much better at using and remembering names than IP addresses. If a name is used as an alias for an IP address, you need to ensure that the name is unique and that it resolves to the correct IP address.

In Windows 2000, there are two types of names to resolve:

➤ *Host names*—For programs that use the Windows Sockets programming interface, such as Web browsers.

➤ *NetBIOS names*—For network programs or services that use the NetBIOS programming interface, such as Client for Microsoft Networks and File and Printer Sharing for Microsoft Networks.

Obtaining IP Addresses

Dynamic Host Configuration Protocol (DHCP) is a TCP/IP standard designed to make administering address configurations easier. It uses a server computer to centrally manage IP addresses. Windows 2000 Server includes the DHCP service to enable the server computer to perform as a DHCP server and configure DHCP-enabled client computers on a network. For more information on DHCP, see Chapter 4.

Registering and Resolving NetBIOS Names

Windows Internet Name Service (WINS) provides a dynamic database service that registers and resolves NetBIOS names to IP addresses used on a network. Windows 2000 Server provides WINS to enable the server computer to emulate a NetBIOS name server, which registers and resolves names for WINS-enabled client computers. For more information on WINS, refer to Chapter 7.

Registering and Resolving DNS Names

The Domain Name System (DNS) is a standard name service for the Internet and TCP/IP. The DNS service lets client computers on a network register and resolve DNS domain names. DNS names are used to find and access resources offered by other computers on a network or other networks, including the Internet. For more information on DNS, see Chapters 5 and 6.

Determining How to Use This Computer with Your TCP/IP Network

Before you install Microsoft TCP/IP on a computer running Windows 2000, you need to know the following:

➤ *Does the network support a dynamic TCP/IP configuration?* A dynamic configuration is the simplest to complete and can be used if another computer on a network is installed as a DHCP server.

➤ *Does the network require a manual TCP/IP configuration?* Some existing networks either do not use DHCP or require that TCP/IP configuration be performed manually for each computer.

If DHCP is not used to configure TCP/IP dynamically, the following information is required:

➤ The IP address and subnet mask for each network adapter on the computer.

➤ The IP address for the default local gateway if there is one.

➤ The name of the DNS domain and the IP addresses of the DNS servers. For Active Directory deployment, the primary DNS suffix of a computer, or primary domain name, is by default the name of the Active Directory domain that the computer has joined. The computer's primary DNS suffix can be changed to be different from the primary domain server of the domain that the computer has joined.

➤ The IP addresses for the WINS servers, if WINS is available on a network.

Installing TCP/IP

1. Open Network and Dial-up Connections, and a window similar to Figure 3.2 will appear.

2. Right-click on the network connection for TCP/IP to be installed and enabled, and then click on Properties.

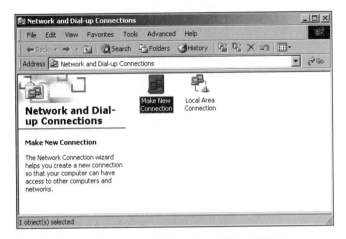

Figure 3.2 The Network and Dial-up Connections window.

3. On the General tab or the Networking tab, if Internet Protocol (TCP/IP) is not in the list of installed components, then do the following:

   a. Click on Install.

   b. Click on Protocol, and then click on Add.

   c. In the Select Network Protocol dialog box, click on Internet Protocol (TCP/IP), and then click on OK.

   d. Verify that the Internet Protocol (TCP/IP) checkbox is selected, and then click on OK.

Configuring TCP/IP Properties

The following section is a walkthrough for configuring TCP/IP properties.

To configure TCP/IP for dynamic addressing:

1. Open Network and Dial-up Connections.

2. Right-click on the network connection you want to configure, and then click on Properties.

3. On the General tab or the Networking tab, click on Internet Protocol (TCP/IP), and then click on Properties.

4. Click on Obtain an IP Address Automatically, and then click on OK.

To disable automatic address configuration:

1. Open Registry Editor.

2. In Registry Editor, navigate to the following registry key:

```
HKEY_LOCAL_MACHINE\SYSTEM\CurrentControlSet\
Services\Tcpip\Parameters\Interfaces\adapter_name
```

3. Create the following entry:

```
IPAutoconfigurationEnabled: REG_DWORD
```

4. Assign a value of 0 to disable Automatic Private IP Addressing (APIPA) support for the selected network adapter.

5. Close Registry Editor.

To configure TCP/IP for static addressing:

1. Open Network and Dial-up Connections.

2. Right-click on the network connection you want to configure, and then click on Properties.

3. On the General tab (for a local area connection) or the Networking tab (all other connections), click on Internet Protocol (TCP/IP), and then click on Properties.

4. Click on Use the Following IP Address, and do one of the following:

   ➤ For a local area connection, in IP Address, Subnet Mask, and Default Gateway, type the IP address, subnet mask, and default gateway addresses.

   ➤ For all other connections, in IP Address, type the IP address.

5. Click on Use the Following DNS Server Addresses.

6. In Preferred DNS Server and Alternate DNS Server, type the primary and secondary DNS server addresses.

7. Click on OK.

To configure TCP/IP to use DNS:

1. Open Network and Dial-up Connections.

2. Right-click on the network connection you want to configure, and then click on Properties.

3. On the General tab (for a local area connection) or the Networking tab (all other connections), click on Internet Protocol (TCP/IP), and then click on Properties.

4. If you want to obtain DNS server addresses from a DHCP server, click on Obtain DNS Server Address Automatically.

5. If you want manually to configure DNS server addresses, click on Use the Following DNS Server Addresses, and in Preferred DNS Server and Alternate DNS Server, type the preferred DNS server and alternate DNS server IP addresses.

6. Click on OK.

To configure TCP/IP to use WINS:

1. Open Network and Dial-up Connections.

2. Right-click on the network connection you want to configure, and then click on Properties.

3. On the General tab or the Networking tab, click on Internet Protocol (TCP/IP), and then click on Properties.

4. Click on Advanced, click on the WINS tab, and then click on Add.

5. In TCP/IP WINS Server, type the IP address of the WINS server, and then click on Add.

6. Repeat Steps 4 and 5 for each WINS server IP address you want to add, and then click on OK.

7. To enable the use of the lmhosts file to resolve remote NetBIOS names, select the Enable LMHOSTS Lookup checkbox. This option is enabled by default.

8. To specify the location of the file that you want to import into the lmhosts file, click on Import LMHOSTS, and select the file in the Open dialog box.

9. To modify the behavior of NetBIOS over TCP/IP behavior, do the following:

   ➤ To enable the use of NetBIOS over TCP/IP, click on Enable NetBIOS over TCP/IP.

   ➤ To disable the use of NetBIOS over TCP/IP, click on Disable NetBIOS over TCP/IP.

   ➤ To have the DHCP server determine the NetBIOS behavior, click on Use NetBIOS Setting from the DHCP Server.

To configure TCP/IP to use an IP Security (IPSec) policy:

1. Open Network and Dial-up Connections.

2. Right-click on the network connection you want to configure, and then click on Properties.

3. On the General tab or the Networking tab, click on Internet Protocol (TCP/IP), and then click on Properties.

4. Click on Advanced.

5. On the Options tab, click on IP Security, and then click on Properties.

6. To enable IPSec, click on Use this IP Security Policy, and then click on the name of a policy.

7. To disable IPSec, click on Do Not Use IPSec.

To configure TCP/IP to use TCP/IP filtering:

1. Open Network and Dial-up Connections.

2. Right-click on the network connection you want to configure, and then click on Properties.

3. On the General tab or the Networking tab, click on Internet Protocol (TCP/IP), and then click on Properties.

4. Click on Advanced.

5. Click on Options, click on TCP/IP filtering, and then click on Properties.

6. Do one of the following:

> ➤ To enable TCP/IP filtering for all adapters, select the Enable TCP/IP Filtering (All Adapters) checkbox.

> ➤ To disable TCP/IP filtering for all adapters, clear the Enable TCP/IP Filtering (All Adapters) checkbox.

7. Based on your requirements for TCP/IP filtering, configure TCP ports, UDP ports, or IP protocols for the allowed traffic.

Configuring Additional or Secondary Methods to Obtain and Resolve NetBIOS and DNS Names

Beyond the configuration of an IP address, subnet mask, default gateway, DNS server, and WINS server, you can do advanced configuration for Windows 2000 TCP/IP including IP, DNS, and WINS settings.

Advanced IP Settings

These include:

> ➤ *Multiple IP addresses*—These can be used for each network connection for multiple IP numbering schemes, including public addresses used for the Internet and private addresses, and for multiple logical IP networks on the same physical network segment.

> ➤ *Default gateways*—Windows 2000 can detect downed routers by using a feature called *dead gateway detection*. If multiple default gateways are configured, failing TCP connections update the IP routing table with the next default gateway in the list.

Advanced DNS Settings

These include:

> ➤ *Multiple DNS servers*—If multiple DNS servers are configured, and TCP/IP fails to receive any response from the current DNS server, TCP/IP will switch to the next DNS server.

> ➤ *Unqualified name resolution*—For unqualified names, you can configure TCP/IP to append either the primary and connection-specific DNS suffixes to the unqualified name for DNS queries, or a series of configured DNS suffixes to the unqualified name for DNS queries.

> ➤ *Connection-specific DNS suffixes*—You can configure each connection in Network and Dial-up Connections to have its own DNS suffix in addition to the primary DNS suffix configured for the computer on the Network Identification tab, which is available under System in Control Panel.

➤ *DNS dynamic update behavior*—If you have DNS servers that support DNS dynamic update, you can enable the DNS dynamic update of the domain name and IP addresses for the computer. If you configure a connection-specific DNS suffix, you can also enable the DNS dynamic update of the domain name and IP addresses for the connection.

Advanced WINS Settings

These include:

➤ *Multiple WINS servers*—If multiple WINS servers are configured, and TCP/IP fails to receive any response from the current WINS server, TCP/IP switches to the next WINS server.

➤ *Enabling and disabling the use of lmhosts files*—If the lmhosts file is enabled, TCP/IP parses the lmhosts file found in the systemroot\System32\Drivers\Etc folder during NetBIOS name resolution. By default, the use of the lmhosts file is enabled.

➤ *Enabling or disabling the use of NetBIOS over TCP/IP*—If the use of NetBIOS over TCP/IP is disabled, NetBIOS programs cannot run over TCP/IP. Computers that are running an operating system other than Windows 2000 may not be able to make a connection. By default, the use of NetBIOS over TCP/IP is specified by the settings obtained from a DHCP server.

Advanced Options

These include:

➤ *Enabling IPSec and specifying an IPSec policy*—If IPSec is configured, secure end-to-end communication of IP-based traffic on a private network or the Internet is used. By default, IPSec is disabled.

➤ *Enabling TCP/IP filtering and specifying TCP/IP traffic*—If TCP/IP filtering is enabled, you can specify the types of TCP/IP traffic for processing.

The ipconfig/all Command

The **ipconfig/all** command is a diagnostic command that displays all current TCP/IP configuration values. It is of particular use on systems running DHCP, allowing users to determine which TCP/IP configuration values have been configured by DHCP.

The ping Command

Use the **ping** command to verify that you have TCP/IP installed and working properly. It is a useful tool in determining if the computer has established a connection to the network and what portions of the network it can talk to. Follow these steps in using the ping command:

1. To quickly obtain the TCP/IP configuration of a computer, open Command Prompt, and then type "ipconfig".

2. At the command prompt, ping the loopback address by typing ping "127.0.0.1". If the **ping** command fails, verify that the computer was restarted after TCP/IP was installed and configured.

3. Ping the IP address of the computer. If the **ping** command fails, verify that the computer was restarted after TCP/IP was installed and configured.

4. Ping the IP address of the default gateway. If the **ping** command fails, verify that the default gateway IP address is correct and that the gateway (router) is operational.

5. Ping the IP address of a remote host (one that is on a different subnet). If the **ping** command fails, verify that the remote host IP address is correct, that the remote host is operational, and that all the gateways (routers) between this computer and the remote host are operational.

6. Ping the IP address of the DNS server. If the **ping** command fails, verify that the DNS server IP address is correct, that the DNS server is operational, and that all the gateways (routers) between this computer and the DNS server are operational.

The nslookup Command

Use the **nslookup** command to verify that you are able to obtain and resolve DNS names. **nslookup** is a diagnostic tool used to display information from DNS name servers. Before using this tool, you should be familiar with how DNS works. **nslookup** is available only if TCP/IP has been installed and has two modes: interactive and noninteractive. If you need to look up only a single piece of data, use the noninteractive mode. If more than one piece of data needs to be looked up, use the interactive mode.

IPX/SPX

IPX and SPX are transport protocols used in Novell NetWare networks. Together, they correspond to the IP and TCP, respectively, used in the TCP/IP suite. IPX/SPX/NetBIOS Compatible Transport Protocol (NWLink) is an implementation of Novell's IPX/SPX and NetBIOS protocols. Windows 2000 clients can use NWLink to access client and server applications on Novell NetWare servers, and, likewise, NetWare clients can use NWLink to access client and server applications on Windows 2000 servers. With NWLink, Windows 2000 computers can communicate with other network devices that use IPX/SPX. You can also use NWLink in small networks with Microsoft client software.

NWLink

NWLink supports two networking application programming interfaces (APIs): NetBIOS and Windows Sockets. APIs allow communication among computers running Windows 2000 and NetWare servers.

The NWLink transport driver is an implementation of the lower-level NetWare protocols, which include IPX, SPX, RIPX (Routing Information Protocol over IPX), and NBIPX (NetBIOS over IPX). IPX controls addressing and routing of packets of data within and between networks. SPX provides reliable delivery through sequencing and acknowledgments. NWLink provides NetBIOS compatibility with a NetBIOS layer over IPX.

Depending on which platform is being used and which resources are to be accessed, you may need to use NWLink in conjunction with other tools. Table 3.6 lists several interoperability options with NWLink.

For a Windows 2000 client to access file and print resources on a NetWare server, Client Service for NetWare must be installed on the Windows 2000 client in addition to NWLink. Non-NetWare computers on a network, which are not running NWLink or another IPX/SPX transport, can access NetWare file and print resources through a computer running Windows 2000 Server that has Gateway Service for NetWare and NWLink installed.

If a Novell NetWare client requires file and print access to a computer running Windows 2000, File and Print Services for NetWare and NWLink must be installed on the computer running Windows 2000. File and Print Services for NetWare is available as a separate product. Users should note that, by default, the file- and print-sharing components of Windows 2000 use NetBIOS over IPX to send messages about file and print sharing. Users can disable NetBIOS so that the file- and print-sharing messages are sent directly over IPX. This is known as *direct hosting*.

Although direct hosting may be more efficient, it can cause an interoperability issue in that a direct hosting client can connect only to a direct hosting server. Direct

Table 3.6 NWLink interoperability options.

Platform	Running	Can Connect to
Windows 2000	NWLink	Client/server applications running on a NetWare server.
Windows 2000	NWLink and Client Service for NetWare or NWLink and Gateway Service for NetWare	NetWare servers for file and print services.
NetWare client	IPX with NetBIOS, Named Pipes, or Windows Sockets support	Computers running Windows 2000 (with NWLink installed) or running IPX applications, such as Microsoft SQL Server.
NetWare client	IPX	Computers running Windows 2000 Server (with NWLink and File and Print Services for NetWare installed) for file and print services.

hosting clients include computers running Microsoft Network Client for MS-DOS, Windows for Workgroups, Windows 95, and Windows 98. Direct hosting servers include computers running Microsoft Network Client for MS-DOS, Windows for Workgroups, Windows 95, Windows 98, Windows NT, and Windows 2000. Table 3.7 lists several interoperability options that use IPX.

Depending on your computer configuration, you may need the following hardware:

➤ Network adapter with a certified Network Driver Interface Specification (NDIS) driver for LAN connectivity

➤ One or more compatible modems and an available COM port

➤ Modem or ISDN adapter (if you are using an ISDN line)

➤ Digital Subscriber Line (DSL) adapter

➤ X.25 card or packet assembler/disassembler (PAD), if you are using X.25

➤ Analog telephone line

➤ Multiport adapter, which may improve performance for multiple connections if your computer is set up for incoming connections

To verify that the hardware is compatible in a computer running Windows 2000, see the Microsoft Windows Hardware Compatibility List at the Microsoft Web site.

To install NWLink:

1. Open Network and Dial-up Connections.

2. Right-click on a local area connection, and then click on Properties.

3. On the General tab, click on Install.

4. In the Select Network Component Type dialog box, click on Protocol, and then click on Add.

Table 3.7   IPX interoperability options.

Platform	Running	Can Connect to
Microsoft Network Client for MS-DOS, Windows for Workgroups, Windows 95, and Windows 98	IPX only (direct hosting)	File- and print-shared resources on computers running Microsoft Network Client for MS-DOS, Windows for Workgroups, Windows 95, Windows 98, Windows NT, and Windows 2000.
Microsoft Network Client for MS-DOS, Windows for Workgroups, Windows 95, Windows 98, Windows NT, and Windows 2000	NetBIOS over IPX	File- and print-shared resources on computers running Microsoft Network Client for MS-DOS, Windows for Workgroups, Windows 95, Windows 98, Windows NT, and Windows 2000.

5. In the Select Network Protocol dialog box, click on NWLink IPX/SPX/NetBIOS Compatible.

6. Set the frame type.

7. Set the external and internal network numbers.

8. Enable/disable the Routing Information Protocol (RIP).

To configure NWLink:

1. Open Network and Dial-up Connections.

2. Right-click on a local area connection, and then click on Properties.

3. On the General tab, click on NWLink IPX/SPX/NetBIOS Compatible Transport Protocol, and then click on Properties.

4. On the General tab, type a value for the internal network number, or leave this setting at the default value of 00000000.

5. Do one of the following:

   ➤ Click on Auto Frame Type Detection, and then click on OK.

   ➤ Click on Manual Frame Type Detection.

   ➤ Click on Add.

   ➤ In the Manual Frame Detection dialog box, in Frame Type, click on a frame type.

   ➤ In Network Number, type a network number, and then click on Add.

   ➤ Repeat these steps for each frame type you want to include, and then click on OK.

To enable RIP on an interface:

1. Open Routing and Remote Access.

2. In the console tree, click on RIP for IPX.

3. In the Details pane, right-click on the interface on which you want to enable RIP, and then click on Properties.

4. On the General tab, select the Enable RIP on this Interface checkbox.

5. Select the Advertise Routes and the Accept Route Advertisements checkboxes.

6. Under Update mode, click on Standard, and then click on OK.

7. For demand-dial interfaces, click on Autostatic, and then click on OK.

NetBIOS

NetBIOS started as a high-level programming language interface for MS-DOS programs. It was used to network IBM PC-compatible microcomputers introduced during the late 1980s. Microsoft and other vendors adopted the NetBIOS interface as the standard in designing their networking system components and programs. This interface uses single-part names, which are limited to 16 characters to identify each network resource. The NetBIOS names can be used only once within a network. Names are dynamically registered when computers start up, services start, or users log on. NetBIOS names can be registered as either unique or group names. A unique name has one address associated with it. A group name has more than one address mapped to it.

Prior to Windows 2000, all MS-DOS and Windows-based operating systems required the NetBIOS naming interface to support network capabilities. With the release of Windows 2000, this interface is no longer required for networking computers; however, most networks still need to integrate legacy operating systems that require NetBIOS network names with computers running Windows 2000. With Windows 2000, Microsoft has continued to provide default support for NetBIOS names to ease interoperability with legacy operating systems. This support is provided mainly in two ways:

➤ Windows 2000 computers that use TCP/IP are enabled by default to provide client-side support for registering and resolving NetBIOS names.

➤ This support is provided through NetBIOS over TCP/IP (NetBT) and can, if desired, be manually disabled.

NetBIOS Name Resolution

NetBIOS name resolution is defined as successfully mapping a NetBIOS name to an IP address. A NetBIOS name is a 16-byte address used to identify a resource on the network. When a NetBIOS process is communicating with a specific process on a specific computer, it uses a unique name. When a NetBIOS process is communicating with multiple processes on multiple computers, it uses a group name.

The File and Printer Sharing for Microsoft Networks service on a computer running Windows 2000 is an example of a process that uses NetBIOS. When a computer starts up, the service registers a unique NetBIOS name based on the computer name. The exact name used by the service is the 15-character computer name plus a 16th character of 0x20. If the computer name is not long enough, it is padded with spaces up to 15 characters. When a user makes a file-sharing connection to a computer running Windows 2000 by name, the File and Printer Sharing for Microsoft Networks service on the file server corresponds to a specific NetBIOS name. Before a file- and print-sharing connection can be established, there must be a TCP connection. For a TCP connection to be established, the NetBIOS name must be resolved to an IP address.

The exact mechanism by which NetBIOS names are resolved to IP addresses depends on the NetBIOS node type. Table 3.8 defines the NetBIOS node types.

A computer running Windows 2000 is B-node by default and becomes H-node when it is configured as a WINS server. Windows 2000 can also use the local database file lmhosts to resolve remote NetBIOS names. It is highly recommended that you configure computers running Windows 2000 with the IP address of your WINS server to allow remote NetBIOS names to be resolved. Active Directory-based computers running Windows 2000 must be configured with the IP address of a WINS server if they communicate with other computers running Windows NT and Windows 2000, Windows 95, or Windows 98 that are not Active Directory-based.

WINS Proxies

WINS proxies help resolve NetBIOS name queries for computers located on routed TCP/IP networks. By default, most computers that are not able to use WINS use broadcasts to resolve NetBIOS name queries and register their NetBIOS names on the network. Configure a WINS proxy to listen on behalf of these computers and query WINS for names not resolved by broadcast. WINS proxies are useful or necessary only on networks that include broadcast NetBIOS. These clients are known as B-node clients.

WINS proxies are used in the following ways:

➤ When a B-node client registers its name, the proxy checks the name against the WINS server database. If the name exists in the WINS database, the proxy will send a negative registration response back to the B-node client attempting to register the name.

Table 3.8   NetBIOS node types.

Node Type	Description
B-node (broadcast)	B-node uses broadcast NetBIOS name queries for name registration and resolution. B-node has two major problems: (1) Broadcasts disturb every node on the network; and (2) Routers typically do not forward broadcasts, so only NetBIOS names on the local network can be resolved.
P-node (peer-peer)	P-node uses a NetBIOS name server (NBNS), such as a WINS server, to resolve NetBIOS names. P-node does not use broadcasts; instead, it queries the name server directly.
M-node (mixed)	M-node is a combination of B-node and P-node. By default, an M-node functions as a B-node. If an M-node is unable to resolve a name by broadcast, it queries an NBNS using P-node.
H-node (hybrid)	H-node is a combination of P-node and B-node. By default, an H-node functions as a P-node. If an H-node is unable to resolve a name through the NBNS, it uses a broadcast to resolve the name.

➤ When a B-node client releases its name, the proxy deletes the client name from its remote name cache.

➤ When a B-node client sends a name query, the proxy attempts to resolve the name either using information locally contained in its cache of remote names or through the use of information it obtains from the WINS server.

Disabling NetBIOS over TCP/IP

Windows 2000 allows select clients to disable NetBT. If DNS is required to provide name registration and resolution on a specified computer used in a specialized or secured role for a network, select clients can disable NetBT services for one or all installed network adapter interfaces on that computer.

When NetBT is disabled, consider the following:

➤ The computer no longer listens for traffic to the NetBIOS datagram service at UDP port 138, the NetBIOS name service at UDP port 137, or the NetBIOS session service at TCP port 139.

➤ If WINS is installed, the computer can no longer function as a WINS server to service WINS clients over this connection unless NetBT is re-enabled.

➤ If the computer needs to participate in WINS as a client, it must be physically multihomed for it to continue communicating with and using a WINS server. Multihomed means that it must have other physical network connections active and available for its use.

➤ For computers operating as WINS clients, any WINS servers configured in TCP/IP properties for the disabled network adapter do not apply to other installed network adapters. For those adapters to use WINS, you must either manually configure a list of WINS servers on the NetBT-enabled connections or provide such a list to these connections from a DHCP server.

A possible use for this configuration setting is when a server computer is multihomed on an internal private network and an exposed external network, such as the Internet. In this situation, disabling NetBT for the installed external network connection makes sense. This lets the dual-homed computer continue to function as either a WINS server or client for the internal network, and WINS clients can still be serviced for connections made using another physical network adapter installed on the computer.

To disable WINS/NetBT name resolution:

1. Open Network and Dial-up Connections.

2. Click on the local area connection to be statically configured and then, from the File menu, click on Properties.

3. In the list of components, click on Internet Protocol (TCP/IP), and then click on Properties.

4. Click on Advanced.

5. Click on the WINS tab.

6. Click on Disable NetBIOS over TCP/IP.

To release and refresh NetBIOS names by using the nbtstat command:

1. Open Command Prompt.

2. At the command prompt, type "nbtstat –RR".

The progress of the release and refresh process is displayed as command-line output. This information indicates if all local NetBIOS names currently registered in WINS for this computer have released and renewed their registration with a WINS server.

NetBEUI

NetBIOS Extended User Interface (NetBEUI) is perfect for use in small workgroups or LANs. Install a NetBIOS gateway and the NetBEUI client protocol on all remote access servers and most Windows networking clients. NetBEUI is not routable, and the only configuration required for the protocol is a computer name. Because this book is targeted for medium to large networks, and is suited for Windows 2000 and Small Business Server networks, we will not cover NetBEUI in any greater detail.

AppleTalk

Apple Macintosh clients can dial in to a remote access server running Windows 2000 by using the remote access Point-to-Point Protocol (PPP) and the AppleTalk LAN protocol. In this configuration, remote access clients negotiate AppleTalk network settings with the remote access server by using the AppleTalk Control Protocol (ATCP).

To configure AppleTalk remote access:

1. Open Routing and Remote Access.

2. Right-click on the server name for which you want to configure AppleTalk remote access, and then click on Properties.

3. On the AppleTalk tab, configure the AppleTalk remote access settings.

Monitoring Network Activity and Protocol Management and Optimization

Administrators can use the Network Monitor tool to capture protocol packets and monitor network activity for different protocols. For more information on using Network Monitor and filtering packets, see Chapter 2.

Using Network Administrative tools to optimize protocols is explained in more detail in Chapter 2 as well.

Binding Network Protocols

For an adapter to communicate over the network, it must be bound to one or more protocols. Binding paths are processed in the order listed. If the network protocol used most frequently is first in the binding list, average connection time is lower. Some protocols are faster than others for certain network topologies. Putting the faster protocol first in the binding list improves performance.

To modify the protocol bindings order:

1. Open Network and Dial-up Connections.

2. Click on the connection you want to modify; then on the Advanced menu, click on Advanced Settings.

3. On the Adapters and Bindings tab, in Bindings for Adapter Name, click on the protocol you want to move up or down in the list, and then click on the Up or Down button.

Chapter Summary

Several core protocols are included in TCP/IP: Address Resolution Protocol (ARP), Internet Protocol (IP), Internet Control Message Protocol (ICMP), Internet Group Management Protocol (IGMP), User Datagram Protocol (UDP), and Transmission Control Protocol (TCP). ARP resolves IP addresses used by TCP/IP-based software to MAC addresses used by LAN hardware. IP is a connectionless, unreliable datagram protocol primarily responsible for addressing and routing packets between hosts. With ICMP, hosts and routers that use IP communication can report errors and exchange limited control and status information. IGMP is a protocol to exchange and update information about host membership in specific multicast groups. UDP provides a connectionless datagram service that offers best-effort delivery. This means that UDP does not guarantee delivery or verify sequencing for any datagrams. TCP is a required TCP/IP standard that provides a reliable, connection-oriented packet delivery service.

Each TCP/IP host is identified by a unique, logical IP address. The network ID or address identifies a network segment within a larger TCP/IP internetwork. The host ID or address identifies a workstation, server, router, or other TCP/IP device within each network.

For TCP/IP-based networks, routing is part of the IP and is used with other network protocol services to provide forwarding between hosts that are located on separate network segments within a larger TCP/IP-based network.

IP is like the mailroom of the TCP/IP protocol. Each incoming or outgoing packet is called an IP datagram and contains two IP addresses: the source address of the sending host and the destination address of the receiving host. IP routers connect TCP/IP network segments and provide the principal means of joining two or more separated IP network segments. IP routers are multihomed hosts that provide packet forwarding for other TCP/IP hosts. IP routers are distinct from other hosts that use multihoming because they must be able to forward IP-based communication between networks for other IP network hosts.

Network programs or services that use the NetBIOS programming interface, such as Client for Microsoft Networks and File and Printer Sharing for Microsoft Networks, use NetBIOS names. NetBIOS uses a server computer to centrally manage IP addresses. Windows 2000 Server includes the DHCP service to enable the server computer to perform as a DHCP server and configure DHCP-enabled client computers on your network. WINS provides a dynamic database service that registers and resolves NetBIOS names to IP addresses used on a network. Windows 2000 Server provides WINS to enable the server computer to emulate a NetBIOS name server, which registers and resolves names for WINS-enabled client computers. DNS is a standard name service for the Internet and TCP/IP. The DNS service allows client computers on a network to register and resolve DNS domain names.

Beyond the configuration of an IP address, subnet mask, default gateway, DNS server, and WINS server, you can do advanced configuration for Windows 2000 TCP/IP, including IP, DNS, and WINS settings. Advanced IP settings include multiple IP addresses and multiple default gateways. You can use multiple IP addresses for each network connection for multiple IP numbering schemes, including public addresses used for the Internet and private addresses, and for multiple logical IP networks on the same physical network segment. If multiple DNS servers are configured, and TCP/IP fails to receive any response from the current DNS server, TCP/IP will switch to the next DNS server. DNS dynamic update can be enabled for the domain name and IP addresses for the computer. If a connection-specific DNS suffix is configured, DNS dynamic update can also be enabled to update the domain name and IP addresses for the connection.

Direct hosting clients include computers running Microsoft Network Client for MS-DOS, Windows for Workgroups, Windows 95, and Windows 98. Direct hosting servers include computers running Microsoft Network Client for MS-DOS, Windows for Workgroups, Windows 95, Windows 98, Windows NT, and Windows 2000.

Computers running Windows 2000 should be configured with the IP address of a WINS server to allow remote NetBIOS names to be resolved. WINS proxies help resolve NetBIOS name queries for computers located on routed TCP/IP networks.

3

Review Questions

1. What is the third layer of the OSI model?

    a. Applications

    b. Transport

    c. Session

    d. Presentation

2. Which of the core protocols included in TCP/IP resolves IP addresses used by TCP/IP-based software to MAC addresses used by LAN hardware?

    a. ARP

    b. IP

    c. ICMP

    d. TCP

3. Which of the core protocols included in TCP/IP provides a connectionless datagram service that offers best-effort delivery?

    a. IGMP

    b. UDP

    c. ICMP

    d. IP

4. Which of the core protocols included in TCP/IP guarantees delivery of IP datagrams?

    a. ICMP

    b. ARP

    c. IP

    d. TCP

5. With the IP address, 131.107.16.200, which numbers indicate the network ID portion?

 a. 131.107

 b. 107.16

 c. 16.200

 d. 131.107.16

6. With the IP address, 131.107.16.200, which numbers indicate the host ID portion?

 a. 131.107

 b. 107.16

 c. 16.200

 d. 131.107.16

7. Which of the following IP addresses would indicate Class C?

 a. 1-126

 b. 192-223

 c. 240-254

 d. 224-239

8. What is the primary function of IP?

 a. Routing

 b. Services

 c. Processing

 d. Internet support

9. Regardless of the type of IP routers you use, what do all IP routers rely on to communicate between network segments?

 a. Special software

 b. Designated hardware

 c. Communication skills

 d. Routing table

10. Which of the following is not done to configure TCP/IP for dynamic addressing?

 a. Open Network and Dial-up Connections

 b. Right-click on the network connection you want to configure, and then click on Add.

 c. On the General tab (for local area connection) or the Networking tab (all other connections), click on Internet Protocol (TCP/IP), and then click on Properties.

 d. Click on Obtain an IP Address Automatically, and then click on OK.

11. Which of the following are transport protocols used in Novell NetWare networks?

    a. IPX/SPX

    b. TCP/IP

    c. NetBIOS

    d. AppleTalk

3

12. A NetBIOS name uses how many bytes in its address to identify a resource on the network?

    a. 8

    b. 12

    c. 16

    d. 32

13. Computers running Windows 2000 are B-node by default, and become what node when they are configured as a WINS server?

    a. A

    b. P

    c. M

    d. H

14. Which protocol is not routable, and the only configuration required for it is a computer name?

    a. AppleTalk

    b. TCP/IP

    c. NetBEUI

    d. IPX/SPX

15. What tool can administrators use to capture protocol packets and monitor network activity for different protocols?

    a. Network Monitor

    b. Network Abilities

    c. Monitoring and Configuration

    d. Packet Capturing

Real-World Projects

Lesha Camille, the IT director of Red National Bank, has already upgraded the bank's 13 computers to a physical and logical star network using 100BaseT Ethernet technology for a higher degree of security and centralized administration.

After setting up the star network, Camille now needs to configure TCP/IP for the network. She has asked you, the network consultant, to help her get all the workstations configured for TCP/IP usage.

Project 3.1

To install TCP/IP, perform the following steps:

1. Open Network and Dial Connections.

2. Right-click on the network connection, and then click on Properties.

3. On the General tab, if Internet Protocol (TCP/IP) is not in the list of installed components, do the following:

4. Click on Install.

5. Click on Protocol, and then click on Add.

6. In the Select Network Protocol dialog box, click on Internet Protocol (TCP/IP).

7. Click on OK.

8. Verify the Internet Protocol (TCP/IP) checkbox is selected, then click on OK.

This will enable TCP/IP on a network; however, it should automatically be installed during the Windows 2000 installation process and will depend largely on the NIC used.

Project 3.2

To configure TCP/IP manually for a network's clients and servers, perform the following steps:

1. Open Network and Dial-up Connections.

2. Right-click on the network connection, and then click on Properties.

3. On the General tab, click on Internet Protocol (TCP/IP), and then click on Properties.

4. Click on Use the Following IP Address.

5. Fill in the IP address for the computer, the subnet mask, and a default gateway (only if routers are present).

6. Click on OK.

This will configure the network's clients and servers statically for TCP/IP. The default gateway can be left blank because this particular network does not have an Internet gateway connection or routers.

3

Note: This network still needs name resolution with either a WINS server or a DNS server. This will be covered in later chapters, but keep it in mind.

CHAPTER FOUR

Dynamic Host Configuration Protocol

After completing this chapter, you will be able to:

✓ Understand how DHCP works

✓ Understand the underlying terminology of DHCP

✓ Understand the difference between user and vendor classes

✓ Understand what DHCP options are and how to apply them

✓ Understand the role of a DHCP server

✓ Automatically configure clients

✓ Authorize DHCP servers for a network

✓ Manage DHCP servers remotely

✓ Identify, troubleshoot, and recover DHCP database data

✓ Understand the role of a DHCP client

✓ Support DHCP clients

✓ Use reservations for clients

✓ Use the DHCP Relay Agent

✓ Use DHCP with Routing and Remote Access Service servers

✓ Use DNS servers with DHCP

ynamic Host Configuration Protocol (DHCP) is a TCP/IP standard for automating, as well as reducing, administrative complexities for host IP configuration management. Through the use of DHCP servers, the DHCP standard lets you manage dynamic assignments of IP addresses and other related configuration details to DHCP-enabled clients on a network. Every computer on a TCP/IP network is required to have a unique computer name and IP address. The host or client's IP address and the related subnet mask for its network together identify both the host computer and the subnet it belongs to. When you move a computer to a different subnet, the IP address has to be changed; with a DHCP server, an IP address can be assigned dynamically to a client from an IP address database on a local network. In TCP/IP-based networks the implementation of DHCP will simplify and reduce the administrative overhead generally involved in reconfiguring IP addresses to computers.

In this chapter, we will discuss how DHCP works and the terminology you will need to understand to use DHCP effectively. We will also discuss planning issues and considerations, as well as how to configure a DHCP client and DHCP servers. We will touch on the use of DHCP with DNS and interoperability issues that can affect a network. Some of these topics will be dealt with in more detail in later chapters, because of the amount of services that are integrated in Windows 2000.

How DHCP Works

DHCP uses a client-server model where the network administrator configures one or more DHCP servers to maintain TCP/IP configuration information and provide it to clients on that network. The server database includes valid configuration parameters for all clients on the network, valid IP addresses maintained in a pool for client allocation, as well as reserved addresses for manual assignment and an IP address lease. The lease defines the length of time a client is assigned an IP address.

With a DHCP server installed on a network, DHCP-enabled clients will be assigned IP addresses and related configuration information dynamically each time they join their network. DHCP clients receive their configuration in the form of an address-lease offer from DHCP servers.

The Benefits of DHCP

DHCP provides several benefits for administering a TCP/IP-based network. It offers safe and reliable configuration free of errors caused by manually typing in values at each computer. DHCP also prevents address conflicts caused by a previously assigned IP address being reused to configure a new computer on a network.

DHCP servers on a network can greatly decrease time spent configuring and reconfiguring computers. DHCP servers can supply a full range of additional configuration values when assigning address leases to clients. Also, with mobile users who change localities often, the DHCP lease-renewal process assures that frequent updates of client configurations can be made directly with DHCP servers.

The Terminology of DHCP

DHCP terminology lays the foundation of what you need to learn for a complete understanding of this standard. The terms introduced here will be referred to throughout the chapter and will be touched on again in future chapters. (Some of these terms relate to IP routing and multicasting, addressed in Chapters 8 and 9.)

➤ *Scope*—The full consecutive range of possible IP addresses for a network. A scope defines a single physical subnet on a network where DHCP services are offered. It also provides the server a way to manage the distribution, assignment, and configuration parameters of clients and their IP addresses on a network.

➤ *Superscope*—An administrative grouping of scopes that supports multiple logical IP subnets on the same physical subnet. A superscope contains a list of member scopes or child scopes that can be activated together. It is not used to configure other details about scope usage. For configuring most properties used within a superscope, you need to configure member scope properties individually.

➤ *Exclusion range*—A limited sequence of IP addresses within a scope, excluded from DHCP service offerings. An exclusion range ensures that the server does not offer any addresses in these ranges to any DHCP client on a network.

➤ *Address pool*—The remaining addresses available within the scope after you define it and apply exclusion ranges. The DHCP server uses pooled addresses for dynamically assigning addresses to DHCP clients.

➤ *Lease*—The length of time a DHCP server specifies that a client can use an assigned IP address. When a lease is made to a client, it is active. Before the lease expires, the client typically needs to renew its address lease assignment with the server. A lease becomes inactive when it expires or is deleted at the server. The duration of a lease determines its expiration as well as when renewal with the server is needed for a client.

➤ *Reservation*—Used by DHCP servers to create permanent address lease assignments. A reservation ensures that specified hardware devices on a subnet can always use the same IP address.

➤ *Option types*—Other client configuration parameters that can be assigned when serving leases to DHCP clients. Commonly used options include IP addresses for default gateways, Windows Internet Name Service (WINS) servers, and Domain Name System (DNS) servers. These option types are enabled and configured for each scope. The DHCP Console permits the configuration of default option types that are used by all scopes added and configured at the server. You can also use the DHCP Console to define and add custom option types if needed, but most options are predefined through Request for Comments (RFC) 2132.

➤ *Options class*—Provides a way for the server to further manage option types for clients. When an options class is added to the server, clients of that class can be provided class-specific option types for their configuration. For Windows 2000, client computers can also specify a class ID when communicating with the server. For earlier DHCP clients that do not support the class ID process, the server can be configured with default classes. Options classes can be of two types: vendor and user.

Microsoft Predefined User Classes

For Windows 2000 Server, Microsoft has predefined several DHCP user classes, for use when assigning DHCP options; the client being assigned needs to be identified as a member of the specified user classes.

The default user class has an unspecified data type and is used to classify clients that do not explicitly identify themselves as members of a user class defined at the DHCP server. By default, this options class is typically used where most DHCP clients are grouped and included. Clients are assigned to this class when they have no concept of a DHCP user class or a DHCP class ID. Classes are also assigned this way for most legacy and older DHCP clients prior to Windows 2000, and for Windows 2000 clients configured with a DHCP class ID unknown to an undefined DHCP server for which the client identifies itself.

The default remote access class RRAS.Microsoft is used to classify clients making a Point-to-Point Protocol (PPP)-type connection through a Routing and Remote Access Service (RRAS) server. This class includes most remote access clients that use DHCP to obtain a lease. RRAS clients are assigned to this class when they have no concept of this user class or its associated reserved class ID string ("RRAS.Microsoft"). Most remote access clients released prior to Windows 2000 fit this description, as well as Windows 2000 clients that are operating as RRAS clients. Options assigned for distribution with this class are in effect only for RRAS clients.

For computers running Windows 2000, additional user classes can be created at the DHCP server and set to show the DHCP class data used as matching ID strings for

DHCP clients. When working with user classes, be sure that the class data set at the client identically matches the ASCII data value as it is set at the server for a user class. Also make sure character data that is used to identify the class is case-sensitive and is entered in matching case for both server and client configurations.

DHCP Options

DHCP provides an internal framework for passing configuration information to clients on your network. Configuration parameters and other control information are carried in tagged data items stored within protocol messages exchanged between the DHCP server and its clients. These data items are called *options*.

Most standard DHCP options are defined in RFCs published by the Internet Engineering Task Force (IETF). The full set of standard DHCP options is described specifically in RFC 2132, "DHCP Options and BOOTP Vendor Extensions."

All DHCP options mentioned in RFC 2132 are predefined for configuration and use at any Windows 2000 DHCP server. You can use the DHCP Console to define new DHCP options at each server. Even though most DHCP servers can assign many options, most DHCP clients are typically designed to request or support only a subset of the full RFC-specified standard options set.

Applying Options

You can manage options using different control levels assigned for each managed DHCP server:

➤ *Server options*—Apply to all scopes defined at a DHCP server.

➤ *Scope options*—Apply specifically to all clients that obtain leases within a particular scope.

➤ *Class options*—Apply only to clients that are identified as members of a specified user or vendor class when obtaining a lease.

➤ *Client options*—Apply only to a single reserved client computer and require a reservation to be used in an active scope.

The DHCP Server

Configuring DHCP servers for a network can be beneficial. The administrator can assign and specify global and subnet-specific TCP/IP parameters centrally for use throughout the entire network. Client computers don't require manual TCP/IP configuration, and when a client computer moves between subnets its old IP address is freed for reuse. The client will reconfigure its TCP/IP settings automatically when the computer is restarted in its new location. If they support RFC 1542, most routers can forward DHCP configuration requests; therefore, DHCP servers are not required on every subnet in the network, or otherwise you will need to install a DHCP relay agent.

Server Usage by Clients

A computer running Windows 2000 becomes a DHCP client if Obtain An IP Address is selected in its TCP/IP properties. When a client computer is set to use DHCP, it accepts a lease offer and can receive from the server temporary use of an IP address known to be valid for the network it is joining, as well as additional TCP/IP configuration parameters in the form of options data.

If conflict detection is configured, the DHCP server attempts to ping each available address in the scope prior to presenting the address in a lease offer to a client. This ensures that each IP address offered to clients is not already in use by a non-DHCP computer using manual TCP/IP configuration.

Servers and Optional Data

In addition to providing an IP address, a DHCP server can be configured to provide optional data to fully configure TCP/IP for clients. One of the most common DHCP option types configured and distributed by the DHCP server during leases is the default gateway (router), which is used to connect a network segment to other network segments; other optional configuration parameters include IP addresses for DNS servers and WINS servers.

Configuring Clients Automatically

For Windows 2000, DHCP clients automatically configure an IP address and subnet mask when started, if a DHCP server is unavailable. IP autoconfiguration can be useful for clients on small private networks, such as small business office or home network environments.

When clients are configured to use a DHCP server, the DHCP client service engages each time the computer starts. For Windows 2000, the DHCP client service uses a five-step process to configure the client with an IP address and other configuration information. This process is as follows (Steps 2 and 3 occur only when a server cannot be found):

1. The DHCP client attempts to locate a DHCP server and obtain a configuration from it.

2. If a DHCP server cannot be found, the DHCP client autoconfigures its IP address and subnet mask using a selected address from the Microsoft-reserved class B network, 169.254.0.0, with the subnet mask, 255.255.0.0.

3. The DHCP client tests for an address conflict by using a gratuitous Address Resolution Protocol (ARP) to make sure that the IP address it has chosen is not already in use on the network. If a conflict is found, the client selects another IP address. For each address conflict, the client will retry autoconfiguration for up to 10 addresses.

4. Once the DHCP client succeeds in selecting an address in the 169.254.0.0 network range not in use, it will configure the interface with this address.

5. The client continues to check for a DHCP server in the background every five minutes. If a DHCP server is found later, the client abandons its autoconfigured information. The DHCP client then uses an address offered by the DHCP server to update its IP configuration settings.

If the DHCP client has previously obtained a lease from a DHCP server, the following modified sequence of events occurs:

1. If the client lease is still valid (not expired) at boot time, the client will try to renew its lease with the DHCP server.

2. If during the renewal attempt the client fails to locate any DHCP server, it will attempt to ping the default gateway that is listed in the lease. Depending on whether the ping fails or succeeds, the DHCP client proceeds as follows:

   ➤ If a ping of the default gateway succeeds, the DHCP client assumes it is still located on the same network where it obtained its current lease and will continue to use the lease. By default, the client will next attempt in the background to renew its lease when 50 percent of its assigned lease time has expired.

   ➤ If a ping of the default gateway fails, the client assumes it has been moved to a network where DHCP services are not available, such as a home network. The client then autoconfigures its IP address as described previously. Once the client is autoconfigured, it will continue to try locating a DHCP server every five minutes in the background and obtaining a lease.

The How-To of Client Configuration

DHCP clients use two different processes to communicate with DHCP servers and to obtain configuration. The lease-process steps vary depending on whether the client is initializing or renewing its lease. The initialization process occurs when a client computer first starts and attempts to join the network. The renewal process occurs after a client has a lease but needs to renew it with the server.

The Initial Lease Process

The first time a DHCP-enabled client starts, it automatically follows an initialization process to obtain a lease from a DHCP server. The DHCP client first broadcasts a DHCP discover message to the local subnet. A DHCP server can then respond with a DHCP offer message (DHCPOFFER) that contains an offered IP address for lease to the client. If no DHCP servers respond to the client discover request, the client can proceed in either of two ways:

➤ If the client is running under Windows 2000 and IP autoconfiguration has not been disabled, the client self-configures an IP address for itself.

➤ If the client is not running under Windows 2000 or IP autoconfiguration is disabled, the client fails to initialize and, if left running, continues sending a DHCP discover message every five minutes in the background until it receives a DHCP offer message from a server.

As soon as it receives the offer message, the client selects the offered address by replying to the server with a DHCP request. The offering server sends a DHCP acknowledgment message (DHCPACK) to approve the lease. Other DHCP options information is included in the acknowledgment. Once the client receives acknowledgment, it will configure its TCP/IP properties using the information in the reply and join the network. Figure 4.1 shows the lease process between the DHCP server and client. A popular way to memorize the process is the acronym ROSA (Request, Offer, Selection, Acknowledgment).

In rare cases, a DHCP server can return a DHCP negative acknowledgment message (DHCPNAK) to the client. This can happen when a client requests an invalid or duplicate address for the network. If a client receives a negative acknowledgment, the current initialization process fails and the client will try again until it receives an acknowledgment.

The Lease Renewal Process

When a DHCP client shuts down and restarts on the same subnet, it obtains a lease for the same IP address it had prior to the shutdown. After 50 percent of the client

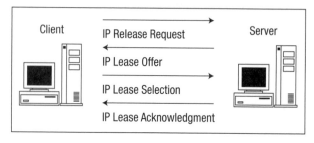

Figure 4.1   The lease process between a DHCP server and client.

lease time elapses, the client will try to renew its lease with the DHCP server by doing the following:

1. The client sends a DHCP request message directly to the server that leased it, to renew and extend its current address lease.

2. If the server is reachable, it typically sends a DHCP acknowledgement message to the client, which renews the current lease.

3. If the client is unable to communicate with its original DHCP server, the client waits until it reaches a rebinding state. Once it reaches this state, it attempts to renew its current lease with any available DHCP server. If a server responds with a DHCP offer message, the client can renew its lease. If the lease expires and no server has been contacted, the client must immediately discontinue using its leased IP address.

4. The client then follows the same process used during its initial startup operation to obtain a new IP address lease. DHCP options information is included in the reply, so if any options information has changed since the client first obtained its lease, the client can update its configuration.

If it is unable to communicate with its original DHCP server, the client waits until it reaches a rebinding state. When the client reaches this state, it attempts to renew its current lease with any available DHCP server. If a server responds with a DHCPOFFER to update the current client lease, the client can renew its lease based on the offering server and continue operation. If the lease expires and no server has been contacted, the client must immediately discontinue using its leased IP address. The client then follows the same process used during its initial startup operation to obtain a new IP address lease.

DHCP Server Authorization

Windows 2000 Server provides integrated security support for networks that use Active Directory. This support adds and uses a class of objects that is part of the base directory scheme that provides for enhancements, such as a list of available IP addresses for the computers that will be authorized to operate as DHCP servers on a network. It also detects unauthorized DHCP servers and prevents them from starting or running on a network.

This section will give some background information about unauthorized DHCP servers on a network. It will explain how servers are authorized in Active Directory to provide the DHCP service and how unauthorized servers are detected and prevented from providing DHCP service.

The Unauthorized Server

When configured correctly and authorized for use on a network, DHCP servers provide a useful and intended administrative service. When an incorrectly configured or unauthorized DHCP server is introduced into a network, however, it can cause problems. When an unauthorized DHCP server starts, it will begin either leasing incorrect IP addresses to clients or negatively acknowledging DHCP clients attempting to renew current address leases. Either of these configurations can produce further problems for DHCP-enabled clients. Clients that obtain a configuration lease from the unauthorized server can fail to locate valid domain controllers, preventing clients from successfully logging on to the network.

To avoid these problems in Windows 2000, servers are verified as legal in the network before they can service clients. This avoids most of the accidental damage caused by running DHCP servers with incorrect configurations or with correct configurations on the wrong network.

Authorizing a Server

The authorization process for DHCP server computers in Active Directory depends on the installed role of the server on your network. In Windows 2000 Server and earlier versions of Windows, each server computer can be installed in one of three roles, or server types:

➤ *Domain controller*—Maintains a copy of the Active Directory service database and provides secure account management for domain member users and computers.

➤ *Member server*—Does not operate as a domain controller but has joined a domain in which it has a membership account in the Active Directory service database.

➤ *Standalone server*—Does not operate as a domain controller or a member server in a domain. Instead, the server is made known to the network through a specified workgroup name shared by other computers. The workgroup name in this instance is used only for browsing purposes and not to provide secured logon access to shared domain resources.

If you deploy Active Directory, all computers operating as DHCP servers must be either domain controllers or domain member servers before they can be authorized in the directory service and provide DHCP service to clients. To authorize a computer as a DHCP server, log on to the network using an account that either has enterprise administrative privileges or has been delegated authority to authorize DHCP servers for an enterprise. Logging on to the network from the computer where the new DHCP server is to be authorized is generally easier. This ensures that other TCP/IP configurations of the authorized computer have been set up correctly prior to authorization.

The account allowed to have Full Control rights to the NetServices container object typically has membership in the Enterprise Administrators group, as it is stored in the enterprise root of the Active Directory service. Install the DHCP service on this computer. Start the DHCP Console and select the computer operating as a DHCP server that is to be added as an authorized server in the directory service database. If the local computer is to be authorized, select Local Computer for Connection when starting the DHCP Console. If another computer on the network is to be authorized, select Remote Computer.

When a DHCP server is authorized, the server computer is added to the list of authorized DHCP servers maintained in the directory service database. You can verify that a server has been added by checking the properties using the Active Directory Sites and Services Console. These properties appear under Configuration, which is a global container maintained at the following folder location relative to the enterprise root: \Configuration\Services\NetServices.

You might choose to let non-enterprise administrators have appropriate security access to delegate the object type to create and modify the list of authorized DHCP servers. This can be useful in cases where the DHCP server is set up and prepared at another location before being shipped to a remote site for installation and authorization for service on the network.

Detecting Unauthorized Servers

Windows 2000 DHCP servers can detect both authorized and unauthorized servers through enhancements for the DHCP standard. These enhancements include the use of information messaging between DHCP servers and the addition of several new vendor-specific option types that communicate information about the root domain.

The Windows 2000 DHCP server uses the following process to detect other DHCP servers running on the same network and determine if they are authorized to provide service:

1. When the DHCP service starts, it sends a DHCP informational message (DHCPINFORM) request to the reachable network, using the local limited broadcast address (255.255.255.255), to locate the root domain on which other DHCP servers are installed and configured. This message includes several vendor-specific option types known and supported by other DHCP servers running Windows 2000 Server.

2. When received by other DHCP servers, these option types enable the query and retrieval of information about the root domain.

3. When queried, other DHCP servers reply with DHCPACKs, both to ac-knowledge and answer with root domain information. In this way, the initializ-ing DHCP server collects and compiles a list of all currently active DHCP

servers on the reachable network, along with the root (of the root domain) used by each server. Usually, it detects one enterprise root, which is the same for all DHCP servers that are reachable and acknowledge the initializing server. If additional enterprise roots are detected, however, each one is queried to determine whether the computer is authorized for DHCP service for those other enterprises discovered during this phase.

4. After a list of all DHCP servers running on the network is built, the next step in the detection process depends on whether a directory service is available from the local computer. Most commonly, there will be only one enterprise root and only a single point for directory authorization of the DHCP server. No restriction exists, however, on authorizing DHCP servers for more than one enterprise root.

5. If the directory service is not available, the initializing server can start if no other DHCP servers are discovered on the network that are part of any enterprise. Where this condition is met, the server successfully initializes and begins serving DHCP clients.

6. The server continues every five minutes to collect information about other DHCP servers running on the network, using DHCPINFORM as it did at startup. Each time, it checks whether the directory service is available. If a directory service is found, the server ensures that it is authorized by the following procedure, depending on whether it is a member server or a standalone server.

   ➤ For member servers, the DHCP server queries the directory service for the DHCP server list of authorized addresses. If the server finds its IP address in the authorized list, it initializes and starts providing DHCP service to clients. If it does not find itself in the authorized list, it does not initialize and stops providing DHCP services.

   ➤ For standalone servers, the DHCP server queries the directory service with the root of the enterprise returned by each of the other DHCP servers to see if it can find itself on the authorized list with any of the reported enterprises. The server initializes and starts providing DHCP services to clients only if it finds its IP address in the authorized list for each of the enterprise roots reported by other DHCP servers. If it does not find itself in the authorized list, it does not initialize and the DHCP service is stopped.

The process of authorizing DHCP servers is useful only for DHCP servers running Windows 2000 Server. Authorization does not apply if DHCP servers are running Windows NT Server 4 and earlier versions or third-party DHCP server software.

For directory authorization to work properly, the first DHCP server introduced on a network must participate in Active Directory. This requires that the server be installed as either a domain controller or a member server. When planning or deploying Active Directory with Windows 2000 DHCP, you should not install your first DHCP server as a standalone.

To enable address conflict detection, click on Start, point to Programs, then to Administrative Tools, and click on DHCP. In the console tree, click on the appropriate DHCP server. On the Action menu, click on Properties, then click on the Advanced tab. For Conflict detection attempts, type a number greater than zero and then click on OK. The number you type determines how many times the DHCP server tests an IP address before leasing it to a client.

When conflict detection attempts are set, the DHCP server uses the Packet Internet Groper (ping) process to test available scope IP addresses before including these addresses in DHCP lease offers to clients. A successful ping means the IP address is in use on the network. When this occurs, the DHCP server does not offer to lease the address to a client. If the ping request fails and times out, the IP address is not in use on the network and the DHCP server offers to lease the address to a client. Each additional conflict detection attempt delays the DHCP server response by a second while waiting for the ping request to time out. This increases the load on the server. A value of no greater than two for ping attempts is recommended.

Remote Management of DHCP Servers

The Windows 2000 Administration Tools included with Windows 2000 Server and Windows 2000 Advanced Server allows the user to manage a DHCP server remotely from another Windows 2000 computer. It contains Microsoft Management Console (MMC) snap-ins and other tools to manage Windows 2000 Server. Once Windows 2000 Administration Tools is installed, an administrator can manage a remote server from that computer.

Database Files for DHCP

The DHCP server database in Windows 2000 Server uses the performance-enhanced Exchange Server storage engine. When the DHCP service is installed, the files shown in Table 4.1 are automatically created in the WINNT\System32\Dhcp directory.

You should not remove or alter the J50.log, J50#####.log, Dhcp.mdb, and Dhcp.tmp files.

The DHCP server database is a dynamic database updated as DHCP clients are assigned or as they release their TCP/IP configuration parameters. Because the DHCP database is not a distributed database like the WINS server database, main-

Table 4.1   DHCP service database files.

File	Description
Dhcp.mdb	The DHCP server database file.
Dhcp.tmp	A temporary file used by the DHCP database as a swap file during database index maintenance operations. This file sometimes remains in the WINNT\System32\Dhcp directory after a system failure.
J50.log and J50#####.log	A log of all database transactions. This file is used by the DHCP database to recover data when necessary.
J50.chk	A checkpoint file.

taining it is less complex. The DHCP database and related Registry entries are automatically backed up at a specific interval (15 minutes by installation default). You can change this installation default by changing the value of BackupInterval in the following Registry key:

```
HKEY_LOCAL_MACHINE\SYSTEM\CurrentControlSet\Services\DHCPServer\
Parameters
```

The DHCP Database

No built-in limit exists for the number of records a DHCP server can store. The size of the database depends upon the number of DHCP clients on the network. The DHCP database grows over time because of clients starting and stopping on the network. The size of the DHCP database is not directly proportional to the number of active client lease entries. Over time, as DHCP client entries become obsolete and deleted, some unused space will remain.

To recover the unused space, you must compact the DHCP database. Starting with Windows NT Server 4, dynamic database compaction occurs on DHCP servers as an automatic background process during idle time after a database update. Although dynamic compacting greatly reduces the need for offline compaction, it does not fully eliminate the need. Offline compaction effectively reclaims space and should be performed about once a month for large and busy networks with 1,000 or more DHCP clients. For smaller networks, manual compaction can be useful when performed every few months. Because dynamic database compaction occurs while the database is in use, stopping the DHCP server is not necessary for it to occur. For manual compacting, however, you must stop the DHCP server and perform compacting offline.

When using or upgrading DHCP databases in earlier versions of Windows NT Server, the DHCP database requires conversion. For Windows 2000 Server, if a previous copy of the DHCP server database is detected during an upgrade, it is automatically converted to the current database version and format. For larger databases, this process can increase the time needed to complete the installation.

Restoring a Server's Data

Restoring the DHCP server database can be useful in situations where the database has become either corrupted or lost. Where DHCP database corruption or loss occurs, Windows 2000 Server provides a progressive set of recovery and repair options for restoration of DHCP data on the server computer. In troubleshooting data corruption problems, use the following general process to detect corruption and restore DHCP service:

1. First, confirm the source of data loss or corruption at the DHCP server. To do so, you can use JetPack.exe to perform a preliminary diagnosis or useful repairs, such as offline database compaction. Additionally, verify that corruption is not related to other problems or conditions with hardware or software changes. Where data loss occurs, verify that the server computer disk drives are operating properly. In most cases, database corruption first appears in the form of Jet database error messages in the System event log.

2. If repair through JetPack.exe compaction fails, perform a quick recovery of the DHCP server based on the available options for server backup. One option is to manually make an offline backup of the DHCP server database files and then copy the server database back during restoration from an archived source, such as a recent tape backup of the server computer disk drives. Another option is to use the Netshell set databaserestore flag command to set the restore flag. This lets the DHCP Server service load a copy of the DHCP database in its default backup directory when re-initialized. When backing up the server computer, use either Windows 2000 backup and restore options or other backup and restoration software.

3. Finally, when other server data recovery options are not available or are tried but unsuccessful, use advanced DHCP recovery options.

The DHCP Client

DHCP clients can be any Microsoft Windows-based clients or others that support and comply with client behavior described in the updated DHCP standards document, RFC 2132.

In most cases, no additional steps are needed to let Windows-based clients use DHCP configuration, because it is the default setting. If a Windows-based client computer is not configured to use DHCP, it can be enabled to do so with a simple configuration change.

DHCP Clients for Microsoft

Microsoft provides DHCP client support for computers running under any of these operating systems:

➤ Windows 2000 (all released versions)

➤ Windows NT (all released versions)

➤ Windows 98

➤ Windows 95

➤ Windows for Workgroups 3.11 (with the Microsoft 32-bit TCP/IP VxD installed)

➤ Microsoft-Network Client 3 for MS-DOS (with the real-mode TCP/IP driver installed)

➤ LAN Manager 2.2c

Microsoft DHCP Client Options

By default, Microsoft-based DHCP clients can recognize and use option types in two categories: information and protocol options. Information options use the DHCP Console to explicitly configure these option types and any associated values provided to clients. These options are not required and can be assigned at your discretion.

Protocol options are implicitly configured values for these options based on properties configured at either the applicable server or one of its scopes. These options are always included in DHCP client/server messages, as they are a required part of protocol design.

Information Options

All Microsoft DHCP clients support a common set of DHCP standard options. This support is provided for all clients running released versions of Windows and MS-DOS operating systems. For Windows 2000 DHCP clients only, some additional DHCP standard and Microsoft-specific options are also supported.

Table 4.2 lists the DHCP standard options that all Microsoft DHCP clients are able to support and use, if provided by the DHCP server during the lease process.

When a DHCP server actively provides these options, clients receive and use the associated values in their local TCP/IP configurations for the period of leased configuration. In addition to these standard options, you can also use or assign Microsoft vendor-specific options when using Microsoft predefined user and vendor classes.

Table 4.2   DHCP standard options for Microsoft clients.

Code	Description
3	Router
6	DNS server
15	DNS domain name
44	WINS server
46	NetBIOS node type

Table 4.3   Internal option types for Microsoft clients.

Code	Description
1	Subnet mask
51	IP address lease time
53	DHCP message type
54	Server identifier
58	Lease renewal time
59	Lease rebinding time

Protocol Options

Table 4.3 lists the internal option types that Microsoft DHCP clients use when communicating with a DHCP server to obtain or renew their leased configurations.

In most cases, the actual values provided with these protocol options are based on Properties set at the applicable DHCP server where the client obtains its address lease. You can also use the DHCP Console to configure or tune these options individually for defined scopes, identifying members of a specified user or vendor class or for a single reserved client.

Supporting Clients

When installing a DHCP server to support a combination of DHCP clients provided by Windows and other operating systems on a network, you might consider if Windows 2000 DHCP servers can assign any of the predefined options that are part of the DHCP standard set of options described in RFC 2132. You can also modify servers to provide additional custom options as needed and requested by DHCP clients that support and request such options. Microsoft DHCP clients, including those running Windows 2000, support and request only a small number of the full standard set of DHCP options in their default configuration. This subset of supported options contrasts with the larger set of options that are predefined for assigned use within the DHCP Console when managing Windows 2000 DHCP servers.

Other DHCP clients provided in systems supplied from other software vendors, such as Unix and Linux, can request and recognize different DHCP options from those commonly supported by default for all released Microsoft DHCP clients. For these other DHCP clients, assign options at the server that are recognized by and configured for the supporting clients.

If DHCP clients are unable to recognize or support an assigned DHCP option provided by the server during leasing, they silently ignore it. Another method to control options assignment is to use vendor- or user-defined classes. In this arrangement, assign options for distribution only to identified members of the applicable class at the DHCP server.

In some advanced deployment cases, you can customize Windows applications for Windows 2000 clients to leverage current DHCP client application programming interfaces (APIs). These APIs are documented as part of the Microsoft Platform SDK available through the Microsoft Developers Network (MSDN). They can enable DHCP client customized behavior—for example, to enable other DHCP options to be requested and used at a Windows 2000 DHCP client.

Using Reservations for Clients

You can reserve a specific IP address for permanent use by a DHCP client. Typically, you will need to do this if the client uses an IP address that was assigned using another method for TCP/IP configuration. If multiple DHCP servers are configured with a scope that covers the range of the reserved IP address, the client reservation must be made and duplicated at each of these DHCP servers. Otherwise, the reserved client computer can receive a different IP address, depending on the responding DHCP server.

To change a reserved IP address for a current client, remove the existing address reservation of the client and then add a new reservation. Any other information about a reserved client can be changed while keeping the reserved IP address. If you reserve an IP address for a new client, or an address that is different from its current one, verify that the DHCP server has not already leased the address. Reserving an IP address in a scope does not automatically force a client currently using that address to stop using it. If the address is already in use, the client using the address must release it by issuing an ipconfig /release command at a command prompt. The DHCP release message name is DHCPRELEASE. To make this happen, type ipconfig /release at the command prompt of a client computer running under Windows 2000.

Reserving an IP address at the DHCP server also does not force the new client for which the reservation is made to move to that address immediately. The client must first issue an ipconfig /release command at a command prompt. The DHCP release message name is DHCPRELEASE. DHCP request message (DHCPREQUEST). To make this happen, type ipconfig /renew at the command prompt of a client computer running under Windows 2000. For clients using Windows 95 or Windows 98, use the Winipcfg.exe program to cause release or renewal of the reserved IP address in DHCP. For clients using MS-DOS, and some clients using other operating systems, you must restart the computer for the change to take effect. Once these changes are made, the IP address is reserved for the reserved client's permanent use each time it renews its lease with the DHCP server.

Reserved clients can have DHCP options configured specifically for their use. When options are configured for a reserved client, these values override any option type parameters distributed via server-based, scope-based, or class-based options assignment. You can also use the **ipconfig** command on computers running earlier versions of Windows NT to release and renew DHCP leases. Not all other **ipconfig** command options are available, however, when executed at clients running under these earlier versions.

The DHCP Relay Agent Component

The DHCP Relay Agent component provided with the Windows 2000 router is a Bootstrap Protocol (BOOTP) relay agent that relays DHCP messages between DHCP clients and DHCP servers on different IP networks. The DHCP Relay Agent is compliant with RFC 1542, "Clarifications and Extensions for the Bootstrap Protocol." For each IP network segment that contains DHCP clients, either a DHCP server or a computer acting as a DHCP Relay Agent is required.

You cannot use the DHCP Relay Agent component on a Windows 2000 Server computer running the DHCP service or the Network Address Translation (NAT) routing protocol with automatic addressing enabled.

Design Considerations for the Relay Agent

You must consider some important design issues before setting up the relay agents on a network. If you have multiple DHCP servers, Microsoft recommends that they be placed on different subnets to achieve a degree of fault tolerance. Each DHCP server should have a unique pool of addresses with common IP addresses in their scopes.

If the DHCP server on the local subnet shuts down, requests are relayed to a remote subnet. The DHCP server at that location can respond to DHCP requests if it maintains a scope of IP addresses for the requesting subnet. If the remote server has no scope defined for the requesting subnet, it cannot provide IP addresses even if it has available addresses for other scopes. If each DHCP server has a pool of addresses for each subnet, then it can provide IP addresses for remote clients whose own DHCP server is offline.

What You Should Do

The following relay agent implementation is recommended for best-routed DHCP network performance: It uses two DHCP servers attached to two different subnets; the relay agents operating on each of the routers that connect the subnets have varied delay intervals (one is set to four seconds, the other uses no delay). This eliminates the risk of undesirable floods of DHCP packets through randomly selected network paths.

What You Shouldn't Do

The following relay agent implementation is not recommended: It has the same number of DHCP servers and subnets as in the previous example, but uses less caution; the risk that DHCP discover messages (DHCPDISCOVERs), which are broadcast by the DHCP clients at startup, will be randomly forwarded or duplicated when destined for the other subnets is much higher. Moreover, the relay agents do not use any delay interval. This increases the likelihood that both relay agents duplicate any client-broadcasted messages, which could potentially flood the remote subnets.

Using DHCPINFORM and the Relay Agent

After the connection negotiation is complete, Windows 2000 and Windows 98 remote access clients send their remote access servers a DHCPINFORM message. DHCP clients use the message to obtain DHCP options. Although remote access clients do not use DHCP to obtain IP addresses for the remote access connection, remote access clients running Windows 2000 and Windows 98 use the DHCPINFORM message to obtain DNS server IP addresses, WINS server IP addresses, and a DNS domain name.

The DHCPINFORM message received by the remote access server is then forwarded to a DHCP server. The remote access server forwards DHCPINFORM messages if it has been configured with the DHCP Relay Agent. The response to the DHCPINFORM message is sent back to the requesting remote access client. If the response contains DNS and WINS server IP address options, then these new values override what was allocated during the connection negotiation process. To facilitate the forwarding of DHCPINFORM messages between remote access clients and DHCP servers, the remote access server uses the DHCP Relay Agent, a component of the Windows 2000 Routing and Remote Access Service (RRAS). To configure the remote access server to use the DHCP Relay Agent, you need to add the Internal interface to the DHCP Relay Agent IP routing protocol in RRAS.

If the remote access server is using DHCP to obtain IP addresses for remote access clients, then the remote access server uses the DHCP Relay Agent to forward DHCPINFORM messages to the DHCP server of the selected LAN interface. If the remote access server is using a static IP address pool to obtain IP addresses for remote access clients, then configure the DHCP Relay Agent with the IP address of at least one DHCP server. Otherwise, the remote access server silently discards DHCPINFORM messages sent by remote access clients.

Routing and Remote Access Servers with DHCP

The DHCP Server service can be deployed along with RRAS to provide remote access clients with a dynamically assigned IP address during connection. When these services are used together on the same server computer, the information provided during dynamic configuration comes in a different way from a typical DHCP configuration for LAN-based clients.

In LAN environments, DHCP clients negotiate and receive configuration information based entirely on settings configured in the DHCP Console for the DHCP server. The available address pool of an active scope on the DHCP server provides a leased IP address. The DHCP server directly manages the address and distributes it to the LAN-based DHCP client. Additional parameters and other configuration information are provided through assigned DHCP options in the address lease. The values and list of options used correspond to option types configured and assigned on the DHCP server.

When an RRAS server provides dynamic configuration for dial-up clients, it selects the Use DHCP to Assign Remote TCP/IP Addresses option. This lets it make advance requests to the DHCP server to obtain and cache DHCP client addresses for dial-up clients. The number of client addresses requested in advance is equal to the number of RRAS ports set to receive calls, plus one additional address. If the server has two analog modem ports and two ISDN adapter ports set to receive calls, it requests five IP addresses from the DHCP server. The first four are for assigning to clients that dial in to the analog and ISDN server ports. The fifth address is reserved for the server itself, so it can configure and use its own IP address when processing connections for dial-up clients.

When the RRAS server uses this type of proactive caching of DHCP address leases for dial-up clients, it records the lease responses it obtains from the DHCP server and its IP address. It then records the client's leased IP address, the time the lease was obtained, the time the lease will expire, and the duration of the lease for later distribution to an RRAS client. All other DHCP options information returned by the DHCP server is discarded. When Server Assigned IP Address is being used, the dial-up client will use an IP address that has been cached by the RRAS server to provide the dynamic IP address configuration. When the IP address is provided to the dial-up client, the client is unaware that the address has been obtained through this intermediate process between the DHCP server and the RRAS server. The RRAS server maintains the lease on behalf of the client. Therefore, the only information that the client receives from the DHCP server is the IP address lease.

In dial-up environments, DHCP clients negotiate and receive dynamic configuration using modified behavior. A leased IP address is obtained from an RRAS server cache of DHCP scope addresses. The RRAS server obtains and renews its cached address pool from a DHCP server. If additional parameters and other configuration information are provided through assigned DHCP options in the address lease that is normally provided by a DHCP server, this information is returned to the RRAS client, based on TCP/IP properties configured on the RRAS server.

Dynamic Configuration

With DHCP, TCP/IP configuration occurs dynamically and automatically when the computer starts. Dynamic configuration requires the configuration of a DHCP server. By default, computers running Windows 2000 are DHCP clients. By properly configuring the DHCP server, TCP/IP hosts can obtain an IP address, subnet mask, default gateway, DNS server, and NetBIOS node type, as shown in Figure 4.2, as well as WINS server configuration information. Dynamic configuration (using DHCP) is recommended for medium to large TCP/IP networks.

Manual Configuration

By manually configuring the properties of the TCP/IP protocol through the properties of a network connection (in Network and Dial-up Connections), you can assign an IP address, subnet mask, default gateway, DNS server, and WINS server. Manual configuration is required in a network with multiple network segments when no DHCP server is present.

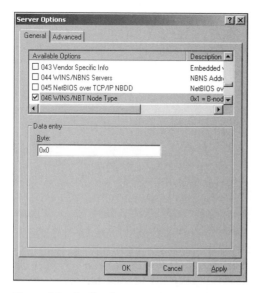

Figure 4.2 Configuring node type.

DHCP and WINS Interoperability

When using DHCP and WINS together on a network, consider using additional DHCP scope options. Specifically, use DHCP options to assign WINS node types (option type 46) and to identify WINS servers for use by DHCP clients (option type 44). In some cases, this can involve adjusting the option types for each physical subnet in which DHCP and WINS are implemented. When both services are deployed, assign a length of time for DHCP lease durations, comparable to the time WINS uses for renew intervals. By default, DHCP leases are three days long, and the WINS renew interval is every six days. When lease lengths for DHCP widely differ from WINS renew intervals, lease-management traffic might increase, which might cause a WINS registration for both services. If the DHCP lease time is shortened or lengthened for clients, then modify the WINS renew interval accordingly.

4

DNS Servers and DHCP

When installing a Windows 2000 DHCP server, configure it to perform updates on behalf of its DHCP clients to any ping remote host rather than ping 1.2.3.4, if the mapping for the system-named remote host was contained in the DNS database. DNS domains should not be confused with Windows 2000 networking domains.

The DHCP for DNS Update

You can use the DHCP server to register and update the pointer (PTR) and address (A) resource records on behalf of its DHCP-enabled clients. This process requires an additional DHCP option (81). When a qualified DHCP client issues this option, it is processed and interpreted by Windows 2000 DHCP servers. They determine how to initiate updates on behalf of the client.

The server might be configured in one of the following ways to process client requests:

➤ *The DHCP server registers and updates client information with its configured DNS servers according to the client request.* Once a new DHCP server is installed, this is the default configuration for Windows 2000 DHCP servers and clients. In this mode, any Windows 2000 DHCP client can request the way in which the DHCP server performs updates of its host (A) and pointer (PTR) resource records. If possible, the DHCP server accommodates the client request for handling updates to its name and IP address information in DNS. This can be set at the applicable DHCP server by configuring the Update DNS Only if DHCP Client Requests option located in Properties on the DNS tab.

➤ *The DHCP server always registers and updates client information with its configured DNS servers.* This is a modified configuration supported for Windows 2000 DHCP servers and clients. In this mode, the DHCP server always performs updates of the client's FQDN and leased IP address information, and both its host (A) and pointer (PTR) resource records, regardless of whether the client has requested performing its own updates. This can be set at the applicable DHCP server by configuring the Always Update DNS option located in Properties on the DNS tab.

➤ *The DHCP server never registers and updates client information with its configured DNS servers.* To set this behavior, the DHCP server must be configured to disable performance of DHCP/DNS proxied updates. By disabling this feature, no client host (A) or pointer (PTR) resource records are updated in DNS for DHCP clients. If necessary, this change in setting can be made at Windows 2000 DHCP servers by clearing the Automatically Update DHCP Client Information in DNS checkbox, which is located in Properties on the DNS tab on the applicable DHCP server or one of its scopes. By default, updates are always performed for newly installed Windows 2000 DHCP servers and any new scopes created for them.

Windows Clients and the DNS Dynamic Update Protocol

DHCP clients running Windows 2000 interact differently from earlier versions of Windows when performing the DHCP/DNS interactions previously described. The following example shows how this process varies in different situations.

The Update Process for Windows 2000 Clients

Windows 2000 DHCP clients interact with the DNS dynamic update protocol in the following situations:

➤ The client has to select and request a lease from a specific DHCP server when lease offers are made simultaneously from several different servers.

➤ To confirm a previously leased IP address after the client system is restarted.

➤ To extend the current IP address lease for the client.

DHCPREQUEST is sent to the server from a client. The server returns a DHCPACK to the client, granting an IP address lease. By default, the client sends a DNS update request to the DNS server for its own forward lookup record, a host (A) resource record. Alternatively, the server can perform this update of the DNS server on behalf of the client if both the client and its configuration are modified accordingly. The server sends updates for the DHCP client's reverse lookup record—a pointer (PTR) resource record—using the process defined by the DNS dynamic update protocol.

The DnsUpdateProxy Security Group

As previously described, you can configure a Windows 2000 DHCP server so that it dynamically registers host (A) and pointer (PTR) resource records on behalf of

DHCP clients. In this configuration, the use of secure dynamic update with Windows 2000 DNS servers might cause stale resource records.

For example, suppose the following event occurs: A Windows 2000 DHCP server (DHCP1) performs a secure dynamic update on behalf of one of its clients for a specific DNS domain name. Because the DHCP server successfully created the name, it becomes the owner of the name. Once the DHCP server becomes the owner of the client name, only that DHCP server can update the name. In some circumstances, this might cause problems. For instance, suppose that DHCP1 later fails. If a second backup DHCP server comes online, it cannot update the client name because it is not the owner of the name.

In a similar example, suppose DHCP1 registered in DNS, on behalf of its client, the name "host.example.microsoft.com", and then the administrator upgraded that computer from an earlier version of Windows to Windows 2000. Because DHCP1 is the owner of this name, the client cannot update its DNS records once the computer is upgraded to Windows 2000.

To solve this problem, Windows 2000 provides a new built-in security group called DnsUpdateProxy. Any object created by the members of this group has no security; the first user (who is not a member of the DnsUpdateProxy group) to modify the set of records associated with a client becomes its owner. Thus, if every DHCP server registering resource records for older clients is a member of this group, the problems discussed earlier are eliminated.

Adding Members to the DnsUpdateProxy Group

You can configure the DnsUpdateProxy security group through Active Directory Users and Computers. If you are using multiple DHCP servers for fault tolerance and you are also securing dynamic updates, add each of the computers operating a Windows 2000 DHCP server as members of the DnsUpdateProxy global security group.

Security Concerns When Using the DnsUpdateProxy Group

Although making all DHCP servers members of this special built-in group helps resolve some concerns about maintaining secure DNS updates, this solution introduces some other security concerns. Any DNS domain names registered by the computer running the DHCP server are nonsecure. The host (A) resource record for the DHCP server itself is an example of such a record. This issue is more significant if the DHCP server (a member of the DnsUpdateProxy group) is installed on a domain controller. To protect against this problem, you can manually specify a different owner for any DNS records associated with the DHCP server itself.

In this case, all service location (SRV), host (A), or alias (CNAME) resource records registered by the Netlogon service for the domain controller are nonsecure. To minimize the problem, do not install a DHCP server on a domain controller.

Another strong argument against running a Windows 2000 DHCP server on a Windows 2000 domain controller is that the DHCP server has full control over all DNS objects stored in Active Directory, because the DHCP server is running under the computer (in this case, the domain controller) account.

DHCP Audit Logging

Windows 2000 DHCP servers include several new logging features and server parameters that provide enhanced auditing capabilities. The following features can now be specified:

➤ The directory path in which the DHCP server stores audit-log files.

➤ A maximum size restriction for the total amount of disk space available for all audit-log files created and stored by the DHCP service.

➤ An interval for disk checking that is used to determine how many times the DHCP server writes audit-log events to the log file before checking for available disk space on the server.

➤ A minimum size requirement for server disk space used during disk checking to determine if sufficient space exists for the server to continue audit logging.

You can selectively enable or disable the audit-logging feature at each DHCP server. Only the directory path in which the DHCP server stores audit-log files can be modified using the DHCP Console. To do so, first select the applicable DHCP server in the console tree. On the Action menu, click on Properties. Next, click on the Advanced tab and edit the audit-log file path as necessary. Other audit-logging parameters described previously are adjusted through Registry-based configuration changes.

How It Works

The audit-logging behavior discussed in this section applies only to the DHCP Server service provided with Windows 2000 Server. It replaces the previous DHCP logging behavior used in earlier versions of Windows NT Server, which do not perform audit checks and use only a single log file named Dhcpsrv.log for logging service events.

The formatted structure of DHCP server logs and the level of reporting maintained for audited logging are the same as in earlier DHCP server versions provided with Windows NT Server.

Naming Audit Logs

The DHCP Server service bases the name of the audit-log file on the current day of the week, as determined by checking the current date and time at the server. For example, when the DHCP server starts, if the current date and time are Wednesday, March 5, 2000, 04:56:42 A.M., then the server audit log file is named DhcpSrvLog.Wed.

Starting a Daily Audit Log

When a DHCP server starts or a new weekday begins (when the local time on the computer is 12:00 A.M.), the server writes a header message in the audit-log file, indicating that logging has started. Then, depending on whether the audit-log file is a new or existing file, the following actions occur:

➤ If the file already existed without modification for more than a day, it is overwritten.

➤ If the file already existed but was modified within the previous 24 hours, the file is not overwritten. Instead, new logging activity is appended to the end of the existing file.

Checking Hard-Drive Space

After audit logging starts, the DHCP server performs disk checks at regular intervals to ensure both the ongoing availability of server disk space and that the current audit-log file does not become too large or that log-file growth is not occurring too rapidly. The DHCP server performs a full disk check whenever the date changes on the server computer by default; the DHCP server performs a periodic disk space check for every 50 events it writes to the audit log. The DHCP server can also detect a date change when the server computer reaches 12:00 A.M. on its locally set Date/Time clock. Each time a disk check is completed, the server determines whether disk space is filled. The disk is considered full if either of the following conditions is true:

➤ Disk space on the server computer is lower than the required minimum amount for DHCP audit logging. By default, if the amount of disk space remaining on the server disk reaches less than 20MB, audit logging is halted.

➤ The current audit-log file is larger than one-seventh of the maximum allotted space or size for the combined total of all audit logs currently stored on the server. At the time of the disk check, the DHCP server compares the exact size (in megabytes) of the current audit-log file with a value obtained by dividing the current value from the maximum number of log files the server permits to be stored simultaneously before overwriting and discarding older log files. By default, seven is the maximum number of log files the server permits to be stored, one for each day of the week. Assuming the default is set, the largest size that the current audit-log file can reach is 1MB.

In either case, if the disk is full, the DHCP server closes the current file and ignores further requests to log audit events until either 12:00 A.M. or disk status is improved and the disk is no longer full. Even if audit-logged events are ignored because of a disk-full condition, the DHCP server continues disk checking every 50 events (or the currently set interval) to determine whether disk conditions have improved. If subsequent disk checks determine that the required amount of server disk space is available, the DHCP server reopens the current log file and resumes logging.

Ending a Daily Audit Log

At 12:00 A.M. local time on the server computer, the DHCP server closes the existing log and moves to the log file for the next day of the week. If the day of the week changes at 12:00 A.M. from Wednesday to Thursday, the log file DhcpSrvLog.Wed is closed and DhcpSrvLog.Thu is opened and used for logging events.

Tools for DHCP

The primary tool to manage DHCP servers is the DHCP Console, which is added to the Administrative Tools folder in Control Panel when a DHCP server is installed for Windows 2000 Server. The DHCP Console appears as an MMC snap-in to further integrate DHCP administration into your total network management. Figure 4.3 provides an example of DHCP Console actions.

After installing a DHCP server, use the DHCP Console to perform several basic administrative server tasks. Right-click on the server or choose Action from the menu bar to see the list of tasks. Create scopes with the New Scope Wizard, as shown in Figure 4.4, and add and configure superscopes and even multicast scopes. View and modify scope properties including setting additional exclusion ranges.

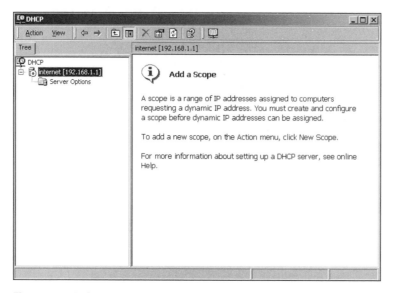

Figure 4.3 DHCP actions.

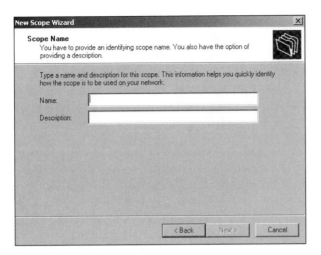

Figure 4.4   New Scope Wizard.

Scopes and superscopes can also be activated from the console, which includes monitoring scope-leasing activity by reviewing the Active Leases for each scope. The DHCP Console allows for the creation of reservations in scopes for clients needing a permanent IP address.

The DHCP Console has optional advanced setup tasks to allow for new custom default option types and to add and configure any user and vendor-defined option classes. The DHCP Console also allows for configuration of server properties, such as audit logging and BOOTP tables. In addition, this version of the DHCP Console contains new features and enhancements, many of which were suggested by network managers. These include enhanced server performance monitoring, more predefined DHCP option types, dynamic update support for clients running earlier versions of Windows, and detection of unauthorized DHCP servers on your network.

Chapter Summary

The DHCP standard provides for managing dynamic assignments of IP addresses and other related configuration details to DHCP-enabled clients on a network by using DHCP servers. DHCP uses the client-server model where the network administrator configures one or more DHCP servers to maintain TCP/IP configuration information and provide it to clients on that network. DHCP clients are provided their configuration in the form of an address-lease offer from DHCP servers.

The DHCP server uses pooled addresses for dynamically assigning addresses to DHCP clients. DHCP servers use reservations to create permanent address lease assignments.

The DHCP Relay Agent service is available only on computers running Windows 2000 Server or Windows NT Server 4.

DHCP options and their values should be predefined for each scope and any superscope. Using more than one DHCP server on the same subnet provides increased fault tolerance for servicing DHCP clients. When started, each DHCP client broadcasts a DHCP discover message (DHCPDISCOVER) to its local subnet to attempt to find a DHCP server. A DHCP server can then respond with a DHCP offer message (DHCPOFFER) that contains an IP address offered for lease to the client.

When a DHCP server is authorized, the server computer is added to the list of authorized DHCP servers maintained in the directory service database. For member servers, the DHCP server queries the directory service for the DHCP server list of authorized addresses. The server initializes and starts providing DHCP services to clients only if the server finds its IP address in the authorized list for each of the enterprise roots reported by other DHCP servers. The process of authorizing DHCP servers is useful only for DHCP servers running Windows 2000 Server.

The DHCP Relay Agent component provided with the Windows 2000 router is a Bootstrap Protocol (BOOTP) that relays DHCP messages between DHCP clients and DHCP servers on different IP networks. For each IP network segment that contains DHCP clients, either a DHCP server or a computer acting as a DHCP Relay Agent is required. If each DHCP server has a pool of addresses for each subnet, then it can provide IP addresses for remote clients whose own DHCP server is offline.

In LAN environments, DHCP clients negotiate and receive configuration information, based entirely on settings configured in the DHCP Console for the DHCP server. The DHCP server directly manages the address and distributes it to the LAN-based DHCP client. All other DHCP options information returned by the DHCP server is discarded. A leased IP address is obtained from an RRAS server cache of DHCP scope addresses. The RRAS server obtains and renews its cached address pool from a DHCP server.

Review Questions

1. DHCP is a standard for automating, as well as reducing, administrative complexities for host IP configuration management for which protocol?

   a. TCP/IP

   b. IPX/SPX

   c. AppleTalk

   d. None of the above

2. What do DHCP servers use to create permanent address lease assignments?

   a. A lease

   b. An exclusion range

   c. An options class

   d. Reservations

3. Which of the following is a limited sequence of IP addresses within a scope?

   a. Superscope

   b. Address pool

   c. Exclusion range

   d. Options class

4. You should limit each DHCP server to having no more than how many scopes defined for use?

   a. 10

   b. 100

   c. 500

   d. 1,000

5. User class IDs can be set and viewed at a Windows 2000 DHCP client using what command?

   a. **ipconfig**

   b. **winipcfg**

   c. **setclass**

   d. **classid**

6. You can manage DHCP servers remotely using what in Windows 2000?

   a. Edit

   b. Manage DHCP

   c. Administration tools

   d. None of the above

7. For which of the following is DHCP client support not provided?

   a. Windows 98

   b. Linux

   c. LAN Manager 2.2c

   d. Windows NT

8. If the server has two analog modem ports and two ISDN adapter ports that are set to receive calls, how many IP addresses does it request from the DHCP server?

   a. 2

   b. 3

   c. 4

   d. 5

9. What additional DHCP options should you consider when using DHCP and WINS together on your network?

   a. Class ID

   b. Network

   c. Scope

   d. WINS

10. What is the maximum number of log files the server permits to be stored, by default?

    a. 1

    b. 5

    c. 3

    d. 7

11. Which of the following options are applied only to clients that are identified as members of a specified user or vendor class?

    a. Server options

    b. Scope options

    c. Class options

    d. Client options

12. Which of the following is not an authorizing DHCP server type?

    a. Domain controller

    b. Stand-alone server

    c. Member server

    d. All are authorizing DHCP server types

13. When using Active Directory, all DHCP servers must be what type of server?

    a. Domain controllers or domain member servers

    b. Domain controller or stand-alone server

    c. Stand-alone or domain member server

    d. It does not matter what type of server they are

14. Which of the following is not a standard DHCP option for a Microsoft client?

    a. Router

    b. DNS domain name

    c. Bridge

    d. NetBIOS node type

15. Which of the following is not an internal option for Microsoft clients?

    a. DNS server

    b. IP Address lease time

    c. Server identifier

    d. Subnet mask

4

Real-World Projects

Lesha Camille, the IT director for Red National Bank, has decided that the bank's network would be better served if a DHCP server were installed to handle both the dynamic allocation and assignment of IP addresses, as well as dynamic DNS updates. The network is already set up for TCP/IP and now has its own class C address.

Camille has proposed the use of DHCP-enabled servers to decrease the stress and overhead involved in manually configuring the network. The reasoning behind migrating to DHCP is that the network has been having tremendous problems with IP address conflicts because of IP addresses being reused or changed by the user. They have already set up a server to be the DHCP server for the network. Now all they have to do is install the DHCP service and configure the scopes and the reservations for the network.

Project 4.1

To install the DHCP server, perform the following steps:

1. Open the Windows Components wizard.

2. Under Components, scroll to Networking Services and click on it.

3. Click on Details.

4. Under Subcomponents of Networking Services, click on Dynamic Host Configuration Protocol (DHCP), and then click on OK.

By following this procedure, the DHCP service will be installed on the server.

Project 4.2

To configure scopes for a network, perform the following steps:

1. In the DHCP Console, right-click on the appropriate server.

2. In the Shortcut menu, choose New Scope, and then click on Next.

3. Type a name and description for the scope, and then click on Next.

4. Enter start and end addresses for the range of addresses the scope will define in the Start Address and End Address fields. Then click on Next.

5. Skip the next two screens. A superscope is not needed here; nor will any IP addresses need to be excluded.

6. The default lease duration is eight days. If this is okay with you, click on Next.

7. In this screen, you can set options for DNS, WINS, gateways, and more. This isn't necessary at the moment, but can be done if desired. Select the No option, and then click on Next.

8. Click on Finish.

This will define a range of addresses for the network that DHCP will use to service client requests. This will also ensure that during the course of use IP addresses will not be in conflict because the same two addresses have been configured on two clients.

Project 4.3

To configure reservations, perform the following steps:

1. Open DHCP.

2. In the console tree, click on Reservations.

3. On the Action menu, click on New Reservation.

4. In New Reservation, type the information required to complete the client reservation.

5. To add the client reservation to the scope, click on Add.

6. Repeat the two previous steps for any other client reservations you want to add, and then click on Close.

The reservations for this scenario are to be set for servers, such as for member servers, the DHCP server, and so on. This will let them have dedicated IP addresses that will not change.

CHAPTER FIVE

Domain Name System (DNS)

After completing this chapter, you will be able to:

✓ Understand the Domain Name System hierarchy

✓ Identify and use Fully Qualified Domain Names (FQDN)

✓ Install the DNS Server Service

✓ Create zone transfers with BIND

✓ Implement Active Directory server support

✓ Implement Windows 2000 DNS Server for clients on the Internet

✓ Identify and understand DNS domain names and namespaces

✓ Deploy DNS servers for optimal performance and efficiency

✓ Integrate Active Directory

✓ Configure DNS clients

✓ Use DNS tools

✓ Verify server configuration

CP/IP requires that every networked node be assigned an IP address, either dynamically via Dynamic Host Configuration Protocol (DHCP) or statically through TCP/IP configuration. It would suffice for the network and TCP/IP to identify a computer by the Media Access Control (MAC) address, a 12-digit hexadecimal number, for example 00-AA-00-62-C6-09, and the 32-digit binary ip address, for example 10011101.00110111.01010101.11010100, or the numeric equivalent, for example 157.55.85.212, but users prefer to refer to a computer by name, for example, SERVER1.

User-friendly names called *hostnames* were introduced to simplify network communications, where a hostname (MyComputer) is mapped back to its IP address (157.55.85.212) and eventually to the MAC address (00-AA-00-62-C6-09). Domain Name System (DNS) provides a mechanism to map the user-friendly hostname to the corresponding IP address. This chapter and Chapter 6 will cover the mapping of hostnames to IP address name resolution using DNS. Chapter 8 covers resolution of NetBIOS names to IP address names. DNS is the preferred name resolution service on the Internet and in Windows 2000 networks.

Domain Name System Hierarchy

DNS, the name service used on the Internet, is based on the Domain Name System Hierarchy developed by Network Solutions Inc. (NSI), formerly Internet Network Information Center (InterNIC). The domain namespace is split among domains—namely, com, edu, gov, int, mil, net, and org—where the three-letter extension represents the type of domain. Com is the largest category of top-level domains in the world. Table 5.1 lists the domain types.

Valid domain names cannot exceed 22 characters and can consist only of letters, numbers, and hyphens. Domain names are case-insensitive, but case is preserved. Most important, every domain name must be unique. Ideally, hostnames are descriptive without introducing unnecessary complexity. Keep in mind that

Table 5.1   Domain types and extensions.

Domain	Type
.com	Commercial
.edu	Education
.gov	Government
.int	International
.mil	Military
.net	Network
.num	Phone numbers
.org	Nonprofit institutions and organizations
.xx	Two-letter country code

hostnames are user-friendly, created to eliminate the need to refer to a computer by IP address. A hostname of COMPUTER45-678912, although valid, defeats the purpose.

Fully Qualified Domain Name (FQDN)

The Fully Qualified Domain Name (FQDN) contains the hostname followed by a period and then the domain name. For example, a computer with the hostname of MyComputer located at Microsoft might have the following FQDN: MyComputer.Microsoft.com. Because hostnames can contain only letters, numbers, and hyphens, we know that this name with a period (.) is not just a hostname. Microsoft may create subdomains, such as marketing and engineering, with two different hosts: MyComputer.Marketing.Microsoft.com and MyComputer. Engineering.Microsoft.com.

Installing the DNS Server Service

DNS is required for Internet use and when implementing Active Directory. When a Windows 2000 Server computer is promoted to domain controller (DC), the option to install a DNS server and add new zones automatically is part of Active Directory installation. Separately installing a DNS server at the server computer is necessary only if it is not a DC or expected to be promoted to one in the future. Note that you must first assign a static ip address and DNS domain name to the Windows 2000 Server before you can install the DNS server service.

If you have selected the option to install and configure a DNS server during the Active Directory Installation wizard, zones will be created based on the DNS name specified while promoting the server to a DC. Other tasks that might also be useful once the first server in the domain is promoted to a DC include changing the zone type from Standard Primary to Active Directory-integrated and changing the update policy for the zone to Allow Only Secure Updates.

If you are deploying DNS to support Active Directory, a simple method for redundancy and fault-tolerance planning is to have a DNS server running on each DC. For each subnet, a good rule to follow is to have two Windows 2000 Server computers configured as DCs that are also running as DNS servers that load and store only Active Directory-integrated zones. By observing these guidelines for simplified DNS and Active Directory configuration, you can enable DNS servers to fully leverage the enhanced benefits of using Active Directory and Windows 2000 DNS servers, such as integrated storage, merged replication of Active Directory and DNS data, and secure authentication when allowing dynamic updates.

5

Zone Transfer with BIND

When transferring a zone between two Windows DNS servers, the DNS Server Service always uses a fast transfer method incorporating compression. This method includes multiple resource records (RRs) in each message sent to complete the transfer of the zone between servers. For Windows 2000 DNS servers, this is the default method used when initiating transfers with other DNS server implementations.

If necessary, you can configure Windows 2000 DNS servers to transfer a zone using the slower uncompressed transfer format. This permits successful zone transfers with DNS servers that do not support the faster transfer method, such as Berkeley Internet Name Domain (BIND) servers before version 4.9.4. When you choose the BIND Secondaries option in Advanced Server properties, no fast transfers are made. By default, the checkbox is cleared to enable fast transfers.

Supporting Active Directory

In many large organizations, DNS is already implemented using other solutions, such as Unix DNS servers that run legacy versions of BIND software. In some cases, these DNS servers are not equipped to support the DNS requirements for deploying Active Directory. This issue can be addressed in one of two ways:

➤ Upgrade any BIND DNS servers to version 8.1.2 or later of the BIND software to meet the DNS requirements for Active Directory support.

➤ Use the DNS service provided with Windows 2000 Server, migrating, if possible, any of your current DNS zones to Windows 2000 DNS servers.

Although the DNS service is recommended to support Active Directory, you can use other DNS server implementations for this purpose. These other implementations, however, should support the following standard specifications:

➤ The service location (SRV) resource record, as described in the Internet draft, "A DNS RR for specifying the location of services (DNS SRV)."

➤ Dynamic updates in DNS, as described in Request for Comments (RFC) 2136.

Support for dynamic updates is recommended but not essential. Support for the SRV resource record is mandatory, because it is required to provide basic DNS support to Active Directory. For example, a DNS server that does not support dynamic updates, such as that provided with Windows NT Server 4.0, supports the DNS requirements of Active Directory because SRV resource record support was added with Service Pack 4.

Windows DNS Server Interoperability

The Windows DNS service can be used and managed with a split DNS configuration when:

➤ Existing DNS servers for root zones will not to be upgraded or migrated to other DNS solutions.

➤ The DNS service and Windows 2000 server are to be deployed and provide management of DNS domain names for use with Active Directory.

You can modify DNS namespace design plans in either of the following ways:

➤ *Create a single new subdomain in the current DNS domain namespace to root your first Active Directory domain*—If an organization has registered and is using a second-level domain name, such as microsoft.com, it can create a single subdomain similar to example.microsoft.com and use this domain to root the DNS domain namespace used by Active Directory. The DNS service is automatically configured to support Active Directory when the first DC is installed. Before a zone for the new subdomain is created at a computer running the DNS Server Service, these subdomains can be delegated away at the primary zone for a second-level domain, similar to microsoft.com. In some cases, another DNS or Unix system administrator might need to be notified to make the delegation.

➤ *Create multiple subdomains based on a DNS second-level domain to support registration of Active Directory in DNS*—If an organization has a registered second-level DNS domain name already in use (such as microsoft.com), it can create subdomains that are delegated to Windows DNS servers and used only for registering DNS names related to Active Directory. This method is more complex to implement, but causes less change to a currently deployed DNS infrastructure that is not Windows-based. With this namespace design, create only those additional subdomains and appropriate zones needed to support Active Directory deployment. For example, the domain name microsoft.com is both the root DNS and the root Active Directory domain name for an organization. For this configuration, you must first create zones for the following subdomains using the DNS snap-in tool at a computer running the DNS service and Windows 2000 Server: _msdcs.microsoft.com, _ldap._tcp.microsoft.com. Before creating these zones, you can delegate these subdomains away at the primary zone for the parent or second-level domain name or notify another DNS administrator who manages these zones.

DNS on the Internet

To establish a presence on the Internet, an individual or business must first apply for and register a second-level domain name with an authorized DNS domain name registration authority. An Internet service provider (ISP) can often obtain a name on behalf of an organization, usually for an additional fee.

Registering a domain name requires several tasks, including:

➤ *Selecting and researching a second-level domain name that is not currently registered or in use*—This is easily accomplished using a WHOIS query engine provided at the Web site for an applicable Internet DNS domain name registrar, Network Solutions at **http://www.networksolutions.com/cgi-bin/whois/whois**. Be prepared to select an alternative name if the WHOIS query indicates your selection is already registered and in use.

➤ *Registering and obtaining at least one IP address valid for use on the Internet*—This address establishes the DNS server on the Internet as the host for the primary copy of the zone based on the second-level domain name. If your ISP is registering your domain name, it can specify the IP addresses for one or two of its servers as primary and secondary for the Internet. As part of the registration process, an applicant must provide at least two currently active DNS servers that are used on the Internet as the primary and secondary servers designated for the new domain. This ensures proper Internet root server configuration and referral for others who query for the registered DNS domain name on the Internet. After you obtain one IP address, you can sometimes arrange to use another company or ISP's DNS server as a secondary server for the zone. In the United States you can also obtain a valid IP address through the American Registry for Internet Numbers (ARIN) at **www.arin.net**. In other countries, contact the Asia Pacific Network Information Centre (APNIC) at **www.apnic.net** or Réseaux Ip Européens (RIPE) at **www.ripe.net** to find out how to register and acquire an IP address.

➤ *Completing the registration application form and submitting it with the registration fee to the appropriate Internet DNS registration authority*—Registrations are typically in force for a limited time and must be periodically renewed.

Here are some related Internet Web sites that might be useful when you select and register an Internet DNS name:

➤ Network Solutions Inc. (NSI), **www.nsiregistry.net**

➤ Internet Corporation for Assigned Names and Numbers (ICANN), **www.icann.org**

➤ Internet Assigned Authority (IANA), **www.iana.org**

Note: *NSI (formerly know as InterNIC) used to be the primary means for domain name registration. A transition to a shared registration system is being worked out.*

DNS Domain Names

DNS was originally defined in RFCs 1034 and 1035. These documents specify elements common to all implementations of DNS-related software, including:

➤ A DNS domain namespace, which specifies a structured hierarchy of domains used to organize names.

➤ RRs, which map DNS domain names to a specific type of resource information for use when the name is registered or resolved in the namespace.

➤ DNS servers that store and answer name queries for resource records.

➤ DNS clients, also known as resolvers, which query servers to look up and resolve names to a type of RR specified in the query.

Understanding DNS Domain Namespaces

The DNS domain namespace, as shown in Figure 5.1, is based on the concept of a tree of named domains. Each level of the tree can represent either a branch or a leaf. A *branch* is a level where more than one name is used to identify a collection of named resources. A *leaf* represents a single name used once at that level to indicate a specific resource.

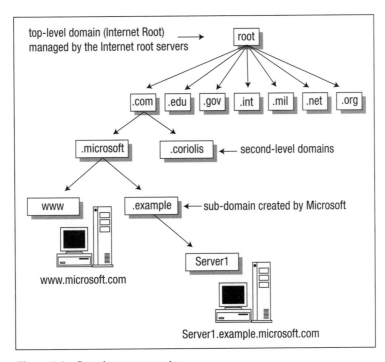

Figure 5.1 Domain namespace tree.

Figure 5.1 shows how Microsoft is assigned authority by the Internet root servers for its own part of the DNS domain namespace tree on the Internet. DNS clients and servers use queries as the fundamental method of resolving names in the tree to specific types of resource information. This information is provided by DNS servers in query responses to DNS clients, which then extract the information and pass it to a requesting program for resolving the queried name.

Keep in mind that DNS servers often function as DNS clients, querying other servers to resolve a queried name.

DNS Domain Namespace Organization

Any DNS domain name used in the tree is technically a domain. Most DNS discussions, however, identify names in one of five ways, based on the level and the way a name is commonly used. For example, the DNS domain name registered to Microsoft (microsoft.com.) is a second-level domain, because it has two parts (known as labels) that indicate it is located two levels below the root or top of the tree. Most DNS domain names have two or more labels, each of which indicates a new level in the tree. Periods are used in names to separate labels.

Table 5.2 lists other terms that describe DNS domain names by their function in the namespace.

Table 5.2   DNS name types.

Name type	Description
Domain Root	The top of the tree, representing an unnamed level. It is sometimes shown as two empty quotation marks (""), indicating a null value. When used in a DNS domain name, it is stated by a trailing period (.) to designate that the name is located at the root or highest level of the domain hierarchy. In this instance, the DNS domain name is considered to be complete and points to an exact location in the tree of names. Names stated this way are FQDNs. They have a single period (.) or a period used at the end, such as example.microsoft.com.
Top-level Domain	Two or three letters indicating a country/region or the type of organization using a name. For example, com indicates a name registered to a business for commercial use on the Internet.
Second-level Domain	Variable-length names registered to an individual or organization for use on the Internet. These names are always based upon an appropriate top-level domain, depending on the type of organization or geographic location where the name is used. Microsoft.com., for example, is the second-level domain name registered to Microsoft by the Internet DNS domain name registrar.
Subdomain	Additional names an organization can create that are derived from the registered second-level domain name. These include names added to grow the DNS tree of names in an organization and divide it into departments or geographic locations. Example.microsoft.com. is a fictitious subdomain assigned by Microsoft for use in documentation example names.
Host or Resource Name	Names that represent a leaf in the DNS tree of names and identify a specific resource. Typically, the leftmost label of a DNS domain name identifies a specific computer on the network. For example, if a name at this level is used in a host (A) RR, it is used to look up the IP address of a computer based on its hostname: Server1.example.microsoft.com., where the first label (Server1) is the DNS hostname for a specific computer on the network.

Interpreting DNS Domain Names

DNS has a method of noting and interpreting the fully qualified path to a DNS domain name similar to the way full paths to files or directories are noted or displayed at a command prompt.

A directory tree path helps point to the exact location of a file stored on your computer. For Windows computers, the backslash (\) indicates each new directory that leads to the exact location of a file. For DNS, the equivalent is a period (.) indicating each new domain level in a name.

For example, the full path to a file called Services would be displayed at a Windows command prompt as:

```
C:\Winnt\System32\Drivers\Etc\Services
```

The full path of the file reads in a left-to-right direction from the highest or most general piece of information (drive C:, the drive where the file is stored) to its most specific information (the file name Services). This example shows five separate levels of hierarchy leading toward the location of the Services file on drive C:

➤ The root folder for drive C: (C:\)

➤ The system root folder where Windows is installed (Winnt)

➤ A system folder where system components are stored (System32)

➤ A subfolder where system device drivers are stored (Drivers)

➤ A subfolder where miscellaneous files used by system and network device drivers are stored (Etc)

For DNS, a domain name with multiple levels would have the following FQDN:

```
Server1.example.microsoft.com.
```

Unlike the file-name path, a DNS FQDN, when read from left to right, moves from its most specific information (the DNS name for a computer called Server1) to its highest or most general piece of information (the trailing period that indicates the root of the DNS name tree). This example shows the four separate DNS domain levels that lead away from the specific host location of Server1:

➤ The "example" domain, which corresponds to a subdomain where the computer name Server1 is registered for use

➤ The "microsoft" domain, which corresponds to the parent domain that roots the "example" subdomain

➤ The "com" domain, which corresponds to the top-level domain designated for use by business or commercial organizations that roots the "microsoft" domain

➤ The full DNS domain name to the root level of the DNS namespace tree

DNS and the Internet

DNS was developed because of the need to provide a name-to-address mapping service for computers on the Internet. Before DNS was introduced in 1987, the practice of mapping user-friendly computer names to IP addresses was done mainly through a shared static file, known as a Hosts file.

Originally, the Internet was small enough to use one centrally administered file that was published and downloaded using FTP for Internet-connected sites. Periodically, each Internet site would update its copy of the Hosts file, and these updated versions were posted to reflect network changes.

As the number of computers on the Internet grew, having one central authority managing a single Hosts file for all Internet hosts became unworkable. The file became increasingly larger, which made it harder to maintain and distribute to all sites in a current and updated form.

The DNS standard provides an alternative to Hosts files. RFCs 1034 and 1035 specify most of the core protocols and have been added to and updated by additional RFCs submitted to the Internet Engineering Task Force (IETF). The IETF reviews and approves new drafts continually, so the standards for DNS evolve and change as needed.

DNS Namespace Planning

Before you begin to use DNS on a network, decide on a plan for the DNS domain namespace. Coming up with a namespace plan involves making some decisions about how DNS naming will be used and what goals will be accomplished in using DNS. Some questions at this stage might include:

➤ Have you previously chosen and registered a DNS domain name for use on the Internet?

➤ Are you going to set up DNS servers on a private network or the Internet?

➤ Are you going to use DNS to support your use of Active Directory?

➤ What naming requirements do you need to follow when choosing DNS domain names for computers?

Your First DNS Domain Name

When setting up DNS servers, you should first choose and register a unique parent DNS domain name for hosting an organization on the Internet—for example, yahoo.com. This name is a second-level domain within one of the top-level domains used on the Internet.

Once you have selected a parent domain name, you can combine it with a location or organizational name to form subdomain names. Take, for example, the domain tree itd.example.yahoo.com, used by the information technology department (itd). A group of programmers working on client/server applications (csa) in this department could have a subdomain named csa.itd.example.yahoo.com. Likewise, another group of workers providing support in this department might use support.itd. example.yahoo.com.

Before deciding on a parent DNS domain name to use on the Internet, perform a search to see if the name is already registered to another organization or person. The Internet DNS namespace is managed by Network Solutions, Inc. (NSI) at **www.networksolutions.com**. In the future, other domain name registrars might also be available.

Planning for Active Directory

If you are using Active Directory, first establish a namespace plan. Before a DNS domain namespace can be properly implemented in Windows 2000, the Active Directory structure needs to be available. Therefore, begin with the Active Directory design and support it with the appropriate DNS namespace.

In Windows 2000, Active Directory domains have DNS names. Start with the registered DNS domain name suffix reserved for use on the Internet, such as excite.com, and combine it with either geographical or divisional names to form full names for the Active Directory domains.

For example, the Windows test group at *PC World* magazine might call its domain wintest.example.pcworld.com. This method of naming ensures that each Active Directory domain name is globally unique. Once employed, these naming methods also make it easy to use existing names as parents for creating additional subdomains and further grow the namespace to accommodate new departments within your organization.

Selecting Names

When creating names, use only characters that are part of the Internet standard character set permitted for use in DNS host naming. Permissible characters are defined in RFC 1123 as follows: all uppercase letters (A-Z), lowercase letters (a-z), numbers (0-9), and the hyphen (-).

Adjusting the naming conventions might prove to be time consuming. To ease the transition from Windows NT 4.0 NetBIOS names to Windows 2000 DNS domain names, the DNS service includes support for extended ASCII and Unicode characters. This additional character support, however, can be used only in a pure Windows 2000 network environment. This is because most other DNS resolver client software is based on RFC 1123, the specification that standardizes Internet host-naming requirements. If you enter a nonstandard DNS domain name during Windows 2000 setup, a warning message appears recommending that you use a standard DNS name instead.

In Windows NT 4.0 and earlier versions, the name used to identify a Windows computer on the network was a NetBIOS name. In Windows 2000, a computer can be identified in either of the following ways:

➤ A NetBIOS computer name, which is optional and used for interoperability with earlier Windows systems

➤ The full computer name, which is a fully qualified domain name for the computer and is its primary name

In addition, a computer might be identified by the FQDN, consisting of the computer name (or hostname) and a connection-specific domain name. The DNS domain name is part of the System properties for the computer and is not related to any specifically installed networking components. Computers running Windows 2000 that do not use either networking or TCP/IP do not have a DNS domain name. Table 5.3 compares NetBIOS and DNS computer names.

To ensure interoperability between NetBIOS and DNS naming, Windows 2000 introduced a new naming parameter called the NetBIOS computer name. The value of this parameter, which is not required in a pure Windows 2000 environment, is derived from the first 15 characters of the DNS full computer name.

When the full computer name is a combination of the computer name and the DNS domain name for the computer, the impact of renaming and making the transition from a NetBIOS namespace to a DNS namespace can be minimal. Users continue to focus on the short computer name. If this name is 15 characters or less,

Table 5.3   A comparison of NetBIOS and DNS computer names.

	NetBIOS computer name	DNS computer name
Type	Flat	Hierarchical
Character restrictions	Unicode characters, numbers, white space. Symbols: ! @ # $ % ^ & ') (. - _ { } ~	Same as for NetBIOS except no white space permitted; period (.) has special reserved meaning
Maximum length	15 character bytes	63 octets per label; 255 octets per FQDN
Name service	Windows Internet Name Service (WINS); NetBIOS broadcast	DNS service

it can be made identical to the NetBIOS computer name. The administrator can then also assign a DNS domain name for each computer. This can be done using remote administration tools.

In this way, the System Properties page can have the settings as illustrated in Table 5.4 on the Network Identification tab.

In addition to support for the internal DNS namespace used by Windows 2000 and Active Directory, many networks require support for resolving external DNS names, such as those used on the Internet. The DNS service provides ways to integrate and manage disjointed namespaces where both external and internal DNS names are resolved on a network.

In deciding how to integrate namespaces, determine which of the following scenarios most closely resembles the situation and proposed use of DNS:

➤ An internal DNS namespace, used only on an organization's network

➤ An internal DNS namespace with referral and access to an external namespace, such as referral or forwarding to a DNS server on the Internet

➤ An external DNS namespace, used only on a public network such as the Internet

If the use of DNS for name service will be limited within a private namespace, there are no restrictions on how it is designed or implemented. For example, you could choose any DNS naming standard, configure DNS servers to be valid root servers for a network's DNS distributed design, or form an entirely self-contained DNS domain tree structure and hierarchy.

When referral to either an external DNS namespace or full DNS service is provided on the Internet, consider the compatibility between the private and external namespaces. Additionally, Internet service requires the registration of parent domain names for an organization.

When you use the DNS console for the first time to add and connect a Windows 2000 DNS server, the root hints file (cache.dns) is automatically initialized for use on a network. This action is transparent and will require no further interaction. Depending on the way DNS is used, however, this file can be updated in one of the following ways:

Table 5.4 Settings on the Network Identification tab.

Settings	Example
Computer name	Longer-than-15-characters-name
NetBIOS computer name	Longer-than-15c
Primary DNS suffix for this computer	Example.microsoft.com

➤ When the root hints file is updated and released, you can get a copy with anonymous FTP to the site, ftp://rs.internic.net/domain/named.root. Note that the root hints file is cache.dsn on a Windows 2000 Server and is named.root on the ftp server.

➤ If no Internet connection exists, remove the default RRs in the root hints file and replace them with Name Server (NS) and Host (A) resource records for the DNS authoritative servers at the root domain of the site. This file can be safely removed entirely from the root domain servers on a private network because the servers at this domain level do not require or use a cache of root hints.

➤ If the cache.dns file is deleted from the private root domain server, the cache directive from the server boot file will also need to be deleted before you restart the DNS service. This needs to be done if the server's DNS service was configured using the Boot From File method instead of the default Boot From Registry option.

DNS Server Planning

When planning for DNS servers, you should do the following:

➤ Perform capacity planning and review server hardware requirements.

➤ Determine how many DNS servers you need and their roles in the network.

➤ When determining the number of DNS servers to use, decide which servers will host primary and secondary copies of zones. Also, if using Active Directory, determine whether the server computer will perform as a DC or a member server for the domain.

➤ Decide where to place DNS servers on a network for traffic loads, replication, and fault tolerance.

➤ Decide if you will use only Windows 2000 DNS servers for all DNS servers or if the network will be operating a mixture of Windows and other DNS server implementations.

Planning Server Capacity

Planning and deploying DNS servers on a network involves examining several aspects of a network and the capacity requirements for any DNS servers intended to be used in it. Some questions to consider:

➤ How many zones is the DNS server expected to load and host?

➤ How large is each zone the server is loading for service (based on the size of the zone file or the number of RRs used in the zone)?

➤ For a multihomed DNS server, how many interfaces are to be enabled for listening to and servicing DNS clients on each of the server's connected subnets?

➤ How many total or overall DNS query requests from all of its clients is a DNS server expected to receive and service?

In many cases, adding more RAM to a DNS server can provide the most noticeable improvements in performance. This is because the DNS Server Service fully loads all of its configured zones into memory at startup. If a server is operating and loading a large number of zones, and dynamic updates occur frequently for zone clients, additional memory can be helpful. Keep in mind that for typical usage, the DNS server consumes system memory as follows:

➤ Approximately 4MB of RAM is used when the DNS server is started without any zones.

➤ For each addition of zones or RRs to the server, the DNS server consumes additional server memory.

➤ The addition of every RR to a server zone uses an average of approximately 100 bytes of server memory.

For example, adding a zone containing 1,000 RRs to a server would require approximately 100K of server memory.

Placing DNS Servers

In general, place DNS servers at a location on the network that is centrally accessible to clients. Using a DNS server on each subnet is often the most practical method. There are several factors to consider when deciding where a DNS server is needed:

➤ If you are deploying DNS to support Active Directory, is the DNS server computer also a DC or likely to be promoted to one in the future?

➤ If the DNS server stops responding, are its local clients able to access an alternative DNS server?

➤ If the DNS server is located on a subnet that is remote to some of its clients, what other DNS servers or name resolution options are available if the routed connection stops responding?

For DNS server installations where the use of Active Directory is an issue, review special interoperability issues and installation details. For all DNS server installations, including those in which the use of Active Directory is not an issue, the following server placement and planning guidelines can be usefully applied:

➤ If a routed LAN and high-speed links are fairly reliable, maybe one DNS server could be used for a larger, multiple subnetted network area. If many client nodes are on a single subnet design, maybe more than one DNS server could be added to the subnet to provide backup and failover if the preferred DNS server stops responding.

➤ When determining the number of DNS servers needed for use, you should assess the effect of zone transfers and DNS query traffic on slower links in the network. Although DNS is designed to help reduce broadcast traffic between local subnets, it does create some traffic between servers and clients that you should review, particularly when used in complexly routed LAN or WAN environments.

➤ Consider the effects of zone transfer over slower-speed links, such as those typically used for a WAN connection. Although the DNS service supports incremental zone transfers, and Windows 2000 DNS clients and servers can cache recently used names, traffic considerations are sometimes still an issue, particularly when DHCP leases are shortened and, as a result, dynamic updates in DNS are performed more frequently. One option for dealing with remote locations on WAN links is to set up a DNS server at these locations to provide caching-only DNS service.

➤ With most installations, at least two server computers should be hosting each of the DNS zones for fault tolerance. DNS was designed to have two servers for each zone: one as a primary server, and the other as a backup or secondary server. When making any final determinations about the number of servers to use, first assess the level of fault tolerance needed for the network.

➤ When administering zone files created by the DNS service, use the DNS console tool to make changes. Another method is to administer all DNS zone files manually using any application that supports file saving in text mode. Whether using a text editor or the DNS console to modify and edit zone files manually, select one method for updating zones and use it consistently. This helps prevent having zone edits overwritten or rejected, which might happen when changing from one method to another.

Integrating Active Directory

For Windows 2000 Server, the DNS Server Service has been carefully integrated into the design and implementation of Active Directory, the next-generation directory service designed by Microsoft for networks using Windows NT technologies. Active Directory provides an enterprise-level tool for organizing, managing, and locating resources in a network.

There are two significant changes when deploying Windows 2000 DNS servers together with Active Directory:

➤ DNS is required for locating Windows 2000 DCs. The Netlogon service uses new DNS server support to provide registration of DCs in a DNS domain namespace.

➤ Windows 2000 DNS servers can use Active Directory for storing and replicating zones. By directory integrating zones, you can use additional Windows 2000 DNS features, such as secure dynamic updates and record aging/scavenging.

How DNS and Active Directory Integrate

When Active Directory is installed on a server computer, promote the server to the role of a DC for a specified domain. After completing this process, specify a DNS domain name for the appropriate Active Directory domain when prompted.

If, during this process, a DNS server authoritative for the specified domain either cannot be located on the network or does not support the DNS dynamic update protocol, a prompt for the option to install a Windows 2000 DNS server will appear. Once Active Directory is installed, you have two options for storing and replicating zones when operating the DNS server at the new DC:

➤ *Standard zone storage, using a text-based file*—Zones stored this way are located in .dns files that are stored in the %SystemRoot%\System32\Dns folder on each computer operating a DNS server. Zone file names correspond to the name chosen for the zone when creating it—for example, if the zone name is example.microsoft.com, the zone file name would be example.microsoft.com.dns.

➤ *Directory-integrated zone storage, using the Active Directory database*—Zones stored this way are located in the Active Directory tree under the domain object container. Each directory-integrated zone is stored in a dnsZone container object identified by the name chosen for the zone when creating it.

The Benefits of Integration

For networks deploying DNS to support Active Directory, directory-integrated primary zones are strongly recommended and provide several benefits. Using multimaster update and enhanced security, based on Active Directory capabilities in a standard zone storage model, DNS updates are conducted based upon a single-master update model. In this model, a single authoritative DNS server for a zone is designated as the primary source for the zone. This server maintains the master copy of the zone in a local file. With this model, the primary server for the zone represents a single fixed point of failure. If this server is not available, update requests from DNS clients are not processed for the zone.

With directory-integrated storage, dynamic updates to DNS are conducted based upon a multimaster update model. In this model, any authoritative DNS server, such as a DC running the Windows 2000 DNS Server Service, is designated as a primary source for the zone. Because the master copy of the zone is maintained in the Active Directory database, which is fully replicated to all DCs, the DNS servers operating at any DC for the domain can update the zone. With the multimaster update model of Active Directory, any of the primary servers for the directory-integrated zone can process requests from DNS clients to update the zone as long as a DC is available and reachable on the network.

Also, with directory-integrated zones, you can use access control list (ACL) editing to secure a dnsZone object container in the directory tree. This feature provides granulated access to either the zone or a specified RR in the zone. For example, an ACL for a zone RR can be restricted so that dynamic updates are allowed only for a specified client computer or a secure group, such as a domain administrators group. This security feature is not available with standard primary zones.

Zones are replicated and synchronized to new DCs automatically whenever a new one is added to an Active Directory domain. Although DNS service can be selectively removed from a DC, directory-integrated zones are already stored at each DC, so zone storage and management is not an additional resource. Also, the methods used to synchronize directory-stored information offer performance improvement over standard zone update methods, which can potentially require transfer of the entire zone.

By integrating storage of DNS zone databases in Active Directory, you can streamline database replication planning for a network. When DNS and Active Directory namespaces are stored and replicated separately, each namespace may need to be planned and administered separately—for example, when using standard DNS zone storage and Active Directory together to design, implement, test, and maintain two different database replication topologies. One replication topology is needed for replicating directory data between DCs, and another topology would be needed for replicating zone databases between DNS servers. This can create additional administrative complexity for planning and designing a network and allowing for its eventual growth. Integrating DNS storage unifies storage management and replication issues for both DNS and Active Directory, merging and viewing them together as a single administrative entity.

Directory replication is faster and more efficient than standard DNS replication because Active Directory replication processing is performed on a per-property basis; thus, only relevant changes are propagated. This allows less data to be used and submitted in updates for directory-stored zones.

Installing the DNS Server Service

Several situations might require adding a primary server and configuring it for a network:

➤ When adding a new DNS server to a network and configuring a new zone for first-time use.

➤ When a zone has already been created at another DNS server and a new server is being added that also needs to load and provide service for the zone.

➤ When a DNS server configured with a zone or zones needs to add a new zone for another domain name, such as a subdomain.

5

Adding a Primary Server for an Existing Zone

The primary server for a zone acts as the zone's point of update. Newly created zones are always this type. Windows 2000 Server uses primary zones in two ways: as standard primary zones or as primary zones integrated with Active Directory.

For standard primary zones, only a single server can host and load the master copy of the zone. If a zone is created as a standard primary zone, no additional primary servers for the zone are permitted. Only one server is allowed to accept dynamic updates and process zone changes.

The standard primary model implies a single point of failure. For example, if for any reason the primary server for a zone is unavailable to the network, no dynamic updates to the zone can be made. Note that queries for names in the zone are not affected and can continue uninterrupted, as long as secondary servers for the zone are available to answer them.

In Windows 2000 Server, however, you can add more primary servers for a zone by using the directory-integrated storage and replication features of the DNS service. To do this, you must change a zone and integrate it into Active Directory.

You can integrate an existing zone into Active Directory by changing the type of zone at the originating primary server where it was created. Once the zone type is changed from standard primary to Active Directory-integrated, add the zone to other DNS servers by configuring them to use the Boot from DS option when they initialize DNS service.

When the Boot from DS option is selected, other DNS servers operating as part of the Active Directory domain namespace—such as DCs for the Active Directory domain—can query the directory and automatically load all directory-integrated zones, which are stored in the directory database. No other steps are necessary. With the Boot from DS option, any DNS servers operating as part of Active Directory are, by default, also primary servers for directory-integrated zones.

Adding a New Primary Zone to an Existing Server

You can add a new primary zone to an existing server whenever additional domains or subdomains are needed in a DNS domain namespace. For example, for a second-level domain such as excite.com, the addition of a primary zone for the new subdomain would be example.excite.com.

In this example, you can create the new zone for the subdomain using the DNS snap-in, by running the Configure New Zone wizard. When finished, create a delegation in the parent zone for the new subdomain to complete the addition of the new subdomain and its primary zone. Once the new primary zone is added, you can perform other zone configuration tasks as needed to fully configure the zone for use.

DNS Client Configuration

You can use the DNS Client Service running in Windows 2000 to resolve DNS domain names. It implements the following features:

➤ *System-wide caching RRs from query responses*—These are added to the client cache as applications query DNS servers. This information is then cached for a set Time-To-Live (TTL) and can be used again to answer subsequent queries.

➤ *RFC-compliant negative caching support*—In addition to caching positive query responses from DNS servers, the DNS Client Service also caches negative query responses. A negative response results when an RR for the queried name does not exist. Negative caching prevents repeating additional queries for names that do not exist; this can adversely affect client system performance. By default, any query information negatively cached is kept for a shorter period of time (no more than five minutes) than is used for positive query responses. This avoids continued negative caching of stale information if the records later become available. Negative caching is a new DNS standard specification defined in RFC 2308.

➤ *Avoidance of unresponsive DNS servers*—The DNS Client Service uses a server search list, ordered by preference. This list includes all preferred and alternative DNS servers configured for each of the active network connections on the system. Windows 2000 rearranges these lists based on the following criteria: Preferred DNS servers have first priority; if no preferred DNS servers are available, then alternative DNS servers are used; unresponsive servers are removed temporarily from these lists.

Setting Computer Names

When setting computer names for DNS, think of the name as the leftmost portion of an FQDN. For example, in comp1.example.microsoft.com, the first part of the name that precedes the first period (.) (comp1) is the name of the computer.

All Windows DNS clients can be configured with a computer name based on any of the standard supported characters defined in RFC 1123 for Internet DNS use. These characters include:

➤ Uppercase letters, A through Z

➤ Lowercase letters, a through z

➤ Numbers, 0 through 9

➤ Hyphens (-)

If both NetBIOS and DNS resolution are being used on a network, use a different computer name for each type of resolution. If WINS lookup is enabled for DNS servers, however, use the same name for both NetBIOS and DNS client computer naming to ensure consistency when other clients attempt to query and resolve names for these computers.

If NetBIOS names are being used to support legacy Microsoft networking technology, the NetBIOS computer names should be revised for use on a network to prepare for migration to a standard DNS-only environment. This prepares a network for long-term growth and interoperability with future naming requirements. As an example, if the same computer name for both NetBIOS and DNS resolution is going to be used, consider converting any special characters, such as the underscore (_), in the current NetBIOS names that do not comply with DNS naming standards. Although these characters are permitted in NetBIOS names, they are incompatible with DNS.

Setting Domain Names

The domain name is used with the client computer name to form the FQDN, or full computer name.

Windows 2000 domain names have two variations: a DNS name and a NetBIOS name. For Windows 2000 computers, the full computer name is used during querying and location of named resources on a network. For earlier version clients, the NetBIOS name is used to locate various types of NetBIOS services that are shared on a network.

An example that shows the need for both NetBIOS and DNS names is the Netlogon service. In Windows 2000 Server, the Netlogon service on a DC registers its service resource records on a DNS server. For Windows NT Server 4 and earlier versions, DCs register a DomainName [1C] entry in WINS to perform the same registration and advertise their availability for providing authentication service to the network.

When a client computer running Windows 2000 is started on the network, it uses the Windows 2000 resolver to query a DNS server for SRV records for its configured domain name. This query is used to locate DCs and provide logon authentication for accessing network resources. If either a client or a DC on the network is running Windows NT Server 4.0 or earlier, Windows 2000 optionally uses the NetBIOS resolver service to query WINS servers, attempting to locate DomainName [1C] entries to complete the logon process.

If the FQDN configured for a Windows client computer is comp1.example. microsoft.com, for example, the domain name is the example.microsoft.com portion of the name.

Domain names should follow the same standards and recommended practices that apply to DNS computer naming described in the previous section. In general, acceptable naming conventions for domain names include the use of letters A through Z, numerals 0 through 9, and the hyphen (-). The use of the period (.) in a domain name is always used to separate its discrete parts, commonly known as labels. Each label corresponds to an additional level defined in the DNS namespace tree.

By default, for Windows 2000, the leftmost label in the full DNS computer name for clients equals the NetBIOS computer name, unless this label is 16 or more characters. When these labels exceed the maximum length for NetBIOS, the NetBIOS computer name is truncated based on the full label that is specified. After a network connection is installed and configured, this name can be changed so that it is not related to the DNS computer name.

Configuring a DNS Servers List

For DNS clients to operate effectively, a prioritized list of DNS name servers must be configured for each computer to use when processing queries and resolving DNS names. In most cases, the client computer contacts and uses its preferred DNS server, which is the first DNS server on its locally configured list. Alternative DNS servers are contacted and used when the preferred server is not available. For this reason, it is important that the preferred DNS server be appropriate for continuous client use under normal conditions.

Configuring a DNS Suffix Search List

For Windows clients, you can configure a DNS domain suffix search list that extends or revises their DNS search capabilities. By adding suffixes to the list, you can search for short unqualified computer names in more than one specified DNS domain. Then, if a DNS query fails, the DNS Client Service can use this list to append other name suffixes to the original name and repeat DNS queries to the DNS server for these alternative FQDNs. For Windows 2000 computers, the following default DNS search behavior is predetermined and used when completing and resolving short, unqualified names:

➤ When the suffix search list is empty or unspecified, the primary DNS suffix of the computer is appended to short unqualified names, and DNS query is used to resolve the resultant FQDN. If this query fails, the computer can try additional queries for alternative FQDNs by appending any connection-specific DNS suffix configured for network connections.

➤ If no connection-specific suffixes are configured, or queries for these resultant connection-specific FQDNs fail, the client can then begin to retry queries based on systematic reduction of the primary suffix, also known as *devolution*. For example, if the primary suffix were example.yahoo.com, the devolution process would retry queries for the short name by searching for it in the yahoo.com and com domains.

➤ When the suffix search list is not empty and has at least one DNS suffix specified, attempts to qualify and resolve short DNS names are limited to searching only those FQDNs made possible by the specified suffix list. If a search fails to find any FQDNs formed as a result of appending and trying each suffix in the list, the query process fails, producing a "name not found" result.

Configuring Multiple Names

In Windows 2000, computers are given DNS names by default. Each computer running Windows 2000 can have its DNS names configured using one of two possible methods:

➤ *A primary DNS domain name*—Applies to the default fully qualified DNS name for the computer and all of its configured network connections.

➤ *A connection-specific DNS domain name*—Can be configured as an alternative DNS domain name that applies only to a single network adapter installed and configured on the computer.

Although most computers do not need to support or use more than one name in DNS, support for configuring multiple connection-specific DNS names is sometimes useful. For example, by using multiple names, a user could specify which network connection to use when connecting to a multihomed computer.

Using Connection-Specific Names

As shown in Figure 5.2, a multihomed server computer named Server1 can be named according to both its primary and connection-specific DNS domain names.

In this example, the server computer Server1 attaches to two separate subnets— Subnet 1 and Subnet 2—which are linked at redundant points using two routers for additional paths between each subnet. Given this configuration, Server1 provides access through its separately named LAN connections, as follows:

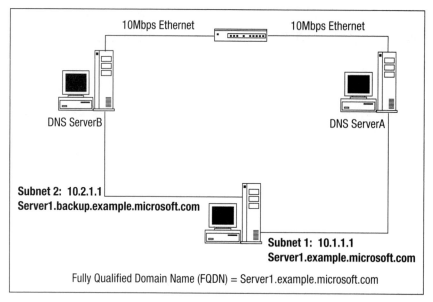

Figure 5.2 Connection-specific DNS domain name.

➤ The name Server1.example.microsoft.com provides access using LAN connection 1 over Subnet 1, a higher-speed (100Mbps) Ethernet LAN, for normal access to users who have typical file and print service needs.

➤ The name Server1.backup.example.microsoft.com provides access using LAN connection 2 over Subnet 2, a lower-speed (10Mbps) Ethernet LAN, for reserved access by server applications, such as troubleshooting server networking problems, performing network-based backup, or replicating zone data between servers.

In addition to the connection-specific DNS names, the computer can also be accessible using either of the two LAN connections by specifying its primary DNS domain name, Server1.example.microsoft.com.

When configured as shown, Windows 2000 can register RRs in DNS according to its three distinct names and sets of IP addresses, as shown in Table 5.5.

Updating Client Information

Updating DNS client information on a computer is sometimes necessary—for example, if a computer is added or removed from an Active Directory domain. In most cases, clients perform dynamic updates for the following changes when entering or leaving a domain:

Table 5.5   DNS names and IP addresses.

DNS name	IP addresses	Description
Server1.example.microsoft.com	10.1.1.1	Primary DNS name for computer. The computer registers Host (A) and Pointer (PTR) resource records for all configured IP addresses under this name in the example.microsoft.com zone.
Server1.example.microsoft.com	10.1.1.1	Connection-specific DNS name for LAN connection 1, which registers A and PTR resource records for IP address 10.1.1.1 in the example.microsoft.com zone.
Server1.backup.example.microsoft.com	10.2.1.1	Connection-specific DNS name for LAN connection 2, which registers A and PTR resource records for IP address 10.2.1.1 in the backup.example.microsoft.com zone.

➤ When a computer is joined to a domain, it adds its A and PTR records to DNS.

➤ When a computer is removed from a domain, it deletes its A and PTR records from DNS.

If dynamic update for zones is enabled, these changes occur automatically.

DNS Tools

Windows 2000 provides a number of utilities for administering, monitoring, and troubleshooting both DNS servers and clients. These utilities include:

➤ The DNS console, which is part of Administrative Tools.

➤ Command-line utilities, such as Nslookup, which can be used to troubleshoot DNS problems.

➤ Logging features, such as the DNS server log, which can be viewed using Event Viewer. File-based logs can also be used temporarily as an advanced debugging option to log and trace selected service events.

➤ Performance monitoring utilities, such as statistical counters to measure and monitor DNS server activity with System Monitor.

The DNS Console

The primary tool to manage Windows 2000 DNS servers is the DNS console, which is provided in the Administrative Tools folder in the Control Panel. The DNS console appears as a Microsoft Management Console (MMC) snap-in, to further integrate DNS administration for total network management.

After the DNS server is installed, you can use the DNS console for these basic administrative server tasks:

➤ Performing initial configuration of a new DNS server

➤ Connecting to and managing a local DNS server on the same computer or remote DNS servers on other computers

➤ Adding and removing forward and reverse lookup zones as needed

➤ Adding, removing, and updating RRs in zones

➤ Modifying how zones are stored and replicated between servers

➤ Modifying how servers process queries and handle dynamic updates

➤ Modifying security for specific zones or RRs

In addition, the DNS console can be used for these tasks:

➤ Performing maintenance on the server, such as starting, stopping, pausing, resuming, or manually updating server data files

➤ Monitoring the contents of the server cache and, as needed, clearing it

➤ Tuning Advanced Server options

➤ Configuring and performing aging and scavenging of stale RRs stored by the server

Keep in mind that you can also operate the DNS console from a non-server computer to administer Windows 2000 DNS servers remotely if the DNS service is installed on them. The DNS console, however, can be used to manage Windows 2000 DNS servers only.

Command-Line Utilities

Windows 2000 provides several command-line utilities. They can be used to manage and troubleshoot DNS servers and clients. The following table describes each of these utilities, which can be run either by typing them at a command prompt or by entering them in batch files for scripted use. Table 5.6 lists these DNS commands.

Table 5.6   DNS commands.

Command	Description
Nslookup	Performs query testing of the DNS domain namespace.
Dnscmd	A command-line interface for managing DNS servers. This utility is useful in scripting batch files to help automate routine DNS management tasks, or to perform simple unattended setup and configuration of new DNS servers on your network.
Ipconfig	Views and modifies IP configuration details used by the computer. For Windows 2000, additional command-line options are included with this utility to help in troubleshooting and supporting DNS clients.

Event Monitoring Utilities

Windows 2000 Server includes two options for monitoring DNS servers: the default logging of event messages to the DNS server log and debug options for trace logging to a text file on the DNS server.

For Windows 2000 Server, server event messages are separated and kept in their own system event log—the DNS server log—which can be viewed using Event Viewer. The DNS server log contains basic events logged by the DNS Server Service. Some additional critical DNS service events are also logged here—for example, when the server starts but cannot locate initializing data, such as zones or boot information stored in the Windows 2000 registry or Active Directory. The event types logged by Windows 2000 DNS servers are predetermined. Event Viewer can also be used to view and monitor client-related DNS events. These appear in the System log and are written by the DNS Client Service at any computers running Windows 2000.

The DNS console can also be used to selectively enable additional debug logging options for temporary trace logging to a text-based file of DNS server activity. The file created and used for this feature, dns.log, is stored in the systemroot\ System32\Dns folder.

Performance Monitoring Utilities

Performance monitoring for Windows 2000 DNS servers can be done using additional service-specific counters that measure DNS server performance. These counters are accessible through System Monitor, which is provided in the Performance console.

With System Monitor, you can create charts and graphs of server performance trends over time for any Windows 2000 DNS servers. These can be further studied and analyzed to determine if you need additional server tuning. By measuring and reviewing server metrics over a period of time, you can determine performance benchmarks and decide if further adjustments can optimize the system.

To open the DNS console:

1. Open Notes.

2. To open DNS, click on Start, point to Programs, point to Administrative Tools, and then click on DNS.

The DNS console is an administrative tool for managing Windows 2000 DNS servers only.

To start or stop a DNS server:

1. Open.

2. In the console tree, click on the applicable DNS server.

3. On the Action menu, point to All Tasks and then click on one of the following:

➤ To start the service, click on Start.

➤ To stop the service, click on Stop.

➤ To interrupt the service, click on Pause.

➤ To stop and then automatically restart the service, click on Restart.

To add a server to the DNS console:

1. Open the On the Action menu, then click on Connect to Computer.

2. From Select Target Computer, select either:

➤ This computer, if the server you want to connect to and manage is located on the same computer you are using to manage it.

➤ The following computer, if the server you want to connect to and manage is located on a remote computer. If you choose to connect to a remote server, specify either its DNS computer name or its IP address.

3. Select the Connect to the Specified Computer Now checkbox, and then click on OK.

To remove a server from the DNS console:

1. Open In the Console Tree, then click on the applicable DNS server.

2. On the Action menu, click on Delete.

3. When prompted to confirm you want to delete this server from the list, click on OK.

To update server data files manually:

1. Open In the Console Tree, then click on the applicable DNS server.

2. On the Action menu, click on Update Server Data Files.

To change the boot method used by the DNS server:

1. Open In the Console Tree, then click on the applicable DNS server.

2. On the Action menu, click on Properties.

3. Click on the Advanced tab.

4. In the Load Zone Data on Startup list, select From Registry, From File, or From Active Directory and Registry.

To change the name-checking method used by the DNS server:

1. In the console tree, click on the applicable DNS server.

2. On the Action menu, click on Properties.

3. Click on the Advanced tab.

4. In the Name Checking list, select Non RFC (ANSI), Strict RFC (ANSI), or Multibyte (UTF8).

Windows 2000 DNS servers support three methods for checking names received and processed during normal server operations:

➤ *Strict RFC (ANSI)*—Strictly enforces RFC-compliant naming rules for all DNS names that the server processes. Names that are not RFC-compliant are treated as errors by the server.

➤ *Non RFC (ANSI)*—Allows names that are not RFC-compliant to be used with the DNS server, such as those that use ASCII characters but are not compliant with RFC host naming requirements.

➤ *Multibyte (UTF8)*—Allows names that use the Unicode eight-bit translation encoding scheme, which is a proposed RFC draft, to be used with the DNS server.

By default, the server uses Non RFC (ANSI) to check names. This option provides loose name checking and allows any DNS names that use standard ANSI or ASCII encoded characters to be received and processed by the server, providing the highest possible interoperability with other DNS servers and host systems.

Verifying Server Configuration

With the DNS console, you can perform either manual or automated verification testing of DNS servers to monitor their ability to process and resolve queries. You access this feature through the Monitoring tab in DNS Server Properties.

Two types of tests are available with this feature:

➤ *A simple query against this DNS server*—Specifies that the DNS server perform a simple or iterative query. This localized query uses the DNS resolver (client) on the server computer to query the local DNS server.

➤ *A recursive query to other DNS servers*—Specifies that the DNS server perform a recursive query. This test is similar in its initial query processing to the previous test in that it uses the local DNS resolver (client) to query the local DNS server, also located on the same computer. In this test, however, the client asks the server to use recursion to resolve an NS-type query for the root of the DNS domain namespace, stated as a single dot (.). This type of query should typically require additional recursive processing and can be helpful in verifying that server root hints or zone delegations have been properly set. Once the tests are selected for use, either click on the Test Now button to manually perform the tests immediately, or have automatic testing performed at a specified time interval. Automated tests are performed periodically when the Perform Automatic Testing at the Following Interval checkbox is selected; they are done according to the duration configured in Time Interval. Results of all selected tests, whether manually or automatically performed, are displayed in the Test Results List box. Typically, this information includes:

➤ The date and time when each query was made.

➤ Additional status results of the specific test used, such as whether the simple or recursive query failed or succeeded.

Chapter Summary

When transferring a zone between two Windows DNS servers, the DNS Server Service always uses a fast transfer method incorporating compression. For Windows 2000 DNS servers, this is the default method used when initiating transfers with other DNS server implementations.

In some cases, these DNS servers are not equipped to support the DNS requirements for deploying Active Directory. Use the DNS service provided with Windows 2000 Server, migrating, if possible, any current DNS zones to Windows 2000 DNS servers. Existing DNS servers for root zones are not to be upgraded or migrated to other DNS solutions. Create multiple subdomains based on a DNS second-level domain to support registration of Active Directory in DNS.

DNS was originally defined in RFCs 1034 and 1035.

A DNS domain namespace specifies a structured hierarchy of domains used to organize names. DNS servers store and answer name queries for RRs. In resolving a name, keep in mind DNS servers often function as DNS clients, querying other servers to fully resolve a queried name.

Any DNS domain name used in the tree is technically a domain. For example, the DNS domain name registered to Microsoft (microsoft.com.) is known as a second-level domain.

In Windows 2000, Active Directory domains have DNS names. To ease the transition from Windows NT 4 NetBIOS names to Windows 2000 DNS domain names, the DNS service includes support for extended ASCII and Unicode characters. If a nonstandard DNS domain name is entered during Windows 2000 setup, a warning message appears recommending that a standard DNS name be used instead. The full computer name is a combination of both the computer name and the DNS domain name for the computer. To ensure interoperability between NetBIOS and

DNS naming in Windows 2000, a new naming parameter called the *NetBIOS computer name* was introduced. The administrator can then also assign a DNS domain name for each computer.

The DNS Client Service running in Windows 2000 is used to resolve DNS domain names and avoid unresponsive DNS servers. The DNS Client Service uses a server search list, ordered by preference. If no preferred DNS servers are available, then alternative DNS servers are used.

Windows 2000 domain names have two variations: a DNS name and a NetBIOS name. For Windows 2000 computers, the full computer name (a fully qualified DNS name) is used during querying and location of named resources on your network.

For DNS clients to operate effectively, a prioritized list of DNS name servers must be configured for each computer to use when processing queries and resolving DNS names. Then, if a DNS query fails, the DNS Client Service can use this list to append other name suffixes to your original name and repeat DNS queries to the DNS server for these alternative FQDNs. In Windows 2000, computers are given DNS names by default. A primary DNS domain name applies as the default fully qualified DNS name for the computer and all of its configured network connections.

Windows 2000 Server includes two options for monitoring DNS servers: the default logging of event messages to the DNS server log and debug options for trace logging to a text file on the DNS server.

Review Questions

1. What is the largest category of top-level domains in use?

   a. .gov

   b. .com

   c. .edu

   d. .org

2. Valid domain names cannot exceed how many characters?

   a. 23

   b. 24

   c. 22

   d. 26

3. To ensure interoperability between NetBIOS and DNS naming in Windows 2000, what new naming parameter was introduced?

   a. FQDN

   b. NetBIOS

   c. WINS

   d. NetBEUI

4. What are the two significant changes when deploying Windows 2000 DNS server together with Active Directory? (Select two answers.)

   a. DNS is required for locating a Windows 2000 DC. The Netlogon service uses new DNS server support to provide registration of DCs in a DNS domain namespace.

   b. DNS is required for locating a Windows 2000 Active Directory zone. The Netlogon service uses new DNS server support to provide registration of Active Directory zones in a DNS domain namespace.

   c. Windows 2000 DNS server can use Active Directory for storing and replicating zones. By directory-integrating zones, you can use additional Windows 2000 DNS features, such as secure dynamic updates and record aging/scavenging.

   d. Active Directory can use Netlogon to store and replicate zones for a DNS server.

5. If both NetBIOS and DNS name resolution are on a network, you can use different computer names for each resolution.

   a. True

   b. False

6. Windows 2000 domain names have what two variations? (Choose two.)

   a. FQDN

   b. DNS name

   c. NetBIOS name

   d. NetBEUI name

7. DNS names can be set using remote administration and other remote configuration services, such as DHCP.

   a. True

   b. False

8. To establish a presence on the Internet, an individual or business must first do what?

    a. Apply for and register an IP address for the organization's network

    b. Apply for and register an AS number

    c. Apply for and register a second-level domain name

    d. Apply for and register a top-level domain name

9. Why was DNS developed?

    a. To confuse people with naming conventions

    b. To provide a name-to-address mapping service for computers on the Internet

    c. To provide IP ARP resolution for computers on the Internet

    d. To make Web surfing easier

10. In Windows 2000, a computer can be identified in what ways? (Choose two.)

    a. NetBIOS computer name

    b. DNS name

    c. FQDN

    d. NetBEUI name

11. What two configurations are required for a Windows 2000 DNS server? (Choose two.)

    a. Dynamic IP address

    b. Static IP address

    c. DNS domain name

    d. DNS resource records

12. If a client expects the best answer that a DNS server can provide without querying other DNS servers, what is the query type?

    a. Recursive

    b. Iterative

    c. Best-efforts

    d. Local

13. If a client expects a complete answer where a DNS server may query other DNS servers, what is the query type?

    a. Recursive

    b. Iterative

    c. Best-efforts

    d. Local

5

14. Which zone contains the master copy of zone file?

   a. Start zone

   b. Primary

   c. Secondary

   d. First

15. Which zone contains a copy of the existing zone file?

   a. Primary

   b. Backup

   c. Copy

   d. Secondary

Real-World Projects

Lesha Camille, the IT director for Red National Bank, is thinking of setting up a DNS domain name for the bank, but is not sure if it is even necessary. She would like to know for future reference what this would entail and what the fees would be for an IP address for the primary and secondary DNS servers if one were needed.

Her goal here is mainly to research options and gather information so she can make an informed decision. She knows that she can do a WHOIS query on the NSI Web site to find out if the domain name she is considering is already in use by another company. She also knows she can check the ARIN Web site for IP address registration information.

Project 5.1

To do a WHOIS query on the NSI Web site, perform the following steps:

1. Open your Web browser.

2. In the address bar of the browser, type "http://www.nsiregistry.net".

3. Press Enter on the keyboard.

4. After the NSI Web site opens, click on Registry WHOIS.

5. In the Search Registry WHOIS field, type a domain name—for example, microsoft.com or yahoo.com.

When a domain name WHOIS query is done on this particular site, the result will tell you the domain name you looked up, the registrar of the domain name, the WHOIS server name, the referral URL, and the name servers for that particular domain name. This information can be vital if your chosen domain name is already being used.

Project 5.2

**To research IP address registration services at the ARIN Web site,
perform the following steps:**

1. Open your browser.

2. In the address bar of the browser, type "http://www.arin.net".

3. Press Enter on the keyboard.

4. After the ARIN homepage loads, scroll down to Registration Services and
   click on that option.

5. After the Registration Services page loads, research the fee schedule for IP
   addresses.

The Registration Services page describes the fee schedule for the various versions
of IP addressing and explains what those fees are based on. Phone numbers appear
on the left side of the screen as the page is scrolled down for the IP Registration
Services Help Desk.

5

CHAPTER SIX

Domain Name System (DNS) Servers

After completing this chapter, you will be able to:

✓ Understand what a DNS server is

✓ Understand what a Dynamic DNS server is

✓ Understand Dynamic Update for DNS

✓ Understand Secure Dynamic Update

✓ Identify and use the different DNS server types

✓ Plan for DNS servers and their capacity

✓ Place DNS servers

✓ Prioritize local subnets for DNS

✓ Understand DNS zones

✓ Understand the differences in zones and domains

✓ Understand zone replication and zone transfer needs

✓ Understand incremental zone tranfers and DNS notify

✓ Understand the aging and scavenging features

✓ Understand DNS database files and DNS-related files

✓ Understand the cache file

✓ Understand the reverse lookup file

✓ Understand the DNS Server boot file

✓ Monitor server performance

✓ Understand the sample DNS server performance test results

✓ Identify DNS server performance counters

This chapter is an overview of Domain Name System (DNS) servers and the different types that can be configured: primary, secondary, caching-only, and multihomed. We will discuss local subnet prioritization for DNS server implementations as well. We will touch on zones and domains to continue building on information from previous chapters, as well as the DNS database file and its resource records (RRs). The last part of this chapter deals with monitoring server performance.

DNS Servers

DNS servers take name requests from clients and resolve these computer or domain names to IP addresses. If the DNS server is not able to resolve the request, it may forward the request to one that can. DNS servers are grouped into different levels, called *domains*. DNS unto itself is a static service; someone has to enter the names and IP addresses manually before the DNS server can resolve them. A network consisting of a single network segment does not need to implement a DNS server because host names can be resolved by broadcasting.

Windows 2000 is more heavily dependent on DNS than was Windows NT 4, because of the implementation of Active Directory. Windows NT and Windows 2000 servers can interoperate as long as the communication is with other Windows-based computers. If the network is operating with the NetBEUI protocol commonly used for small workgroups, it will need a gateway service enabled because it is not routable. If you are performing routing between servers, you must use a routable protocol, such as TCP/IP. Windows NT attempts to send computer names across TCP/IP; if there is a router between two PCs, Windows NT will rely on a Windows Internet Name Service (WINS) server to pass the computer name and other NetBIOS information between the two computers. This environment would be better served if all the DNS servers were upgraded to Windows 2000 servers, thus avoiding interoperability issues.

The four types of DNS server implementations are:

➤ *Primary*—The primary point of update

➤ *Secondary*—Used for backup purposes

➤ *Caching-only*—Caches learned names

➤ *Multihomed*—Services more than one subnet

We will discuss each type of DNS server, but first we are going to explain the dynamic domain name server (DDNS) and its use of dynamic updates for a DNS server implementation.

Dynamic Domain Name Server (DDNS)

DDNS is fully integrated with the DNS service and the Dynamic Host Configuration Protocol (DHCP) service in Windows 2000 Server to gain all the benefits of the TCP/IP protocol and Internet-standards-based name resolution. This integration allows for name resolution maintenance that is dynamic, so the DNS service does not have to be administered or updated manually on the server.

When DDNS is enabled, it can perform forward lookups for existing WINS servers. This lets DDNS clients resolve names registered with WINS. Windows 2000 Server uses the WINS service for backward compatibility issues so that existing hosts configured for WINS won't have to be reconfigured.

Dynamic Update

DNS client computers can register and dynamically update their RRs with a DNS server whenever changes occur. This reduces the need for manual administration of zone records, especially for clients that frequently move or change locations and use DHCP to obtain an IP address.

Windows 2000 provides client and server support for the use of dynamic updates, as described in Request for Comments (RFC) 2136. For DNS servers, the DNS service allows dynamic update to be enabled or disabled on a per-zone basis at each server configured to load either a standard primary or directory-integrated zone. By default, client computers running under any version of Windows 2000 dynamically update their host (the 'A' or address record) RRs in DNS when configured for TCP/IP.

How Windows 2000 Clients Update DNS Names

Computers that run Windows 2000 are, by default, statically configured for TCP/IP and attempt to dynamically register host address records (A) and pointer records (PTR, usually for reverse lookup) RRs for IP addresses configured and used by their installed network. All computers, by default, register records based on their full computer name. For Windows 2000 computers, the primary full computer name, a fully qualified domain name (FQDN), is based on the primary DNS suffix of the computer, appended to the computer name.

Both of these settings are displayed or configured from the Network Identification tab in System Properties. You can send for dynamic updates when an IP address is added, removed, or modified in the TCP/IP properties configuration for any installed network connection or when an IP address lease changes or renews with the DHCP server—for example, when you start the computer or use the **ipconfig /renew** command. The **ipconfig /registerdns** command manually forces a refresh of the client name registration in DNS.

When one of the previous events triggers a dynamic update, the DHCP client service sends updates. This is designed so that if a change to the IP address information occurs because of DHCP, corresponding updates in DNS are performed to synchronize name-to-address mappings for the computer. The DHCP client service performs this function for all network connections used on the system, including those not configured to use DHCP.

Dynamic updates are performed differently for Windows 2000 computers that use DHCP to obtain their IP addresses. The update process described in this section assumes Windows 2000 installation defaults are in effect. You can tune specific names and update behavior where advanced TCP/IP properties are configured to use nondefault DNS settings. In addition to the full computer name (or primary name), you can configure connection-specific DNS names, as well as register or update them in DNS.

How Dynamic Update Works

For Windows 2000, dynamic updates are typically requested when either a DNS name or IP address changes on the computer. Suppose a client named oldhost is first configured in System Properties with the names shown in Table 6.1.

In this example, no connection-specific DNS domain names are configured for the computer. Later, the computer is renamed newhost, resulting in the changes on the system, as shown in Table 6.2.

Once the name change is applied in System Properties, Windows 2000 prompts you to restart the computer. When the computer restarts Windows, the DHCP client service performs a sequence of events to update DNS:

1. First the DHCP client service sends a Start of Authority (SOA) query using the DNS domain name of the computer. The client computer uses the currently configured FQDN of the computer (such as newhost.example.microsoft.com) as the name specified in the query.

2. Then an authoritative DNS server for the zone containing the client FQDN responds to the SOA query. For standard primary zones, the primary server returned in the SOA query response is fixed and static. It always matches the

Table 6.1 Example computer and DNS names.

Computer Name	DNS Domain Name of Computer	Full Computer Name
Oldhost	example.microsoft.com	oldhost.example.microsoft.com

Table 6.2 Example computer name changes.

Computer Name	DNS Domain Name of Computer	Full Computer Name
Newhost	example.microsoft.com	newhost.example.microsoft.com

exact DNS name as it appears in the SOA resource record stored with the zone. If the zone being updated is directory-integrated, any DNS server loading the zone can respond and dynamically insert its own name as the primary server of the zone in the SOA query response.

3. The DHCP client service then attempts to contact the primary DNS server. The client processes the SOA query response for its name to determine the IP address of the DNS server authorized as the primary server for accepting its name. It then performs a sequence of steps—as needed—to contact and dynamically update its primary server.

4. The DHCP client service sends a dynamic update request to the primary server determined in the SOA query response. If the update succeeds, no further action is taken. If this update fails, the client sends a Name Server (NS) query for the zone name specified in the SOA record. When it receives a response to this query, it sends an SOA query to the first DNS server listed in the response. After the SOA query is resolved, the client sends a dynamic update to the server specified in the returned SOA record. If the update succeeds, no further action is taken. If it fails, then the client repeats the SOA query process by sending to the next DNS server listed in the response.

5. Once the primary server that can perform the update is contacted, the client sends the update request, and the server processes it. The contents of the update request include instructions to add A (and possibly PTR) RRs for newhost.example.microsoft.com and remove these same record types for oldhost.example.microsoft.com, the name that was previously registered. The server also checks to ensure that updates are permitted for the client request. For standard primary zones, dynamic updates are not secured, so any client attempt to update succeeds. For Active Directory-integrated zones, updates are secured and performed using directory-based security settings.

6. Dynamic updates are sent or refreshed periodically. By default, Windows 2000 sends a refresh once every 24 hours. If the update results in no changes to zone data, the zone remains at its current version and no changes are written. Updates result in actual zone changes or increased zone transfer only if names or addresses actually change. Names are not removed from DNS zones if they become inactive or are not updated within the refresh interval. DNS does not use a mechanism to release or tombstone names, although DNS clients do attempt to delete or update old name records when a new name or address change is applied.

7. When the DHCP client service registers A and PTR resource records for a Windows 2000 computer, it uses a default caching time-to-live (TTL) of 15 minutes for host records. This determines how long other DNS servers and clients cache a computer's records when they are included in a query response.

Secure Dynamic Update

For Windows 2000, DNS update security is available only for zones that are integrated into Active Directory. Once you directory-integrate a zone, access control list (ACL) editing features are available in the DNS console, so you can add or remove users or groups from the ACL for a specified zone or RR.

By default, dynamic update security for Windows 2000 DNS servers and clients is to use unsecured dynamic update first. If an unsecured update is refused, clients try to use secure update. Also, clients use a default update policy that permits them to attempt to overwrite a previously registered RR, unless they are specifically blocked by update security.

Once a zone becomes Active Directory-integrated, Windows 2000 DNS servers default to allowing only secure dynamic updates. When using standard zone storage, the default for the DNS Server service is not to allow dynamic updates on its zones. For zones that are either directory-integrated or use standard file-based storage, you can change the zone to allow all dynamic updates, which permit all updates to be accepted, bypassing the use of secure updates. For Windows 2000 Server, the DHCP Server service can perform proxy registration and updates of DNS records for legacy clients that do not support dynamic updates.

If you use multiple Windows 2000 DHCP servers on your network and configure your zones to allow secure dynamic updates only, you need to use the Active Directory Users and Computers MMC snap-in to add your DHCP server computers to the built-in DnsUpdateProxyGroup. This will permit all of your DHCP servers the secure rights to perform proxy updates for any of your DHCP clients.

For Windows 2000, the use of secure dynamic updates can be compromised by running a DHCP server on a domain controller when Windows 2000 DHCP Server is configured to perform registration of DNS records on behalf of its clients. To avoid this issue, deploy DHCP servers and domain controllers on separate computers. If you are unconcerned about security of reverse lookup records, then this precaution is advisable only if the DHCP server is configured to perform registration of host (A) records on behalf of its clients.

DNS Server Types

As mentioned previously, you can use four DNS server implementation types in a network environment. Each type has a specific use to meet different network needs, and each is configured differently to reflect those needs.

To install a DNS server:

1. Click on Start.

2. Point to Settings.

3. Click on Control Panel.

4. Double-click on Add/Remove Programs.

5. Click on Add/Remove Windows Components button, as shown in Figure 6.1.

Primary Name Server

The primary server for a zone acts as the zone's point of update. Windows 2000 Active Directory has a multimaster replication engine, whereas conventional DNS servers use single-master replication. Network administrators can centralize and simplify overall system management by not having to maintain a separate replication topology for DNS. Using Active Directory with new features and enhancements will provide greater reliability.

Adding a Primary Server for an Existing Zone

The primary servers at the zone's point of update when created are always this type. With Windows 2000 Server, you can use primary zones in one of two ways: as standard primary zones or primary zones integrated with Active Directory.

For standard primary-type zones, only a single server can host and load the master copy of the zone. If you create a zone and keep it as a standard primary zone, no additional primary servers for the zone are permitted. Only one server is allowed to accept dynamic updates and process zone changes.

The standard primary model suggests a single point of failure. If for any reason the primary server for a zone is unavailable to the network, no dynamic updates to the zone will be made. The queries for names in the zone are not affected and can continue uninterrupted as long as secondary servers for the zone are available to respond.

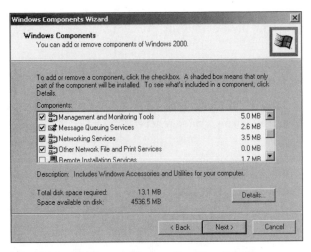

Figure 6.1   Add/Remove Windows Components button.

In Windows 2000 Server, you can add primary servers to a zone by using the directory-integrated storage and replication features of the DNS service. To do this, you need to change a zone and integrate it into Active Directory. You can integrate an existing zone into Active Directory by changing the type of zone at the originating primary server where it was first created. Once the zone type is changed from standard primary to Active Directory-integrated, you can add the zone to other DNS servers by configuring them to use the Boot from DS option when they initialize the DNS service.

When the Boot from DS option is selected, other DNS servers operating as part of the Active Directory domain namespace can query the directory and automatically load all directory-integrated zones that are stored in the directory database. No other steps are necessary. With the Boot from DS option, any DNS servers operating as part of Active Directory are by default also primary servers for directory-integrated zones.

Secondary Name Servers

DNS design specifications recommend that at least two DNS servers be used to host each zone. For directory-integrated primary zones, secondary servers are supported but not required. Secondary servers can provide a means to offload DNS query traffic in areas of the network where a zone is heavily queried and used. Additionally, if a primary server is down, a secondary server can provide some name resolution in the zone until the primary server is available.

Implementing and Configuring

When adding a secondary server, locate it as close as possible to clients with a big demand for names used in a zone. Also, consider placing secondary servers across a router, either on other subnets when on a routed LAN or across WAN links. This will provide for good use of a secondary server as a local backup in cases where an intermediate network link is slow or becomes the point of failure between DNS servers and clients in that zone.

Because a primary server always maintains the master copy of updates and changes to the zone, a secondary server relies on DNS zone transfer mechanisms to obtain its information and keep it current. Issues such as using either full or incremental zone transfers are more applicable with secondary servers.

Advantages

In considering the impact of secondary server zone transfers, consider their advantage as a backup source of information and measure this against the added cost they impose on your network infrastructure. A simple rule is that for each secondary server added, network usage increases, and so does the time required to synchronize the zone at all secondary servers.

Secondary servers are most heavily used for forward lookup zones. If you are using reverse lookup zones, you can assume that you do not need to add as many secondary servers for those zones. Typically, a secondary server for a reverse lookup zone is not used outside of the network and subnet that correspond to the reverse zone.

Caching-Only Servers

Caching-only DNS servers do not host any zones and thus are not authoritative for a particular domain. They are servers that build a local cache of names they learned while performing queries for their clients. This information is then available when answering subsequent client queries.

Implementing and Configuring

To install a caching-only DNS server, install a DNS server on the server computer. Do not configure the DNS server to load any zones and verify server root hints (i.e., DNS root servers' IP addresses) are configured or updated correctly. When operating the computer as a DNS server, you should manually configure TCP/IP and use a static IP address.

Advantages

When this server is started, it has no cached information, which is obtained over time as client requests are serviced. If you have a slow-speed WAN link between sites, this option might be ideal, because after the cache is built, traffic will decrease. Also the caching-only server does not perform zone transfers, which are network intensive in WAN environments. A caching-only DNS server can even be valuable at a local site where a separate domain or zone is not needed or cannot be created.

Multihomed DNS Servers

DNS servers that are multihomed are set up as such because they have to service multiple subnets. They can be set up as any of the DNS server types. They will most likely be primary name servers but can also be master name servers or caching-only servers. The only real feature that sets them apart is having multiple network interfaces. Multihomed DNS servers add to the complexity of configuring the DNS service.

When multihomed DNS servers configure the DNS service, they can selectively enable and bind only to IP addresses that are specified in the DNS console. By default, the DNS service binds to all IP interfaces configured for the computer. This can include any additional IP addresses configured for a single network connection. DNS servers can restrict DNS service for selected IP addresses. When this feature is used, the DNS service listens for and answers only those DNS requests that are sent to the IP addresses specified on the Interface tab in Server Properties.

When to Specify Interfaces

By default, the DNS service listens to all IP addresses and accepts all client requests sent to its default service port, which is User Datagram Protocol (UDP) 53 or Transmission Control Protocol (TCP) 53 for zone transfer requests. Some DNS resolvers require that the source address of a DNS response be the same as the destination address used in the query. If these addresses differ, clients can reject the response. To accommodate these resolvers, you can specify the list of allowed interfaces for the DNS server. When a list is set, the DNS service binds sockets to allow only the IP addresses used on the computer.

In addition to providing support for clients that require explicit bindings to be used, specifying interfaces can be useful for other reasons—especially if you don't want some IP addresses or interfaces or if the server computer is configured to use a large number of IP addresses and you do not want the added expense of binding to all of them.

Additional Considerations

When configuring additional IP addresses and enabling them for use with the Windows 2000 DNS server, consider that additional system resources will be consumed at the server computer. DNS server performance overhead increases slightly, which can affect DNS query reception for the server. Although Windows 2000 provides the means to configure multiple IP addresses for use with any installed network adapters, there is no performance benefit for doing so. Even if the DNS server is handling multiple zones registered for Internet use, you do not have to have different IP addresses registered for each zone.

When adding IP addresses for multihomed DNS server use, each address might only slightly increase server performance. Realize that when a large number of IP addresses are enabled for use, server performance can degrade noticeably. In general, when adding network adapter hardware to the server computer, assign only a single primary IP address for each network connection. Whenever possible, remove nonessential IP addresses from existing server TCP/IP configurations as well.

Server Planning for DNS

When planning DNS servers, you need to perform capacity planning and review server hardware requirements, as well as determine how many DNS servers are needed and their role in the network. When considering the number of DNS servers to use, decide which ones will host primary and secondary copies of zones. Also, if using Active Directory, determine whether the server computer will perform as a domain controller or a member server for the domain. Decide where DNS servers are going to be placed on the network, taking into consideration traffic loads, replication, and fault tolerance. Decide whether to use only Windows 2000 DNS servers for all DNS servers or to operate a mixture of Windows and other DNS server implementations.

Server Capacity Planning

Planning and deploying DNS servers on a network involves examining several aspects of a network and the capacity requirements for any DNS servers intended for use in it. Some questions to consider include:

➤ How many zones are the DNS servers expected to load and host?

➤ For each zone the server is loading for service, how large is the zone (based on the size of the zone file or the number of RRs used in the zone)?

➤ For a multihomed DNS server, how many interfaces are to be enabled for listening to and servicing DNS clients on each of the server's connected subnets?

➤ How many total or overall DNS query requests, from all of its clients, is a DNS server expected to receive and service?

In many cases, adding RAM to a DNS server can provide the most noticeable improvements in performance. This is because the DNS server service fully loads all of its configured zones into memory at startup. If your server is operating and loading a large number of zones, and dynamic updates occur frequently for zone clients, additional memory can be helpful. Keep in mind that for typical usage, the DNS server consumes system memory as follows:

➤ The DNS server uses approximately 4MB of RAM when you start it without any zones.

➤ For each addition of a zone or RR, the DNS server consumes additional server memory.

➤ For the addition of every RR to a server zone, an average of approximately 100 bytes of server memory is used. For example, if you add a zone containing 1,000 RRs to a server, it will require approximately 100KB of server memory.

In determining server plans, start by reviewing sample DNS server performance test results collected by the Windows 2000 DNS development and testing teams. In addition, use DNS server-related counters provided for use with Windows 2000 monitoring tools to obtain performance measurements for Windows 2000 DNS servers deployed on a network.

Note: The previous recommendations are not intended to indicate maximum performance or limitations for Windows 2000 DNS servers. These numbers are approximate and can be influenced by the type of RRs entered in zones, the number of RRs with the same owner name, and the number of zones in use at a specific DNS server.

Where to Place DNS Servers

In general, place DNS servers at a location on a network that is centrally accessible to clients. It is often most practical to use a DNS server on each subnet. Consider these questions when deciding where the network needs a DNS server:

➤ If deploying DNS to support Active Directory, is the DNS server computer also a domain controller or likely to be promoted to one in the future?

➤ If the DNS server stops responding, are its local clients able to gain access to an alternative DNS server?

➤ If the DNS server is located on a subnet that is remote to some of its clients, what other DNS servers or name resolution options are available if the routed connection stops responding?

For all DNS server installations, including those in which the use of Active Directory is not an issue, you can use the following server placement and planning guidelines. If a routed LAN and high-speed links are fairly reliable, one DNS server might be sufficient for a larger, multiple subnetted network area. For a high number of client nodes on a single subnet design, add more than one DNS server to the subnet to provide backup and failover if the preferred DNS server stops responding.

When determining the number of DNS servers needed, assess the effect of zone transfers and DNS query traffic on slower links in your network. Although DNS is designed to help reduce broadcast traffic between local subnets, it does create some traffic between servers and clients that you should review, particularly when used in complexly routed LAN or WAN environments.

Consider the effects of zone transfer over slower speed links, such as those typically used for a WAN connection. Although the DNS service supports incremental zone transfers and Windows 2000 DNS clients and servers can cache recently used names, traffic considerations are sometimes still an issue, particularly when DHCP leases are shortened and, as a result, dynamic updates in DNS are performed more frequently. One option for dealing with remote locations on WAN links is to set up a DNS server at these locations to provide caching-only DNS service.

With most installations, at least two server computers should be hosting DNS zones for fault tolerance. DNS was designed to have two servers for each zone: one as a primary server and the other as a backup or secondary server. When making any final determinations about the number of servers to use, first assess the level of fault tolerance the network needs.

When only a single Windows 2000 server is used on a small LAN in a single-subnet environment, configure the single server to simulate both the primary and secondary servers for a zone. For best results and simplified DNS administration, consider using the DNS service supplied with Windows 2000 Server for all DNS servers. When administering zone files created by the DNS service, use the DNS console tool to make changes.

Another option is to administer all DNS zone files manually using any application that supports file saving in text mode. Select one method for editing zone files—whether it is manually in a text editor or by using the DNS console to modify them—and use it consistently for updating zones. This will help prevent having zone edits overwritten or rejected, which can happen if changes come from one method to another.

Prioritizing Local Subnets

By default, the DNS service uses local subnet prioritizing as the method for giving preference to IP addresses on the same network when a client query resolves to a host name that is mapped to more than one IP address. This feature requires that the client application attempt to connect to the host using its closest and usually fastest IP address connection. The DNS service uses local subnet priority as follows:

1. The DNS service determines if local subnet prioritization is needed to order the query response. If more than one A resource record matches the queried host name, the DNS service can reorder the records by their subnet location. If the queried host name matches only a single A resource record, or if the IP network address of the client does not match an IP network address for any of the mapped addresses in an answer list of multiple RRs, no prioritizing is necessary.

2. For each RR in the matched answer list, the DNS service determines which records match the subnet location of the requesting client.

3. The DNS service reorders the answer list so that A resource records that match the local subnet of the requesting client are placed first in the answer list.

4. Prioritized by subnet order, the answer list is returned to the requesting client.

Simple Local Network Prioritizing

A multihomed computer, multihomed.example.microsoft.com, has three A resource records for its three separate host IP addresses in the example.microsoft.com zone. A separate A resource record is used for each of the host's addresses, which appear in this order in the zone:

```
multihomed    IN  A   192.168.1.27
multihomed    IN  A   10.0.0.14
multihomed    IN  A   172.16.20.4
```

If a DNS client resolver at IP address 10.4.3.2 queries the server for the IP addresses of host multihomed.example.microsoft.com, the DNS service notes that the originating IP network address (10.0.0.0) of the client matches the network class A portion of the 10.0.0.4 address in the answer list of RRs. The DNS service then reorders the addresses in the response as follows:

```
multihomed   IN  A   10.0.0.14
multihomed   IN  A   192.168.1.27
multihomed   IN  A   172.16.20.4
```

If the IP address of the requesting client has no local network match with any of the RRs in the answer list, then the list is not prioritized.

Complex Local Subnet Prioritizing

Only a few minor differences are apparent if you are working in a network that uses IP subnetting (nondefault subnet masks). If more than one address matches in the network portion, then the matching addresses are further ordered and the RR having the closest matching subnet address is placed first.

For example, a multihomed computer, multihomed.example.microsoft.com, has four A resource records for four separate host IP addresses in the example.microsoft.com zone. Two of these IP addresses are for nonlocal networks. The other two share a common IP network address but, because IP subnetting is used, represent different physical subnetted network connections based on their custom subnet mask value of 255.255.248.0. These example RRs appear in the following order in the zone:

```
multihomed   IN  A   192.168.1.27
multihomed   IN  A   172.16.22.4
multihomed   IN  A   10.0.0.14
multihomed   IN  A   172.16.31.5
```

If the IP address of the requesting client is 172.16.22.8, both of the IP addresses that match the same IP network as the client, 172.16.0.0, are returned at the top of the answer list to the client. In this example, however, the 172.16.22.4 address is placed ahead of 172.16.31.5, because it matches the client IP address down through the 172.16.20.0 subnet address.

```
multihomed   IN  A   172.16.22.4
multihomed   IN  A   172.16.31.5
multihomed   IN  A   192.168.1.27
multihomed   IN  A   10.0.0.14
```

Using a custom or nondefault subnet mask value with all IP addresses on your network imposes IP subnetting. Local subnet priority supersedes the use of round-robin rotation for multihomed names. When round robin is enabled, however, RRs continue to be rotated using round robin as the secondary method of sorting the response list.

DNS Zones

DNS allows a namespace to be divided into zones that store name information about one or more DNS domains. The zone becomes the authoritative source for information about the domain for each DNS domain name included in a zone. To understand zones better, you first must know the differences between zones and domains. Understanding zone replication and zone transfers, including incremental transfers and DNS notify, will also help.

The Differences between Zones and Domains

DNS zones and domains look and sound very much alike and can be confusing. A domain is any tree or subtree within the DNS namespace that often relates to an Active Directory domain. DNS domains should not be confused with Windows 2000 and Active Directory networking domains (physical network structures or groups of computers).

A zone in a DNS database is a subtree of the database that is administered as a single entity. As an administrative unit, it can contain a single domain or a domain with subdomains. A DNS zone is administered with one or more name servers.

A zone starts as a storage database for a single DNS domain name. If you add other domains below the domain used to create the zone, they can either be part of the same zone or belong to another zone. Once you add a subdomain, it can either be managed and included as part of the original zone records or delegated away to another zone created to support the subdomain.

Why Zone Replication and Zone Transfers Are Needed

If you use a single server that is not responding, queries for names in that zone can fail. A secondary name server provides availability and fault tolerance when resolving name queries. For additional servers to host a zone, zone transfers are required to replicate all copies of the zone to the other servers that host the zone.

If you add a new server to the network and configure it as a new secondary server for an existing zone, it performs a full initial transfer of the zone to obtain a full copy of records for the zone. Earlier DNS server implementations use a full transfer for a zone when the zone requires updating after changes are made. For Windows 2000 Server, the DNS service supports incremental zone transfers. This is a revised process for intermediate changes.

Incremental Zone Transfers

Incremental transfers that are supported by both a DNS server acting as the source for a zone and any servers that copy the zone from it provide a more efficient method of propagating zone changes and updates. In earlier DNS implementations, any request for an update of a zone required a full transfer of the entire zone database. With an incremental transfer, you can use a different type of query to let the secondary server pull only those zone changes it needs to synchronize its copy of the zone with its source—either a primary or secondary copy of the zone maintained by another DNS server.

An incremental zone transfer lets you determine differences between the source and replicated versions of the zone. If the zones are the same version, as indicated by the serial number field in the SOA resource record of each zone, no transfer is made. If the serial number for the zone is greater than at the requesting secondary server, a transfer is made of only those changes to RRs for each incremental version of the zone. For this incremental query to succeed and changes to be sent, the primary DNS server for the zone must keep a history of incremental zone changes to use when answering these queries. This means less traffic on a network, and zone transfers are done much faster.

DNS Notify

Windows DNS servers support DNS Notify, an update to the original DNS protocol specification that permits a means of initiating notification to secondary servers when zone changes occur (RFC 1996). DNS notification implements a push mechanism for notifying a select set of secondary servers for a zone when it is updated. Servers that are notified can then initiate a zone transfer to pull zone changes from their primary servers and update their local replicas of the zone.

To be notified by the DNS server acting as their configured source for a zone, each secondary server must first have its IP address in the notify list of the source server. When using the DNS console to manage zones loaded at Windows 2000 DNS servers, you will find this list maintained in the Notify dialog box, which is accessible from the Zone Transfer tab located in Zone Properties.

The DNS console permits the contents of the notify list to restrict or limit zone transfer access to only those secondary servers specified in the list. This can help stop attempts by unknown or unapproved DNS servers to pull zone updates.

The following is a brief summary of the typical DNS notification process for zone updates so the normal zone transfer process can continue:

1. The local zone at a DNS server acting as a master server is updated. When the zone is updated at the master or source server, the serial number field in the SOA resource record is also updated, indicating a new local version of the zone.

2. The master server sends a DNS notify message to other servers that are part of its configured notify list.

3. All secondary servers that receive the notify message then respond by initiating a zone transfer request back to the notifying master server.

Use DNS notification only to notify secondary servers for a zone. You do not need DNS notification for replication of directory-integrated zones. This is because any DNS server that loads a zone from Active Directory automatically polls the directory to update and refresh the zone approximately every 15 minutes. In these cases, configuring a notify list can actually degrade system performance by causing unnecessary additional transfer requests for the updated zone.

Aging and Scavenging

Windows 2000 DNS servers support aging and scavenging features. These features provide the mechanism for removing stale RRs that can accumulate in zone data over time and present problems. Stale RRs take up space on the server and increase time to load the zone data. Because of this, DNS server performance suffers. Also, a server might use a stale RR to answer queries addressed to the server, which could cause clients to experience name resolution problems on the network.

To solve these problems, the Windows 2000 DNS server can scavenge stale records; it can search the database for records that have aged and delete them. Administrators can control aging and scavenging by specifying which servers can scavenge zones, which zones can be scavenged, and which records must be scavenged if they become stale.

The DNS server uses an algorithm that ensures that it does not accidentally scavenge the records that must remain, provided that all the parameters are correctly configured. By default, the aging and scavenging mechanism is disabled at Windows 2000 DNS servers. All parameters should be completely understood before aging and scavenging is enabled. Otherwise, the server could be accidentally configured to delete records that should not be deleted. If a record is accidentally deleted, not only will users fail to resolve queries for that record, but also any user can create the record and take ownership of it, even on zones configured for secure dynamic update.

Before you can use the aging and scavenging features of Windows 2000 DNS, several conditions must be met:

➤ Scavenging and aging must be enabled both at the DNS server and on the zone.

➤ RRs must either be dynamically added to zones or manually modified to be used in aging and scavenging operations.

➤ Typically, only those RRs added dynamically using the DNS dynamic update protocol are subject to aging and scavenging.

Caching and Time to Live

The TTL field is optional for most records. It indicates a length of time used by other DNS servers to determine how long to cache information for a record before expiring and discarding it. Most RRs created by the DNS server service have a minimum or default TTL of one hour from the SOA record; this prevents overlong caching by other DNS servers. You can, however, specify a record-specific TTL that overrides the default. You may also use a value of zero (0) for RRs that contain important data that should not be cached for use after the current query is completed.

Negative Caching

Negative caching is the storage of the fact that the requested information does not exist. In the same way that you can cache the fact that an RR exists and has a particular value, you can cache a nonexistent RR or name server.

Negative caching is useful in that it reduces the response time for negative answers. It also reduces the number of messages that have to be sent between resolvers and name servers, decreasing overall network traffic generated by these messages. A large proportion of the DNS traffic on the Internet could be eliminated if all resolvers implemented negative caching.

DNS Database Files and DNS-Related Files

The Windows 2000 DNS implementation has related files incorporated into it so that it can be configured for various reasons, relating mainly to interoperability issues. Each file—the Berkeley Internet Name Domain (BIND) boot configuration file, cache.dns, root.dns, and zone_name.dns—has its own functionality that relates to the proper functioning of the DNS service.

The DNS console does not create the BIND boot configuration file; however, as an optional configuration for the DNS server service, it can be copied from another DNS server running the BIND server implementation. To use this file with the DNS server service, you need to click on the Boot from File option in Server Properties. On BIND servers, this file is often called named.boot.

The cache.dns file is used to preload RRs into the DNS server names cache. Windows 2000 DNS servers use this file to help locate root servers on either a network or the Internet. By default, this file contains DNS resource records that prime the local cache of the server with the addresses of authoritative root servers for the Internet. If you are setting up a DNS server to resolve Internet DNS names, the information in this file is required unless another DNS server is enabled for use as a forwarder to resolve these names.

Note: Traffic to the Internet root servers is heavy, but because host names are not usually resolved at this level, the load can be reasonably handled. Instead, the root hints file provides referral information that can be useful during DNS name resolution to redirect a query to other servers that are authoritative for names located beneath the root. For DNS servers operating privately on your internal network, the DNS console can learn and replace the contents of this file with internal root servers on your network, provided they are reachable through the network when you are setting up and configuring new DNS servers. It can be updated using the DNS console from the Root Hints tab located under the applicable server properties. This file preloads the server names cache when it is started.

The root.dns, or root zone, file can appear at a computer running as a Windows 2000 DNS server, if it is configured as a root server for a network.

The zone_name.dns file is used when a standard zone, either primary or secondary, is added and configured for a server. Files of this type are not created or used for primary type zones that are directory-integrated, which are stored in the Active Directory database.

Note: You can find all of these files in the %SystemRoot%\System32\Dns folder on the server computer.

Database File

By default, Microsoft Windows NT comes with a file called place.dns. It is a template that you can use to build a database file. Microsoft recommends copying this file to another file with a name that matches your domain. The database file, zone.dns, stores RRs for a domain. You should edit and rename this file before using it on a production DNS server. Naming this file the same as the zone it represents is generally a good idea. The database file always begins with an SOA record, which is responsible for defining the general parameters of the DNS zone.

The database file may also contain name server records that list additional DNS servers. This is the file that will be replicated between primary and secondary servers. Another optional component of a database file is a host record, which you use to make a static association between a host name and an IP address.

Another component of a database file is a canonical name (CNAME) record, explained in more detail later in the chapter. With this record you can assign more than one host name to a single IP address, allowing you to use multiple aliases to a single domain.

To update server data files manually:

1. Click on Start.

2. Point to Programs.

3. Point to Administrative Tools.

4. Click on DNS.

For standard primary zones, this procedure causes the DNS server immediately to write its in-memory changes out to disk for storage with the zone file. Normally, these changes are written only at predefined update intervals and only when the DNS server is shut down. For Active Directory-integrated zones, this procedure does not apply because most changes to directory-integrated zone data are written immediately back to the applicable directory-integrated zone database.

Name Server Records

You can use Name Server (NS) resource records to assign authority to specified servers for a DNS domain name in two ways:

➤ By indicating authoritative DNS servers for any subdomains that are delegated away from the zone.

➤ By making a list of authoritative servers for the domain so those servers can be made known to others that request information about this domain (zone).

In the case of assigning servers with host names in the same zone, corresponding address RRs are normally used in the zone to resolve the names of specified servers to their IP addresses. For servers that are specified using this RR as part of a zone delegation to a subdomain, the NS resource record usually contains out-of-zone names. For the out-of-zone names to be resolved, you may need address RRs for the specified out-of-zone servers. When these out-of-zone address records are needed to provide delegation, they are known as *glue records*.

Database File Records

The DNS database file has a number of records associated with it. Each record has a purpose within the database for the proper function of the DNS implementation on a name server.

Start of Authority Record

Zones are based on the concept of server authority. When a DNS server is configured to load a zone, it uses two types of RRs to determine the authoritative properties of the zone:

➤ *SOA*—Indicates the name of origin for the zone and contains the name of the server that is the primary source for information about the zone.

➤ *NS*—Notates which DNS servers are designated as authoritative for the zone. A server listed in the NS record becomes known to others as an authoritative server for the zone. This means that any server specified in the NS resource record is to be considered an authoritative source by others and is able to answer with certainty any queries made for names included in the zone.

The SOA and NS records are required for any zone and are typically the first RRs listed in files. By default, the Add New Zone wizard automatically creates these records when a new primary zone is added using the DNS snap-in.

The SOA resource record is always first in any standard zone. It indicates the DNS server that either originally created it or is now the primary server for the zone. It is also used to store other properties, such as version information and timings that affect zone renewal or expiration. These properties affect how often transfers of the zone are done between servers authoritative for the zone.

The SOA resource record contains the following fields:

➤ *Primary Server (the owner)*—The Primary DNS server's host name.

➤ *Responsible Person*—Contains the email address of the person responsible for administering the zone. Note that a period (.) is used instead of an at sign (@) in the email name. For example, Some_Admin@Microsoft.com would be Some_Admin.Microsoft.com.

➤ *Serial Number*—The version or revision level of the zone file; it is also used to synchronize replication.

➤ *Refresh Interval*—The time, in seconds, that a secondary DNS server waits before querying its source for the zone to attempt renewal of the zone. The default field is 900 seconds.

➤ *Retry Interval*—The time, in seconds, a secondary server waits before retrying a failed zone transfer. The default value is 600 seconds.

➤ *Expire Interval*—The time, in seconds, before a secondary server stops responding to queries after a lapsed refresh interval where the zone was not refreshed or updated. The default value is 86,400 seconds.

➤ *TTL Value*—The minimum default value applied to all RRs. The default value is 3,600 seconds.

The following is an example of an SOA resource record:

```
@   IN  SOA     nameserver.microsoft.com.  Some_Admin.microsoft.com.
(   1           ; serial number
3600            ; refresh    [1h]
600             ; retry      [10minutes]
86400           ; expire     [1d]
3600 )          ; min TTL    [1h]
```

To modify the SOA record for a zone:

1. Open DNS by clicking on Start | Programs | Administrative Tools | DNS.

2. In the console tree, click on the applicable zone.

3. On the Action menu, click on Properties.

4. Click on the SOA tab.

5. Make the appropriate changes desired.

6. Click on OK to save changes.

Host (A) Address Resource Record

A host (A) address RR maps a DNS domain name to an IP version 4, 32-bit address. An example of a host address RR: host1.example.microsoft.com.

The fields used in a host RR include:

➤ *Owner*—Indicates the DNS domain name that owns an RR. This name is the same as that of the console tree node where an RR is located.

➤ *TTL*—For most RRs, this field is optional. It indicates a length of time used by other DNS servers to determine how long to cache information for a record before expiring and discarding it. (Default TTL is one hour from the SOA.)

➤ *Class*—Contains standard mnemonic text indicating the class of the RR. For example, a setting of "IN" indicates that the RR belongs to the Internet class, which is the only one supported by Windows 2000 DNS servers. This field is required.

➤ *Type*—Contains standard mnemonic text indicating the type of the RR. For example, a mnemonic of "A" indicates that the RR stores host address information. This field is required.

➤ *Record-specific data*—A required, variable-length field that contains information describing the resource. The format of this information varies according to the type and class of the RR.

Canonical Name (CNAME) Record

An Alias (CNAME) RR is sometimes called a canonical name. It maps an aliased or alternative DNS domain name in the owner field to a canonical or primary DNS domain name specified in the canonical_name field. The canonical or primary DNS domain name used in the data is required and must resolve to a valid DNS domain name in the namespace.

These records allow for more than one name to point to a single host, so the same computer could host both an FTP server and a Web server. For example, the server names ftp and www are registered using CNAME RRs that map to the DNS host name, such as server-1, for the server computer that hosts these services.

CNAME RRs are recommended when:

➤ A host specified in an address RR in the same zone needs to be renamed.

➤ A generic name for a well-known server, such as www, needs to resolve to a group of individual computers, with each having an individual address RR that provides for the same service.

In this example, a computer named host-a.example.microsoft.com needs to function as both a Web server named **www.example.microsoft.com**. and an FTP server named **ftp.example.microsoft.com**. To achieve the intended use for naming this computer, add and use the following CNAME entries in the **example.microsoft.com** zone:

```
host-a    IN  A      20.0.0.10
ftp       IN  CNAME  host-a
www       IN  CNAME  host-a
```

Be conservative in adding alias records to zones. Avoid using CNAME records where they do not need to alias host names used in host address RRs. Also, ensure that any alias names are not used in other RRs.

Pointer (PTR) Record

Pointer (PTR) resource records support the reverse lookup process, based on zones created and rooted in the in-addr.arpa domain. These records are used to locate a computer by its IP address and resolve this information to the DNS domain name for that computer. In most cases, each record provides information that points to another DNS domain name location, such as a corresponding host address RR in a forward lookup zone.

You can add PTR resource records to a zone by doing the following:

➤ Manually create a PTR resource record for a static TCP/IP client computer using the DNS snap-in.

➤ If you are running Windows 2000, you can use the DHCP client service to dynamically register and update the PTR resource record in DNS when an IP configuration change occurs.

➤ All other DHCP client computers can have their PTR RRs registered and updated by the DHCP server if they obtain their IP lease from a qualified server. The Windows 2000 DHCP service provides this capability.

Host Information Record

The host information (HINFO) resource record specifies the type of CPU and operating system in the cpu_type and os_type fields, respectively, for the host DNS domain name in the owner field. Well-known CPU and operating system types that are most often used are noted in RFC 1700. This information can be used by application protocols, such as FTP, which uses special procedures when communicating with computers of a known CPU and operating system type.

Mail Exchanger Record

Email applications use the Mail Exchanger (MX) resource record to locate a mail server based on a DNS domain name used in the destination address for the recipient of a message. For example, a DNS query for the name example.microsoft.com could be used to find an MX resource record, enabling an email application to forward or exchange mail to a user with the email address user@example.microsoft.com.

An MX record provides message routing to a specified mail exchange host that is acting as a mail exchanger for a specified DNS domain name. MX records use a 16-bit integer to indicate host priority in message routing where multiple mail exchange hosts are specified. For each mail exchange host specified in this record type, a corresponding host address record is needed. A two-digit preference value indicates preferred ordering if multiple exchanger hosts are specified.

Service Locator Record

The service locator (SRV) resource record allows multiple servers providing a similar TCP/IP-based service to be located using a single DNS query operation. In Windows 2000 Server, it provides the means to locate domain controllers that use Lightweight Directory Access Protocol (LDAP) service over TCP port 389.

Locating Active Directory domain controllers in Windows 2000 requires SRV resource records. Typically, you can avoid manual administration of the SRV resource record when installing Active Directory.

By default, the Active Directory installation wizard attempts to locate a DNS server configured in any of its TCP/IP client properties, for any of its active network connections. If a DNS server is contacted, the configuration process is complete. If a DNS server is not found, a Windows 2000 DNS server can be installed locally and automatically configured with a zone that is based on the Active Directory domain.

AAAA Resource Record

The AAAA RR is used to define a relationship between a computer name and an IP address in IPv6 format. These are currently very rare, but as IP ranges are depleted under the existing notation, they will become the standard.

The fields used in an AAAA RR include:

➤ *Name field*—Enter the name of the host that you are assigning to a specific IP address. This host is considered to own the IP address. The host's TCP/IP name can be found in the Windows NT Network control panel.

➤ *IPv6 Address field*—Enter the IPv6 format static IP Address that is being assigned to the host.

➤ *Comment field*—enter a descriptive comment for this resource record in this field. This is an optional field.

➤ *Associations button*—Click this button to invoke the Record Associations dialog box. This dialog box is provided as a convenient way to create other resource records that are related to the currently selected AAAA record. For example, use it to add related CNAME records.

Only create AAAA records for static IP addresses. You can use dynamic DNS to create AAAA records for local computers that obtain an IPv6 lease from the DHCP server. IPv6 format IP Addresses should not be made part of a lease pool and should not be assigned to a user through the Meta IP RADIUS Framed IP Protocol attribute or the Attributes tab of the Meta IP/User dialog box. Assigning the same IP Address in more than one area will result in an IP address conflict (between the static address and valid DHCP lease).

Cache File

Cache.dns is used to preload RRs into the DNS server names cache. Windows 2000 DNS servers use this file to help locate root servers on either your network or the Internet.

By default, this file contains DNS resource records that prime the local cache of the server with the addresses of authoritative root servers for the Internet. If you are setting up a DNS server to resolve Internet DNS names, the information in this file is required unless you enable the use of another DNS server as a forwarder to resolve these names.

Traffic to the Internet root servers is heavy, but because host names are not usually resolved at this level, the load can be reasonably handled. Instead, the root hints file provides referral information that can be useful during DNS name resolution to redirect a query to other servers that are authoritative for names located beneath the root.

For DNS servers operating privately on your internal network, the DNS console can learn and replace the contents of the cache file with internal root servers on your network, provided they are reachable through the network when you are setting up and configuring new DNS servers. It can be updated using the DNS console from the Root Hints tab located under the applicable server properties.

The Reverse Lookup File

In most DNS lookups, clients perform a forward lookup, which is a search based on the DNS name of another computer as stored in an address RR. This type of query expects an IP address as the resource data for the response.

DNS also provides a reverse lookup process. This lets clients use a known IP address during a name query and look up a computer name based on its address. A reverse lookup takes the form of a question, such as, "Can you tell me the DNS name of the computer that uses the IP address 194.158.1.10?"

DNS was not originally designed to support this type of query. One issue for supporting the reverse query process is the difference in how the DNS namespace organizes and indexes names and how IP addresses are assigned. If the only method to answer the previous question were to search in all domains in the DNS namespace, a reverse query would take too long and require too much processing to be useful.

To resolve this issue, a special in-addr.arpa domain was defined in the DNS standards and reserved in the Internet DNS namespace to provide a practical and reliable way to perform reverse queries. To create the reverse namespace, subdomains within the in-addr.arpa domain are formed using the reverse ordering of the numbers in the dotted-decimal notation of IP addresses.

This reversed ordering of the domains for each octet value is needed because, unlike DNS names, when IP addresses are read from left to right, they are interpreted in the opposite manner. When an IP address is read, it is viewed from its most generalized information from left to right, with the IP network address in the first part of the address to the more specific information the IP host address contains in the last part. For this reason, you must reverse the order of IP address octets when building the in-addr.arpa domain tree. With this arrangement, administering lower limbs of the DNS in-addr.arpa tree can be given to companies as they are assigned a specific or limited set of IP addresses within the Internet-defined address classes.

The in-addr.arpa domain tree, as built into DNS, requires that an additional RR type, the PTR, be defined. This RR is used to create a mapping in the reverse lookup zone that typically corresponds to a host-address-named RR for the DNS computer name of a host in its forward lookup zone.

The in-addr.arpa domain applies for use in all TCP/IP networks that are based on IP version 4 addressing. The New Zone wizard automatically assumes that you are using this domain when creating a new reverse lookup zone.

If you are installing DNS and configuring reverse lookup zones for an IP version 6 network, you can specify an exact name in the New Zone wizard. This will permit you to create reverse lookup zones in the DNS console that can support IP version 6 networks, which uses a different special domain name, the ip6.int domain.

For Windows 2000 Server, the DNS snap-in provides a means to configure a subnetted reverse lookup "classless" zone when the Advanced view is selected. This allows a zone to be configured in the in-addr.arpa domain for a limited set of assigned IP addresses, where a nondefault IP subnet mask is used.

Boot File

The boot file that starts Windows 2000 is used only to make changes to the DNS through the editing of text files and not through the DNS Manager. In such cases, the boot file controls the startup behavior of the DNS. The partition boot sector is a portion of a hard-disk partition that contains information about the disk's file system and a short machine language program that loads the Windows operating system.

To change the boot method used by the DNS server:

1. Open DNS.

2. In the console tree, click on the applicable DNS server.

3. On the Action menu, click on Properties.

4. Click on the Advanced tab.

5. In the Load Zone Data on Startup list, select From Registry, From File, or From Active Directory and Registry.

Windows 2000 DNS servers use information stored in the Windows 2000 Registry to initialize for service and load any zone data for use at the server. As added options, the DNS server can be configured to boot from a file or, in Active Directory environments, with supplemented local Registry data, with zone data retrieved for directory-integrated zones stored in the Active Directory database. To use this method, the file must be a text file named boot.dns, located in the \Winnt\System32\Dns folder.

Monitoring Server Performance

Because DNS servers are of critical importance in most environments, monitoring their performance can be extremely useful. It provides a benchmark for predicting, estimating, and optimizing DNS server performance. In troubleshooting DNS servers where server performance has degraded over time or during periods of peak activity, Windows 2000 Server provides a set of DNS server performance counters that you can use with System Monitor to measure and monitor various aspects of server activity.

Sample DNS Server Performance Test Results

The DNS development and testing team compiled some statistics as a profile of DNS server performance during preliminary testing of Windows 2000 Server. The team used two different DNS server hardware configurations and measured overall DNS query and dynamic update activity, along with processor utilization. Table 6.3 shows the results of these tests.

During the collection of these measurements, the monitored DNS server was processing both queries and dynamic updates simultaneously. The numbers in the table reflect this.

For dynamic updates, standard primary type zones were used, not Active Directory-integrated zones. When directory integration is used for zones, the rate at which dynamic updates can be processed decreases, because the DNS server must additionally write to and rely upon the Active Directory database. In addition, if a zone is configured to accept only secure dynamic updates, the update rate can decrease. Network performance might also be a factor in these cases because the directory database may require network activity to process updates.

These measurements were not intended to indicate maximum performance or server limitations for Windows 2000 DNS servers. The objectives of the tests were to sample typical DNS server performance and obtain a working benchmark based on standard available hardware. This information could serve as a basis to begin server capacity planning. The test numbers are approximate and can be influenced by the types of RRs entered in zones, the number of RRs with the same owner name, and the number of zones in use at a specific DNS server.

DNS Server Performance Counters

Windows 2000 Server provides a set of DNS server performance counters that you can use with System Monitor to measure and monitor various aspects of server activity, such as:

➤ Overall DNS server performance statistics, or the number of overall queries and responses processed by a DNS server.

➤ UDP or TCP counters for measuring DNS queries and responses that are processed, respectively, using either of these transport protocols.

➤ Dynamic update and secure dynamic update counters, for measuring registration and update activity generated by dynamic clients.

Table 6.3 The test results.

Server Configuration	Queries/Sec	Dynamic Updates/Sec	Processor Utilization
Intel P-II 400-MHz dual-processor	900	100	30%

➤ Memory usage counters, for measuring system memory usage and memory allocation patterns created by operating the server computer as a Windows 2000 DNS server.

➤ Recursive lookup counters, for measuring queries and responses when the DNS server service uses recursion to look up and fully resolve DNS names on behalf of requesting clients.

➤ WINS lookup counters, for measuring queries and responses made to WINS servers when the WINS lookup integration features of the DNS server service are used.

➤ Zone transfer counters, including specific counters for measuring: all zone transfer (AXFR), incremental zone transfer (IXFR), and DNS zone update notification activity.

6

Chapter Summary

The DNS service running in Windows 2000 Server provides an RFC-compliant DNS name server. The DNS service allows clients to dynamically update RRs, based on the DNS dynamic update protocol (RFC 2136). Computers running Windows 2000 can dynamically register their DNS names and IP addresses.

Zone transfers are used between DNS servers to replicate information about a portion of the DNS namespace.

Name servers take name requests from clients and resolve computer (or domain) names to IP addresses. A DNS server resolves domain names to IP addresses. A TCP/IP host configured with the IP address of a DNS server will send DNS name queries to the DNS server for resolution. If the computer is running Active Directory-based Windows 2000, a DNS server is required.

The primary server for a zone acts as the zone's point of update. Add a new DNS server when no additional primary servers for the zone are permitted.

A secondary server is required to add and configure the zone to appear to other DNS servers in the network, for standard primary zones. Additionally, if a primary server is down, a secondary server can provide some name resolution in the zone until the primary server is available.

For multihomed DNS servers, you can configure the DNS service to selectively enable and bind only to IP addresses that you specify using the DNS console. By restricting the DNS service for selected IP addresses, DNS server performance overhead will decrease slightly, which can affect DNS query reception for the server.

When determining the number of DNS servers to use, decide which servers will host primary and secondary copies of zones. Decide whether to use only Windows 2000 DNS servers for all your DNS servers or to operate a mixture of Windows and other DNS server implementations.

DNS was designed to have two servers for each zone: one as a primary server and the other as a backup or secondary server. For best results and simplified DNS administration, consider using the DNS service supplied with Windows 2000 Server for all DNS servers.

For additional servers to host a zone, zone transfers are required to replicate all copies of the zone to the other servers that host the zone.

Windows DNS servers support DNS Notify, an update to the original DNS protocol specification that permits a means of initiating notification to secondary servers when zone changes occur (RFC 1996).

Cache.dns is used to preload RRs into the DNS server names cache. Windows 2000 DNS servers use this file to help locate root servers either on a network or the Internet.

Review Questions

1. Name servers take name requests from where and resolve computer (or domain) names to IP addresses?

    a. Servers

    b. The Internet

    c. Clients

    d. None of the above

2. Stating that someone has to enter the names and IP addresses manually before the DNS server can resolve them means that DNS is what kind of service?

    a. Dynamic

    b. Static

    c. WINS

    d. None of the above

3. What protocol is usually used for small workgroups and isn't routable?

    a. NetBEUI

    b. TCP/IP

    c. IPX/SPX

    d. WINS

4. Dynamic DNS is fully integrated with DNS to get all the benefits of what protocol and Internet-standards-based name resolution, without maintaining name resolution manually, as was the case previously?

   a. NetBEUI

   b. TCP/IP

   c. SPX/IPX

   d. None of the above

5. What enables clients using DDNS for name resolution still to access hosts that are not registered in DDNS but are registered in WINS?

   a. Integration with DNS

   b. Integration with DHCP

   c. Both a and b

   d. None of the above

6. What does dynamic update enable?

   a. DNS client computers to register

   b. DNS computers dynamically to update their RRs with a DNS server whenever changes occur

   c. DNS computers to connect to the Internet

   d. Both a and b

7. Windows 2000 gives you the option of choosing one of two ways to use primary zones. What are they?

   a. Primary master zones or primary master zones integrated with Active Directory

   b. Standard primary zones or primary zones integrated with WINS

   c. Standard primary zones or primary zones integrated with Active Directory

   d. Primary master zones or primary master zones integrated with WINS

8. If you decide to use the standard primary zone, how many servers can host and load the master copy of the zone?

   a. 1

   b. 2

   c. 3

   d. 4

9. It is recommended that at least how many DNS servers should be used to host each zone?

    a. 1

    b. 2

    c. 3

    d. None of the above

10. Caching-only DNS servers do not do what?

    a. Retain their information for more than one month

    b. Host any zones and are not authoritative for a particular domain

    c. There is no such thing as a caching-only DNS server

    d. None of the above

11. What choices is it important to make when planning for your DNS servers?

    a. Perform capacity planning

    b. Review server hardware requirements

    c. Determine how many DNS servers are needed

    d. Determine their role in the network

    e. All of the above

12. In many cases, doing what to a DNS server can provide the most noticeable improvements in performance?

    a. Adding storage space

    b. Reducing user access levels

    c. Adding RAM

    d. Adding virus-scanning software

13. Approximately how much RAM is used when the DNS server is started without any zones?

    a. 6MB

    b. 2MB

    c. 8MB

    d. 4MB

14. What is used to offload DNS query traffic in areas of the network where a zone is heavily queried?

    a. Backup name server

    b. Secondary name server

    c. Primary name server

    d. Offload name server

15. Which of the following files does not relate to using and configuring DNS servers and clients for use under Windows 2000?

   a. BIND boot configuration file

   b. Cache.dns

   c. Root.dns

   d. Config.dns

16. Which of the following files is used when a standard zone (either primary or secondary) is added and configured for the server?

   a. Cache.dns

   b. Root.dns

   c. Zone_name.dns

   d. Config.dns

17. What does CNAME stand for?

   a. Client name

   b. Current name

   c. Canonical name

   d. Compatible name

18. Which RR is always the first in any standard zone?

   a. CNAME

   b. SOA

   c. Name Server

   d. PTR

19. Which RR specifies the type of CPU and operating system in the cpu_type and os_type fields, respectively, for the host DNS domain name in the owner field?

   a. Mail Exchanger

   b. Service Locator

   c. HINFO

   d. CNAME

20. Windows 2000 DNS servers use information stored where to initialize for service and load any zone data for use at the server?

   a. System BIOS

   b. System Registry

   c. DNS configuration dialog box

   d. DNS does not load zone data for server use

6

Real-World Projects

James, the IT director for the Puddin' International Restaurant Products Corporation, wants to implement a caching-only DNS server for the company's network. The company's LAN is supported by a cable modem connection and its employees are always experiencing performance issues with name resolution when looking up Web sites.

The DNS server that is going to be implemented will ensure faster name resolution overall for the company's LAN; it will also act as a back up should the ISP's DNS server be changed or go offline.

James has asked you, the network consultant, to help him set up the DNS server, as well as configure the clients on the LAN to use the IP address of the company's DNS server first, then the DNS server of their ISP.

Project 6.1

To install a DNS server with the DNS service, perform the following steps:

1. In the Control Panel, double-click on Add/Remove Programs.

2. Click on Add/Remove Windows Components.

3. In the Components window, click on Networking Services and then click on Details.

4. In Subcomponents of Networking Services, select the Domain Name System (DNS) checkbox, click on OK, then click on Next.

5. In Copy Files From, type the full path of the distribution files and then click on OK.

This procedure will install the DNS service onto the computer that will be used as a DNS server. The next process would be to configure the DNS server as caching-only.

Project 6.2

To configure a DNS server as caching-only, perform the following steps:

1. Open DNS.

2. In the console tree, click on the appropriate server.

3. In the Action Menu, click on Configure Server.

4. In the Configure DNS Server wizard, check the option, "Do not create a forward lookup zone."

5. Click on Finish.

6. Right click on the Local Area Connection icon (from the taskbar or Network and Dial-up Connections folder), click on Properties.

7. In the Local Area Connection Properties dialog box, select Internet Protocol (TCP/IP), then click on Properties.

8. In the Internet Protocol (TCP/IP) properties dialog box, check the option, "Use the following DNS server address."

9. For the preferred DNS server, use the IP address of the server that was just configured.

This will create a caching-only server; the file for the server will build up based on usage. The file that will be created will be based on the usage of the clients and will be done automatically.

6

Note: This server can also be set up as a secondary server in a forward lookup zone that keeps a backup copy of the DNS files from the primary zone server of the ISP.

Project 6.3

To configure the network clients to use the caching-only DNS server, perform the following steps:

This process will vary depending on the operating system the clients use.

1. Open Internet Protocol (TCP/IP) Properties.

2. In the Internet Protocol (TCP/IP) Properties dialog box, select the option, "Use the following DNS server address."

3. In the Preferred DNS server, add the IP address for the caching-only DNS server.

4. In the Alternate DNS server, add the ISP's DNS server's IP address.

5. Click on OK.

This will configure the clients on the network to look first at the caching-only server on the network, where the ISP's DNS server can be put in as the alternate DNS server. This will ensure that should the ISP's DNS server for any reason be unavailable or vice versa, clients will still be able to resolve names to addresses on the Internet.

CHAPTER SEVEN

Windows Internet Name Service (WINS)

After completing this chapter, you will be able to:

✓ Determine when and where to use NetBIOS name servers

✓ Install and configure WINS

✓ Install and configure WINS clients

✓ Implement and configure WINS proxy for non-WINS clients

✓ Perform WINS name query and resolution

✓ Implement WINS database replication

✓ Configure DHCP server for WINS

✓ Use the NBTSTAT utility

✓ Use Microsoft Management Console (MMC)

✓ Perform WINS database backup

✓ Restore WINS database

✓ Understand WINS database scavenging and compaction

For those who are new to both Windows 2000 and Windows Internet Name Service (WINS), this chapter begins by defining WINS and covers installation, administration, and troubleshooting in detail. WINS is no longer required in Windows 2000, so you might be wondering, why cover this subject? The main reason is that although pure Windows 2000 networks do not need WINS, other networks that are not using Windows 2000 will.

It is imperative that you know when and where to use WINS, not only for certification testing, but also to ensure compatibility and optimal performance with existing network segments as well as across WANs. You should become thoroughly educated in existing WINS networks so that you are prepared to replace WINS name resolution with Domain Name System (DNS) name resolution. If you are not familiar with how to remove WINS name resolution from your existing network, then pay special attention to the section in this chapter that discusses the integration of WINS with both DNS and Dynamic Host Configuration Protocol (DHCP).

This chapter covers the steps necessary to ensure database integrity and optimal performance. You will learn how to perform maintenance tasks, such as scavenging and backup. This chapter will cover database fault tolerance with the use of WINS replication. It will also address the planning and placement of WINS servers as required for optimal performance. We will explore both graphical and command-line utilities to help you analyze and troubleshoot WINS traffic on a Windows 2000 network.

WINS Overview

WINS provides a dynamic replicated database service that can register and resolve NetBIOS names to IP addresses on a network. Windows 2000 Server provides WINS, which enables the server computer to act as a NetBIOS name server and to register and resolve names for WINS-enabled client computers, as described in the NetBIOS over TCP/IP (NetBT) standards. NetBIOS names are required for establishing networking services in earlier versions of Microsoft operating systems. Although the NetBIOS naming protocol can be used with network protocols other than TCP/IP (such as NetBEUI or IPX/SPX), WINS was designed specifically to support NetBT. WINS simplifies managing the NetBIOS namespace in TCP/IP-based networks.

You do not need WINS and NetBT if you are using only Windows 2000 servers and clients. DNS is the preferred name resolution for pure Windows networks. If you use Windows NT version 3.5x, Windows NT 4, Windows 95, Windows 98, or Windows 3.x, however, WINS is still required because those operating systems use NetBIOS name resolution and NetBIOS sessions to create file- and print-sharing connections.

Windows 2000 provides integration between DNS and WINS. If a Windows 2000 DNS server cannot resolve a fully qualified domain name (FQDN), it converts the FQDN to a NetBIOS name and queries a configured WINS server. The IP address returned by the WINS server is forwarded to the DNS client.

WINS provides the following benefits for administering your TCP/IP-based network:

➤ A dynamic name-to-address database that maintains support for computer name registration and resolution.

➤ Centralized management of the name-to-address database, alleviating the need for managing lmhosts files.

➤ Reduction of NetBIOS-based broadcast traffic on subnets, by permitting clients to query WINS servers to directly locate remote systems.

➤ Support for earlier Windows and NetBIOS-based clients on your network, permitting these types of clients to browse lists for remote Windows domains without requiring a local domain controller to be present on each subnet.

➤ Support for DNS-based clients by enabling those clients to locate NetBIOS resources when WINS lookup integration is implemented.

NetBIOS Names

A NetBIOS name is a 16-byte address that identifies a NetBIOS resource on the network. A NetBIOS name is either a unique (exclusive) or group (nonexclusive) name. The first 15 bytes of each name are user-specified, indicating either: a unique name, identifying a resource associated with a single user or computer on the network; or a group name, identifying a resource associated with a group or collection of users or computers on the network. Unique names are typically used to send network communications to a specific process on a computer. Group names are used to send information simultaneously to multiple computers.

Microsoft NetBIOS clients use the 16th character in each NetBIOS name to indicate information about the resource that the name is being used to register on the network. It is always exactly the 16th character; NetBIOS names shorter than 15 characters in length are padded with blank spaces. You can view locally cached NetBIOS names by typing "nbstat –n" at the command prompt, as shown in Figure 7.1. In the following section, we will discuss the type description for the second column shown in the **NBSTAT –n** command-line results for each cached NetBIOS name. The 16th character is for defining resource types, always expressed as hexadecimal values.

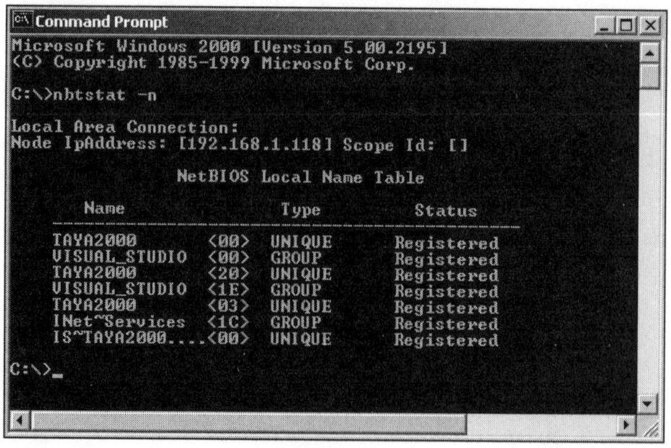

Figure 7.1 The NBTSTAT utility.

Type Description

The NetBIOS local name for a local computer will display as command-line output listing the name type. These are general types for select use. The **NBTSTAT –n** command output indicates in the second column the results of the type description for each cached NetBIOS name. This column will contain one of the following entries:

➤ *Unique*—Associates the computer specified by name in Computer Name and a single IP address in IP Address for this static mapped entry. When this type is selected, three types of records are statically added to the WINS database for the specified computer name. These are the [00h]WorkStation, [03h]Messenger, and [20h] File Server types.

➤ *Group*—Also referred to as a normal group. This type is used to add a static entry for the computer, specified by name in a static mapping, to a workgroup used on your network. If this type is used, the IP address for the computer is not stored in WINS, but is resolved through local subnet broadcasts.

➤ *Domain Name*—Indicates a domain name [1C] mapped entry for locating Windows NT domain controllers.

➤ *Internet Group*—Used for special user-defined administrative groups. You can use this to group resources. For example, you can indicate a group of file or print servers for organizing shared resources that are visible when browsing your network. Each Internet group is represented by a shared group name of [20h] type in the WINS database.

➤ *Multihomed*—Registers a unique name for a computer that has more than one IP address (either multiple adapters, each using a single address, or one network adapter configured with multiple IP addresses).

NetBIOS Unique Names

The first column shown in the results of the **NBTSTAT –n** command shows the computer name padded to exactly 15 characters, followed by a single hexadecimal character indicating the service available for the computer. There is a separate line for each service available on a single computer. These services, such as computer_name[00h], a unique computer name used by NetBIOS, are described below:

➤ computer_name[00h]—Registered by the Workstation Service on the WINS client. In general, this is called the NetBIOS computer name.

➤ computer_name[03h]—Registered by the Messenger Service on the WINS client. The client uses this service when sending and receiving messages. This name is usually appended to both the NetBIOS computer name for the WINS client computer and the name of the user currently logged on to that computer when sending messages on the network.

➤ computer_name[06h]—Registered by the Routing and Remote Access Service on the WINS client (when the service is started).

➤ domain_name[1Bh]—Registered by each Windows NT Server 4 domain controller running as the domain master browser. This name record is used to permit remote browsing of domains. When a WINS server is queried for this name, it returns the IP address of the computer that registered the name.

➤ computer_name[1Fh]—Registered by the Network Dynamic Data Exchange (NetDDE) services. This appears only if the NetDDE services are started on the computer.

➤ computer_name[20h]—Registered by the Server service on the WINS client. This service provides points of service to the WINS client to provide sharing of its files on the network.

➤ computer_name[21h]—Registered by the Remote Access Service (RAS) client on the WINS client (when the RAS client is started).

➤ computer_name[BEh]—Registered by the Network Monitoring Agent Service. It appears only if the service is started on the WINS client computer. If the computer name has fewer than 15 characters, the remaining character spaces are padded with plus (+) symbols.

➤ computer_name[BFh]—Registered by the Network Monitoring Utility (included with Microsoft Systems Management Server). If the computer name has fewer than 15 characters, the remaining character spaces are padded with plus (+) symbols.

7

➤ username[03h]—Registered in the WINS database. Each user name for currently logged-on users is registered by the Server service component, so those users can receive any net send commands sent to the user name. If more than one user logs on with the same user name, only the first computer logged on with that name registers the name.

NetBIOS Group Names

The first column shown in the results of the NBTSTAT −n command may also contain a domain name padded to exactly 15 characters, followed by a single hexadecimal character indicating the service available for the computer. There is a separate line for each group service available on a single computer. The domain_name[00h] is a NetBIOS group name used by the Workstation Service. Other group services are described here:

➤ domain_name[00h]—Registered by the Workstation Service so that it can receive browser broadcasts from LAN Manager-based computers.

➤ domain_name[1Ch]—Registered for use by the domain controllers within the domain. These contain up to 25 IP addresses.

➤ domain_name[1Dh]—Registered for use by master browsers (described later in this chapter), of which there is only one per subnet. Backup browsers use this name to communicate with the master browser, retrieving the list of available servers from the master browser. WINS servers always return a positive registration response for domain_name[1D], even though the WINS server does not register this name in its database. Therefore, when a WINS server is queried for the domain_name[1D], it returns a negative response, which forces the client to broadcast for name resolution.

➤ group_name[1Eh]—Used for a normal group name. Any computers configured to be network browsers can broadcast to this name and listen for broadcasts to this name to elect a master browser. A statically mapped group name uses this name to register itself on the network. When a WINS server receives a name query for a name ending with [1E], the WINS server always returns the network broadcast address for the local network of the requesting client. The client can then use this address to broadcast to the group members. These broadcasts are for the local subnet and should not cross routers.

➤ group_name[20h]—A special group name called the Internet Group is registered with WINS servers to identify groups of computers for administrative purposes. For example, "printersg" could be a registered group name used to identify an administrative group of print servers.

➤ —__MSBROWSE__[01h]—This special NetBIOS group name is registered by the master browser for each subnet. When a WINS server receives a name query for this name, the server always returns the network broadcast address for the local network of the requesting client.

NetBIOS Node Types

The exact mechanism by which NetBIOS names are resolved to IP addresses depends on the NetBIOS node type that is configured for the node. Request for Comments (RFC) 1001, "Protocol Standard for a NetBIOS Service on a TCP/UDP Transport: Concepts and Methods," defines the NetBIOS node types, as listed in Table 7.1. In each case, you proceed to a subsequent step only if the previous step was not successful.

A popular memorization technique for H-node (hybrid) is as follows: CWBLHD (Can We Buy Large Hard Drives), where C = cache, W = WINS, B = broadcast, L = lmhosts, H = hosts, and D = DNS. Remember that P-node does not use broad-

7

Table 7.1   NetBIOS node types.

Node Types	Order of Name Resolution
B-node (broadcast)	1. Query the NetBIOS name cache on the node
	2. Broadcast a message on the local subnet. (Other nodes can report IP address if stored in their cache.)
	3. Query lmhosts file, if enabled.
	4. Query hosts file, if enabled.
	5. Query DNS if enabled.
P-node (peer-to-peer)	1. Query the NetBIOS name cache on the node.
	2. Query WINS if enabled.
	3. Query lmhosts file, if enabled.
	4. Query hosts file, if enabled.
	5. Query DNS, if enabled.
M-node (mixed)	1. Query the NetBIOS name cache on the node.
	2. Broadcast on the local subnet.
	3. Query WINS, if enabled.
	4. Query lmhosts file, if enabled.
	5. Query hosts file, if enabled.
	6. Query DNS, if enabled.
H-node (hybrid)	1. Query the NetBIOS name cache on the node.
	2. Query WINS, if enabled.
	3. Broadcast on the local subnet.
	4. Query lmhosts, if enabled.
	5. Query hosts, if enabled.
	6. Query DNS, if enabled.

cast because it is peer-to-peer; then you have CWLHD. Also, remember that B-node uses broadcast rather than WINS, so removing the W, we have CBLHD. M-node (mixed) simply mixes or changes the order of broadcast and WINS, resulting in CBWLHD.

B-node (broadcast) has two major problems: (1) Broadcasts consume bandwidth and computer resources; and (2) routers typically do not forward broadcasts, so only NetBIOS names on the local network can be resolved.

P-node (peer-to-peer) uses a NetBIOS name server (NBNS), such as a WINS server, to resolve NetBIOS names. P-node does not use broadcasts; instead, it queries the name server directly.

M-node (mixed) is a combination of B-node and P-node. By default, M-node functions as B-node. If M-node is unable to resolve a name by broadcast, it queries an NBNS using P-node.

H-node (hybrid) is a combination of P-node and B-node. By default, H-node functions as P-node. If H-node is unable to resolve a name through the NBNS, it uses a broadcast to resolve the name.

Computers running Windows 2000 are B-node by default and become H-node when they are configured with a WINS server. Use the TCP/IP utility IPCONFIG by typing "ipconfig /all" at the command prompt to identify the node type, as shown in Figure 7.2, where Node Type = Hybrid.

Windows 2000 can also use a local lmhosts file to resolve remote NetBIOS names. The lmhosts file is stored in the WINNT\System32\Drivers\Etc folder. An example lmhosts file is shown in Figure 7.3. Note that the IP address is entered first, followed by the NetBIOS name. The #PRE indicates that the mapping will be preloaded into cache. The #DOM:domain_name indicates that the mapping is for a domain controller for domain_name.

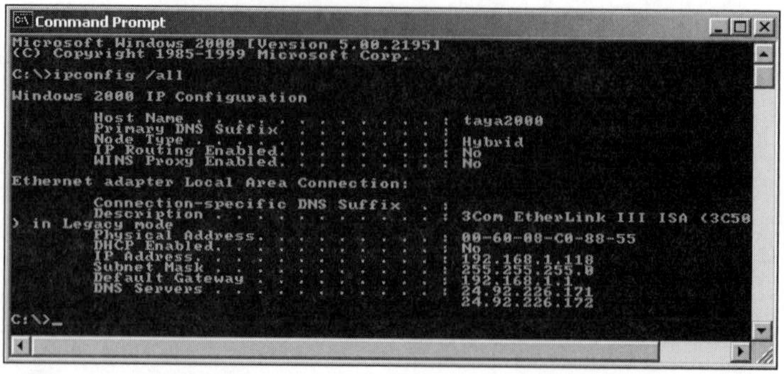

Figure 7.2   The IPCONFIG utility.

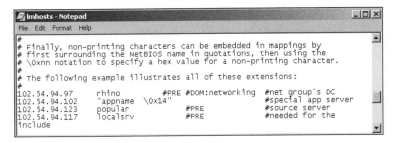

Figure 7.3 Sample lmhosts file.

You should configure computers running Windows 2000 with the IP address of your WINS server, so remote NetBIOS names can be resolved. You must configure Active Directory–based computers running Windows 2000 with the IP address of a WINS server if they are to communicate with other computers running Windows NT, Windows 2000, Windows 95, or Windows 98, which are not Active Directory–based.

NetBIOS Before Windows 2000

For Windows 2000, the Netlogon service and potentially other network services will register in DNS. In earlier versions of Windows NT, however, all network services were registered using only NetBIOS names. NetBIOS names are used by earlier versions of Microsoft operating systems to identify and locate computers and other shared or grouped resources needed to register or resolve names for use on the network. If you use Windows NT 3.5x, Windows NT 4, Windows 95, Windows 98, or Windows 3.x, WINS is still required because those operating systems use NetBIOS name resolution and NetBIOS sessions to create file- and print-sharing connections.

Also, legacy network command-line applications (such as the various net commands) use NetBIOS names to access these services. Other NetBIOS-based computers, such as Windows for Workgroups, LAN Manager, and LAN Manager for Unix hosts, use NetBIOS names.

In versions of Windows earlier than Windows 2000, WINS is used in conjunction with DHCP to register NetBIOS names and dynamically configure the client with the WINS server IP address. In this case, a DHCP-enabled host queries a DHCP server for an IP address; the DHCP server then allocates a WINS server to the DHCP client as a DHCP option. After the DHCP lease allocation process is complete, the NetBIOS name and its associated IP address are registered in the WINS database by the DHCP client.

For networks with servers running Windows 2000 Server and all other computers running Windows 2000 Professional, NetBIOS is no longer required for TCP/IP-based networking. When deciding whether to use WINS, you should consider the following questions:

➤ *Do I have any legacy computers on my network that require the use of NetBIOS names?* Remember that all networked computers that run under any previously released Microsoft operating system, such as versions of MS-DOS, Windows, or Windows NT, require NetBIOS name support. Windows 2000 is the first Microsoft operating system that no longer requires NetBIOS naming. Therefore, NetBIOS names may still be required on your network to provide basic file and print services and support for many legacy applications.

➤ *Are all computers on my network configured and able to support the use of another type of network naming, such as DNS?* Network naming is still a vital service for locating computers and resources throughout your network, even when NetBIOS names are not required. Before you decide to eliminate WINS or NetBIOS name support, be sure that all computers and programs on your network are able to function using another naming service, such as DNS.

➤ *What are the two major methods of performing network name resolution?* The first is host name resolution, which is Windows sockets-based and implements the gethostbyname () API to search for a host IP address based on a queried host name. This method relies on either a hosts file or querying DNS to perform resolution of the name. The second is NetBIOS name resolution, which uses the NetBIOS redirector to search for an address based on a queried NetBIOS name. This method relies on either an lmhosts file or querying WINS to perform resolution of the name.

WINS clients running under Windows 2000 are configured by default first to use DNS to resolve names that are longer than 15 characters or that use periods (".") within the name. For names that have fewer than 15 characters and do not use periods, DNS is also used as a final option after a WINS query fails, if the client is configured to use a DNS server.

If you are running a pure Windows 2000 environment, review that DNS is currently configured and can be used by all client computers on your network to resolve names. If you have a mixed environment of computers running under Windows 2000 and other platforms (such as Unix), confirm that these other hosts can rely on using only DNS for host name resolution.

➤ *Is your network a single subnet or routed with multiple subnets?* If your entire network is made up of a single small LAN that occupies one physical network segment and has fewer than 50 clients, you can probably do without a WINS server. All computers that run under Windows 2000—and most earlier

Microsoft-based WINS clients—are configured as hybrid node (H-node) type clients and can use either of the following methods to handle NetBIOS requests to resolve or register names:

➤ Direct (point-to-point) contact with a WINS server, if one is configured.

➤ Broadcast of the NetBIOS request to the local subnet. For small networks, the latter option is typically an effective and simple solution for providing NetBIOS name service to a small number of LAN-based clients.

NetBIOS Name Servers

If NetBIOS name resolution is required, you need to determine the number of WINS servers you need. Consider the location of routers on your network and the distribution of clients in each subnet. On a smaller network, a single WINS server can service up to 10,000 clients for NetBIOS name resolution requests. Larger networks require more, depending on the number of client connections per server. You can install the WINS server either on the same system as the DNS server or separately. You also need to install a backup WINS server elsewhere in the network, either on the same system as a Windows 2000 domain controller or separately.

The preconfigured WINS settings provide the optimal configuration for most conditions and should be used in most WINS network installations. If you modify the default settings, be sure that the need to do so is clear and that you understand all of the implications.

Static WINS entries require further administrative action to ensure their successful and intended use. Static entries, however, can be useful for specific purposes, such as safeguarding against WINS registration of the names used by critically important servers. For example, a static entry in WINS can prevent other computers from taking over the use of the name of a critical server while that server is unavailable because WINS will not let that client register its name.

The biggest disadvantage of using static WINS entries is that it complicates administration of name and address changes in your network. For example, if either the IP address or the computer name of a static WINS entry changes, you might have to update other configurations manually, such as DHCP servers, DNS servers, end systems, and lmhosts files.

If you decide to use static WINS entries, consider the following suggestions for configuring other WINS and DHCP service properties and avoiding common problems:

➤ For each IP address used in static WINS mapping, consider using a corresponding client address reservation to reserve the IP address at the DHCP server.

➤ If you use static WINS entries only to support temporary changes on your network, keep the default Migrate On setting selected in the WINS Console.

➤ When Migrate On is selected, any temporary unique or multihomed static entries you add can be challenged and dynamically updated by clients. An attempt later by any client to dynamically register a unique or multihomed name entry over an existing static entry of the same name results in a challenge process.

➤ In the challenge, the IP address in the static mapping is compared with any IP address that the named client attempts to dynamically register in WINS. If the two addresses are different and the static IP address is determined no longer to be active or in use, the IP mapping can be migrated (from static to dynamic mapping) and the IP address is updated in WINS.

➤ If you use static WINS entries on a permanent basis, you can disable Migrate On. This prevents a dynamic WINS entry from overriding a static WINS entry that maps to the name and address of a critical server on your network.

➤ Schedule consistency checking for an off-peak time. For Windows 2000 Server, WINS consistency checking is available through the WINS snap-in. You should use this feature periodically to check the WINS database for consistency. Consistency checking is network- and resource-intensive for the WINS server computer, however. For this reason, run WINS consistency checks during times of low traffic, such as at night or on weekends.

Configuring Replication Partners

In general, push/pull is a simple and effective way to ensure full WINS replication between partners. Configuring your server to enable automatic partner configuration will ensure that other WINS servers on a network will be discovered and added as replication partners. In the Replication Partners property sheet, check the box on the Advanced tab, as shown in Figure 7.4.

Automatic partner configuration is useful for small networks where single subnet LAN environments exist. Automatic configuration can be used in routed networks but should be limited to routed subnets with three or fewer WINS servers. Automatic replication configuration monitors multicast announcements from other WINS servers and automatically adds the IP addresses for discovered servers to the local list of replication partners and configures both servers as push and pull partners. Then it configures pull replication for two-hour intervals.

Push Partners

A push partner is a WINS server that notifies (pushes) other WINS servers of the need to replicate their database entries at a configured interval. To configure a WINS server to use push replication, you can choose from several WINS Console

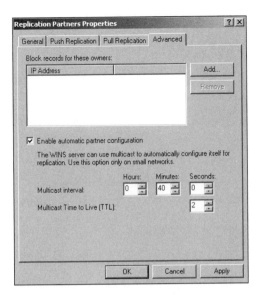

Figure 7.4 Replication Partners Advanced tab.

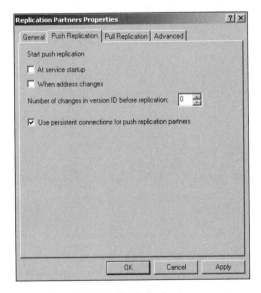

Figure 7.5 Push Replication tab.

configurable options, as shown in Figure 7.5. For example, you can enable WINS to push (notify) configured partners when one of these events occurs:

➤ The WINS server starts.

➤ An IP address change occurs for a name-to-address mapping in the WINS server database.

➤ A value is specified for the Number of Changes in Version ID Before Replication, either globally for all push partners or individually for specific push partners. WINS can use this value as a threshold for determining how many incremental changes must be made to the database before it starts push replication to its partners.

In the figure, the Use Persistent Connections for Push Replication Partners checkbox is selected. This can affect how WINS handles the value of Number of Changes in Version ID Before Replication.

By default, persistent connections are not used and replication with partners does not occur except at configured intervals. You can change this default, but you must first set a specified minimum number of update changes to WINS. Without the use of persistent connections, Number of Changes in Version ID Before Replication requires a minimum value of 20.

With persistent connections enabled for push replication, the default value of 0 causes the local WINS server to send a push trigger and notify its push partners each time an update occurs. An update is defined as an incremental increase to the highest version ID in the local WINS database for records the server owns. This can occur when a new name record is registered and added locally or if an IP address change occurs for an existing record.

With persistent connections, you can reduce the update frequency for push notifications by specifying a nonzero value. If you use a value greater than zero, WINS starts push replication only when the highest ID for records it owns has increased an equal number of times.

Pull Partners

A pull partner is a WINS server that requests (pulls) replication of updated WINS database entries from other WINS servers at a configured interval. This is done by requesting entries with a higher version ID than the last entry received from its configured partner.

You can enable WINS to pull (request) a replication with its configured partners when one of the following events occurs:

➤ The WINS server starts.

➤ A set amount of time has elapsed. The amount of time between pull replications is indicated in the Replication interval, as shown in Figure 7.6, which can be specified either globally for all pull partners or individually for specific partners. When the time has elapsed for each interval, WINS sends a pull replication trigger to its pull partners. The partners can then respond with incremental changes, if any have been made since the last time replication occurred. Additionally, you have the administrative option of manually sending a pull replication trigger to another pull partner of the selected WINS server.

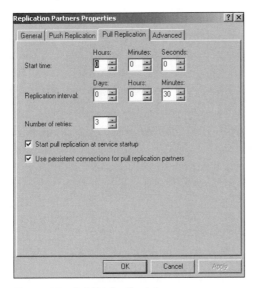

Figure 7.6 Pull Replication tab.

For most WINS installations, avoid the use of limited replication partnerships (Push Only or Pull Only) between WINS servers. In some large enterprise WINS networks, limited replication partnering can effectively support replication over slow WAN links. When you plan limited WINS replication, however, note the design and configuration when choosing to use limited replication partnerships.

For best results in WINS replication and convergence, use a hub-and-spoke design model. Convergence is a critical part of WINS planning. To review convergence for your WINS network design, ask the following question for each of your WINS servers:

Note: How long does it take for a change in WINS data at one WINS server to replicate and appear at other WINS servers in the network?

In most cases, the hub-and-spoke model provides a simple and effective planning method for organizations that require full and speedy convergence with minimal administrative intervention. For example, you can use this model for organizations with centralized headquarters or a corporate data center (the hub) and several branch offices (the spokes). A second, redundant hub (that is, a second WINS server in the central location) can increase the fault tolerance for WINS.

Too many WINS servers on a network can complicate any problems that arise. Be conservative when adding WINS servers to your network, using as few as possible to support all clients while maintaining acceptable performance from each server. If you are designing a WINS installation that includes more than 20 WINS servers, seek assistance from Microsoft Product Support Services before completing your plans.

WINS network traffic during client registration can be much less than for DHCP, which uses client broadcasts to discover servers. By default, most WINS clients first try to communicate using directed point-to-point datagrams with their configured primary WINS servers. One WINS server adequately supports a small routed internetwork, but use at least two WINS servers to provide a fault-tolerant WINS installation.

To make the most of server performance, purchase hardware with optimal disk performance characteristics to handle WINS, which causes frequent and intensive activity on server hard disks. To provide for the best performance, consider RAID solutions that improve disk-access time when you purchase new hardware to use as a WINS server. You should view WINS as part of a full performance evaluation of the server. By monitoring system hardware performance in the most demanding areas of utilization (CPU, memory, and disk input/output), you can make the best assessments of when a WINS server is overloaded and should be upgraded.

When using multihomed WINS servers, you will do well to configure all server IP addresses as replication partners with other WINS servers. Using a multihomed WINS server as a router or gateway between disjointed networks is not recommended.

Although manual compaction of the WINS server database is not as important for Windows 2000 Server as it was for earlier versions, it is still useful. For disk defragmentation and improved server disk performance, use offline WINS compaction regularly (monthly or weekly). Then, monitor any changes to the size of the server database file, wins.mdb, which is located in the systemroot\System32\WINS\ folder.

At each offline compaction, it is useful to check the file size of wins.mdb, both before and after compaction, to measure growth and reduction. This information can be helpful in determining the actual benefits to using offline compaction. Based on this information, you can then gauge how often to repeat offline compaction for measurable gains.

Besides using tape backup of the WINS server, the WINS Console offers a backup option, which you can use to restore a server database if corruption occurs.

In earlier versions of Windows NT, you could manually configure clients to use only a primary and secondary WINS server. For Windows 2000, you can configure WINS clients (either manually or through DHCP) to use up to 12 WINS servers. You can either statically configure this list, using the Internet Protocol (TCP/IP) Properties dialog box, or distribute it to DHCP clients, using Option 44. A larger list of WINS servers gives clients additional fault tolerance for WINS when their configured primary WINS server is not available.

Use NBTSTAT –RR to register and troubleshoot client connectivity. For Windows 2000, the **NBTSTAT –RR** command-line option supports purging of remote names from the local NetBIOS names cache and forces immediate renewal and re-registration of local client names. You can use this command-line option to refresh the client entries in WINS and replicate them to other replication partners without requiring a client reboot.

Each WINS server that you install on your network must register its own set of NetBIOS unique and group names in WINS. To prevent WINS service problems that can occur when a WINS record splits (that is, when names registered for a particular WINS server are owned by different WINS servers), each WINS server computer should point only to its own IP address when configuring its TCP/IP properties.

Installing and Configuring the WINS Service

7

Windows 2000 Server has a variety of core components, including a number of administrative tools that Setup installs automatically. In addition, you can choose from a number of optional components that extend the functionality of Windows 2000 Server. You can install these components during Setup, or you can add them later through the Windows Components Wizard. To activate the Windows Component Wizard through the Add/Remove Programs utility found in the Control Panel, select the Add/Remove Windows Components button on the left, choose Networking Services, and then click on the Details button. In the following screen, select WINS and then click on OK, as shown in Figure 7.7.

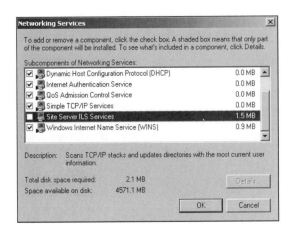

Figure 7.7 Windows Component Wizard.

Configure WINS through the WINS Console, an administrative tool used to manage WINS servers. Open the WINS Console by clicking on Start, point to Programs and then to Administrative Tools, and click on WINS. You can start and stop the WINS service by highlighting the desired server, and then on the Action menu, point to All Tasks and click on one of the following:

➤ To start the service, click Start

➤ To stop the service, click Stop

➤ To interrupt the service, click Pause

➤ To stop and then automatically restart the service, click Restart

You can also perform most of these tasks at a command prompt by using the following commands:

➤ **net start wins**

➤ **net stop wins**

➤ **net pause wins**

➤ **net continue wins**

Installing and Configuring WINS Clients

This section covers the steps to install and configure WINS clients that are using the TCP/IP service. It also covers the configuration of WINS DHCP-enabled clients and how to release their client names.

Configuring WINS for TCP/IP Clients

To configure WINS for TCP/IP clients, complete the following steps:

1. Open Network and Dial-up Connections.

2. Right-click on the network connection you want to configure, and then click on Properties.

3. On the General tab (for a local area connection) or the Networking tab (all other connections), click on Internet Protocol (TCP/IP), and then click on Properties.

4. Click on Advanced, click on the WINS tab, and then click on Add.

5. In TCP/IP WINS server, type the IP address of the WINS server, and then click on Add.

6. Repeat Steps 4 and 5 for each WINS server IP address you want to add, and then click on OK.

7. To enable the use of the lmhosts file to resolve remote NetBIOS names, select the Enable LMHOSTS lookup checkbox. This option is enabled by default.

8. To specify the location of the file that you want to import into the lmhosts file, click on Import LMHOSTS, and select the file in the Open dialog box.

9. To modify the behavior of NetBT behavior, do the following:

   ➤ To enable the use of NetBIOS over TCP/IP, click on Enable NetBIOS over TCP/IP.

   ➤ To disable the use of NetBIOS over TCP/IP, click on Disable NetBIOS over TCP/IP.

   ➤ To have the DHCP server determine the NetBIOS behavior, click on Use NetBIOS Setting from the DHCP Server.

Enabling and Disabling the Use of NetBT

If you disable NetBT, you may not be able to connect to computers that are running operating systems other than Windows 2000. If it is disabled, NetBIOS programs cannot run over TCP/IP. Therefore, you may not be able to connect to computers that are running an operating system other than Windows 2000. By default, the use of NetBT is specified by the settings obtained from a DHCP server.

You can no longer configure the NetBIOS scope ID on the WINS tab. To configure the NetBIOS scope ID, set the following Registry value to the name of the scope ID you want to use:

```
HKEY_LOCAL_MACHINE\SYSTEM\CurrentControlSet\Services\NetBT\Parameters\ScopeID
```

Configuring WINS for DHCP-Enabled Clients

Windows 2000 clients are configured by default to use a DHCP server to obtain an IP address. No further client-side configuration is needed.

Instead, configure your DHCP server to assign WINS-related option types needed to let DHCP-enabled clients on your network use WINS. In most cases, WINS clients need to be provided only these two NetBT option types for basic WINS configuration: 44 (WINS servers) and 46 (WINS node type). These options must be configured at the DHCP server providing each client its dynamically leased IP address.

Releasing Names

Name release occurs when a WINS client computer finishes using a particular name. In releasing its name, a WINS client notifies its WINS server (or potentially other computers on the network) that it is no longer using its registered name. A WINS-enabled client releases its name during normal shutdown and/or when a user enters the **NBTSTAT -RR** command.

The WINS server marks the related database entry for the host as released. If the entry remains released for a period of time, the WINS server marks the entry as *tombstoned*, updates the version ID for the entry, and notifies other WINS servers of the change. The WINS server returns a release confirmation message to the WINS client. If a name entry is marked as released, the WINS server can immediately update or revise a marked name entry when a new registration request arrives from a WINS client with the same name but with a different IP address. This is possible because the WINS database shows that the WINS client at the old IP address is no longer using that name. For example, this can happen when a DHCP-enabled laptop changes subnets.

Name release is most often used to simplify WINS registration for clients that shut down and restart on the network. If a computer releases its name during a normal shutdown, the WINS server does not challenge the name when the computer reconnects. If a proper shutdown does not occur, the name registration with a new IP address causes the WINS server to challenge the previous registration. When the challenge fails (because the client computer is no longer using the old IP address), the registration succeeds.

In some cases, a client is not able to release its name by contacting the WINS server, so it must use broadcasts to release a name. This can happen when a WINS-enabled client shuts down without receiving confirmation of its name release by the WINS server.

Implementing and Configuring a WINS Proxy for Non-WINS Clients

A WINS proxy is a WINS client computer configured to act on behalf of other host computers that cannot directly use WINS. A proxy helps resolve NetBIOS name queries for computers located on routed TCP/IP networks. By default, most computers not able to use WINS use broadcasts to resolve NetBIOS name queries and register their NetBIOS names on the network. You can configure a WINS proxy to listen on behalf of these computers and to query WINS for names not resolved by broadcast. WINS proxies are useful or necessary only on networks that include NetBIOS broadcast-only (or B-node) clients. For most networks, WINS-enabled clients are common and WINS proxies are typically not needed.

WINS proxies are WINS-enabled computers that listen for B-node NetBIOS name service functions (name registration, name release, and name query) and can respond for those names that are remote and not used on the local network. Proxies communicate directly with a WINS server to retrieve the information necessary to respond to these local broadcasts.

WINS proxies are used in the following ways:

➤ When a B-node client registers its name, the proxy checks the name against the WINS server database. If the name exists in the WINS database, the proxy might send a negative registration response to the B-node client attempting to register the name.

➤ When a B-node client releases its name, the proxy deletes the client name from its remote names cache.

➤ When a B-node client sends a name query, the proxy attempts to resolve the name using information either locally contained in its cache of remote names or through the use of information it obtains from the WINS server.

By default, WINS proxies cache remote name mappings that it queries in WINS for six minutes, but this value is configurable with a minimum value of one minute. Because WINS servers do not respond to broadcasts, you should configure a computer as a WINS proxy on each subnet that contains non–WINS computers that must use broadcasts to resolve NetBIOS names. When a WINS proxy answers a query for a multihomed client or a group record containing a list of IP addresses, only the first listed address is returned to the B-node client.

Name Registration

Name registration occurs when a WINS client requests the use of a NetBIOS name on the network. The request may be for a unique (exclusive) or a group (shared) name. NetBIOS applications can also register one or more names. A WINS server can accept or reject the name registration request by issuing either a positive or negative name registration response to a client.

If the name does not exist in the database, it is accepted as a new registration and the following steps occur:

1. The name for host is entered with a new version ID, given a time stamp, and marked with the owner ID of the WINS server.

2. The time stamp is calculated based on adding the value of the Renew interval (which, by default, is six days) set on the WINS server to the current date and time of the server.

3. A positive registration response is sent back to the client with a Time-to-Live (TTL) value equal to the time stamp recorded for the name.

If the name is already entered in the database with the same IP address as that being requested, the action taken depends on the state and ownership of the existing name. If the entry is marked as active and the entry is owned by the server, the server updates the time stamp for the record and returns a positive response to the client. If the entry is marked as being either released or tombstoned, or if the entry is owned by another WINS server, the registration is treated as a new registration. Time stamp, version ID, and ownership are all updated, and a positive response is returned.

When the name exists in the WINS database but with a different IP address than that being requested, and the entry is in the active state, the node holding the name is challenged to determine if it still exists on the network. In this case, the WINS server could perform a challenge of the name as follows:

1. Send a Wait for Acknowledgment (WACK) response to the requesting client (HOST-C), specifying a time in the TTL field that the client should be prepared to wait for a response.

2. Issue a name query request to the node currently registered for this name in the server database. If the node still exists, it sends a positive response to the WINS server. The WINS server, in turn, sends a negative name registration response to the requesting client, rejecting the name registration.

3. If a positive response is not received from the first challenge query, two subsequent name query requests are made. After three attempts with no response, the challenge process is complete and a positive registration response is returned to the requesting client. The name is updated in the server database for the new client registration.

Unlike WINS-enabled clients, which can directly contact a WINS server, non-WINS clients (such as NetBT B-node clients) must register and then continuously defend their names by sending and replying to broadcast name queries within the local network.

NetBIOS names are registered with WINS and are normally released when the computer is properly shut down. If the computer is not properly shut down, or is not able to contact a WINS server during shutdown, you can use the **NBTSTAT** command to refresh in WINS the local names for this computer. This can be useful for mobile or portable computers that are moved to different locations on a network.

Burst Handling

WINS servers can now support handling of high-volume (burst) server loads. Bursts occur when a large number of WINS clients actively and simultaneously try to register their local names in WINS. This can happen, for example, after a power failure. When power is restored, many users start and register their names simultaneously on the network, creating high levels of WINS traffic. With burst-mode support, a WINS server can respond positively to these client requests, even before it processes and physically enters those updates in the WINS server database.

Burst mode uses a burst-queue size as a threshold value. This value determines how many name registration and name refresh requests sent by WINS clients are processed normally, before burst-mode handling is started. By default, the value is 500. A WINS server initiates burst handling whenever the number of WINS client registration requests exceeds the burst queue size.

In burst handling, additional client requests are immediately answered with a positive response by the WINS server. The response also includes a varied TTL to clients, which helps regulate the client registration load and distribute processing of the requests over time. This slows the refresh and retry rate for new WINS clients and regulates the burst of WINS client traffic.

For example, if the burst queue size is 500 entries, and more than 500 requests are active, the WINS server replies immediately to the next 100 WINS client registration requests by sending early success responses with a starting TTL value of five minutes. For each additional round of 100 client requests, five minutes more are added to the TTL up to a maximum of 50 minutes. If WINS client traffic still arrives at burst levels, the next round of 100 client requests is answered with the initial TTL value of five minutes, and the entire process for incrementing the response TTL is repeated.

This behavior continues until the WINS server reaches its maximum intake level of 25,000 name registration and refresh queries. At this point, the WINS server begins dropping queries.

Using the WINS Console, you can configure the level of burst handling used by the server. This modifies the size of the burst queue to accommodate either a low, medium, or large burst situation, as shown in Figure 7.8.

Name Query and Resolution

This section explains how browsing a network is done for domains in routed WANs that use NetBT. Domains used in this type of environment are likely to be controlled by computers running earlier versions of Windows NT operating

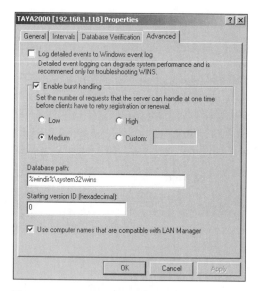

Figure 7.8 WINS burst configuration.

systems. In this environment, WINS provides effective browsing of shared resources located in remote domains on other physical networks.

The Computer Browser service is used by Windows-based computers operating on each subnet. Computers designated as browsers maintain the browse lists, which contain all shared resources used on the network. Browsing is required by some network applications provided in earlier versions of Windows, such as My Network Places, the **NET VIEW** command, and Windows NT Explorer.

For example, when a user at a computer running Windows 95 opens My Network Places, the application displays a list of domains and computers. The computer obtains a copy of the browse list from a browser computer functioning in that role on the same subnet. Most computers on the network operate as non-browsers, but computers running the Computer Browser service can become potential browsers for each subnet. For computers active as browsers on the network and maintaining copies of the browse list, Windows NT assigns special browser roles.

Browser Roles

A browser is a network computer that tracks the location, availability, and identity of shared devices. Browser roles are arranged in a hierarchical organization that provides for a fair level of fault tolerance. This organization should reflect itself on the network. The following sections describe the browser roles.

Domain Master Browser

➤ Used only in domain environments. By default, the primary domain controller (PDC) for a domain operates in this role.

➤ Collects and maintains the master browse list of available servers for its domain, as well as any names for other domains and workgroups used in the network.

➤ Distributes and synchronizes the master browse list for master browsers on other subnets that have computers belonging to the same domain.

Master Browser

➤ Collects and maintains the list of available network servers in its subnet.

➤ Fully replicates its listed information with the domain master browser to obtain a complete browse list for the network.

➤ Distributes its completed list to backup browsers located on the same subnet.

Backup Browser

➤ Receives a copy of the browse list from the master browser for its subnet.

➤ Distributes the browse list to other computers upon request.

Potential Browser

➤ Under normal conditions, operates similarly to a non-browser.

➤ Capable of becoming a backup browser if instructed to do so by the master browser for the subnet.

Non-Browser

➤ Does not maintain a browse list.

➤ Can operate as a browse client, requesting browse lists from other computers operating as browsers on the same subnet.

➤ Configured so it cannot become a browser.

Under some conditions, such as failure or shutdown of a computer, a designated computer with a specified browser role, browsers, or potential browsers may change to a different role of operation. For example, a backup browser can become a master browser if the computer that is acting as a master browser is taken offline or its network connection removed. This is typically performed through a browser election.

Browser Processes

Browsing services in earlier versions of Windows operating systems can be understood in terms of three key processes:

➤ *Collection of browsing information*—Browse lists are made up of computers that share resources through the use of the Server service. Periodically, every computer running this service broadcasts a host announcement message for its configured domain or workgroup name to the local subnet. The master browser for each subnet collects and processes these announcements on an ongoing basis. When the master browser on a subnet receives a host announcement, it compares the name of the sending computer with its current browse list. If the name already appears, it is refreshed in the list. If the name does not appear, it is added to the list.

➤ *Distribution of browsing information*—Browse lists are distributed to backup browsers by the master browser for the subnet. Periodically, the master browser must broadcast an announcement message for its configured domain or workgroup name to the local subnet. This message confirms the master browser's presence on the network. If the master browser fails to announce itself for a period of time, a browser election can occur. Once a master browser is either present or (in the event of a failure) replaced, other backup browsers periodically contact it to obtain an updated copy of the browse list that it maintains for the subnet.

➤ *Servicing of browse requests from clients*—When a browse client computer starts on a subnet, it broadcasts a request to the master browser for a list of the backup browsers on the subnet. The master browser responds to this request and provides the client a list of three backup browsers. The browse client then randomly selects one of the backup browsers from the list and contacts it for a copy of the browse list. For subsequent browse list requests, the client continues to use the list of backup browsers provided by the master browser during its startup and does not repeat the broadcast. The success of this process depends first upon the client getting a response from its master browser, and second upon its ability to resolve the names of backup browsers it selects from the list.

Planning Browsing Services

For Windows 2000, browsing functionality in many cases can be accomplished by publishing services in the Active Directory through the use of global catalogs. The following are additional considerations to keep in mind when planning browsing services across a routed TCP/IP-based network:

➤ Computers running earlier versions of Windows operating systems (Windows NT Workstation, Windows NT Server, Windows for Workgroups, and Windows 95 and 98) can perform the master browser and backup browser roles.

➤ Only computers running an earlier version of Windows NT Server and operating as the PDC for a domain typically perform the domain master browser role.

➤ Only domains can span multiple subnets. Workgroups cannot span multiple subnets and can view other workgroups only on the same subnet.

WINS acts as a directory service for NetBIOS names and IP addresses. The use of WINS can improve browsing for WANs through the following enhancements:

➤ WINS-enabled clients can directly query their configured WINS server for NetBIOS names used to implement browsing and domain services.

➤ If a domain master browser is a WINS-enabled client, it queries WINS periodically (every 12 to 15 minutes) to obtain a list of all domains stored in the WINS database.

These enhancements make it possible for WINS to assist in fully browsing the entire network and resources shared in remote domains. Implementing this enhanced browsing involves the use of WINS in two ways:

➤ Names for remote domains are registered in WINS and replicated to all WINS servers used in the network.

➤ WINS-enabled clients use a modified process of WINS query and directed communication with computers in the remote domain to obtain browse list information about servers and shared resources in these remote domains.

NetBT clients can use broadcasts to their local subnets for <domain> [1D] names. When this happens and the domain is located at a remote subnet or site, the query fails. Under these circumstances, browsing is not possible unless you make and maintain special configurations. Without WINS, each domain master browser would need static information entered in an lmhosts file to further process a client request. This would require careful administration to maintain and update static lmhosts files at each domain master browser in the enterprise.

With WINS, clients can leverage the replicated names database more effectively and administrators can eliminate reliance on lmhosts management. The process used by WINS clients to resolve a browser request for a remote domain name is different from the process used by non-WINS (NetBIOS broadcast-only) computers or to obtain information about local domains on the same subnet.

Some reasons for a negative response from a WINS server include:

➤ The remote [1b] name queried was found to be for a workgroup, not a domain.

➤ The PDC for the remote domain is not a WINS client.

➤ The PDC for the remote domain is a WINS client, but the PDC and the browsing client are not sharing a common WINS database (replication is not occurring).

If receiving negative responses from the WINS server, the WINS client should do the following:

1. It makes a connection with its local master browser (on the same subnet as the client) and requests the name of the master browser of the desired domain or workgroup.

2. The local master browser returns the name of the master browser that advertised the domain or workgroup.

3. The client resolves the unique name of the <master_browser> [20] that advertised the domain or workgroup.

4. The client then makes a connection with that master browser to request a list of servers in the domain or workgroup.

5. The list of servers in the domain or workgroup is returned to the client.

WINS Database Replication

To be effective with WINS databases, you need to pay careful attention to network planning or an existing network topology. You can configure WINS scenarios for optimum performance, based on this premise. Replicating across WANs will need the best performance possible through greater utilization of the overall network. The speed of persistent connections will be the primary factor in the performance of replication between partners.

Configuration Scenarios

Before configuring replication, you should first carefully design and review your WINS replication topology. For WANs, this planning can be critical to the success of your deployment and use of WINS. In general, WINS offers you the following options when you are configuring replication:

➤ You can manually configure WINS replication for a WAN environment.

➤ For some larger campus networks, you might also configure WINS to replicate within a LAN environment.

➤ In smaller or bounded LAN installations, you might consider enabling and using WINS automatic partner configuration for simplified setup of WINS replication.

➤ In some larger or more global installations, you might have to configure WINS across untrusted Windows NT domains.

Replication across WANs

When configuring WINS replication, the most important planning issues are slower WAN links and total length of time required for all replicated changes in the WINS database to converge and achieve consistency on the network. The frequency of WINS database replication between WINS servers is a major planning issue. The WINS server database should be replicated frequently enough to prevent the downtime of a single WINS server from affecting the reliability of the mapping information in other WINS servers. The time interval between replications should not be so small, however, that it interferes with network throughput.

Network topology can influence your decision on replication frequency. For example, if your network has multiple hubs connected by relatively slow WAN links, you can configure WINS database replication between WINS servers on the slow links to occur less frequently than replication on the LAN or on fast WAN links. This reduces traffic across the slow links and reduces contention between replication traffic and WINS client name queries.

Persistent Connections

You can now configure each WINS server to maintain a persistent connection with one or more replication partners. This increases the speed of replication and eliminates the overhead of opening and terminating connections. For Windows 2000 Server, WINS introduces persistent connections between WINS server replication partners. This feature is helpful because, typically, WINS servers disconnect from their replication partners each time replication is completed. In many cases, where WINS servers are interconnected through high-speed LAN links, keeping connections open is preferable to closing them after replication is completed.

For earlier versions of WINS, servers had to establish new WINS-server connections each time replication was performed. Each connection required a modest number of processor cycles. For efficiency, network managers often configured systems to accumulate a larger number of changes before connecting for replication. These reconnections sometimes caused delays (perhaps as long as several minutes) in the replication process, which meant that inconsistencies in server data commonly existed when WINS was updated.

Persistent connections increase the speed of replication because a server can immediately send records to its partners, without incurring the cost of establishing temporary connections each time. Every record is immediately updated across the network upon registration in WINS, making replication more consistent. The bandwidth that persistent connections use is minimal because the connection is usually idle.

Configuring DHCP Server for WINS

When using DHCP and WINS together on your network, you can choose additional DHCP scope options. A Scope is a range of addresses. Specifically, use DHCP options to assign WINS node types (option type 46) and to identify WINS servers for use by DHCP clients (option type 44). In some cases, this can involve adjusting these option types for each physical subnet in which DHCP and WINS are implemented.

Assign a length of time for DHCP lease durations comparable to the time WINS uses for renew intervals, when both services are deployed. By default, DHCP leases are three days in length, and the WINS renew interval is six days. If lease lengths for DHCP widely differ from WINS renew intervals, the effect on your network can be an increase in lease-management traffic and might cause a WINS registration for both services. If you shorten or lengthen the DHCP lease time for clients, then modify the WINS renew interval accordingly.

If a large percentage of clients use NetBIOS and you are using DNS, consider using WINS lookup on your DNS servers. If WINS lookup is enabled on Microsoft DNS Service, WINS is used for final resolution of any names not found using DNS resolution. The WINS forward lookup and WINS-R reverse lookup records are supported only by DNS. If you use servers on your network that do not support DNS, use DNS Manager to ensure that these WINS records are not propagated to DNS servers that do not support WINS lookup.

If you have a large percentage of computers running Windows 2000 on your network, consider creating a pure DNS environment. This involves developing a migration plan to upgrade legacy WINS clients to Windows 2000. Support issues involving network name service are simplified by using a single naming and resource locator service (such as WINS and DNS) on your network.

For multihomed WINS servers, where more than one local network connection appears in the Network and Dial-up Connections folder, Windows 2000 does not guarantee the binding order for NetBIOS. Therefore, for a multihomed WINS server to function properly, all installed connections should be configured as routable interfaces.

All multihomed WINS servers should have their primary IP addresses assigned to each network connection, configured as push and pull replication partners at other servers that can be reached through each of the respective connections. When configuring replication partners, you can ensure a specific network connection is used by specifying an IP address for the remote multihomed server you are adding at a WINS server.

Otherwise, when replication partners are specified and resolved by a name entered in the WINS Console, a packet generated by WINS could use any of the installed interfaces and their respective IP addresses. This seemingly random behavior results from WINS referring to its local IP routing table, which contains all of the installed IP interfaces, before it sends packets to the remote server.

Monitoring and Managing

Windows 2000 includes tools for monitoring and managing WINS—for example, the NBTSTAT –n command-line utility to verify client NetBIOS names. The Microsoft Management Console (MMC) offers a customizable administrative tool that will allow for remote management of WINS. The WINS Console offers its own backup service for the WINS database and its Registry entries. Another part of managing WINS is known as *scavenging*. Understanding what scavenging is will help define the need for it. Scavenging the WINS database is a necessary evil that you can set up to be done automatically at configured intervals. The WINS database can also be restored and compacted through the WINS Console.

Using NBTSTAT

To verify WINS registration of client NetBIOS names, type "nbtstat -n" at the command prompt on the WINS client computer. This will list the local NetBIOS names table for the WINS client computer. Verify that each name indicates Registered in the Status column, such as shown in this sample command output:

```
Node IpAddress: [10.0.0.1] Scope Id: []
      NetBIOS Local Name Table
   Name           Type          Status
------------------------------------------
BRADMA8        <20> UNIQUE    Registered
BRADMA8        <00> UNIQUE    Registered
WORKGROUP      <00> GROUP     Registered
INet~Services  <1C> GROUP     Registered
IS~BRADMA8.....<00> UNIQUE    Registered
BRADMA8        <03> UNIQUE    Registered
ADMINISTRATOR  <03> UNIQUE    Registered
WORKGROUP      <1E> GROUP     Registered
WORKGROUP      <1D> UNIQUE    Registered
.._MYBROWSE__.<01> GROUP     Registered
```

The Status column should indicate a status of Registered, Registering, or Conflict.

When the name is shown to be either Registered or Registering, you can type "nbtstat -RR" to release and refresh registration of the local NetBIOS names of the client with WINS.

When the Status column indicates a conflict for the name, try either of the following to resolve the conflicted name state at the client computer:

➤ For Windows 2000 WINS clients, you can selectively disconnect and reconnect the network connection in the Network and Dial-up Connections folder to force the release and refresh of all client NetBIOS names in WINS.

➤ For earlier versions of Windows, shut down and restart the system to achieve similar results.

After the release/refresh process is completed, repeat nbtstat -n to verify that all local names have a status of Registered in WINS.

*Note: Perform this step only if the name in conflict is critically necessary for the WINS client to maintain visibility or locate other computers on the network. Names that fit this description might include the [00h] and [20h] type names, if they match the client NetBIOS computer name. The need to resolve a name conflict for other types of names might be less critical to support needs. You can also use the **NBTSTAT** command to perform other useful procedures related to WINS client support.*

Microsoft Management Console

With Windows 2000 Administration Tools, included on the Windows 2000 Server and Windows 2000 Advanced Server CD sets, you can manage a server remotely from any computer running Windows 2000. Windows 2000 Administration Tools contains MMC snap-ins and other tools you can use to manage computers running Windows 2000 Server. These tools are not provided with Windows 2000 Professional.

Once Windows 2000 Administration Tools is installed on a computer, an administrator can manage a remote server from that computer.

To open WINS, click on Start, point to Programs, then to Administrative Tools, and click on WINS. For information about using WINS, click on the Action menu, and then click on Help.

You can perform a search of records by name, owner, or record type by simply right-clicking on Active Registrations in MMC, as shown in Figure 7.9.

WINS Database Backup

The WINS Console provides its own backup feature for the WINS server database. Begin by right-clicking on the WINS server name, as shown in Figure 7.10. After

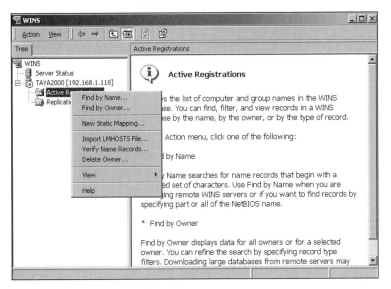

Figure 7.9 WINS administration from MMC.

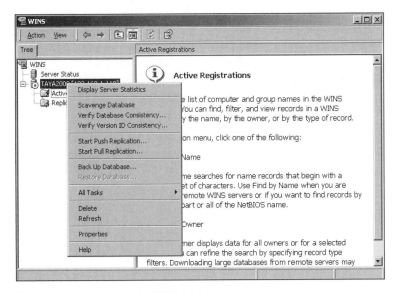

Figure 7.10 Backing up the WINS database.

you specify a backup directory for the database, WINS performs complete database backups every three hours, by default.

You should also periodically back up the Registry entries for the WINS server.

You can choose to back up the WINS database during server shutdown by selecting the option on the General tab of the WINS property sheet, as shown in Figure 7.11.

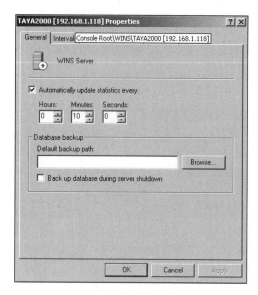

Figure 7.11 WINS database properties General tab.

Scavenging the Database

Scavenging the WINS server database consists of deleting obsolete information that remains after changes occur. Like any database, the WINS server database of address mappings needs to be periodically scavenged and backed up. The local WINS server database sometimes retains both released and old entries that were registered at another WINS server and replicated to the local WINS server. Automatic scavenging takes place at intervals defined by the relationship between the Renew and Extinction intervals you specify on the Interval tab of the WINS property sheet, as shown in Figure 7.12. You can also manually clean the database.

Table 7.2 shows the results of scavenging the WINS database for a WINS server. The first column shows the record criteria and state of any database entries before scavenging is started. The second column indicates the state of the same entries after the scavenging process.

To modify backup settings, complete the following steps:

1. Open WINS (click on Start, point to Programs, then to Administrative Tools, and click on WINS).

2. In the console tree, click on the applicable WINS server.

3. On the Action menu, click on Properties.

4. On the General tab, under Database Backup, modify default backup settings as needed.

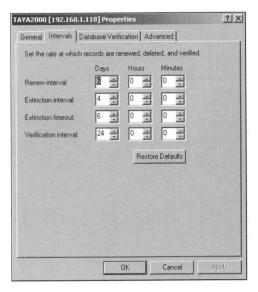

Figure 7.12   Intervals property sheet.

Table 7.2   The results of scavenging a WINS database.

Before Scavenging	After Scavenging
Active names, owned by this WINS server, where the Renew interval has expired.	Marked as Released.
Active names, replicated from other servers, where the Verification interval has expired.	Revalidated.
Released names owned by this WINS server where the Extinction interval has expired.	Marked as Tombstoned.
Tombstoned names where Extinction timeout has expired.	Deleted and removed from the database.
Tombstoned or deleted names replicated from other servers.	Removed from the database.

5. To view a description of a dialog box item, right-click on the item, and then click on What's This?

Restoring the WINS Database

To restore the WINS database, complete the following steps:

1. Stop WINS.

2. Delete all files in the folder path on the WINS server computer where you are restoring the database. This path is determined by the current setting of Database Path, which is located on the Advanced tab in server Properties.

3. Open WINS.

4. In the console tree, click on the applicable WINS server.

5. On the Action menu, click on Restore Database.

6. In the Browse for Folder dialog box, click on the same folder (such as C:\) that was used previously to back up the local WINS database, and then click on OK.

7. To open WINS, click on Start, point to Programs, then to Administrative Tools, and click on WINS.

In Step 1, wait for WINS to stop completely before proceeding. A busy server might require several minutes before it can stop WINS and you can proceed with restoring the database.

When you restore the database, WINS requires that the backup path used for restoration match the one you originally specified in server Properties. By default, this path is the root folder on the system partition. If you specify a different path, be sure to use that same path given in Step 6 above.

WINS does not permit you to restore the server databases remotely from another computer.

The restore option is available only when viewing a computer on which WINS is stopped. In some cases, you might need to refresh the WINS Console to activate the restore option. If necessary, click on Refresh from the Action menu to refresh the server node so that the WINS Console detects that WINS is stopped on the server.

In case of database corruption, the WINS database can be restored from the backup. You can sometimes repair WINS database corruption by incrementing the starting version count for the WINS server and restarting the server.

Compacting the WINS Database

Scavenging and compaction are additional maintenance operations that you can use selectively to help reduce database size and reclaim disk space that is no longer used by the database. For Windows 2000 Server, WINS automatically performs dynamic compaction at periodic intervals, so manual compaction is not generally necessary.

The lmhosts File

The lmhosts file is a static file that assists with remote NetBIOS name resolution on computers that cannot respond to NetBIOS name-query broadcasts. It contains NetBIOS name-to-IP address mappings. Its function is similar to that of the hosts file; the difference is that you can use the hosts file to map DNS domain names for host computers to their IP addresses.

Computers in a Microsoft-based network can resolve NetBIOS names in several ways. If one method fails, they try the next method, in a fixed order. In a broadcast-based network, the computer first checks its NetBIOS names cache. Normally, the cache contains the name only if it was used recently, but names can be preloaded from an lmhosts file into the cache.

If static name-to-address mappings are entered in the lmhosts file using the #PRE notation, then these names are considered to be preloaded into the NetBIOS names cache and are used first to resolve a name query, before a NetBIOS subnet broadcast or WINS query is used.

After the local cache is checked, WINS servers are contacted (if they are configured and reachable) before the name query is broadcast locally on the client subnet to attempt resolution of the name. If these methods fail, the client (if enabled to do so) can later refer to an lmhosts file again to further search for and obtain the name-to-IP address mapping—for example, to resolve a name used by another computer located on another subnet located across a router from the client.

Limitations of lmhosts Files

Despite the many uses of the lmhosts file, it has some limitations. Its greatest limitation is that it is a static file. Because of this, entries must be updated if the name or the IP address of the computer changes.

An IP address for a client might change for several reasons:

➤ It changes (physically moves) to another subnet within your routed LAN.

➤ The computer is a portable and changes to another site, such as a remote dial-up user dialing in from home through remote access to your network.

➤ The DHCP server leases the client a different IP address after its lease expires.

When such changes occur, they must also be propagated to all the computers that need access to the resource with the changed name-to-IP-address mapping. A centrally maintained lmhosts file can reduce some of the manual administration needed to propagate new or revised mappings to the required computers. Entering and changing the mappings is still a manual, labor-intensive process, however. Although maintaining an lmhosts file centrally is certainly preferable to keeping one on each computer, this solution can be feasible only for an organization with a small number of servers and clients. On larger networks, a central file becomes too complicated to maintain and is not a viable or recommended solution.

Note: The WINS Console supports the ability to import static mappings from an lmhosts file into a WINS server database, creating static type WINS entries.

Chapter Summary

Windows 2000 Server provides WINS, which enables the server computer to act as a NetBIOS name server, and register and resolve names for WINS-enabled client computers, as described in the NetBT standards. When a WINS server is queried for a name, it returns the IP address of the computer that registered this name.

Name registration occurs when a WINS client requests the use of a NetBIOS name on the network. WINS-enabled clients can directly query their configured WINS server for NetBIOS names used to implement browsing and domain services. Names for remote domains are registered in WINS and replicated to all WINS servers used in the network.

You can view node type by typing "ipconfig /all" in a command prompt window. This is an overall way of troubleshooting node problems.

When using multihomed WINS servers, you should configure all server IP addresses as replication partners with other WINS servers. A larger list of WINS servers gives clients additional fault tolerance for WINS when their configured primary WINS server is not available.

Configure WINS through the WINS Console, an administrative tool used to manage WINS servers. Open the WINS Console by clicking on Start, pointing to Programs, then to Administrative Tools, and click on WINS.

WINS proxies helps resolve NetBIOS name queries for computers located on routed TCP/IP networks By default, most computers not able to use WINS use broadcasts to resolve NetBIOS name queries and register their NetBIOS names on the network.

The frequency of WINS database replication among WINS servers is a major planning issue. Before configuring replication, you should first carefully design and review your WINS replication topology.

For Windows 2000 Server, WINS introduces persistent connections between WINS server replication partners. Persistent connections increase the speed of replication because a server can immediately send records to its partners, without incurring the cost of establishing temporary connections each time.

To verify WINS registration of client NetBIOS names, type "nbtstat -n" at the command prompt on the WINS client computer. This displays a list of the local NetBIOS names table for the WINS client computer.

The local WINS server database sometimes retains both released and old entries that were registered at another WINS server and replicated to the local WINS server. Automatic scavenging takes place at intervals defined by the relationship between the renew and extinction intervals you define on the Interval tab of the WINS property sheet to clean up obsolete information.

Review Questions

1. Which of the following types appended to a NetBIOS name indicates a workstation?

   a. 00h

   b. 20h

   c. 01h

   d. 10h

2. Which of the following types appended to a NetBIOS name indicates a file server?

   a. 00h

   b. 20h

   c. 01h

   d. 10h

3. Which of the following is not a NetBIOS node type?

   a. P-node

   b. C-node

   c. M-node

   d. H-node

4. Which of the NetBIOS node types does not use broadcasts?

   a. M-node

   b. P-node

   c. H-node

   d. B-node

5. What combination of nodes is M-node?

   a. B-node and H-node

   b. H-node and P-node

   c. B-node and P-node

   d. None of the above

6. Which of the following NetBIOS-based computers use NetBIOS names?

   a. Windows for Workgroups

   b. LAN Manager

   c. LAN Manager for Unix hosts

   d. All of the above

7. What is a WINS pull partner that pulls, or requests, replication of updated WINS database entries from other WINS servers at a configured interval?

   a. Client

   b. Workstation

   c. Application

   d. Server

8. What is the minimum number of WINS servers recommended to provide a fault-tolerant WINS installation?

   a. 1

   b. 3

   c. 2

   d. 4

9. Configuring all server IP addresses as replication partners with other WINS servers is best when using what type of WINS server?

   a. Internet Group

   b. Multihomed

   c. Unique

   d. Group

10. For Windows 2000, you can configure WINS clients to use up to how many servers?

    a. 8

    b. 10

    c. 6

    d. 12

11. Which of the following do you use to register and troubleshoot client connectivity?

    a. NBSTAT -RR

    b. REGEDIT

    c. STATNB-RR

    d. None of the above

12. Which of the following statements best defines a WINS proxy?

    a. A client computer configured to act on behalf of other host computers that cannot directly use WINS

    b. A server computer configured to act on behalf of other host computers that cannot directly use WINS

    c. A client computer configured to directly use WINS

    d. None of the above

13. What type of network requires WINS proxy agents to help resolve NetBIOS name queries for computers located on routed networks?

    a. Networks with Unix hosts or other non-WINS clients

    b. Networks with Windows 95 clients

    c. Networks with Windows 98 clients

    d. Networks with Windows NT clients

14. Which of the following statements describes how WINS proxies are used?

    a. Checks the B-node name registrations against the WINS server database

    b. Deletes the released client names from its remote names cache

    c. Attempts to resolve the name queries using information either locally contained in its cache of remote names or through the use of information it obtains from the WINS server

    d. All of the above

15. Name registration occurs when a WINS client requests the use of a NetBIOS name on the network. What are the two types of names?

    a. Group and shared

    b. Unique and exclusive

    c. Unique and group

    d. IP and NetBIOS

16. At what point are NetBIOS names registered with WINS and normally released?

    a. When the computer is properly shut down

    b. When the lease time expires

    c. When the current user logs off

    d. When a computer with the same name is turned on

17. What does the term WACK stand for?

    a. Windows Acknowledgment

    b. Wait for Acknowledgment

    c. WINS Acknowledgment

    d. Write Acknowledgment

7

18. What is the default burst-queue size?

    a. 400

    b. 500

    c. 300

    d. 1,000

19. NetBIOS group names are registered by what?

    a. Master browsers

    b. Default browsers

    c. Name registry

    d. None of the above

20. How can you configure WINS replication for a WAN environment?

    a. Manually only

    b. Automatically only

    c. Manually or automatically

    d. You do not configure WINS replication; it is self-configuring

Real-World Projects

James and Lesha Spoon both work for ACM Corporation. ACM implemented two WINS servers, A and B, to provide fault tolerance and enjoy greater performance on the NetBT network. The databases are now in place and only need to be configured for replication. Replication of the WINS database from Server A to Server B will provide a backup should Server A fail. Replication of the WINS database from Server B to Server A will provide a backup should Server B fail.

The two replication scenarios available are push and pull. Configuring a WINS server as a push partner causes the server to replicate its database after a number of changes has been made to the database. The number of changes is configured as the threshold. Once the threshold is met, the database is replicated, regardless of the time since the last replication. This type of replication ensures that the two WINS servers will never be out of synch by more than the number of the threshold.

Configuring a WINS server as a pull partner causes the server to query another WINS server for database changes. The query occurs based on time. The backup server initiates a pull at predetermined time intervals—for example, on the hour or every half-hour. Even if there are no changes to replicate, the backup server will query the other server as scheduled. WINS replication based on time intervals is most useful over slow WAN links. If the backup database is located on the other end of a slow WAN link, configure replication to occur during off-peak times, avoiding 8 a.m. login traffic.

Note: You can back up a server based on both time and number of changes. This is accomplished by configuring a server as both a push and a pull partner and configuring the backup server as both a push and a pull partner. James decides to configure WINS Server A and WINS Server B so that each would provide a backup of the other's WINS database. He configured Server A to push its data after every 30 changes. He then configured Server B to pull data every hour. Lesha explained to James that this configuration provided a backup for the WINS database only on Server A and did not provide a backup strategy for Server B. What should be done to correct this problem?

You can configure replication to occur based on two conditions: on a regular or preset time interval; or once a number of changes has occurred to the database. To establish a complete backup of both servers based strictly on number of changes, you would configure both as push partners. To establish a complete backup of both servers based strictly on number of times, you would configure both as pull partners. Alternatively, to establish a complete backup of both servers, you would configure just one of the servers as both a push and pull partner. This alternative solution creates a backup of the server based on number of changes and backs up the other server based on time.

7

Project 7.1

To install two Windows 2000 Servers with TCP/IP and WINS (locate one server on a remote LAN and one server on a local LAN), perform the following steps:

Note: If you do not have a remote LAN, you can simulate one with the use of two modems and two phone lines.

1. Point to Start.

2. Point to Settings.

3. Click on Control Panel.

4. Double-click on System.

5. On the Advanced tab, click on Startup and Recovery.

6. Under System Startup, in the default operating system list, click on the operating system to start if one is not selected from the list displayed during startup.

7. In the Display List of Operating Systems For box, type the number of seconds the list should be displayed before the default operating system automatically starts.

8. During the installation process, the computer will prompt you to enter the TCP/IP address and WINS address for the server. Complete this entry at that time.

After completing the installation, James and Lesha are now ready to configure either push or pull WINS partners.

Project 7.2

To configure the WINS servers as push and pull partners, perform the following steps:

1. Using MMC, establish the servers first as pull partners. Keep reducing the time between replication updates. See how the replication traffic affects your network performance.
   a. Open WINS.
   b. In the console tree, click on Replication Partners.
   c. On the Action menu, click on Properties.
   d. Click on the Pull Replication tab.
   e. Select the Use Persistent Connections for Pull Replication Partners checkbox.
   f. The amount of time between pull replications is indicated in the Replication interval, which can be specified either globally for all pull partners or individually for specific partners.

2. Using MMC, establish the servers as two-way push partners. Keep reducing the threshold. See how the replication traffic affects your network performance.
   a. Open WINS.
   b. In the console tree, click on Replication Partners.
   c. On the Action menu, click on Properties.
   d. Click on the Push Replication tab.
   e. Select the Use Persistent Connections for Push Replication Partners checkbox.

James and Lesha created a pull partner WINS server so that it requests replication of updated WINS database entries from other WINS servers at a configured interval. They created a push partner WINS server to notify other WINS servers of the need to replicate their database entries at a configured interval.

Project 7.3

To delete a server's WINS database, perform the following steps:

1. Stop the WINS service on this computer.

2. Open Add/Remove Programs.

3. Click on Add/Remove Windows Components.

4. In Windows 2000 Components, select Networking Services from the list of components, and then click on Details.

5 In Subcomponents of Networking Services, scroll to Windows Internet Name Service (WINS) and clear the checkbox.

The reason James and Lesha deleted the database is to see what will happen during the time intervals between replications of the WINS database for each server and how it will affect the WINS clients on the network.

CHAPTER EIGHT

IP Routing

After completing this chapter, you will be able to:

✓ Understand routing concepts

✓ Define IP routing

✓ Define routing interfaces, devices, and ports

✓ Identify IP routing protocols

✓ Identify routing infrastructures

✓ Implement a Windows 2000 router

✓ Set up static IP routing

✓ Deploy static IP routing

✓ Set up RIP-for-IP routing

✓ Deploy RIP-for-IP routing

✓ Set up OSPF routing

✓ Deploy OSPF routing

✓ Understand how to deploy a single-area internetwork with OSPF

✓ Understand the use of router administration and management tools

The Routing and Remote Access Service for Microsoft Windows 2000 Server is a full-featured software router and an open platform for routing and internetworking. It offers routing services to businesses in local area network (LAN) and wide area network (WAN) environments. The Routing and Remote Access service combines and integrates the separate routing and remote access services of Windows NT 4 and is an enhancement of the Routing and Remote Access Service (also known as RRAS) for Windows NT 4.

An advantage of the Routing and Remote Access Service is integration with the Windows 2000 Server operating system. The Routing and Remote Access Service delivers many cost-saving features and works with a wide variety of hardware platforms and hundreds of network adapters. The Routing and Remote Access Service is extensible with application programming interfaces (APIs) that developers can use to create custom networking solutions and that new vendors can use to participate in the growing business of open internetworking.

Routing Concepts

Routing is the transference of data across an internetwork from a source host to a destination host. Routing can be understood in terms of two processes: host routing and router routing.

Host Routing

When a host using a routable protocol wants to send data to another host, it must first obtain the internetwork address of the destination. The host obtains the destination internetwork address through address resolution by referencing its logical name. An example would be how TCP/IP hosts use Domain Name System (DNS) name resolution to resolve a DNS domain name to an IP address.

Once the host has obtained the destination internetwork address, the source network and the destination network addresses are compared. When the source and destination hosts are on the same network, the packets are sent directly to the destination host by the source without the use of a router. The source host sends the packet to the destination by addressing the packet to the destination's physical address. This is known as a *direct delivery*, in which the destination internetwork address and the destination physical address are for the same end system.

When the source and destination hosts are on different networks, the packets to the destination cannot be directly delivered by the source. Instead, the source delivers them to an intermediate router by addressing the packet to the router's physical address. This is known as an *indirect delivery*, in which the destination internetwork address and the destination physical address are not for the same end system. During an indirect delivery, the sending host forwards the packet to a router on its network by determining the router corresponding to the first hop or by discovering the entire path from the source to the destination.

Host Determination of the First Hop

IP-sending hosts determine the physical address of the first-hop router in the following ways:

➤ *By using processes such as a host routing table*—A host routing table on the host yields the forwarding address of the router to be used to reach the desired destination network ID. An example is the IP routing table on a Microsoft TCP/IP host.

➤ *By dynamically updating host routing tables*—Dynamic updates of host routing tables are done by a TCP/IP facility that dynamically updates the host routing table with better routes, as packets are sent to destinations. An IP router sends the Internet Control Message Protocol (ICMP) redirect message to a sending host, informing it of a better route to a destination host. The better route becomes a host route in the routing table. TCP/IP for Windows 2000 supports the dynamic update of the IP routing table based on the receipt of the ICMP Redirect message.

➤ *Eavesdropping*—Eavesdropping TCP/IP hosts have the ability to listen to the routing protocol traffic used by routers. This is also known as wiretapping. Eavesdropping hosts have the same routing information as the routers. An example of eavesdropping is Silent RIP, which is the ability of a TCP/IP host to listen to Routing Information Protocol (RIP) for IP routing traffic exchanged by RIP routers and update its routing table.

➤ *By using default routes*—Default routes simplify the configuration of hosts and routers. They reduce the overhead associated with each host having routes for all the networks in the internetwork. The default route and its forwarding address to the default router are used when no other routes to the destination network are found. The default gateway for TCP/IP hosts is a default router.

➤ *By querying the network for the best route*—For hosts without a routing table or a configured default router, the sending host can determine the physical address of the first-hop router by querying the routers on the network. A query for the best route to a specified destination network address is sent as a broadcast or multicast packet. The sending host analyzes the responses from the routers and chooses the best router. An example of this querying process is the RIP GetLocalTarget message sent by an IPX host. The RIP GetLocalTarget message contains a desired destination IPX network ID. IPX routers on the sending host's network that can reach the destination IPX network ID send a response to the sending host. Based on the RIP responses from the local routers, the sending host chooses the best router to forward the IPX packet.

8

Host Determination of the Entire Path

When using some routable protocols, the sending host does more than determine the first hop. The source host goes through a route-discovery process and determines the path between the sending host and the destination. The list of networks or routers is then included in the Network layer header and is used by the routers to forward the packet along the indicated path. This is known as *source routing*.

In source routing, the routers are only acting as store and forward devices because the sending host has already made the routing decisions. Source routing is not typically implemented as a method of routing because the path needs to be either known or discovered. Source route-discovery processes tend to be traffic intensive and slow. IP routing is normally done through routing decisions made by sending hosts and IP routers based on local routing tables. In network testing and debugging situations, however, sometimes the desired course of action is to specify an exact route through the IP internetwork that overrides the path that would normally be taken. This is known as *IP source routing*.

In IP source routing, the entire route is specified by the sending host through the IP addresses of successive IP routers between the source and destination. At each IP router, the IP datagram is addressed to the next router using the Destination IP address field of the IP header. IP supports two types of source routing: The first type is *loose source routing*, in which the IP address of the next router can be one or more routers away (multiple hops); the second type is *strict source routing*, in which the next router must be a neighboring router (single hop).

Router Routing

When a router is forwarded a packet that is not destined for that router, the router must deliver it either to the destination host or to another router. If the destination network matches a network to which the router is attached, the router forwards the packet to the destination host by addressing the packet to the destination host's physical address. The router performs a direct delivery to the destination. Conversely, if the destination network is not directly attached, the router forwards the packet to an intermediate router. The intermediate router chosen is based on the forwarding address of the optimal route in the routing table. The router forwards the packet by addressing the packet to the intermediate router's physical address. The router performs an indirect delivery to the next router in the path to the destination. Figure 8.1 illustrates router routing.

Routing Tables

During the routing process, the routing decisions of hosts and routers are aided by a database of routes known as the *routing table*. The routing table is not exclusive to a router. Depending on the routable protocol, a host may also have a routing table that may be used to decide the best router for the packet to be forwarded. An IP host has a routing table. An IPX host does not.

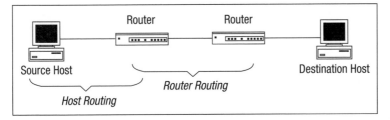

Figure 8.1 Router routing.

Routing Table Structure

A routing table consists of several fields:

➤ *Network ID field*—Contains the identification number for a network route or an internetwork address for a host route.

➤ *Forwarding Address field*—Contains the address to which the packet is to be forwarded. The forwarding address can be a network interface card (NIC) address or an internetwork address. The Forwarding Address field may be blank for network IDs to which the end system or router is directly attached.

➤ *Interface field*—Indicates the network interface that is used when forwarding packets to the network ID. This is a port number or other type of logical identifier. For example, the interface for a 3Com EtherLink III NIC may be referred to as ELNK3 in the routing table.

➤ *Metric field*—Indicates the cost of a route. If multiple routes exist to a given destination network ID, the metric is used to decide which route is to be taken. The route with the lowest metric is the preferred choice. Some routing algorithms store only a single route to any network ID in the routing table, even when multiple routes exist. In this case, the metric is used by the router to decide which route to store in the routing table.

Metrics can indicate different ways of expressing a route preference:

➤ *Hop Count*—A common metric that indicates the number of routers or hops in a path to the network ID.

➤ *Delay*—A measure of time required for the packet to reach the network ID. Delay is used to indicate the speed of the path—LAN links have a low delay, WAN links have a high delay—or a congested condition of a path.

➤ *Throughput*—The effective amount of data that can be sent along the path per second. Throughput is not necessarily a reflection of the bit rate of the link, as a very busy Ethernet link may have a lower throughput than an unutilized 64Kbps WAN link.

➤ *Reliability*—A measure of the path constancy. Some types of links are more prone to link failures; with WAN links, leased lines are more reliable than dial-up lines.

➤ *Lifetime field*—Indicates the lifetime that the route is considered valid. When routes are learned through the exchange of information with other routers, this is an additional field. Learned routes have a finite lifetime. To keep a learned route in the routing table, the route must be refreshed through a periodic process. If a learned route's lifetime expires, it is removed from the routing table. The timing out of learned routes provides a way for routers to reconfigure themselves when the topology of an internetwork changes because of a downed link or a downed router. Figure 8.2 shows the general structure of a typical routing table.

Static and Dynamic Routers

For routing between routers to work efficiently in an internetwork, routers must have knowledge of other network IDs or be configured with a default route. On large internetworks, the routing tables must be maintained so that the traffic always travels along optimal paths. How the routing tables are maintained defines the distinction between static and dynamic routing.

Static Routing

A router with manually configured routing tables is a *static router*. A network administrator, with knowledge of the internetwork topology, manually builds and updates the routing table, programming all routes in the table. Static routers can work well for small internetworks, but, because of their manual administration, they do not scale well to large or dynamically changing internetworks.

Static routers are not fault tolerant. The lifetime of a manually configured static route is infinite, and, therefore, static routers do not sense and recover from downed routers or downed links. A good example of a static router is a multihomed computer running Windows 2000. Creating a static IP router with Windows 2000 is as simple as installing multiple NICs, configuring TCP/IP, and enabling IP routing.

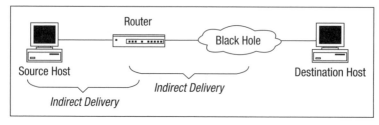

Figure 8.2 The general structure of a routing table.

Dynamic Routing

A router with dynamically configured routing tables is a *dynamic router*. Dynamic routing consists of routing tables that are built and maintained automatically through an ongoing communication between routers. This communication is facilitated by a routing protocol, a series of periodic or on-demand messages containing routing information that is exchanged between routers. Except for their initial configuration, dynamic routers require little ongoing maintenance and, therefore, can scale to larger internetworks.

Dynamic routing is fault tolerant. Dynamic routes learned from other routers have a finite lifetime. If a router or link goes down, the routers sense the change in the internetwork topology through the expiration of the lifetime of the learned route in the routing table. This change can then be propagated to other routers so that all the routers on the internetwork become aware of the new internetwork topology. The ability to scale and recover from internetwork faults makes dynamic routing the better choice for medium, large, and very large internetworks.

IP Routing

8

In general terms, routing is the process of forwarding packets to connected networks. For TCP/IP-based networks, routing is part of the IP and is used in combination with other network protocol services to provide forwarding capabilities between hosts that are located on separate network segments within a larger TCP/IP-based network.

IP is the mailroom of the TCP/IP protocol, where IP data sorting and delivery take place. Each incoming or outgoing packet is called an *IP datagram*. An IP datagram contains two IP addresses: the source address of the sending host and the destination address of the receiving host. Unlike hardware addresses, the IP addresses within a datagram remain the same as it travels across a TCP/IP network. Routing is the primary function of IP. IP datagrams are exchanged and processed on each host by using IP at the Internet layer.

Above the IP layer, transport services on the source host pass data in the form of Transmission Control Protocol (TCP) segments or User Datagram Protocol (UDP) messages to the IP layer. The IP layer assembles IP datagrams with source and destination address information that is used to route the data through the network. The IP layer then passes datagrams down to the network interface layer. At this layer, data-link services convert IP datagrams into frames for transmission over network-specific media on a physical network. This process happens in reverse order on the destination host.

Each IP datagram contains a source and destination IP address. IP layer services on each host examine the destination address of each datagram, compare this address with a locally maintained routing table, and then decide what further forwarding action to take. IP routers are attached to two or more IP network segments that are enabled to forward packets between them.

IP Routers

TCP/IP network segments are interconnected by *IP routers*, which are devices that pass IP datagrams from one network segment to another. IP routers provide the primary means of joining two or more physically separated IP network segments. All IP routers share two essential characteristics: They are multihomed hosts, and they provide packet forwarding for other TCP/IP hosts.

You can implement IP routers by using a variety of hardware and software products. Box-based routers that are dedicated hardware devices running specialized software are common. Alternatively, you can use routing solutions based on software, such as the Routing and Remote Access Service, which runs on a computer running Windows 2000 Server. Regardless of the type of IP routers you use, all IP routers rely on the use of a routing table to communicate between network segments.

Routing Interfaces, Devices, and Ports

The Windows 2000 remote access router views the installed networking equipment as a series of routing interfaces, devices, and ports. A *routing interface* is a physical or logical interface over which unicast or multicast packets are forwarded. A *device* represents hardware or software that creates physical or logical point-to-point connections. A *port* is a communication channel that supports a single point-to-point connection.

Routing Interface

The Windows 2000 router uses a routing interface to forward unicast IP, IPX, or AppleTalk packets and multicast IP packets. The three types of routing interfaces are:

➤ *LAN interface*—A physical interface that typically represents a local area connection using LAN technology, such as Ethernet or token ring. A LAN interface reflects an installed network adapter. An installed WAN adapter is sometimes represented as a LAN interface. For example, some frame relay adapters create a separate logical LAN interface for each configured virtual circuit. LAN interfaces are always active and typically do not require an authentication process to become active.

➤ *Demand-dial interface*—A logical interface that represents a point-to-point connection, based on either a physical connection, such as two routers connected over an analog phone line that uses modems, or a logical connection, such as two routers connected over a virtual private network (VPN) connection that uses the Internet. Demand-dial connections are either on-demand (the point-to-point connection is established only when needed) or persistent (the point-to-point connection is established and then remains in a connected state). Demand-dial interfaces typically require an authentication process to become connected. The equipment needed by a demand-dial interface is a port on a device.

> *IP-in-IP tunnel interface*—A logical interface that represents a tunneled point-to-point connection. IP-in-IP tunnel interfaces do not require an authentication process to become connected.

Device

A *device* is the hardware or software that provides ports that demand-dial and remote access connections used to establish point-to-point connections. A device can be physical, such as a modem, or virtual, such as a VPN protocol. It can support a single port, such as a modem, or multiple ports, such as modem bank hardware that can terminate 64 different incoming analog phone calls. An example of a virtual multiport device is the Point-to-Point Tunneling Protocol (PPTP) or Layer Two Tunneling Protocol (L2TP). Each of these protocols supports multiple VPN connections.

Port

A *port* is a channel of a device that supports a single point-to-point connection. For single-port devices such as modems, the device and the port are indistinguishable. For multiport devices, the port is the subdivision of the device over which a separate point-to-point communication is possible. For example, Primary Rate Interface (PRI) ISDN adapters support two separate channels called B channels. The ISDN adapter is a device. Each B channel is a port, because a separate point-to-point connection occurs over each one.

IP Routing Protocols

In dynamic IP routing environments, the use of IP routing protocols propagates IP routing information. The two most common IP routing protocols used on intranets are RIP and Open Shortest Path First (OSPF).

The same intranet can use multiple routing protocols. In this case, configure preference levels to determine which routing protocol is the preferred source of learned routes. The preferred routing protocol is the source of the route that is added to the routing table, regardless of the metric of the learned route. For example, if the metric of an OSPF learned route is five and the metric of the corresponding RIP learned route is three, and OSPF is the preferred routing protocol, then the OSPF route is added to the IP routing table and the RIP route is ignored.

RIP for IP

RIP is designed for exchanging routing information within a small to medium-size internetwork. The biggest advantage of RIP is that it is extremely simple to configure and deploy. Its biggest disadvantage is its inability to scale to large or very large internetworks. The maximum hop count used by RIP routers is 15. Networks that are 16 hops or more away are considered unreachable. As internetworks grow larger in size, the periodic announcements by each RIP router can cause excessive traffic. Another disadvantage of RIP is its high recovery time. When the internetwork topology changes, the RIP routers may take several minutes to reconfigure themselves to the new internetwork topology. While the internetwork reconfigures itself, routing loops may form that result in lost or undeliverable data.

Initially, the routing table for each router includes only the networks that are physically connected. A RIP router periodically sends announcements that contain its routing table entries to inform other local RIP routers of the networks it can reach. RIP version 1 uses IP broadcast packets for its announcements; RIP version 2 uses multicast or broadcast packets for its announcements.

RIP routers can also communicate routing information through triggered updates. These updates occur when the network topology changes and updated routing information is sent reflecting those changes. Triggered updates are sent immediately rather than waiting for the next periodic announcement. For example, when a router detects a link or router failure, it updates its own routing table and sends updated routes. Each router that receives the triggered update modifies its own routing table and propagates the change.

OSPF for IP

OSPF is designed for exchanging routing information within a large or very large internetwork. The biggest advantage of OSPF is that it is efficient; it requires little network overhead even in very large internetworks. The biggest disadvantage of OSPF is its complexity; it requires proper planning and is more difficult to configure and administer.

OSPF uses a Shortest Path First (SPF) algorithm to compute routes in the routing table. The SPF algorithm computes the shortest path between the router and all the networks of the internetwork. SPF-calculated routes are always loop-free.

Instead of exchanging routing table entries as RIP routers do, OSPF routers maintain a map of the internetwork that is updated after any change to the network topology. This map, called the *link state database*, is synchronized among all the

OSPF routers and is used to compute the routes in the routing table. Neighboring OSPF routers form an *adjacency*, which is a logical relationship among routers to synchronize the link state database. Changes to internetwork topology are efficiently flooded across the entire internetwork to ensure that the link state database on each router is synchronized and accurate at all times. Upon receiving changes to the link state database, the routing table is recalculated.

As the size of the link state database increases, memory requirements and route computation times increase. To address this scaling problem, OSPF divides the internetwork into areas that are connected to each other through a backbone area. Each router keeps a link state database only for those areas connected to the router. Area border routers (ABRs) connect the backbone area to other areas. Figure 8.3 shows a diagram of an OSPF internetwork.

Routing Infrastructure

The routing infrastructure is the entire structure of the routed internetwork. The infrastructure has important attributes to consider when you are deciding on which routable protocols and routing protocols to use.

Single Path vs. Multipath

In a single-path routing infrastructure, only a single path exists between any two networks in the internetwork. While this may simplify the routing tables and the packet-flow paths, single-path internetworks are not fault tolerant. A fault can be sensed with a dynamic router, but the networks across the failure are unreachable for the duration of the fault. A downed link or a downed router must be brought back up before packets can be delivered successfully across the downed link or router.

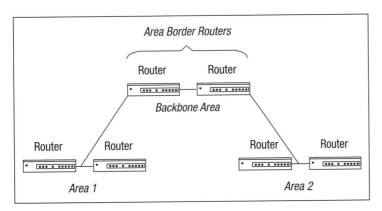

Figure 8.3   An OSPF internetwork.

In a multipath routing infrastructure, multiple paths exist between networks in the internetwork. Multipath internetworks are fault tolerant when dynamic routing is used, and some routing protocols, such as OSPF, can balance the load of network traffic across multiple paths with the same metric value. Multipath internetworks, however, can be more complex to configure and can have a higher probability of routing loops during convergence when using distance vector–based routing protocols.

Flat vs. Hierarchical

In a flat routing infrastructure, each network ID is represented individually in the routing table. The network IDs have no network/subnet structure and cannot be summarized. RIP-based IPX internetworks use flat network addressing and have a flat routing infrastructure.

In a hierarchical routing infrastructure, groups of network IDs can be represented as a single routing table entry through route summarization. The network IDs in a hierarchical internetwork have a network/subnet/sub-subnet structure. A routing table entry for the highest level (the network) is also the route used for the subnets and sub-subnets of the network. Hierarchical routing infrastructures simplify routing tables and lower the amount of routing information that is exchanged, but they require more planning. IP implements hierarchical network addressing, and IP internetworks can have a hierarchical routing structure.

In the hierarchical infrastructure, the internetwork can be divided into routing domains (also known as regions or areas). A *routing domain* is a collection of contiguous networks connected by routers that share the routing information for the routes within the domain. A common routing domain called the *backbone* connects routing domains. The routers within the domain perform intra-domain routing. Domain routers connected to the backbone perform inter-domain routing.

Autonomous Systems

Very large internetworks need to be divided into separate entities known as autonomous systems. An *autonomous system (AS)* is a portion of the internetwork under the same administrative authority. The administrative authority can be an institution or corporation but can also be defined by the use of a routing protocol such as OSPF. The contiguous portion of an IP internetwork that is using OSPF to distribute routing information is under OSPF administrative authority and is, therefore, an OSPF AS. The AS may be further divided into regions, domains, or areas that define a hierarchy within the AS.

Interior Gateway Protocols (IGPs) are used to distribute routing information within an AS. Exterior Gateway Protocols (EGPs) are used to distribute routing information between ASs. Figure 8.4 illustrates an AS with IGPs and EGPs.

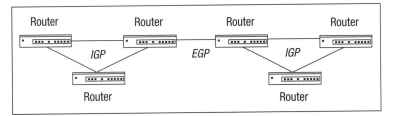

Figure 8.4   An AS with IGPs and EGPs.

Interior Gateway Protocols

IGPs are intra-AS routing protocols that distribute routes within the AS in either a flat or hierarchical manner.

The following are IGPs for IP internetworks:

➤ *RIP for IP*—A Request for Comments (RFC)-based distance vector IGP.

➤ *OSPF*—An RFC-based link state IGP.

Exterior Gateway Protocols

EGPs are inter-AS routing protocols. They define the way that all of the networks within the AS are advertised outside of the AS. This can include a list of network routes in a flat routing infrastructure or a list of summarized network routes in a hierarchical routing infrastructure. EGPs are independent of the IGPs used within the AS. EGPs can facilitate the exchange of routes between ASs that use different IGPs.

The following are EGPs for IP internetworks:

➤ *Exterior Gateway Protocol (EGP)*—An RFC-based EGP developed for use between ASs on the Internet. It is no longer used on the Internet because of its lack of support for complex, multipath environments and Classless Inter-Domain Routing (CIDR).

➤ *Border Gateway Protocol (BGP)*—An RFC-based EGP currently used between ASs on the Internet. BGP overcomes the weaknesses of EGP.

Implementing a Windows 2000 Router

Before you install the Windows 2000 router, all hardware needs to be installed and working. Depending on your network and requirements, you might need the following hardware:

➤ A LAN or WAN adapter with a certified Network Driver Interface Specification (NDIS) driver

➤ One or more compatible modems and an available COM port

➤ A multiport adapter for acceptable performance with multiple remote connections.

➤ X.25 smart cards if you are using an X.25 network

➤ An ISDN adapter if you are using an ISDN line

To verify the compatibility of all hardware in a computer running Windows 2000 Server, you should check the Hardware Compatibility List (HCL) on the Microsoft Web site.

Installation

When you install Windows 2000 Server, the routing component is automatically installed, but the Routing and Remote Access service is installed in a disabled state. To enable the service, click on Start, point to Programs, point to Administrative Tools, and then click on Routing and Remote Access.

By default, the local computer is listed as a server. To add another server in the console tree, right-click on Server Status and then click on Add Server. In the Add Server dialog box, click on the applicable option and then click on OK.

In the console tree, right click on the server you want to enable, and then click on Configure and Enable Routing and Remote Access. Follow the instructions in the Routing and Remote Access wizard.

Setting Up Static IP Routing

A static routed IP internetwork does not use routing protocols such as RIP for IP or OSPF to communicate routing information between routers. All of the routing information is stored in a static routing table on each router. You need to ensure that each router has the appropriate routes in its routing table so that traffic can be exchanged between any two endpoints on the IP internetwork.

A static routed IP environment is best suited to a small, single-path, static IP internetwork:

➤ *A small internetwork* is defined as 2 to 10 networks.

➤ *Single-path* means that there is only one path for packets to travel between any two endpoints on the internetwork.

➤ *Static* means that the topology of the internetwork does not change over time.

The disadvantages of static routing are:

➤ *No fault tolerance*—If a router or link goes down, static routers do not sense the fault and inform other routers of the fault. Although this is a concern on large, corporate internetworks, a small office (with two routers and three networks based on LAN links) does not go down often enough to justify deploying a multipath topology and a routing protocol.

➤ *Administrative overhead*—If you add a new network to the internetwork or remove one from it, you must manually add or remove routes to that network. If you add a new router, it must be properly configured for the routes of the internetwork.

Deploying Static IP Routing

If static routing is appropriate for your IP internetwork, you can perform the following steps to deploy it:

1. Draw a map of the topology of your IP internetwork that shows the separate networks and the placement of routers and hosts (non-router computers that run TCP/IP).

2. For each IP network (a cabling system bounded by one or more routers), assign a unique IP network ID (also known as an IP network address).

3. Assign IP addresses to each router interface. Common industry practice is to assign the first IP addresses of a given IP network to router interfaces. For example, for an IP network ID of 192.168.100.0 with a subnet mask of 255.255.255.0, the router interface is assigned the IP address of 192.168.100.1.

4. For peripheral routers, configure a default route on the interface that has a neighboring router. The use of default routes on peripheral routers is optional.

5. For each non-peripheral router, compile a list of routes that need to be added as static routes to the routing table for that router. Each route consists of a destination network ID, a subnet mask, a gateway (or forwarding) IP address, a metric (number of router hops to reach the network), and the interface to be used to reach the network.

6. For non-peripheral routers, add the static routes compiled in Step 5 to each router. You can add static routes by using Routing and Remote Access or the route command. If you use the route command, use the -p option to make the static routes persistent.

7. When your configuration is complete, use the ping and tracert commands to test connectivity between host computers so that all routing paths are checked.

8

Setting Up RIP-for-IP Routing

A RIP-for-IP routed internetwork uses the RIP-for-IP routing protocol to dynamically communicate routing information among routers. Deployed properly, a RIP-for-IP environment automatically adds and removes routes as networks are added to and removed from the internetwork. Ensure that each router is properly configured so that the RIP-based route announcements are sent and received by all RIP routers on the internetwork.

RIP-for-IP Considerations

To prevent problems, consider the following design issues before implementing RIP for IP.

Decreased Diameter

The maximum diameter of RIP internetworks is 15 routers. The diameter is a measure of the size of an internetwork in terms of hops or other metrics. The Windows 2000 router, however, considers all non-RIP learned routes to be at a fixed hop count of two. Static routes, even those for directly connected networks, are considered non-RIP learned routes. When a Windows 2000 RIP router advertises its directly connected networks, it advertises them at a hop count of two, even though there is only one physical router to cross. Therefore, a RIP-based internetwork that uses Windows 2000 RIP routers has a maximum physical diameter of 14 routers.

RIP Costs

RIP uses the hop count as a metric to determine the best route. Using the number of routers to cross as the basis for selecting the best route may lead to undesired routing behavior. For example, if two sites are connected using a T1 link and a lower-speed satellite link as a backup, both links are considered the same metric. The router is free to choose between two routes of the same lowest metric.

If the router chooses the satellite link, then the slower backup link is used rather than the higher-bandwidth link. To prevent the satellite link from being chosen, assign a custom cost to the satellite interface. For example, assign a cost of two to the satellite interface (rather than the default of one), and then the best route is always the T1 link. If the T1 link goes down, the satellite link is chosen as the next best route.

Deploying RIP for IP

While basic RIP version 1 functionality is easy to configure and deploy, RIP version 2 and advanced RIP capabilities, such as peer security and route filtering, require additional configuration and testing. To make troubleshooting and problem isolation easier, deploy your RIP-based internetwork in the following stages: Set up basic RIP and make sure it is working; then add advanced capabilities one at a time, testing after each feature is added.

Deploying RIP

To deploy RIP, you can perform the following steps:

1. Draw a map of the topology of your IP internetwork that shows the separate networks and the placement of routers and hosts.

2. For each IP network (a cabling system bounded by one or more routers), assign a unique IP network ID.

3. Assign IP addresses to each router interface. Common industry practice is to assign the first IP addresses of an IP network to router interfaces. For example, for an IP network ID of 192.168.100.0 with a subnet mask of 255.255.255.0, the router interface is assigned an IP address of 192.168.100.1.

4. For each Windows 2000 router interface, designate whether that interface will be configured for RIP version 1 or 2. If an interface is configured for RIP version 2, designate whether the version 2 announcements will be broadcast or multicast.

5. By using Routing and Remote Access, add the RIP routing protocol and configure the appropriate interfaces for RIP version 1 or 2 for each Windows 2000 router.

6. When configuration is complete, allow a few minutes for the routers to update each other's routing tables and then test the internetwork.

Setting Up OSPF Routing

An OSPF-routed internetwork uses the OSPF routing protocol to dynamically communicate routing information between routers. Deployed properly, an OSPF environment automatically adds and removes routes as networks are added to and removed from the internetwork. Ensure that each router is properly configured so that the OSPF-based route advertisements are propagated to OSPF routers on the internetwork.

External Routes and ASBRs

The set of OSPF routers in an organization defines an OSPF AS. By default, only OSPF routes corresponding to directly connected network segments are propagated within the AS. An external route is any route that is not within the OSPF AS. External routes can come from many sources:

➤ Other routing protocols such as RIP for IP (version 1 or 2)

➤ Static routes

➤ Routes set on the router through Simple Network Management Protocol (SNMP)

External routes are propagated throughout the OSPF AS through one or more autonomous system boundary routers (ASBRs). An ASBR advertises external routes within the OSPF AS. For example, if there is a need to advertise the static routes of a Windows 2000 router, enable that router as an ASBR.

Deploying OSPF

Deploying OSPF requires careful planning and configuration at three levels:

➤ Autonomous system

➤ Area

➤ Network

Autonomous System Planning

For planning the OSPF AS, follow these steps:

1. Subdivide the OSPF AS into areas that can be easily summarized by using summary routes.

2. Designate the backbone area.

3. Assign area IDs.

4. Identify virtual links.

5. Identify ABRs.

6. Identify stub areas.

7. Identify ASBRs.

Area Planning

For planning each router, follow these steps:

1. Add the areas to which the router is connected.

2. If the area is a stub area, enable it as a stub area.

3. If the router is an ABR, optionally configure the ranges that summarize the IP networks within the area.

4. If the router is an ABR that uses a virtual link, add the virtual interface.

5. If the router is an ASBR, enable ASBR and configure optional external route filters.

Network Planning

For each IP address for each router interface that uses OSPF, follow these steps:

1. Add the interface to the OSPF routing protocol.

2. Enable OSPF on the interface.

3. Configure the interface for the appropriate area ID.

4. Configure the interface for the appropriate router priority.

5. Configure the interface for the appropriate link cost.

6. Configure the interface for the appropriate password.

7. Configure the interface for the appropriate network type.

8. If the interface is a single-adapter frame relay (or X.25 or ATM) interface, configure the non-broadcast multiple access (NBMA) neighbors.

8

Deploying a Single-Area OSPF Internetwork

Although OSPF is a routing protocol designed to scale to very large internetworks, the planning and implementation of a large-scale OSPF internetwork is complex and time-consuming. You don't need a large or very large internetwork to take advantage of the advanced features of OSPF, however.

In the Windows 2000 implementation of OSPF, the default values for global and interface settings make creating a single-area OSPF internetwork with minimal configuration very easy. The single area is the backbone area (0.0.0.0).

Default Global Settings

The OSPF default global settings are as follows:

➤ The router identification is set to the IP address of the first IP binding at the time of the installation of the OSPF routing protocol.

➤ The router is not configured as an OSPF ASBR.

➤ A single area, the backbone area, is configured and enabled for a plaintext password. It is not configured as a stub area and there are no address ranges.

➤ There are no configured virtual interfaces, and external routes are not filtered.

A single-area OSPF internetwork requires no changes to the OSPF default global settings.

Default Interface Settings

The OSPF default interface settings for LAN interfaces are as follows:

➤ By default, OSPF is not enabled to run over the interface.

➤ The area ID is set to the backbone area (0.0.0.0).

➤ The router priority is set to 1. With multiple OSPF routers on the same network with the same router priority, the OSPF designated router and backup designated router are elected based on the router with the highest router ID.

➤ The cost is set to 2.

➤ The password is set to 12345678.

➤ The network type is set to broadcast for LAN interfaces.

➤ There are no configured neighbors.

➤ The hello interval is set to 10 seconds.

➤ The dead interval is set to 40 seconds.

For a single-area OSPF internetwork, the only required change to the OSPF default interface settings is to enable OSPF to run over the interface.

OSPF Deployment

To deploy an OSPF single-area internetwork that consists of LAN interfaces, perform the following steps on each Windows 2000 router:

➤ Enable the Routing and Remote Access Service.

➤ Add the OSPF routing protocol.

➤ Add the routing interfaces of the router to the OSPF routing protocol, enabling OSPF for each interface.

Administration and Management Tools

Routing and Remote Access Service is the primary administration and management tool for configuring the Windows 2000 router. You can find it in the Administrative Tools folder in Control Panel. With Routing and Remote Access, you can do the following:

➤ Configure and enable, disable, start, and stop the Routing and Remote Access Service.

➤ Manage local and remote routers.

➤ Configure routing behavior and routing protocols.

➤ Configure demand-dial routing behavior.

➤ Configure remote access policies.

➤ Monitor active connections.

➤ Save the current routing configuration to a file and load previous configurations from a file.

➤ Local administrator and server operator accounts can use Routing and Remote Access. If the computer is a member of a domain, domain administrator and server operator accounts can use Routing and Remote Access.

➤ Use the **Netsh** command-line utility to configure Windows 2000 remote access routers locally from a Windows 2000 command prompt. This utility can use script files to automate configuration tasks.

Each Windows Server platform has different administration tools available, as follows:

➤ Windows 2000 routers, use the Routing and Remote Access administrative tool or the **Netsh** command-line utility.

➤ With Windows NT 4 RRAS routers, use the Routing and RAS Admin administrative tool.

➤ With Windows NT 4 RAS servers, use the Remote Access Admin administrative tool.

Also, command-line utilities, such as ping, tracert, pathping, and a tracing function, are available for managing and troubleshooting routers and routing connections.

Using Ping

If you are having connectivity problems, you can use the **ping** command to check the destination IP address and record the results. The **ping** command displays whether the destination responded and how long it took to receive a reply. If an error occurs in the delivery to the destination, the **ping** command displays an error message.

You can use the **ping** command to:

➤ Ping a computer by its address to determine that TCP/IP is functioning.

➤ Ping the local router to determine whether the router is running.

➤ Ping beyond the local router.

To check connectivity by using the **ping** command, at the command prompt, type "ping" and the target IP address. A response of "Destination net unreachable" means there was no route to the destination. If this occurs, check the routing table on the router listed in the "Reply from" address in the "Destination net unreachable" message. A response of "Request timed out" means that no response to the ping occurred in the default time period (one second).

Using Tracert

If you are having connectivity problems, use the **tracert** command to check the path to a destination IP address and record the results. The **tracert** command displays the series of IP routers that are used in delivering packets from a computer to the destination and how long it takes on each hop. If the packets are unable to be delivered to the destination, the **tracert** command displays the last router that successfully forwarded the packets. For more information about the **tracert** command, type "tracert -?" at a command prompt.

The most common use of **tracert** is **tracert IP address [-d]**, which returns a list of the routers that are crossed to get to an IP address. By using the -d option, the router path is displayed faster because tracert does not try to resolve the names of the routers in the path.

Chapter Summary

A router with dynamically configured routing tables is known as a dynamic router. Dynamic routing consists of routing tables that are built and maintained automatically through an ongoing communication between routers. Dynamic routing is fault tolerant. Dynamic routes learned from other routers have finite lifetimes.

Routing is the primary function of IP. Each IP datagram contains a source and destination IP address. IP routers are attached to two or more IP network segments that are enabled to forward packets to each other. TCP/IP networks or subnets are interconnected by IP routers, which are devices that pass IP datagrams from one network segment to another. IP routers provide the primary means of joining two or more physically separated IP network segments. All IP routers share two essential characteristics: they are multihomed hosts, and they provide packet forwarding for other TCP/IP hosts.

Windows 2000 Server and Advanced Server support a variety of routing protocols including RIP for IP and OSPF. Windows 2000 Server and Advanced Server also provide an open Application Programming Interface (API) for the development of additional routing protocols.

A routing domain is a collection of contiguous networks connected by routers that share the routing information for the routes within the domain. A common routing domain called the backbone connects routing domains. The routers within the domain perform intra-domain routing. Domain routers connected to the backbone perform inter-domain routing.

EGPs are inter-AS routing protocols. A static routed IP internetwork does not use routing protocols such as RIP for IP or OSPF to communicate routing information between routers. All of the routing information is stored in a static routing table on each router.

Review Questions

1. Routing is the process of transferring data across an internetwork from a destination host to a source host.

   a. True

   b. False

2. The destination internetwork address and the destination physical address are not for the same end system in:

   a. Direct delivery

   b. Indirect delivery

   c. Intermediate delivery

   d. Routing delivery

3. This field indicates the network interface that is used when forwarding packets to the network ID.

   a. Network ID

   b. Forwarding Address

   c. Interface

   d. Metric

4. This field indicates the lifetime that the route is considered valid.

   a. Lifetime

   b. Network ID

   c. Interface

   d. Metric

5. Which of these is a common metric that indicates the number of routers in the path to the network ID?

   a. Delay

   b. Throughput

   c. Reliability

   d. Hop count

6. Routing is the primary function of what protocol?

   a. TCP

   b. IP

   c. ASP

   d. RIP

7. The maximum hop count used by the RIP protocol is:

   a. 5

   b. 10

   c. 15

   d. 20

8. A small internetwork is defined as having how many networks?

   a. 2 to 10

   b. 5 to 20

   c. 2 to 20

   d. 1 to 6

9. If connectivity problems exist, this command can be used to check the path to the destination IP address and record the results.

   a. **tracert**

   b. **pathping**

   c. **tracing**

   d. **ping**

10. Which tool is used for administering Windows NT with the RRAS upgrade?

    a. Routing and Remote Access

    b. Routing and RAS Admin

    c. Remote Access Admin

    d. Any of the above

11. Which tool is used for administering a Windows 2000 router?

    a. Routing and Remote Access

    b. Routing and RAS Admin

    c. Remote Access Admin

    d. Any of the above

12. How should you set the cost to prevent a satellite link from being selected by default?

    a. 0

    b. 1

    c. 2

    d. A negative number, like –1

13. What is the destination address for a message being sent to a remote host?

    a. The MAC address of the host

    b. The IP address of the host

    c. The MAC address of the default gateway

    d. The IP address of the default gateway

14. Which command is used to configure a Windows 2000 router?

    a. **netsh**

    b. **ipconfig**

    c. **route**

    d. **SMNP**

15. Which of the following are multihomed hosts? [Select all that apply]

    a. Workstation with one network card

    b. Server with two network cards where the ip addresses are 191.1.2.3 and 191.4.5.6 using the default subnet mask

    c. Server with two network cards where the ip addresses are 168.1.2.3 and 168.1.4.5 using the subnet mask of 255.255.255.0

    d. A router

    e. A hub

    f. A switch

    g. Gateway server with two network cards where the IP addresses are 24.1.2.3 and 24. 4.5.6 using the default subnet mask

Real-World Projects

The Red Family Doctors Office has recently opened another office in downtown Chicago. The two offices are in the same building, one above the other. They need to communicate with one another to share client and accounting information.

They have two multihomed computers for the network segments they will be connecting. The computers already have Windows 2000 Server installed. You decide to show them how to enable the Routing and Remote Access Service and set up RIP for IP for their networking needs. In addition, you show them how to enable IP forwarding for the network segments.

Project 8.1

To enable the Routing and Remote Access Service, perform the following steps:

1. Click on Start.

2. Point to Programs.

3. Point to Administrative Tools.

4. Click on Routing and Remote Access.

5. To add another server in the console tree, right-click on Server Status.

6. Click on Add Server.

7. In the Add Server dialog box, click on the option for the server you want to add, then click on OK.

8. In the console tree, right-click on the server you want to enable.

9. Click on Configure and Enable Routing and Remote Access.

10. Follow the instructions in the Routing and Remote Access wizard.

This will enable the servers as routers. It will get you started in adding the protocol that is desired for use with the routers.

Project 8.2

To enable IP forwarding, perform the following steps:

1. Click on Start, then click on Run.

2. In the dialog box type, "regedt32" and click on OK.

3. In the Registry editor, navigate to this key:

   `HKEY_LOCAL_MACHINE\SYSTEM\CurrentControlSet\Services\Tcpip\Parameters.`

4. Select the following entry: IPEnableRouter:REG_DWORD:0.

5. Change value to 1; when you do, it will appear as 0x1.

6. Exit the Registry editor.

This will enable IP forwarding for the server and the network as well. If IP forwarding is not enabled on the servers, then information being sent from computer to computer between the cable connections will not be sent or may appear as being sent but won't be received. You enabled IP forwarding because you knew that by default it is not enabled.

Project 8.3

To enable RIP for IP, perform the following steps:

1. Assign the IP addresses to the cable modem interfaces. Assign an internal IP address to the interface for each network segment—for example, if the first IP address is 192.168.1.1 for the cable modem, the second address for the network interface would be 192.168.1.2; this second address will be the default gateway for clients on the network.

2. Open Routing and Remote Access.

3. In the console tree, click on RIP.

4. Right-click on the interface for the cable modem, then click on Properties.

5. On the General tab, in Outgoing packet protocol, click on RIP version 2 Broadcast.

6. On the General tab, in Incoming packet protocol, click on RIP version 1 and 2, then click on OK.

Make sure you do this for both routers, then let them propagate their learned routes for their router tables. This will work as long as there are not 14 hops between the routers on the network. The Red Family is pleased with you, because you were able to link its two network segments.

8

CHAPTER NINE

Multicasting and Network Address Translation

After completing this chapter, you will be able to:

✓ Install the Internet Group Management Protocol

✓ Deploy multicast routing

✓ Configure multicast boundaries, heartbeat, and scopes

✓ Install and configure Network Address Translation

✓ Implement Internet connection sharing with network address translation

✓ Choose the appropriate Network Address Translation design

✓ Deploy Network Address Translation

✓ Use NAT editors

In this chapter, we will explore IP multicasting and Network Address Translation (NAT). The sections concerning multicasting will discuss what multicasting is, what the Internet Group Management Protocol (IGMP) protocol is and how it functions. Also, we will touch on multicast forwarding, multicast routing, and configuring multicast boundaries and heartbeat. In addition, we'll be touching on background information and IP multicast video conferencing. Multicasting is very important to companies that desire to send information from one address to several addresses either within a company intranet, internetwork, or across the Internet.

Through our discussion of NAT, we will overview what NAT is and how it relates to Internet connection sharing as well as NAT design issues. We will also cover how to deploy NAT and how to configure small office or home office (SOHO) network computers. When this chapter is complete, you will have a solid understanding of what NAT and multicasting are, and how to use them on a network.

Multicasting Overview

Multicasting is useful for the point-to-multipoint delivery of information on an internetwork. There are three mechanisms for point-to-multipoint delivery. First, information can be sent to each endpoint individually by using unicast addresses. The disadvantages of this method are the duplication of network traffic and the overhead of maintaining a list of unicast endpoints. Second, information can be sent in a single packet by using a broadcast address. The advantages of this method are the use of a single packet and no overhead for keeping lists of recipients. The disadvantages for the use of broadcast packets are that they disturb all nodes on a network, and routers do not forward broadcasts. A broadcast packet reaches everyone on a network, but not everyone on the internetwork.

Third, information can be sent in a single packet using a multicast address. The advantages of this method are the use of a single packet and no overhead for keeping lists of recipients. Unlike broadcast packets, multicast traffic does not disturb those nodes that are not listening for it. Routers can be multicast-capable and forward the multicast packet to all networks where there is at least one node listening.

Internet Group Management Protocol

The use of IP multicasting in TCP/IP networks is defined as a TCP/IP standard in RFC 1112, "Internet Group Management Protocol (IGMP)." In addition to defining address and host extensions for how IP hosts support multicasting, this RFC also defines the IGMP version 1. RFC 2236 defines IGMP version 2. Both versions of IGMP provide a protocol to exchange and update information about host membership in specific multicast groups.

What Is IP Multicasting?

Multicast IP traffic is sent to a single address, but is processed by multiple hosts. Only host computers that belong to the multicast group receive and process IP traffic sent to the group's reserved IP address. The set of hosts listening on a specific IP multicast address is called a multicast group.

Important IP multicasting aspects include the following:

➤ Group membership is dynamic, allowing hosts to join and leave the group at any time. The capability of hosts to join multicast groups is performed through the sending of IGMP messages.

➤ Groups are not limited by size, and members can be spread across multiple IP networks (if connecting routers support the propagation of IP multicast traffic and group membership information). A host can send IP traffic to the group's IP address without belonging to the corresponding group.

Multicast Addressing

IP multicast addresses are reserved and assigned from within the Class D address range from 224.0.0.0 through 239.255.255.255. Table 9.1 shows a partial list of well-known Class D addresses used by Windows 2000 components that are reserved for IP multicasting and registered with the Internet Assigned Numbers Authority (IANA).

A single IP address within the Class D reserved range identifies each multicast group. Each group's reserved IP address is shared by all the host members for the group, and they listen for and receive any IP messages sent to the group's IP address. IP multicast addresses are mapped to a reserved set of media access control multicast addresses.

Table 9.1   Reserved Class D addresses.

IP Multicast Address	Description
224.0.0.0	Base address (reserved).
224.0.0.1	The All Hosts multicast group that contains all systems on the same network segment.
224.0.0.2	The All Routers multicast group that contains all routers on the same network segment.
224.0.0.5	The Open Shortest Path First (OSPF) AllSPFRouters address. Used to send OSPF routing information to all OSPF routers on a network segment.
224.0.0.6	The OSPF AllDRouters address. Used to send OSPF routing information to OSPF designated routers on a network segment.
224.0.0.9	The RIP Version 2 group address. Used to send RIP routing information to all RIP v2 routers on a network segment.
224.0.1.24	WINS server group address. Used to support autodiscovery and dynamic configuration of replication for WINS servers.

IGMP Messages

IGMP is used to exchange membership status information between IP routers that support multicasting and members of multicast groups. Individual member hosts report host membership in a multicast group, and multicast routers periodically poll membership status. Table 9.2 lists the IGMP message types.

Multicast Forwarding

Multicast forwarding, the intelligent forwarding of multicast traffic, is provided by the Windows 2000 TCP/IP protocol and the Windows 2000 IGMP routing protocol for interfaces running in IGMP router mode.

The Windows 2000 TCP/IP protocol performs the following multicast forwarding functions:

1. It receives and processes all multicast traffic. The TCP/IP protocol receives and processes all multicast traffic on interfaces that are configured for IGMP router mode. All IP multicast traffic is either forwarded to a process running on the router or intelligently forwarded to network segments that contain either multicast group members or routers connected to downstream network segments that contain multicast group members.

2. It forwards multicast packets to the appropriate interfaces. Upon receipt of a multicast packet, TCP/IP consults a multicast forwarding table to decide whether to forward the packet to any of its other attached interfaces.

Interfaces running in IGMP router mode perform the following multicast forwarding functions:

1. They place the network adapter in multicast promiscuous mode. IGMP router mode sets the network adapter to multicast promiscuous mode. In multicast promiscuous mode, all multicast packets received by the network adapter are passed to the Windows 2000 networking layers for processing. Not all network adapters are capable of multicast promiscuous mode.

2. They track multicast group membership. The IGMP router mode interface listens for IGMP Membership Report messages on locally attached networks

Table 9.2   IGMP message types.

IGMP Message Type	Description
Host membership report	When a host joins a multicast group, it sends an IGMP host membership report message, declaring its membership in a specific host group. IGMP host membership report messages are also sent in response to an IGMP host membership query sent by a router.
Host membership query	Used by a multicast router to periodically poll a network for group members.
Leave group	Sent by a host when the host leaves the group.

and compiles a list of multicast accounting information as a series of {receiver network, multicast group} pairs. The receiver network is the IP network ID of a listening node. The multicast group is the specific multicast address that is registered by a listening node. The multicast capable router does not track the IP addresses of the hosts that are listening, only the IP network ID where at least one host is listening. To ensure that hosts are still listening on their registered multicast addresses, the IGMP router periodically queries each network. The response to the query is an IGMP Membership Report. If there are multiple IGMP routers on a single network, one IGMP router is elected the querier and performs all periodic queries.

3. They update the TCP/IP multicast forwarding table. Based on the current state of listening hosts on IGMP router mode interfaces, the TCP/IP multicast forwarding table is updated with the appropriate entries.

Multicast Routing

Multicast routing is the propagation of multicast listening information that is provided by multicast routing protocols, such as Distance Vector Multicast Routing Protocol (DVMRP). Windows 2000 does not provide any multicast routing protocols. However, the Windows 2000 IGMP routing protocol, IGMP router mode, and IGMP proxy mode can be used to provide multicast forwarding in a single router intranet or when connecting a single router intranet to the Internet.

Single-Router Intranets

For an intranet that connects multiple networks by using a single router, enable IGMP router mode on all router interfaces to provide multicast forwarding support between multicast sources and multicast listening hosts on any network.

Single-Router Intranets and the Internet

If the Windows 2000 router is attached to the MBone (Multicast Backbone) through an Internet service provider (ISP), IGMP proxy mode can be used to send and receive multicast traffic to and from the Internet.

In Figure 9.1, IGMP proxy mode is enabled on the Internet interface and IGMP router mode is enabled on the intranet interface. Multicast hosts register themselves locally, and the IGMP proxy mode interface registers their memberships to the multicast capable router at the ISP. Multicast traffic from the Internet is forwarded to the ISP router. The ISP router forwards the multicast traffic to the Windows 2000 router, which then forwards the traffic to listening hosts on an intranet.

When an intranet host sends multicast traffic, it is forwarded over the IGMP proxy mode interface to the ISP router. The ISP router then forwards it to the

9

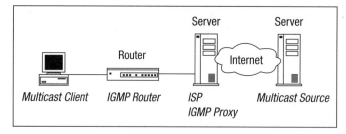

Figure 9.1   IGMP Proxy Mode and IGMP Router Mode.

appropriate downstream router. In this way, Internet hosts can receive multicast traffic sent by intranet hosts.

To add the IGMP routing protocol, perform the following steps:

1. Open Routing and Remote Access.

2. In the console tree, click on General.

3. Right-click on General, and then click on New Routing Protocol.

4. In the Select Routing Protocol dialog box, click on IGMP Version 2, Router and Proxy, and then click on OK.

To enable IGMP router and IGMP proxy mode, perform the following steps:

1. Open Routing and Remote Access.

2. In the console tree, click on IGMP.

3. Right-click on IGMP, and then click on New Interface.

4. In Interfaces, click on the interface to enable, and then click on OK.

5. In the General dialog box, verify that the Enable IGMP checkbox is selected.

6. Under Mode, do one of the following:

   ➤ To enable IGMP router mode, click on IGMP Router.

   ➤ To enable IGMP proxy mode, click on IGMP Proxy.

To configure IGMP router settings, perform the following steps:

1. Open Routing and Remote Access.

2. In the console tree, click on IGMP.

3. In the Details pane, right-click on the interface to configure, and then click on Properties.

4. Click on the Router tab, and then configure the appropriate settings.

Multicast Boundaries and Heartbeat

Windows 2000 supports multicast boundaries, which provides two kinds of boundaries: scope-based boundaries and time-to-live based boundaries. Windows 2000 also supports multicast heartbeat for multicast connectivity.

Multicast Boundaries

Multicast boundaries are administrative barriers to the forwarding of IP multicast traffic. Without boundaries, an IP multicast router forwards all appropriate IP multicast traffic. Multicast boundaries can be created by specifying a range of IP addresses, known as a multicast scope, or by the value of the Time to Live (TTL) field in the IP header.

Note: A scope-based boundary prevents the forwarding of IP multicast traffic with a specified group IP address or range of IP addresses. TTL-based boundaries prevent the forwarding of IP multicast traffic with a TTL less than a specified value. A TTL-based boundary applies to all multicast packets regardless of the multicast group. TTL-based boundaries are less effective than scope-based boundaries.

To configure multicast boundaries, perform the following steps:

1. Open Routing and Remote Access.

2. In the console tree, click on General.

3. In the Details pane, right-click on the interface to configure multicast boundaries for, and then click on Properties.

4. On the Multicast Boundaries tab, do the following:

   a. To add a scope to the list of multicast scope boundaries, in Scope, click on a configured scope, and then click on Add.

   b. To remove a scope from the list of multicast scope boundaries, in Scoped Boundaries, click the on scope, and then click on Remove.

   c. To enable TTL scoping, select the Activate TTL boundary checkbox, and in TTL Value, click on the arrows to set a TTL value. To set a rate limit, in Rate Limit (KBps), type the rate in kilobytes per second.

Multicast Heartbeat

Multicast heartbeat provides the capability for a Windows 2000 router to listen for a regular multicast notification to a specified group address to verify that IP multicast connectivity is available on the network. If the heartbeat is not received within a configured amount of time, the Windows 2000 router sets a flag on the configured interface. A program can provide notification that the multicast heartbeat is no longer present by polling the status of this flag.

To configure multicast heartbeat, perform the following steps:

1. Open Routing and Remote Access.

2. In the console tree, click on General.

3. In the Details pane, right-click on the interface that you want to configure multicast heartbeat for, and then click on Properties.

4. On the Multicast Heartbeat tab, select the Enable Multicast Heartbeat Detection checkbox, and do the following:

   a. To add a multicast heartbeat group, in Multicast Heartbeat Group, type the IP address of the multicast heartbeat group.

   b. To configure a quiet time before alerting, in Quiet Time Before Alerting (minutes), click on the arrows to set a quiet time in minutes.

Using Multicast Scopes

Multicast scopes are supported through the use of Multicast Address Dynamic Client Allocation Protocol (MADCAP), a new proposed standard protocol for performing multicast address allocation. The MADCAP protocol describes how multicast address allocation servers can dynamically provide IP addresses to hosts on a network.

Typically, a MADCAP client might also be a multicast server (MCS) used to support IP multicasting. An MCS, such as a server computer running the Site Server Internet Location Server (ILS) service, manages the shared or group use of the allocated multicast IP address and streams data traffic to members that share the use of the specified group address.

Once an MCS is configured and has allocated a group IP address to use, any multicast clients that have registered their membership with the MCS can receive streams sent to this address. By registering with the MCS, clients can participate efficiently in the stream process to obtain such items as real-time video or audio network transmissions. The MCS also manages the multicast group list, updating its membership and status, so that all current members receive multicast traffic.

Background on Multicast Addresses

Ordinarily, DHCP scopes would be used to provide client configurations by allocating ranges of IP addresses from the standard address classes: Class A, B, or C. By using DHCP scopes, IP addresses can be assigned from the ranges provided by these addresses so that DHCP clients can be configured for unicast or point-to-point directed communication. The multicast address range uses an additional address class, Class D, which includes IP addresses that range from 224.0.0.0 to

239.255.255.255. Addresses in this class are used for multicasting only and not for regular DHCP scopes.

In all TCP/IP networks, each host is required to first be configured with its own IP address taken from one of the standard address classes. Then they must be assigned this required unicast IP address before a host can be configured to support and use secondary IP addresses, such as a multicast IP address.

Another difference between unicast and multicast addresses is that a group of TCP/IP host computers are intended to share a multicast IP address. This is not normally the case with unicast IP addresses, which are not shared and are assigned individually to one configured host.

When the destination address for an IP datagram is an IP multicast address, the datagram is forwarded to all members of a multicast group, which is a set of hosts identified by the address. The membership of a multicast group is dynamic in that individual hosts can join or leave the group at any time. Membership and use of multicast groups is unrestricted, membership can be any size, and hosts can be members of many multicast groups.

Multicast group addresses can be permanently reserved or temporarily assigned and used as needed on a network. For a permanent group IP address to be reserved for Internet use, it must be registered with the IANA. For multicast IP addresses not permanently reserved with the IANA, any Class D addresses that remains unreserved can then be used dynamically to assign and form temporary multicast groups. These temporary groups can exist as long as one or more hosts on the network are configured with the group address and actively share its use.

Determining the Ranges to Use for Multicast Scopes

When deciding the IP address ranges to use for multicast scopes with a MADCAP server, there are two overall best practices recommended by the Multicast Allocation (malloc) working group, which is an Internet Engineering Task Force (IETF) consisting of industry volunteers who help establish multicast address allocation standards. The first best practice is *administrative scoping* and the second is *global scoping*.

Administrative scoping is most useful when using multicast IP addresses privately in a network. It is similar to private IP addressing, which is used currently in the unicast IP address spaces (for example, the use of the 10.0.0.0 network address space). With administrative scoping, the range most recommended to begin with is the 239.192.0.0 range. This range is known as the IPv4 Organization Local Scope and has a subnet mask of 255.252.0.0 that has a NetID that is14 bits in length. It is intended for use by an entire organization setting multicast scopes privately for its own internal or organizational use. This address can create a considerable number of addresses up to 2^{18} or 262,144 group addresses for use in all subnets within an organization's network.

Global scoping is the practice most useful when using multicast group IP addresses in a public network address space, particularly on the Internet. Because most organizations requiring one or more public addresses have probably already been assigned some public unicast IP addresses. For MADCAP, the 233.0.0.0 range of the Class D address space is recommended for use as a global scope range.

When the 233.0.0.0 range is used, a network registry, such as the IANA, allocates and reserves the first 8 bits of the range (for example, the "233" portion of the range). The next 16 bits, the two middle octet numbers of addresses in the range, are based on a previously assigned Autonomous System (AS) number. This number is recorded with the applicable IANA registry for a region.

If an organization has already registered IP addresses with a regional network registry, they will have an autonomous system (AS) number. This can be looked up easily by using the WHOIS database system on the Internet. If the IP addresses will be obtained through an ISP, contact the provider to find out what the AS number will be for the network. AS numbers are allocated to regional registries by the IANA. To obtain an AS number for a network, apply directly to the American Registry for Internet Numbers (ARIN) if you are in the United States.

The last 8 bits in the address are local use bits. These provide the IP address range from which to configure any multicast scopes for group addresses for use publicly on the Internet. With this global scoping system in use, a subnet mask of 255.255.255.0 should be applied. This provides each organization with an assigned AS number of up to 255 multicast group addresses for use on the Internet.

MADCAP and DHCP

The Windows 2000 DHCP Server service supports both the DHCP and MADCAP protocols. These protocols function separately and are not dependent on each other. For example, a DHCP client might or might not be a MADCAP client and a MADCAP client might or might not be a DHCP client.

It's also worth mentioning that the DHCP Server service can be used to deploy MADCAP servers independent of how DHCP servers are used on a network. For example, to install Windows 2000 DHCP for MADCAP service only:

➤ Create multicast scopes.

➤ Do not create other scopes or superscopes.

Only where other scopes or superscopes are configured does the server computer also function as a DHCP server. Multicast scopes and MADCAP only provide a mechanism for dynamically allocating IP address configuration for multicast ranged IP addresses. Other network configuration details are normally required to enable multicasting for deployment needs. Multicast scopes do not require or support the use of DHCP options, but can be configured with a finite lifetime, enabling the multicast scope to expire and be removed by the server.

To create a multicast scope, perform the following steps:

1. Open DHCP.

2. In the console tree, click on the applicable DHCP server.

3. On the Action menu, click on New Multicast Scope.

4. Follow the instructions in the New Multicast Scope Wizard.

Understanding NAT

With NAT in Windows 2000, a home or small office network can be configured to share a single connection to the Internet. NAT consists of a translation component, an addressing component, and a name resolution component.

The translation component on a router on which NAT is enabled acts as a network address translator, translating the IP addresses and TCP/UDP port numbers of packets that are forwarded between the private network and the Internet.

The addressing component of a NAT computer provides IP address configuration information to the other computers on the home network. The addressing component is a simplified DHCP server that allocates an IP address, a subnet mask, a default gateway, and the IP address of a DNS server. The computers on the home network must be configured as DHCP clients in order to receive the IP configuration automatically. The default TCP/IP configuration for computers running Windows 2000, Windows NT, Windows 95, and Windows 98 is as a DHCP client.

The name resolution component of a NAT computer becomes the DNS server for the other computers on the home network. When the NAT computer receives name resolution requests, it forwards the name resolution requests to the Internet-based DNS server for which it is configured and returns the responses to the home network computer.

Because NAT includes addressing and name resolution components that provide DHCP and DNS services for hosts on the private network, the DHCP service or the DHCP Relay Agent cannot be run as long as NAT addressing is enabled.

Internet Connection Sharing and NAT

To connect a small office or home office (SOHO) network to the Internet, one of two methods can be used: a routed connection or a translated connection.

1. A routed connection is where the computer running Windows 2000 Server acts as an IP router that forwards packets between SOHO hosts and Internet hosts. Although conceptually simple, a routed connection requires knowledge

of IP address and routing configuration for SOHO hosts and the Windows 2000 router. However, routed connections allow all IP traffic between SOHO hosts and Internet hosts.

2. A translated connection is where the computer running Windows 2000 Server acts as an network address translator, which is an IP router that translates addresses for packets being forwarded between SOHO hosts and Internet hosts. Translated connections that use computers running Windows 2000 Server require less knowledge of IP addressing and routing and provide a simplified configuration for SOHO hosts and the Windows 2000 router. However, translated connections may not allow all IP traffic between SOHO hosts and Internet hosts.

In Windows 2000 Server, a translated connection to the Internet can be configured by using either the Internet connection sharing feature of Network and Dial-Up Connections or the NAT routing protocol provided with the Routing and Remote Access service. Both Internet connection sharing and NAT provide translation, addressing, and name resolution services to SOHO hosts.

Internet connection sharing does not allow further configuration beyond the configuration of applications and services on the SOHO network. For example, Internet connection sharing is designed for a single IP address obtained from an ISP and does not allow the range of IP addresses allocated to SOHO hosts to be changed.

The NAT routing protocol is designed to provide maximum flexibility in the configuration of the computer running Windows 2000 Server and to provide a translated connection to the Internet. NAT requires more configuration steps; however, each step of the configuration is customizable. The NAT protocol allows for ranges of IP addresses from the ISP and the configuration of the range of IP addresses allocated to SOHO hosts. Table 9.3 summarizes the features and capabilities that Internet connection sharing and NAT have to offer.

As stated earlier, Internet connection sharing and NAT are features of Windows 2000 Server that are designed to connect SOHO networks to the Internet. Internet connection sharing and NAT are not designed to directly connect separate SOHO networks together or connect networks within an intranet. They also were not

Table 9.3 A summary of the features and capabilities of Internet connection sharing and NAT.

Internet Connection Sharing	Network Address Translation
Single checkbox configuration	Manual configuration
Single public IP address	Multiple public IP addresses
Fixed address range for SOHO hosts	Configurable address range for SOHO hosts
Single SOHO interface	Multiple SOHO interfaces

designed to directly connect branch office networks to a corporate network or connect branch office networks to a corporate network over the Internet.

To enable NAT addressing:

1. Open Routing and Remote Access.

2. In the console tree, click on NAT.

3. Right-click on NAT, and then click on Properties.

4. On the Address Assignment tab, select the Automatically Assign IP Addresses By Using DHCP checkbox.

5. If applicable, in IP address and Mask, configure the range of IP addresses to allocate to DHCP clients on the private network.

6. If applicable, click on Exclude, configure the addresses to exclude from allocation to DHCP clients on the private network, and then click on OK.

Private Network Addressing

To communicate on the Internet, only addresses that have been allocated by the Internet Network Information Center (InterNIC) can be used. Addresses allocated by InterNIC can receive traffic from Internet locations and are known as public addresses. A typical small business or home office is allocated a public address (or addresses) from its ISP, who has received a range of public addresses from InterNIC.

To allow multiple computers in the SOHO to communicate on the Internet, each computer must have its own public address. This requirement places great stress on the available pool of public addresses. To relieve this stress, InterNIC has provided for an address reuse scheme by reserving network IDs for private internetworks. The private network IDs include:

➤ 10.0.0.0 with the subnet mask 255.0.0.0

➤ 172.16.0.0 with the subnet mask 255.240.0.0

➤ 192.168.0.0 with the subnet mask 255.255.0.0

Private addresses cannot receive traffic from Internet locations. Therefore, if an intranet is using private addresses and communicating with Internet locations, the private address must be translated to a public address. A network address translator is placed between an intranet that uses private addresses and the Internet, which uses public addresses. Outgoing packets from the intranet have their private addresses translated by the network address translator into public addresses. Incoming packets from the Internet have their public addresses translated by the network address translator into private addresses.

IP addresses from InterNIC's private IP network IDs: 10.0.0.0 with a subnet mask of 255.0.0.0, 172.16.0.0 with a subnet mask of 255.240.0.0, and 192.168.0.0 with a subnet mask of 255.255.0.0 should be used on a private network. By default, NAT uses the private network ID 192.168.0.0 with the subnet mask of 255.255.255.0 for a private network.

Using an IP network ID on the Internet that has not been allocated by InterNIC or an ISP, is known as illegal or overlapping IP addressing. If you are using overlapping public addresses, the Internet resources of the overlapping addresses cannot be reached. For example, by using 1.0.0.0 with the subnet mask of 255.0.0.0, any Internet resources of the organization that is using the 1.0.0.0 network cannot be reached. Also, specific IP addresses can be excluded from the configured range. Excluded addresses are not allocated to private network hosts.

Single or Multiple Public Addresses

If you are using a single public IP address allocated by an ISP, no other IP address configuration is necessary. If you are using multiple IP addresses allocated by an ISP, the NAT interface must be configured with the range of public IP addresses. For the range of IP addresses given an ISP, it must be determined whether the range of public IP addresses can be expressed by using an IP address and a subnet mask.

If you have been allocated a number of addresses that are powers of 2 (2, 4, 8, 16, and so on), the range can be expressed by using a single IP address and subnet mask. For example, if you are given the four public IP addresses 200.100.100.212, 200.100.100.213, 200.100.100.214, and 200.100.100.215 by an ISP, these four addresses can be expressed as 200.100.100.212 with a subnet mask of 255.255.255.252.

If IP addresses are not expressible as an IP address and a subnet mask, they can be entered as a range or series of ranges by indicating the starting and ending IP addresses.

Allowing Inbound Connections

Normal NAT usage from a home or small business allows outbound connections from the private network to the public network. Programs such as Web browsers that run from the private network create connections to Internet resources. The return traffic from the Internet can cross the NAT because the connection was initiated from the private network.

To allow Internet users to access resources on a private network, perform the following steps:

1. Configure a static IP address configuration on the resource server including IP address (from the range of IP addresses allocated by the NAT computer), subnet mask (from the range of IP addresses allocated by the NAT computer),

default gateway (the private IP address of the NAT computer), and DNS server (the private IP address of the NAT computer).

2. Exclude the IP address being used by the resource computer from the range of IP addresses being allocated by the NAT computer.

3. Configure a special port. A special port is a static mapping of a public address and port number to a private address and port number. A special port maps an inbound connection from an Internet user to a specific address on a private network. By using a special port, a Web server can be created on a private network that is accessible from the Internet.

Configuring Applications and Services

Applications and services may need to be configured to work properly across the Internet. For example, if users on a SOHO network want to play Quake Arena (a popular multiplayer first person computer game) with other users on the Internet, NAT must be configured for the application.

To configure Internet connection sharing for applications and services:

1. Open Network and Dial-up Connections.

2. Right-click on the shared connection, and then click on Properties.

3. On the Sharing tab, verify the Enable Internet Connection Sharing For This Connection checkbox is selected, and then click on Settings.

4. To configure a network application for the computers sharing the connection, on the Applications tab, click on Add, and then do the following:

   a. In Name Of Application, type an easily recognized name for the application.

   b. In Remote Server Port Number, type the port number of the remote server where the application resides, and then click on either TCP or UDP.

   c. In TCP or UDP or both, type the port number for the port on the home network that the application will connect to. Some applications require TCP and UDP port numbers.

5. To configure a service to provide to users on remote networks, on the Services tab, click on Add, and then do the following:

   a. In Name Of Service, type an easily recognized name for the service.

   b. In Service Port Number, type the port number of the computer where the service resides, and then click on either TCP or UDP.

   c. In Name Or Address Of Server Computer On Private Network, type the name or TCP/IP address of the computer on the home network where the service resides.

VPN Connections from a Translated SOHO Network

To access a private intranet using a virtual private network (VPN) connection from a translated SOHO network, the Point-to-Point Tunneling Protocol (PPTP) can be used to create a VPN connection from a host on the SOHO network to the VPN server of the private intranet over the Internet. The NAT routing protocol has a NAT editor for PPTP traffic. Layer Two Tunneling Protocol (L2TP) over Internet Protocol Security (IPSec) connections do not work across the NAT computer.

Deploying NAT

To deploy NAT for a SOHO network, the NAT computer as well as the other computers on the small office or home network need to be configured.

To configure the NAT computer, perform the following steps:

1. Install and enable the Routing and Remote Access service. In the Routing and Remote Access Server Setup wizard, choose the options for Internet connection server to set up a router with the NAT routing protocol. After the wizard is finished, the entire configuration for NAT is complete. If the Routing and Remote Access service is already enabled, complete steps 2 through 8 as needed; otherwise setup is finished.

2. Configure the IP address of the home network interface. For the IP address of the LAN adapter that connects to the home network, configure the following: IP address: 192.168.0.1 and Subnet mask: 255.255.255.0 No default gateway. The IP address in the preceding configuration for the home network interface is based on the default address range of 192.168.0.0 with a subnet mask of 255.255.255.0, which is configured for the addressing component of NAT. If this default address range is changed, then change the IP address of the private interface for the NAT computer to be the first IP address in the configured range. Using the first IP address in the range is a recommended practice, not a requirement of the NAT components.

3. Enable routing on the dial-up port. If the connection to the Internet is a permanent connection that appears in Windows 2000 as a LAN interface (such as DDS, T-Carrier, Frame Relay, permanent ISDN, xDSL, or cable modem) or if you are connecting a computer running Windows 2000 to another router before connecting to the Internet, and the LAN interface is configured with an IP address, subnet mask, and default gateway either statically or through DHCP, skip to step 6.

4. Create a demand-dial interface to connect to an ISP that is enabled for IP routing and uses the dial-up equipment and the credentials that will be used to dial the ISP.

5. Create a default static route that uses the Internet interface. For a default static route, select the demand-dial interface (for dial-up connections) or LAN interface (for permanent or intermediate router connections) that is used to connect to the Internet. The destination is 0.0.0.0 and the network mask is 0.0.0.0. For a demand-dial interface, the gateway IP address is not configurable.

6. Add the NAT routing protocol.

7. Add the Internet and home network interfaces to the NAT routing protocol.

8. Enable NAT addressing and name resolution.

The NAT addressing feature only assigns addresses from a single range that corresponds to a single subnet. If multiple home network LAN interfaces are added to the NAT routing protocol, a single subnet configuration (where all LAN interfaces are connected to the same network) is assumed. If the LAN interfaces correspond to different networks, connectivity between clients on different networks who receive addresses from the NAT computer may not be possible.

Configuring Other Computers on the Small Office or Home Network

Configure the TCP/IP protocol on the other computers on the small office or home network to obtain an IP address automatically, and then restart them. When the computers on the home network receive their IP address configuration from the NAT computer, they are configured with:

➤ IP address (from the address range of 192.168.0.0 with a subnet mask of 255.255.255.0).

➤ Subnet mask (255.255.255.0).

➤ Default gateway (the IP address of the interface for the NAT computer on the small office or home network).

➤ DNS server (the IP address of the interface for the NAT computer on the small office or home network).

Advanced NAT Translation Settings

To configure advanced NAT translation settings, when given a range of IP addresses from an ISP, configure the range of IP addresses on the Internet interface. If there are services running on the private network that need to be accessed by users from the Internet, add a special port that maps the public IP address and port number to a private IP address and port number.

NAT Editors

Normal NAT relies on the translation of:

1. The IP addresses in the IP header.

2. The TCP port numbers in the TCP header.

3. The UDP port numbers in the UDP header.

Any translation beyond these three items requires additional processing and additional software components called NAT editors. A NAT editor makes modifications to the IP packet beyond the translation of the IP address in the IP header, the TCP port in the TCP header, and the UDP port in the UDP header.

HyperText Transfer Protocol (HTTP) traffic on the World Wide Web (WWW), for example, does not require a NAT editor because HTTP traffic only requires the translation of the IP address in the IP header and the TCP port in the TCP header. The following list identifies two situations where NAT editors are required:

➤ *The IP address, TCP port, or UDP port is stored in the payload*—The File Transfer Protocol (FTP), for example, stores the dotted decimal representation of IP addresses in the FTP header for the FTP PORT command. If the NAT does not properly translate the IP address within the FTP header and adjust the data stream, then connectivity problems may occur.

➤ *TCP or UDP is not being used to identify the data stream*—The PPTP's tunneled data, for example, does not use a TCP or UDP header. Instead, a Generic Routing Encapsulation (GRE) header is used, and the Tunnel ID is stored in the GRE header to identify the data stream. If the NAT does not properly translate the Tunnel ID within the GRE header, then connectivity problems may occur.

Windows 2000 includes built-in NAT editors for the following protocols:

➤ FTP

➤ Internet Control Message Protocol (ICMP)

➤ PPTP

➤ NetBIOS over TCP/IP

Additionally, the NAT routing protocol includes proxy software for the following protocols:

➤ H.323

➤ Direct Play

➤ LDAP-based ILS registration

➤ Remote Procedure Call (RPC)

Chapter Summary

Multicast IP traffic is sent to a single address but is processed by multiple hosts. Only host computers that belong to the multicast group receive and process IP traffic sent to the group's reserved IP address. The set of hosts listening on a specific IP multicast address is called a multicast group.

IP multicast addresses are reserved and assigned from within the Class D address range from 224.0.0.0 through 239.255.255.255. A single IP address within the Class D reserved range identifies each multicast group. All the host members for the group share each group's reserved IP address, and they listen for and receive any IP messages sent to the group's IP address. IP multicast addresses are mapped to a reserved set of media access control multicast addresses.

All IP multicast traffic is either forwarded to a process running on the router or intelligently forwarded to network segments that contain either multicast group members or routers connected to downstream network segments that contain multicast group members.

MADCAP is built on a client/server model, where multicast conference hosts request addresses from a MADCAP server. The Multicast Conference TAPI Service Provider resolves conference names to IP multicast addresses using the conference descriptors stored on the Site Server ILS server.

With NAT in Windows 2000, a home or small office network can be configured to share a single connection to the Internet. NAT consists of a translation component, an addressing component, and a name resolution component.

Internet connection sharing and NAT are features of Windows 2000 Server that are designed to connect SOHO networks to the Internet. Internet connection sharing and NAT are not designed to directly connect separate SOHO networks together or connect networks within an intranet.

By default, NAT uses the private network ID 192.168.0.0 with the subnet mask of 255.255.255.0 for the private network. If using a single public IP address allocated by an ISP, no other IP address configuration is necessary. If using multiple IP addresses allocated by an ISP, the NAT interface must be configured with the range of public IP addresses.

Review Questions

1. Which of the following is not a mechanism for point-to-multipoint delivery?

   a. Send the information to each endpoint individually by using unicast addresses

   b. Send the information in a single packet by using a broadcast address

   c. Send the information in a single packet by using a multicast address

   d. Send the information in multiple packets by using multicast addresses

2. Multicast IP traffic is sent to multiple addresses and is processed by multiple hosts.

   a. True

   b. False

3. IP multicast addresses are reserved and assigned within which IP address class range?

   a. A

   b. B

   c. C

   d. D

4. What is the IP multicast address for the WINS server group address?

   a. 224.0.1.24

   b. 224.0.0.9

   c. 224.0.0.6

   d. 224.0.0.5

5. All but one of the following is a step in configuring multicast heartbeat.

   a. Open Routing and Remote Access

   b. In the Console tree, click on General

   c. In the Details pane, right-click on the interface to configure multicast heartbeat for, and then click on Properties

   d. On the Multicast Heartbeat tab, clear the Enable Multicast Heartbeat Detection checkbox

6. The multicast address range uses an additional address class that includes IP addresses in a range starting with 224.0.0.0 and ending with:

   a. 224.224.224.224

   b. 239.255.255.255

   c. 240.0.0.0

   d. 224.224.224.0

7. The bulk of Internet traffic is what kind of traffic?

    a. Multicast

    b. Unicast

    c. Point-to-Point

    d. None of the above

8. NAT consists of all but one of the following components.

    a. Translation component

    b. Client/server component

    c. Addressing component

    d. Name resolution component

9. By default, NAT uses which private network ID with the subnet mask 255.255.255.0 for a private network?

    a. 10.0.0.0

    b. 172.16.0.0

    c. 192.168.0.0

    d. 255.255.0.0

9

10. When the home computers on the home network receive their IP address configuration from the NAT computer, they are configured with all but one of the following:

    a. ISP

    b. Subnet mask

    c. Default gateway

    d. IP address

11. What is used to send and receive multicast traffic to and from the Internet?

    a. ICMP proxy mode

    b. IGMP proxy mode

    c. NAT proxy mode

    d. Proxy server

12. If you use private IP addresses on the Internet, what might occur?

    a. IP address overlapping

    b. InterNIC will bill you for using the IP addresses

    c. Your IP addresses will never work

    d. They will not be seen by public IP addresses

13. Which of the following group addresses is used by RIP?

    a. 224.0.0.5

    b. 224.0.0.6

    c. 224.0.0.9

    d. 224.0.0.10

14. Which of the following messages is sent by a multicast router?

    a. A leave group message to request a misbehaving member to leave the multicast group

    b. A status message to ensure connectivity

    c. Host membership query

    d. Host membership report

15. Windows 2000 includes built-in NAT editors for which of the following protocols? [Select all that apply]

    a. FTP

    b. ICMP

    c. PPTP

    d. NetBIOS over TCP/IP

Real-World Projects

After years of a rewarding career as an IT director, Lesha Camille has decided to pursue a lifetime dream of working for herself out of her home. She has set up a home office network with three Windows 2000 Professional computers and a Windows 2000 server. The server has been wired to the Internet by a cable modem from a local ISP. The address for the server is being provided through a DHCP server from the ISP, so she doesn't need to worry about using a static public address. Also, the ISP provided a DNS server address for the network; this address is static and will have to be manually configured for the server and clients. As an added service, the ISP is hosting Lesha Camille's company Web page, so that she doesn't have to own a Web server.

Everything is in place for Lesha; all she needs to do now is implement NAT and Internet connection sharing to get her network up and running. She has asked you, a network consultant she is familiar with, to help her out. The two of you will be doing the configuration details together, so it can be done faster. Also, it gives her a chance to network with you and see if you would be a good candidate for future projects.

As a benefit to her network, Lesha also wants to enable the computer game Asheron's Call, a Microsoft first person role-playing adventure game. One of the companies she did some work for previously had a similar game that the employees played on designated days as a stress management tool and simply to just make work fun. The game is an Internet game that has to be played on the Internet; there is no other choice.

Project 9.1

To implement NAT on a Windows 2000 server, perform the following steps:

1. Open Routing and Remote Access.

2. In the console tree, click on NAT.

3. Right-click on NAT, and then click on Properties.

4. On the Address Assignment tab, select the Automatically Assign IP Addresses By Using DHCP checkbox.

5. If applicable, in IP address and Mask, configure the range of IP addresses to allocate to DHCP clients on the private network.

The address range to be allocated to the client computers on the network will range from 192.168.1.1 to 192.168.1.4. The first address should be reserved for the server interface that will service the clients on the network. The interface for the Internet connection is already taken care of because it is receiving its IP address through DHCP from the ISP. A static IP address can be assigned to the Internet connection interface; the public address would be provided by the ISP, but would have additional charges.

Project 9.2

To configure the Windows 2000 Professional client computers to obtain their addresses dynamically, perform the following steps:

1. On the Desktop, right-click on My Computer.

2. Click on Properties.

3. In the Network Connection Tab, select TCP/IP, and then click on Properties.

4. In the IP Address tab, click on the Obtain IP Address Automatically option.

5. In the DNS entry, select the appropriate option.

Setting up the clients in this fashion allows them to receive their addresses dynamically from the NAT computer. The configured NAT computer will assign the addresses through DHCP for each client computer on the network, so they can share the Internet connection.

Project 9.3

To configure applications for Internet connection sharing, perform the following steps:

1. Open Network and Dial-Up Connections.

2. Right-click on the shared connection, and then click on Properties.

3. On the Sharing tab, verify that the Enable Internet Connection Sharing For This Connection checkbox is selected, and then click on Settings.

4. To configure a network application for the computers sharing the connection, on the Applications tab, click on Add, and then do the following:

   a. In Name Of Application, type an easily recognized name for the application.

   b. In Remote Server Port Number, type the port number of the remote server where the application resides, and then click on either TCP or UDP.

   c. In TCP or UDP or both, type the port number for the port on your home network that the application will connect to. Some applications require TCP and UDP port numbers.

After configuring Acheron's Call for the network, you will be able to play it on one computer. Multiple licenses will be required if all client computers will have the game on them. Test it to see if a connection can be made, and then let the fun begin. If you actually use this game for this exercise, you will know that it is working when it connects to the MSN Gaming Zone; otherwise it will tell you that the connection couldn't be made.

This method will work for any application that requires the use of Internet connection sharing. For those familiar with Internet connection sharing under Windows 98, remember that NAT is a client/server model, so you can use hub connections instead of crossover cabling.

CHAPTER TEN

Remote Access

After completing this chapter, you will be able to:

✓ Understand what remote access is

✓ Identify the components of a dial-up network

✓ Identify the components of a virtual private network (VPN)

✓ Understand remote-access protocols

✓ Understand VPN tunneling protocols

✓ Understand Transmission Control Protocol/Internet Protocol (TCP/IP) and remote access

✓ Differentiate between authentication and authorization

✓ Understand what remote-access policies are

✓ Understand Remote Access Server (RAS) policy administration models

✓ Install the RAS

Windows 2000 Remote Access Server (RAS), part of the integrated Routing and Remote Access Service (RRAS), connects remote or mobile workers to an organization's network. Remote users can work from a location as though their computers are a part of their organization's physical network.

Users run remote-access software and initiate a connection to the RAS. The RAS, which is a computer running Windows 2000 Server and RRAS, authenticates users and provides service sessions until the connection is terminated by the user or network administrator. Services available to a local area network (LAN)-connected user can include file and print sharing, Web server access, and messaging.

Remote-access clients use standard tools to access resources. Clients can use Windows Explorer to make drive connections and connect to printers. These connections are persistent, so users do not need to reconnect to network resources during remote sessions. Because drive letters and the universal naming convention (UNC) have full support by remote access, most commercial and custom applications work without modification.

Remote-Access Connectivity

A RAS running Windows 2000 provides remote-access connectivity using dial-up networking or virtual private networking.

Dial-Up Networking

Dial-up networking is where a remote-access client makes a nonpermanent dial-up connection to a physical port on a RAS by using the service of a telecommunications provider, such as analog telephone, integrated services digital network (ISDN), or X.25. An example of dial-up networking is when a dial-up networking client dials the telephone number of one of the ports of a RAS. Dial-up networking over an analog telephone or ISDN is a direct physical connection between the dial-up networking client and the dial-up networking server. Data encryption over a dial-up connection is not required but is possible.

Components of a Dial-Up Network

Windows 2000 remote-access dial-up networks include components for dial-up servers and clients, LAN and remote-access protocols, wide area network (WAN) options, Internet support, and security options.

➤ *Dial-up servers*—RASs running Windows 2000 can be configured to provide dial-up networking access to an entire network or to restrict access to the shared resources of the RAS only.

➤ *Dial-up clients*—Remote-access clients running Windows NT, Windows 2000, Windows 98, Windows 95, Windows for Workgroups, MS-DOS, LAN Manager dial-up networking or remote access, or Apple Macintosh can all connect to a RAS running Windows 2000.

➤ *LAN and remote-access protocols*—Application programs that transport information using LAN protocols. Remote-access protocols negotiate connections and provide framing for LAN protocol data sent over WAN links. Windows 2000 remote-access dial-up networks support LAN protocols such as TCP/IP, Internetwork Packet Exchange (IPX), AppleTalk, network basic input/output system (NetBIOS) Enhanced User Interface (NetBEUI), Unix, Apple Macintosh, and Novell NetWare resources that enable access to the Internet. Windows 2000 remote-access dial-up networks support remote-access protocols such as Point-to-Point Protocol (PPP), Serial-Line Internet Protocol (SLIP), and Microsoft RAS Protocol (MS-RAS).

➤ *WAN options*—Clients can dial in using standard telephone lines and a modem or modem pool. Faster links are possible using ISDN. Remote-access clients can also connect to RASs using X.25 or asynchronous transfer mode (ATM). Direct connections are supported through an RS-232C null modem cable, a parallel port connection, or an infrared connection.

➤ *Internet support*—Complete services for Internet access are provided. A computer running Windows 2000 Server can be configured for an Internet Service Provider (ISP), which offers dial-up Internet connections to PPP clients. A computer running Windows 2000 can dial in to an Internet-connected computer running Windows NT Server 3.5 or later or to any one of a variety of industry standard PPP or SLIP-based Internet servers.

➤ *Security options*—Logon and domain security as well as security hosts, data encryption, Remote Authentication Dial-In User Service (RADIUS), smart cards, remote-access policies, and callback are supported to provide secure network access for dial-up clients.

Virtual Private Networking

Virtual private networking is the creation of a secure, point-to-point connection across a private or public network, such as the Internet. A virtual private networking client uses special TCP/IP-based protocols called *tunneling protocols* to make a virtual call to a virtual port on a virtual private networking server. An example of virtual private networking is when a virtual private networking client makes a virtual private networking connection to a RAS that is connected to the Internet. The RAS answers the virtual call, authenticates the caller, and transfers data between the virtual private networking client and the corporate network.

Components of a VPN

A Windows 2000 VPN includes components for VPN servers, VPN clients, LAN and remote-access protocols, tunneling protocols, WAN options, Internet support, and security options.

➤ *VPN servers*—RASs running Windows 2000 can be configured to provide access to an entire network or to restrict access to just the resources of the VPN server.

➤ *VPN clients*—Individual users who obtain a remote-access VPN connection or routers that obtain a router-to-router VPN connection are VPN clients. Windows NT version 4.0 and later, Windows 95, and Windows 98 VPN clients can create remote-access VPN connections to a RAS running Windows 2000 that acts as a VPN server. Computers running Windows 2000 Server, or Windows NT Server version 4.0 and RRAS can create router-to-router VPN connections. VPN clients can also be any non-Microsoft Point-to-Point Tunneling Protocol (PPTP) client or Layer 2 Tunneling Protocol (L2TP) client that uses IP security (IPSec).

➤ *LAN and remote-access protocols*—Application programs that transport information using LAN protocols. Remote-access protocols negotiate connections and provide framing for LAN protocol data sent over WAN links. Windows 2000 remote access supports LAN protocols such as TCP/IP, IPX, AppleTalk, and NetBEUI, which all enable access to Internet, Unix, Apple Macintosh, and Novell NetWare resources. For VPN connections, Windows 2000 remote access supports the PPP.

➤ *Tunneling protocols*—VPN clients use tunneling protocols to create secure connections to a VPN server. Windows 2000 includes PPTP and L2TP.

➤ *WAN options*—VPN servers can be connected to the Internet using permanent WAN connections such as T1 or Frame Relay. VPN clients are connected to the Internet by permanent WAN connections or by standard analog telephone lines or ISDN.

➤ *Internet support*—Complete services for VPNs on the Internet are provided. A Windows 2000 Server can be configured as a VPN server, which offers secure connections to remote-access clients or dial-on-demand routers.

➤ *Security options*—Logon and domain security as well as security hosts, data encryption, RADIUS, smart cards, IP packet filtering, and caller ID are supported to provide secure network access for VPN clients.

Remote-Access Protocols

Remote-access protocols control transmission of data over WAN links. The operating system and LAN protocols that are used on remote-access clients and servers dictate which remote-access protocol your clients can use. Three types of remote-access protocols are supported by Windows 2000 RAS: PPP, SLIP, and MS-RAS.

PPP

Windows 2000 Server supports the PPP, a set of industry standard framing and authentication protocols that enable remote-access solutions to function in a multivendor network. PPP is recommended because of its flexibility, its role as an industry standard, and its future flexibility with client and server hardware and software.

PPP support enables computers running Windows 2000 to dial in to remote networks through any server that complies with the PPP standard. PPP compliance also enables a server to receive calls from and provide network access to other vendors' remote-access software.

The PPP architecture also enables remote-access clients to use any combination of IPX, TCP/IP, NetBEUI, and AppleTalk. Remote-access clients running Windows NT, Windows 2000, Windows 98, or Windows 95 can use any combination of TCP/IP, IPX, and NetBEUI as well as programs written to the Windows Sockets (Winsock), NetBIOS, or IPX interface. Microsoft remote-access clients do not support the use of the AppleTalk protocol over a remote-access connection.

SLIP

SLIP is an older remote-access standard typically used by Unix RASs. Remote-access clients running Windows 2000 support SLIP and can connect to any RAS using the SLIP standard. This permits clients running Windows NT version 3.5 or later to connect to the large installed base of Unix servers. A RAS running Windows 2000, however, does not support SLIP clients.

MS-RAS

MS-RAS is a proprietary remote-access protocol that supports the NetBIOS standard. MS-RAS is supported in all previous versions of Microsoft RAS and is used on Windows NT version 3.1, Windows for Workgroups, MS-DOS, and LAN Manager clients.

A remote-access client dialing from a computer running Windows NT version 3.1 or Windows for Workgroups must use the NetBEUI protocol. The RAS acts as a NetBIOS gateway for the remote client, providing access to resources over the NetBEUI, NetBIOS over TCP/IP, or NetBIOS over IPX protocols.

VPN Tunneling Protocols

Virtual private networking supports PPTP, an industry standard, and L2TP, which is currently a Request for Comments (RFC)-based standard.

10

PPTP

PPTP is a de facto industry standard tunneling protocol first supported in Windows NT 4. PPTP is an extension of PPP and leverages the authentication, compression, and encryption mechanisms of PPP.

PPTP is installed with RRAS. By default, PPTP is configured for five PPTP ports. PPTP ports can be enabled for inbound remote-access and dial-on-demand routing (DDR) connections using the Routing and Remote Access Wizard. PPTP and Microsoft Point-to-Point Encryption (MPPE) provide the primary VPN services of encapsulation and encryption of private data.

Encryption

The PPP frame is encrypted with MPPE using encryption keys generated from the Microsoft Challenge Handshake Authentication Protocol (MS-CHAP v1 or v2 with version 2 recommended) or the Extensible Authentication Protocol–Transport Layer Security (EAP-TLS) authentication process. Virtual private networking clients must use either the MS-CHAP or the EAP-TLS authentication process for the payloads of PPP frames to be encrypted. PPTP takes advantage of the underlying PPP encryption and encapsulates a previously encrypted PPP frame.

It is possible to have a nonencrypted PPTP connection where the PPP frame is sent in plain text. Nonencrypted PPTP connections are not recommended for virtual private network connections over the Internet, however, because communications of this type are not secure.

L2TP

L2TP is an RFC-based tunneling protocol that is in the process of becoming an industry standard. Unlike PPTP, L2TP in Windows 2000 does not utilize MPPE to encrypt PPP datagrams. L2TP relies on IPSec for encryption services.

The combination of L2TP and IPSec is known as *L2TP over IPSec*. The result is that L2TP-based VPN connections are a combination of L2TP and IPSec. Both the VPN client and server must support L2TP and IPSec. L2TP over IPSec provides the primary VPN services of encapsulation and encryption of private data.

L2TP is installed with RRAS. By default, L2TP is configured for five L2TP ports. L2TP ports can be enabled for inbound remote-access and DDR connections using the Routing and Remote Access Wizard.

Encryption

L2TP messages are encrypted with IPSec encryption mechanisms using encryption keys generated from the IPSec authentication process. It is possible to have a non-IPSec-based L2TP connection that is not encrypted, where the PPP frame is sent in plain text. A nonencrypted L2TP connection is not recommended for VPN connections over the Internet, however, because communications of this type are not secure.

TCP/IP and Remote Access

TCP/IP is the most popular LAN protocol. Its routing and scaling capabilities provide maximum flexibility in an enterprise-wide internetwork. On a TCP/IP internetwork, IP addresses must be provided to hosts. Hosts might also require methods for name resolution. This section explains IP addressing and name resolution for RASs running Windows 2000 and remote-access clients for TCP/IP networks.

Assigning IP Addresses to Remote Access Clients

Each remote computer that connects to a RAS running Windows 2000 through PPP on a TCP/IP network is provided an IP address automatically. The RAS obtains the IP address allocated to the remote-access client from a Dynamic Host Configuration Protocol (DHCP) server or a static range of IP addresses assigned to the RAS by the administrator.

RAS and DHCP

When the RAS is configured to use DHCP to obtain IP addresses, the DHCP server obtains 10 IP addresses from a DHCP server. The RAS uses the first IP address obtained from DHCP for itself, then allocates subsequent addresses to TCP/IP-based remote-access clients as they connect. IP addresses that are freed when remote-access clients disconnect are reused. When all 10 IP addresses are used, the RAS obtains 10 more. When RRAS is stopped, all IP addresses obtained through DHCP are released.

If a DHCP server is not available when RRAS is started, then Automatic Private IP Addressing (APIPA) addresses from the range of 169.254.0.1 through 169.254.255.254 are used.

The RAS uses a specific LAN interface to obtain DHCP-allocated IP addresses for remote-access clients. To manually select a RAS LAN interface, perform the following eight steps from the RAS server:

1. Open the Routing and Remote Access Microsoft Management Console (MMC).

2. Highlight the RAS Server

3. Select Action | Properties.

4. Select the IP tab.

5. Select the adapter to use to obtain DHCP addresses for dial-up clients, as shown in Figure 10.1.

6. From the Security tab, click the Authentication Methods button, as shown in Figure 10.2.

10

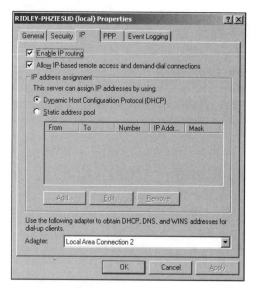

Figure 10.1 RAS IP tab.

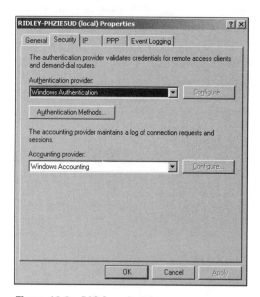

Figure 10.2 RAS Security tab.

7. From the Authentication Methods dialog box, check all the desired server authentication methods, as shown in Figure 10.3.

8. From the PPP tab, select PPP options like Multilink and Software Compression, as shown in Figure 10.4.

By default, RRAS randomly picks a LAN interface to use. For a RAS with multiple adapters, select the adapter that is connected to a network segment where DHCP-allocated addresses can be obtained.

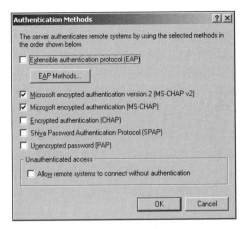

Figure 10.3   RAS Authentication Methods dialog box.

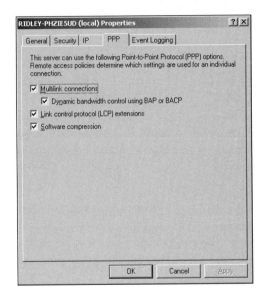

Figure 10.4   RAS PPP tab.

RAS Static IP Address Pools

A static pool of IP addresses is entered as one or more ranges of IP addresses. Each range of IP addresses can be entered as a starting IP address and an ending IP address for the range, or a starting IP address and the number of IP addresses in the range. With previous versions of Windows NT, the address pool is entered as a range of IP addresses with exceptions. In Windows 2000, the ability to configure exceptions can be duplicated by using multiple ranges. The RAS uses the first IP address in the first range.

If the static IP address pool consists of ranges of IP addresses that are a subset of the range of IP addresses for the network where the RAS is attached, then the ranges of IP addresses in the remote-access IP address pool must not be assigned to other TCP/IP nodes statically or through DHCP. If the static IP address pool consists of ranges of IP addresses that are for a separate subnet, then either enable an IP routing protocol on the RAS computer or add static IP routes consisting of the IP address and the subnet mask of each range to the routers of the intranet. Otherwise, remote-access clients cannot receive traffic from resources on the intranet.

Remote-access clients running Windows 2000 can also use a preassigned IP address specified in their RAS phone books. In this case, configure the RAS running Windows 2000 through remote-access policies to permit users to request a specific address, and configure the dial-in properties of the user account with static IP addresses.

Authentication vs. Authorization

The distinction between authentication and authorization is important to understanding why connection attempts are accepted or denied. Authentication is the verification of the credentials of the connection attempt. This process consists of sending the credentials from the remote-access client to the RAS in a plain text or an encrypted form using an authentication protocol. Authorization is the verification that the connection attempt is allowed. Authorization occurs after successful authentication. For connection attempts to be accepted, the connection attempt must be both authenticated and authorized. It is possible to authenticate the connection attempt by using valid credentials, but not to authorize it. The connection attempt is denied in this case.

If a RAS is configured for Windows authentication, Windows 2000 security is used to verify the credentials for authentication, and the dial-in properties of the user account and locally stored remote-access policies are used to authorize the connection. If the connection attempt is both authenticated and authorized, the connection attempt is accepted.

If the RAS is configured for RADIUS, the credentials of the connection attempt are passed to the RADIUS server for authentication and authorization. If the connection attempt is both authenticated and authorized, the RADIUS server sends an accept message to the RAS, and the connection attempt is accepted. If the connection attempt is not authenticated or not authorized, the RADIUS server sends a reject message to the RAS, and the connection process is denied.

Remote-Access Dial-In Permissions

After a RAS is installed, specify from which users the RAS can accept a connection. For Windows 2000, authorization is determined by the dial-in properties on the user account and remote-access policies. User accounts do not need to be created for remote-access users only. RASs use the user accounts specified in the available user accounts databases according to Windows 2000 security.

How Security Works

The following steps describe what happens during a call from a remote-access client to a RAS running Windows 2000 that is configured to use Windows authentication:

1. A remote-access client dials a RAS.

2. The server sends a challenge to the client.

3. The client sends an encrypted response that consists of a username, a domain name, and a password to the server.

4. The server checks the response against the appropriate user accounts database.

5. If the account is valid, the server uses the dial-in properties of the user account and remote-access policies to authorize the connection.

6. If callback is enabled, the server calls the client back and continues the connection negotiation process.

Steps 2 and 3 assume that the remote-access client and the RAS use the MS-CHAP version 1 or CHAP. The process of sending client credentials may vary for other authentication protocols. If the RAS is a member of a domain and the user response does not contain a domain name, then the domain name of the RAS is used. To use a domain name other than the domain name of the RAS, set the following registry value to the name of the domain that you want to use:

```
HKEY_LOCAL_MACHINE\System\CurrentControlSet\Services\RasMan\PPP\
  ControlProtocols\BuiltIn\DefaultDomain
```

Security after the Connection Is Made

After passing remote-access authentication and connecting to the LAN, remote-access clients log on to the Windows 2000 domain. After a successful domain logon process, the user's domain credentials are used to access resources for which they have permission. Remote-access clients are subject to Windows 2000 security, just as they are at the office. Remote-access clients cannot do anything for which they lack sufficient rights, nor can they access resources for which they do not have permission.

The RAS must authenticate remote-access clients before they can access or generate traffic on the network. This authentication is a separate step from logging on to Windows 2000. User passwords and the authentication procedure can be encrypted when they are transmitted over telephone lines.

A remote-access client's access can be restricted to the shared resources of the RAS only, and not the network to which the RAS is attached. A tight control of what information is available to remote-access clients can limit a client's exposure in the event of a security breach.

Account Lockout

The account lockout feature can be set to specify how many times a remote-access authentication fails against a valid user account before the user is denied access. Account lockout is especially important for remote-access VPN connections over the Internet. Malicious users on the Internet can attempt to access an organization's intranet by sending credentials (valid username, hypothetical password) during a VPN connection authentication process. During a dictionary attack, the malicious user sends hundreds or thousands of credentials by using a list of passwords based on common words or phrases.

With account lockout enabled, a dictionary attack is thwarted after a specified number of failed attempts. For network administration, decide on two account lockout variables:

➤ *The number of failed attempts to allow before future attempts are denied*—After each failed attempt, a failed attempts counter for the user account is increased. If the user account's failed attempts counter reaches the configured maximum, future attempts to connect are denied. A successful authentication resets the failed attempts counter when its value is less than the configured maximum. In other words, the failed attempts counter does not accumulate beyond a successful authentication.

➤ *How often to reset the failed attempts counter*—Periodically reset the failed attempts counter to prevent inadvertent account lockouts due to normal mistakes by users when typing in their passwords.

Changing settings in the Windows 2000 registry on the server that provides the authentication enables the account lockout feature. If the RAS is configured for Windows authentication, modify the registry on the RAS. If the RAS is configured for RADIUS and Windows 2000 Internet Authentication Service (IAS) is being used, modify the registry on the IAS server.

To enable account lockout, set the MaxDenials value entry in the registry to 1 or greater. MaxDenials is the maximum number of failed attempts allowed before the account is locked out. Set the MaxDenials value entry in the following registry subkey:

```
HKEY_LOCAL_MACHINE\SYSTEM\CurrentControlSet\Services\RemoteAccess\
    Parameters\AccountLockout
```

By default, MaxDenials is set to 0, which means that account lockout is disabled.

To modify the amount of time before the failed attempts counter is reset, set the ResetTime (mins) value entry in the registry to the required number of minutes. Set the ResetTime (mins) value entry in the following registry subkey:

```
HKEY_LOCAL_MACHINE\SYSTEM\CurrentControlSet\Services\RemoteAccess\
    Parameters\AccountLockout
```

By default, ResetTime (mins) is set to 0xb40 or 2,880 minutes (48 hours).

Introduction to Remote-Access Policies

In Windows NT versions 3.5x and 4.0, authorization is based on the Grant dial-in permission to user option in the User Manager or the Remote Access Admin utility. Callback options are also configured on a per-user basis.

In Windows 2000, authorization is granted based on the dial-in properties of a user account and remote-access policies. Remote-access policies are a set of conditions and connection settings that give network administrators more flexibility in authorizing connection attempts. Windows 2000 RRAS and Windows 2000 IAS both use remote-access policies to determine whether to accept or reject connection attempts. In both cases, the remote-access policies are stored locally.

With remote-access policies, authorization can be granted or denied based on the time of day and day of the week, the Windows 2000 group to which the remote-access user belongs, the type of connection being requested, and so on. Settings that limit the maximum session time, specify the authentication and encryption strengths, and set Bandwidth Allocation Protocol (BAP) policies can also be configured.

It is important to remember that with remote-access policies, a connection is authorized only if the settings of the connection attempt match at least one of the remote-access policies (subject to the conditions of the dial-in properties of the user account and the profile properties of the remote-access policy). If the settings of the connection attempt do not match at least one of the remote-access policies, the connection attempt is denied regardless of the dial-in properties of the user account.

For RASs running Windows 2000, remote-access policies are administered from RRAS. For Windows 2000 IAS servers, remote-access policies are administered from IAS.

Local vs. Centralized Policy Management

Remote-access policies are stored locally on a RAS or an IAS server. To centralize management of a single set of remote-access policies for multiple remote-access or VPN servers, perform the following steps:

10

1. Install the Windows 2000 IAS as a RADIUS server on a computer.

2. Configure IAS with RADIUS clients that correspond to each of the Windows 2000 remote-access or VPN servers.

3. On the IAS server, create the central set of policies to be used by all Windows 2000 RASs.

4. Configure each of the Windows 2000 RASs as a RADIUS client to the IAS server.

When a Windows 2000 RAS is configured as a RADIUS client to an IAS server, local remote-access policies stored on the RAS are no longer used. Centralized management of remote-access policies is also used with RASs running Windows NT 4 with RRAS enabled. The server running Windows NT 4 with RRAS can be configured as a RADIUS client to an IAS server. A RAS running Windows NT 4 without RRAS cannot be configured to take advantage of centralized remote-access policies.

Elements of a Remote-Access Policy

A remote-access policy is a named rule that consists of conditions, remote-access permissions, and profiles.

Conditions

Remote-access policy conditions are attributes that are compared with the settings of the connection attempt. If there are multiple conditions, then all of the conditions must match the settings of the connection attempt for the connection attempt to match the policy.

Remote-Access Permission

If all of the conditions of a remote-access policy are met, remote-access permission is granted or denied. The Grant remote-access permission option or the Deny remote-access permission option can be used to set remote-access permission for a policy.

Remote-access permission is also granted or denied for each user account. The user remote-access permission overrides the policy remote-access permission. When remote-access permission on a user account is set to the Control access through Remote Access Policy option, the policy remote-access permission determines whether the user is granted access.

Granting access through the user account permission setting or the policy permission setting is only the first step in accepting a connection. The connection attempt is then subjected to the settings of the user account properties and the policy profile properties. If the connection attempt does not match the settings of the user account properties or the profile properties, the connection attempt is rejected. By default, the Deny remote-access permission option is selected.

Profile

A remote-access policy profile is a set of properties that are applied to a connection when the connection is authorized through the user account permission setting or the policy permission setting. A profile consists of the following groups of properties:

➤ Dial-in constraints

➤ IP

➤ Multilink

➤ Authentication

➤ Encryption

➤ Advanced

Dial-In Constraints

For a policy profile, dial-in constraint properties can include idle disconnect time, maximum session length, day and time limits, dial-in number to call, and specific dial-in media.

➤ *Idle disconnect time*—The time after which a connection is disconnected when there is no activity. By default, this property is not set, and the RAS does not disconnect an idle connection.

➤ *Maximum session length*—The maximum amount of time that a connection is connected. The RAS disconnects the connection after the maximum session length. By default, this property is not set, and the RAS has no maximum session limit.

➤ *Day and time limits*—The days of the week and the hours of each day that a connection is allowed. If the day and time of the connection attempt do not match the configured day and time limits, the connection attempt is rejected. By default, this property is not set, and the RAS has no day or time limits. The RAS does not disconnect active connections that are connected at a time when connection attempts are not allowed.

➤ *Dial-in number*—A specific telephone number that a caller must use for a connection to be allowed. If the dial-in number of the connection attempt does not match the configured dial-in number, the connection attempt is rejected. By default, this property is not set, and the RAS allows all dial-in numbers.

10

➤ *Specific dial-in media*—The specific types of media (such as modem, ISDN, or VPN) that a caller must use for a connection to be allowed. If the dial-in medium of the connection attempt does not match the configured dial-in media, the connection attempt is rejected. By default, this property is not set, and the RAS allows all dial-in media types.

IP

IP properties that specify whether a specific IP address for a connection requested by the client can be set. By default, the RAS automatically allocates an IP address, and the client is not allowed to request a specific IP address.

IP packet filters for remote-access policy profiles can be configured to define the traffic allowed across the connection after the connection has been made. Profile packet filters can be used to configure IP traffic that is allowed out of the connection to the client or into the connection from the client on an exception basis: all traffic except traffic specified by the filters or no traffic except traffic specified by the filters is allowed. Remote-access policy profile filtering applies to all connections that match the remote-access policy.

Multilink

Multilink properties that enable Multilink and determine the maximum number of ports that a Multilink connection can be set. Additionally, BAP policies that determine BAP usage and when extra BAP lines are dropped can be set. Multilink and BAP properties are specific to Microsoft Windows 2000 remote access. By default, Multilink and BAP are disabled. The RAS must have Multilink and BAP enabled for the Multilink properties of the profile to be enforced.

Authentication

Authentication properties can be set to enable the types of authentication allowed for a connection and to specify the EAP type that must be used. Additionally, the EAP type can be configured. By default, MS-CHAP version 1 (MS-CHAP v1) and MS-CHAP version 2 (MS-CHAP v2) are enabled. The RAS must have the corresponding authentication types enabled for the authentication properties of the profile to be enforced.

Encryption

Encryption properties for a policy profile can set with encryption strengths. The encryption strength settings can be no encryption, basic encryption, strong, and strongest.

➤ *No encryption*—When the No Encryption option is selected, nonencrypted connections are allowed. To require encryption, clear the No Encryption option.

➤ *Basic encryption*—For the Basic For dial-up and PPTP-based VPN connections, MPPE with a 40-bit key is used. For L2TP over IPSec-based VPN connections, a 56-bit Data Encryption Standard (DES) encryption is used.

➤ *Strong*—For the Strong For dial-up and PPTP-based VPN connections, MPPE with a 56-bit key is used. For L2TP over IPSec-based VPN connections, 56-bit DES encryption is used.

➤ *Strongest*—For the Strongest For dial-up and PPTP-based VPN connections, MPPE with a 128-bit key is used. For L2TP over IPSec-based VPN connections, triple DES (3DES) encryption is used.

Advanced

Advanced properties can be set to specify the series of RADIUS attributes that are sent back to the RADIUS client by the IAS server. RADIUS attributes are specific to performing RADIUS authentication and are ignored by the RAS. By default, the Framed-Protocol attribute is set to PPP, and the Service-Type attribute is set to Framed. The only attributes used by the RAS are Account-Interim-Interval, Framed-Protocol, Framed-MTU, Reply-Message, and Service-Type.

Remote-Access Policy Administration Models

10

In Windows 2000, there are three primary models for administering remote-access permissions and connection settings: access by user, access by policy in a native-mode domain, and access by policy in a mixed-mode domain. These administration models are recommended ways of controlling remote access. Remote access can be administered through a mixture of these models, but do so carefully to produce the intended results. Improper configuration may lead to connection attempts that are rejected when they should be accepted and connection attempts that are accepted when they should be rejected.

Access by User

In the access-by-user administration model, remote-access permissions are determined by the remote-access permission setting on the Dial-In tab of the user account. Remote-access permission can be enabled or disabled on a per-user basis by setting the remote-access permission to Allow access or Deny access.

The remote-access permission setting on the remote-access policy is effectively overridden if the user remote-access permission is set to Allow access or Deny access. Remote-access policy conditions and profile properties, however, can be modified to enforce connection settings, such as encryption requirements and idle time-outs.

The access-by-user model can be administered with multiple remote-access policies. Each remote-access policy has its own profile settings. These settings must be configured carefully, because a connection attempt may be rejected even when the remote-access permission on the user account is set to Allow access. If a connection attempt matches the conditions of a policy but does not match the profile settings or any of the remote-access policies, the connection attempt is rejected.

The access-by-user administration model can control three behaviors:

➤ Explicit allow permission for the user account is set to Allow access, and the connection attempt matches the conditions of a policy subject to the settings of the profile and the dial-in properties of the user account.

➤ Explicit deny permission for the user account is set to Deny access.

➤ Implicit deny connection attempts do not match the conditions of any remote-access policies.

In Windows 2000, the access-by-user administration model is equivalent to administering remote access on a Windows NT 4 RAS.

The access-by-user administration model can be used on a standalone RAS, a RAS that is a member of a Windows 2000 native-mode domain, a RAS that is a member of a Windows 2000 mixed-mode domain, or a RAS that is a member of a Windows NT 4 domain. The access-by-user administration model can be used for Windows NT 4 RAS or IAS servers.

Access by Policy in a Native-Mode Domain

In the administration model for accessing by policy in a native-mode domain, the remote-access permission on every user account is set to Control access through Remote Access Policy. Remote-access permissions are determined by the remote-access permission setting on the remote-access policy; therefore, the remote-access permission setting on the remote-access policy determines whether remote-access permission is allowed or denied.

In the administration model for accessing by policy in a native-mode domain, three behaviors can be controlled:

➤ Explicit allow remote-access permission on the remote-access policy is set to Grant remote access permission, and the connection attempt matches the conditions of the policy subject to the settings of the profile and the dial-in properties of the user account.

➤ Explicit deny remote-access permission on the remote-access policy is set to Deny remote access permission, and the connection attempt matches the conditions of the policy.

➤ Implicit deny connection attempts do not match the conditions of any remote-access policies.

Using this administration model, if no remote-access policies are added and the default remote-access policy named "Allow access if dial-in permission is enabled" is not changed, then no users are allowed remote access. The remote-access permission on the default remote-access policy is set to Deny remote access permission. If you change the setting to Grant remote access permission, then all users are allowed remote access. The administration model for accessing by policy in a native-mode domain also applies to standalone RASs that are not members of a domain.

Access by Policy in a Mixed-Mode Domain

In the administration model for accessing by policy in a mixed-mode domain, the remote-access permission on every user account is set to Allow access, the default remote-access policy is deleted, and separate remote-access policies are created to define the types of connections that are allowed. On a RAS running Windows 2000 that is a member of a Windows 2000 mixed-mode domain, the Control access through Remote Access Policy option is not available for remote-access permission on the user account. If a connection attempt matches the conditions of a policy subject to the profile and user account dial-in settings, then the connection is accepted. This administration model also applies to RASs running Windows 2000 that are members of a Windows NT 4 domain.

In the administration model for accessing by policy in a mixed-mode domain, three behaviors can be controlled:

➤ With Explicit allow, the connection attempt matches the conditions of a policy subject to the settings of the profile and the dial-in properties of the user account.

➤ With Explicit deny, the connection attempt matches the conditions of a policy but not the settings of the profile. An explicit deny can be set in this administration model by enabling the Restrict Dial-in to this number only dial-in constraint and typing a number that does not correspond to any dial-in number being used by the RAS.

➤ With Implicit deny, the connection attempt does not match the conditions of any remote-access policies.

Be sure to delete the default remote-access policy named "Allow access if dial-in permission is enabled"; otherwise, all users can obtain a remote-access connection.

10

Installing the RAS

To enable and configure the RAS, log on as a member of the Administrators group.

Installing the Software

When Windows 2000 Server is installed, the remote-access component is installed automatically; however, RRAS is installed in a disabled state.

To enable RRAS, perform the following steps:

1. Open the Routing and Remote Access MMC.

2. By default, the local computer is listed as a server. To add another server, right-click Server Status, and then select Add Server.

3. In the Add Server dialog box, select the applicable option, and then select OK.

4. In the console tree, right-click the server you want to enable, and then select Configure and Enable Routing and Remote Access.

5. Follow the instructions in the Routing and Remote Access Wizard.

Chapter Summary

Users run remote-access software and initiate a connection to the RAS. The RAS, which is a computer running Windows 2000 Server and RRAS, authenticates users and provides services sessions until they are terminated by the user or network administrator. Remote-access clients use standard tools to access resources. A RAS running Windows 2000 provides two different types of remote-access connectivity: dial-up networking and virtual private networking.

When the RAS is configured to use DHCP to obtain IP addresses, the DHCP server obtains 10 IP addresses from a DHCP server. The RAS uses the first IP address obtained from DHCP for itself, then allocates subsequent addresses to TCP/IP-based remote-access clients as they connect. IP addresses that are freed when remote-access clients disconnect are reused. When all 10 IP addresses are used, the RAS obtains 10 more.

The RAS must authenticate remote-access clients before they can access or generate traffic on the network. Remote-access clients can have access restricted to the shared resources of the RAS only, preventing access to the network to which the RAS is attached.

In the access-by-user administration model, remote-access permissions are determined by the remote-access permission on the Dial-in tab of the user account. Remote-access permission can be enabled or disabled on a per-user basis by setting the remote-access permission to Allow access or Deny access.

The access-by-user administration model can be used on a standalone RAS, a RAS that is a member of a Windows 2000 native-mode domain, a RAS that is a member of a Windows 2000 mixed-mode domain, or a RAS that is a member of a Windows NT 4 domain.

In the administration model for accessing by policy in a mixed-mode domain, the remote-access permission on every user account is set to Allow access, the default remote-access policy is deleted, and separate remote-access policies are created to define the types of connections that are allowed. On a RAS running Windows 2000 that is a member of a Windows 2000 mixed-mode domain, the Control access through Remote Access Policy option is not available for remote-access permission on the user account.

Review Questions

1. What is the security feature that denies access after a configured number of failed authentication attempts?

   a. MS-CHAP v2

   b. AppleTalk client support

   c. Account lockout

   d. Remote-access policy

2. What is the set of conditions and connection settings that allow network administrators more flexibility in setting access permissions and connection attributes?

   a. EAP

   b. Remote-access policies

   c. Remote-access permissions

   d. BAP

3. Which of the following are types of remote-access protocols supported by Windows 2000 remote access?

   a. PPP

   b. SLIP

   c. MS-RAS

   d. All of the above

10

4. Microsoft remote-access clients over a remote-access connection do not support the use of which protocol?

   a. AppleTalk

   b. IPX/SPX

   c. TCP/IP

   d. NetBEUI

5. A RAS running Windows 2000 supports SLIP clients.

   a. True

   b. False

6. How many ports are configured by default for PPTP?

   a. 1

   b. 15

   c. 5

   d. 9

7. How many IP addresses does the DHCP server initially obtain for a RAS configured for DHCP?

   a. 5

   b. 10

   c. 15

   d. 20

8. It is possible to have nonencrypted PPTP connections where the PPTP frame is sent in plaintext.

   a. True

   b. False

9. What kind of server needs to support VPN clients using L2TP and IPSec?

   a. RFC

   b. VPN

   c. PPTP

   d. P2TP

10. In a remote-access policy, attributes that are compared with the settings of the connection attempt are known as:

   a. Conditions

   b. Remote-access permissions

   c. Profile

   d. None of the above

11. What happens when you connect to the corporate network via VPN when the DHCP server is down?

    a. You are unable to connect.

    b. You are not able to connect if you are using TCP/IP but will connect if you are using a different protocol.

    c. You will automatically receive an IP address via Automatic Private IP addressing.

    d. You will connect and use a static IP used only when the DHCP server is down.

12. Where do you configure RAS client IP addresses?

    a. RAS IP tab

    b. RAS DHCP Manager

    c. On each client

    d. RAS DHCP tab

13. Where do you configure RAS to use software compression?

    a. RAS Compression tab

    b. RAS Options menu

    c. RAS PPP tab

    d. Software compression is not a RAS option

14. Where are individual user access rights configured?

    a. On the client computer

    b. RAS Clients tab

    c. RAS does not allow individual user access rights

    d. User Accounts Dial-in tab

15. What should you do to require RAS encryption?

    a. Check the Require Encryption box

    b. Clear the No Encryption box

    c. Check the No Encryption box

    d. Check the Allow Encryption box

10

Real-World Projects

The Red Family Law Firm has decided to implement remote access for three of its lawyers so they can do some of their work from home. The lawyers need access to the entire network to utilize the firm's vast information resources. The firm's network administrator needs to configure a server purchased with Windows 2000 Server preloaded for dial-in remote access.

Project 10.1

To enable RRAS, perform the following steps:

1. Open the Routing and Remote Access MMC.

2. By default, the local computer is listed as a server. To add another server, right-click Server Status, and then select Add Server.

3. In the Add Server dialog box, select the applicable option, and then select OK.

4. In the console tree, right-click the server you want to enable, and then select Configure and Enable Routing and Remote Access.

5. Follow the instructions in the Routing and Remote Access Wizard.

By default RRAS is installed in a disabled state. It must be enabled and started on the target server to be used.

Project 10.2

To create a remote-access policy, perform the following steps:

1. Open the Routing and Remote Access MMC.

2. Right-click Remote Access Policies, and then select Add New Policy.

3. Follow the instructions in the Add Remote Access Policy Wizard.

It is a good idea to add the Windows group to the new policy. When defining the permissions, make them appropriate to the user. For example, if a remote user needs to be able to print documents to the network from a remote location, then give that user permission for printing.

CHAPTER ELEVEN

Security

After completing this chapter you will be able to:

✓ Enable IPSec

✓ Configure tunnel mode

✓ Implement policies and procedures

✓ Configure Point-to-Point Tunneling Protocol

✓ Configure Layer 2 Tunneling Protocol

✓ Understand Kerberos authentication

✓ Use Public Key Certificate Server

This chapter teaches users and administrators how to implement security measures on their networks and Windows 2000 Servers. Included in this chapter are the different protocols and how to configure security and reduce problems that can arise from lack of security. Windows 2000 introduces several new security features to help you implement the level of security that your organization needs.

In its simplest form, security ensures that people logging on to your network are who they say they are. When you create trust relationships between Windows domains or Kerberos v5 realms, Windows security can limit access to sensitive data or specific resources to only those people to whom you want to grant access, both within and outside your organization.

Windows 2000 security can also ensure that the data you store on disk or send over private or public networks is protected from unauthorized access. You can use Encrypting File System (EFS) to protect data stored on disk. IP security and Point-to-Point Tunneling Protocol (PPTP) encryption can protect data on your network as well as data transmitted over the Internet.

Internet Protocol Security (IPSec)

IPSec is a suite of cryptography-based protection services and security protocols. Because it requires no changes to applications or protocols, you can easily deploy IPSec for existing networks. It provides machine-level authentication and data encryption for Virtual Private Networking (VPN) connections that use the Layer 2 Tunneling Protocol (L2TP). IPSec negotiates between your computer and its remote tunnel server before an L2TP connection is established, securing both passwords and data.

The IPSec Security Association (SA) determines encryption. An SA is a combination of a destination address, a security protocol, and a unique identification value called a Security Parameters Index (SPI). The available encryptions include:

➤ Data Encryption Standard (DES) with a 56-bit key, which is designed for international use and adheres to United States export encryption laws.

➤ Triple DES (3DES), which uses two 56-bit keys and is designed for high-security environments in North America.

IPSec provides the following:

➤ *Confidentiality*—IPSec traffic is encrypted. Captured IPSec traffic is unintelligible without knowledge of the encryption key.

➤ *Authentication*—IPSec traffic is digitally signed with the shared encryption key, so that the receiver can verify that the IPSec peer sent it.

➤ *Data integrity*—IPSec traffic contains a cryptographic checksum that incorporates the encryption key. The receiver can verify that the packet was not modified in transit.

Using IP Security Policy Management

Windows IPSec is a key line of defense against internal, private network, and external attacks. It is designed to encrypt data as it travels between two computers, protecting it from modification and interpretation if anyone were to see and intercept it on the network. IPSec is controlled using a policy configuration that you create using the IP Security Policy Management snap-in.

To add the IPSec snap-in, complete the following steps:

1. Click on Start, click on Run, type "mmc", and then click on OK.

2. On the Console menu, click on Add/Remove Snap-in.

3. Click on Add, and then double-click on IP Security Policy Management.

4. Follow the instructions that appear on the screen.

Security Features of TCP/IP for Windows 2000

TCP/IP for Windows 2000 incorporates security features that provide protection of the TCP/IP data as it is sent on the network and configuration of the types of local host traffic that are processed.

To configure TCP/IP to use an IPSec policy:

1. Open Network and Dial-Up Connections.

2. Right-click on the network connection that you want to configure, and then click on Properties.

3. On the General tab (for a local area connection) or the Networking tab (all other connections), click on Internet Protocol (TCP/IP), and then click on Properties.

4. Click on Advanced.

5. On the Options tab, click on IP Security, and then click on Properties.

6. To enable IP security, click on Use This IP Security Policy, and then click on the name of a policy.

7. To disable IP security, click on Do Not Use IPSEC. IPSec defaults to Do Not Use as shown in Figure 11.1.

11

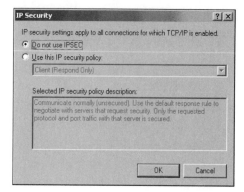

Figure 11.1 The IP Security Properties dialog box.

IPSec Policy Properties

IPSec policies can be applied to local computers, domain members, domains, Organizational Units, or any Group Policy object in Active Directory. Your organization's IPSec policies should be based on your organization's written guidelines for secure operations. Policies may store multiple security actions, called *rules*, so that one policy may be applied to multiple computers.

There are two storage locations for IPSec policies:

➤ Active Directory

➤ Locally defined in the Registry for stand-alone computers and computers that are not always part of a trusted Windows 2000 domain. If the computer is temporarily unconnected from a trusted Windows 2000 domain, the policy information is cached in the local Registry.

Windows includes predefined policies, which can be activated, modified to meet your needs, or used as a template for your own custom policies. Each policy you define should apply to a scenario in your security plan. Special configuration settings may apply if you are assigning policies to a Dynamic Host Control Protocol (DHCP) server, Domain Name System (DNS), Windows Internet Naming Service (WINS), Simple Network Management Protocol (SNMP), or remote access server.

Group Policy

IPSec policies that are assigned to a Group Policy object in Active Directory become part of Group Policy and are transferred to the member computers each time Group Policy propagates.

When assigning an IPSec policy in Active Directory, consider the following:

➤ IPSec policies assigned to a domain policy will override any active, local IPSec policy only when that computer is connected to the domain.

➤ IPSec policies assigned to an Organizational Unit will override an IPSec policy assigned to the domain policy for any member computers of that Organizational Unit. The IPSec policy assigned to the lowest-level Organizational Unit will override an IPSec policy assigned to a higher-level Organizational Unit for any member computers of that Organizational Unit.

Predefined IPSec Policies

Windows 2000 provides a set of predefined IPSec policies. By default, all predefined policies are designed for computers that are members of a Windows 2000 domain. They may be assigned without further action, modified, or used as a template for defining custom policies.

Client (Respond Only)

Client (Respond Only) is used for computers that should not secure communications most of the time. For example, intranet clients may not require IPSec except when requested by another computer. This policy enables the computer on which it is active to respond appropriately to requests for secured communications. The policy contains a default response rule, which enables negotiation with computers requesting IPSec. Only the requested protocol and port traffic for the communication is secured. See Figure 11.2 for Client (Respond Only) policy description.

Server (Request Security)

Server (Request Security) is used for computers that should secure communications most of the time. An example would be servers that transmit sensitive data. In this policy, the computer accepts unsecured traffic, but always attempts to secure

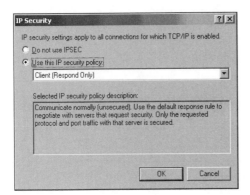

Figure 11.2   Client (Respond Only) policy description.

additional communications by requesting security from the original sender. This policy allows the entire communication to be unsecured if the other computer is not IPSec-enabled. See Figure 11.3 for Secure Server policy description.

Secure Server (Require Security)

Secure Server (Require Security) is used for computers that always require secure communications. An example would be a server that transmits highly sensitive data or a security gateway that protects the intranet from the outside. This policy rejects unsecured incoming communications, and outgoing traffic is always secured. Unsecured communication is not allowed, even if a peer is not IPSec-enabled. See Figure 11.4 for Secure Server policy description.

Predefined Rules

Like the predefined policies, the default response rule is provided for activation without further action, or it may be modified to fit specific needs. It is added to each new policy you create, but not automatically activated. It is used for any computers that do not require security, but must be able to appropriately respond when another computer requests secured communications.

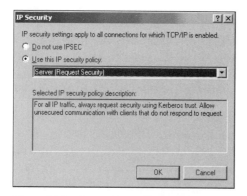

Figure 11.3 Secure Server (Request Security) policy description.

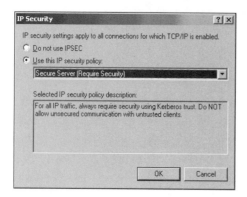

Figure 11.4 Secure Server (Require Security) policy description.

Predefined Filter Actions

Like the predefined rules, predefined filter actions are provided for activation without further action or modification or as a template for defining custom filter actions. They are available for activation in any new or existing rule:

➤ *Require Security*—High security. Unsecured communication is not allowed.

➤ *Request Security (Optional)*—Medium to low security. Unsecured communication is allowed to enable communication with computers that do not or cannot negotiate IPSec.

To restore predefined IPSec policies:

1. In IP Security Policy Management, click on the IP Security Policies folder.

2. Click on Action, point to All Tasks, and then click on Restore Default Policies.

3. Click on Yes.

To export an IPSec policy:

1. In IP Security Policy Management, click on the IP Security Policies folder.

2. Click on Action, point to All Tasks, and then click on Export Policies.

3. Type the path and the name of the file to which you want the policy information saved.

4. Click on Save.

To import an IPSec policy:

1. In IP Security Policy Management, click on IP Security Policies.

2. Click on Action, point to All Tasks, and then click on Import Policies.

3. Type the path and the name of the file from which you are importing the IPSec policy information.

4. If you want to override all existing policies with the imported information, select the Delete All Existing Policy Information checkbox.

5. Click on Open.

IPSec Connection Types

For each IPSec rule, you must define which connection types on your computer will be affected. The connection types apply to all connections in Network and Dial-Up Connections on the computer for which you are configuring IPSec policy.

Each rule has one connection type setting:

➤ *All Network Connections*—The rule will apply to communications sent via any of the network connections you have configured on the computer.

➤ *Local Area Network (LAN)*—The rule will only apply to communications sent via LAN connections you have configured on the computer.

➤ *Remote Access*—The rule will only apply to communications sent via any remote access or dial-up connections you have configured on the computer.

To specify IPSec connection types:

1. In IP Security Policy Management, right-click on the policy you want to modify, and then click on Properties.

2. Click on the rule you want to modify, and then click on Edit.

3. On the Connection Type tab, select the type of network connections to which this rule will apply:

➤ To apply this rule to all network connections you have created on the computer, click on All Network Connections.

➤ To apply this rule to all LAN connections you have created on the computer, click on Local Area Network (LAN).

➤ To apply this rule to any remote or dial-up connections you have created on the computer, click on Remote Access.

Most intranet clients do not need to communicate securely. However, a group of servers in the network may store highly sensitive information, which some intranet clients will need to access. All computers have computer accounts in an Active Directory domain or object. The computers are grouped into Active Directory Organizational Units for security reasons, which enables the appropriate assignment of IPSec policies based on the function of the computers.

Servers that store and exchange highly sensitive information belong to the Highest Security Servers Organizational Unit. Other servers that may use unsecured communication to enable data exchange with non-IPSec capable computers in the domain belong to the Secure Servers Organizational Unit. Clients that require the capability to appropriately respond when secure communications are required belong to the Secure Computers group. Clients that do not require the capability to talk to the secure servers belong to the default Computers group. When you group computers into Organizational Units, you can assign IPSec policies to only those computers that require IPSec. It also allows the appropriate level of security to be assigned avoiding excessive security overhead. In this scenario, Active Directory stores the IPSec policies for all computers. High security between the clients and the domain controller is unnecessary: Kerberos-related exchanges between the clients and the domain controller are already encrypted, and the IPSec policy transmission from Active Directory to the member computers is protected by Windows LDAP (Lightweight Directory Access Protocol) security. IPSec should be combined here with access control security. User permissions are still a necessary part of using security to protect access to the file shares available on any of the Highest Security or Very Secure Servers. IPSec secures the network level traffic, so that attackers cannot interpret or modify the data.

Virtual Private Networking with IPSec

The entire process of encapsulation, routing, and de-encapsulation is called *tunneling*. Tunneling hides, or encapsulates, the original packet inside a new packet. This new packet may have new addressing and routing information, which enables the new packet to travel through networks. When tunneling is combined with privacy, the original packet data (as well as the original source and destination) is not revealed to those listening to traffic in the network. The network could be any internetwork: a private intranet or the Internet. Once the encapsulated packets reach their destination, the encapsulation header is removed and the original packet header is used to route the packet to its final destination.

The tunnel itself is the logical data path through which the encapsulated packets travel. To the original source and destination peer, the tunnel is usually transparent and appears as just another point-to-point connection in the network path. The peers are unaware of any routers, switches, proxy servers, or other security gateways between the tunnel's beginning point and the tunnel's end point. When tunneling is combined with privacy, it can be used to provide Virtual Private Networks (VPN).

In Windows 2000, two types of tunneling are provided that use IPSec:

➤ Layer 2 Tunneling Protocol (L2TP/IPSec), in which L2TP provides encapsulation and tunnel management for any type of network traffic and IPSec in transport mode provides the security for the L2TP tunnel packets.

➤ IPSec in tunnel mode, in which IPSec itself does the encapsulation for IP traffic only.

Before using either type of tunneling, a complete understanding of the functionality should be obtained. For more information, see "Virtual Private Networking and IPSec" in the Windows 2000 Server Resource Kit.

The encapsulated packets travel through the network inside the tunnel. For example, say the network is the Internet. The gateway may be an edge gateway that stands between the outside Internet world and the private network—a router, firewall, proxy server, or other security gateway. Also, two gateways may be used inside the private network to protect traffic across less trusted parts of the network.

L2TP and IPSec

IPSec and L2TP are combined to provide both tunneling and security for IP, IPX, and other protocol packets across any IP network. IPSec can also perform tunneling without L2TP, but it is only recommended for interoperability when one of the gateways does not support L2TP or PPTP.

11

L2TP encapsulates original packets inside a PPP frame, performing compression when possible, and then inside a UDP (User Datagram Protocol) type packet assigned to port 1701. Because the UDP packet format is an IP packet, L2TP automatically uses IPSec to secure the tunnel based on the security settings in the user configuration of the L2TP tunnel. The IPSec Internet Key Exchange (IKE) protocol negotiates security for the L2TP tunnel using certificate-based authentica-tion by default. This authentication uses computer certificates, not user certificates, to verify that both source and destination computers trust each other. If IPSec transport security is successfully established, then L2TP negotiates the tunnel including compression and user authentication options and performs access control based on the user identity. Thus, L2TP/IPSec is the easiest, most flexible, most interoperable, and more secure tunneling option for both client remote access VPN and gateway-to-gateway VPN tunnels.

Configuration for L2TP/IPSec VPN remote access clients is performed using Network and Dial-up Connections. Configuration for the VPN remote access server and for gateway-to-gateway tunnels is performed using the Routing and Remote Access console.

The original packet header carries the original and ultimate source and destination addresses (addresses used on the private network), and the outer IP header contains the source and destination addresses of the tunnel end points (addresses used in the public network). The L2TP header carries tunnel control information. The PPP header identifies the protocol of the original packet, for example, IP or IPX. For more information on L2TP/IPSec, see Network and Dial-Up Connections in Windows 2000 Server Help.

IPSec Tunneling

The primary reason for using IPSec tunnel mode is for interoperability with other routers, gateways, or end-systems that do not support L2TP/IPSec or PPTP VPN tunneling technology. IPSec tunnel mode is supported only in gateway-to-gateway tunneling scenarios as well as for certain server-to-server or server-to-gateway configurations as an advanced feature. The *Microsoft Windows 2000 Server Resource Kit* chapter on IPSec describes these scenarios and configurations in more detail and should be understood before using IPSec tunnel mode. IPSec tunnel mode is not supported for client remote access VPN scenarios. L2TP/IPSec or PPTP should be used for client remote access VPN.

The two formats of IPSec packets can also be used in tunnel mode:

➤ Encapsulating Security Payload (ESP) Tunnel Mode

➤ Authentication Header (AH) Tunnel Mode

The original IP header (which is the original packet header) usually carries the ultimate source and destination addresses, whereas the outer IP header usually contains the source and destination address of security gateways. The ESP tunnel format always provides strong integrity and authenticity for traffic carried inside the tunnel. The ESP tunnel is used mainly to provide privacy for the tunneled packets using DES or 3DES encryption. The level of encryption is specified in the Filter Action of the tunnel rule, and thus could also be configured for no encryption if the content of the tunnel traffic does not require privacy.

The new IP and ESP headers encapsulate the original packet between the ultimate source and destination. The Signed area indicates where the packet has been protected with integrity. The Encrypted area indicates that the entire original packet may be encrypted.

The information in the new IP header is used to route the packet from origin to the tunnel destination end point; usually a security gateway. The integrity hash does not protect the new IP ESP header. The *integrity hash* is the Internet Engineering Task Force (IETF) Request For Comments (RFC) design to allow the packet header to be modified by network components as necessary to provide additional services, such as changing the source or destination IP address or giving it higher priority over other packets.

AH tunnel mode does not provide encryption privacy for the contents of the tunnel, it only provides strong integrity and authenticity.

The entire packet is signed for integrity, including the new tunnel header. Thus, no change in the source or destination address can be made once the packet is sent by the source of the tunnel. The IETF RFC design still allows for a few fields in the new IP header to be modified by network components to provide priority for certain packets and to delete stray or old packets. ESP and AH can be combined to provide tunneling, which includes both integrity for the entire packet and confidentiality for the original IP packet.

IPSec tunnels provide security for "IP only" traffic. The tunnel is configured to protect traffic either between two IP addresses or between two IP subnets. If the tunnel is used between two hosts instead of between two gateways, the outer IP address is the same as the inner IP address. In Windows 2000, IPSec does not support protocol-specific, port-specific, or application-specific tunnels. Configuration is performed using the IPSec Policy console by specifying a security rule containing a filter to describe the traffic that goes into the tunnel, a filter action for securing the tunnel, and an authentication method to be used by the tunnel end points. Three types of authentication are supported: certificates, preshared key, and Kerberos.

To specify an IPSec tunnel:

1. In the details pane of IP Security Policy Management, right-click on the policy you want to modify, and then click on Properties.

2. Select the rule you want to modify, and then click on Edit.

3. On the Tunnel Setting tab, specify the computer that will be the tunnel end point.

Point-to-Point Tunneling Protocol

The Point-to-Point Tunneling Protocol (PPTP) is a de facto industry standard tunneling protocol first supported in Windows NT 4. PPTP is an extension of the Point-to-Point Protocol (PPP) and leverages the authentication, compression, and encryption mechanisms of PPP. PPTP is installed with the Routing and Remote Access Service. By default, PPTP is configured for five PPTP ports. You can enable PPTP ports for inbound remote access and demand-dial routing connections by using the Routing and Remote Access Wizard.

PPTP and Microsoft Point-to-Point Encryption (MPPE) provide the primary VPN services of encapsulation and encryption of private data.

Encapsulation

A PPP frame (an IP datagram, an IPX datagram, or a NetBEUI frame) is wrapped with a Generic Routing Encapsulation (GRE) header and an IP header. In the IP header is the source and destination IP address that correspond to the VPN client and VPN server.

Encryption

The PPP frame is encrypted with MPPE by using encryption keys generated from the MS-CHAP or EAP-TLS authentication process. VPN clients must use either the MS-CHAP or EAP-TLS authentication protocol in order for the payloads of PPP frames to be encrypted. PPTP takes advantage of the underlying PPP encryption and encapsulates a previously encrypted PPP frame.

L2TP Defined

L2TP is networking technology that supports multiprotocol VPNs, which enable remote users to access corporate networks securely across the Internet. Like PPTP, it can be used to provide the securing of tunneled end-to-end Internet connections through other remote access technologies, such as Internet access provided through DSL (Digital Subscriber Line).

Unlike PPTP, L2TP is not dependent on vendor specific encryption technologies for a fully secured and successful implementation. For this reason, it is likely to become the standard for securing VPN connections throughout the Internet.

To add PPTP or L2TP ports:

1. Open Routing And Remote Access.

2. In the console tree, click on Ports.

3. Select Routing And Remote Access.

4. In the Ports Properties dialog box, click on either WAN Miniport (PPTP) or WAN Miniport (L2TP), and then click on Configure.

5. In Maximum ports, type the number of ports, and then click on OK.

Kerberos V5 Authentication

Kerberos v5 is the primary security protocol for authentication within a domain. The Kerberos v5 protocol verifies both the identity of the user and network services. This dual verification is known as *mutual authentication*. The Kerberos Vv5 authentication mechanism issues tickets for accessing network services. These tickets contain encrypted data including an encrypted password that confirms the user's identity to the requested service. Except for entering a password or smart card credentials, the entire authentication process is invisible to the user.

An important service within Kerberos v5 is the Key Distribution Center (KDC). The KDC runs on each domain controller as part of Active Directory, which stores all client passwords and other account information.

The Kerberos v5 authentication process works as follows:

1. The user on a client system, using a password or a smart card, authenticates to the KDC.

2. The KDC issues a special ticket-granting ticket (TGT) to the client. The client system uses this TGT to access the ticket-granting service (TGS), which is part of the Kerberos v5 authentication mechanism on the domain controller.

3. The TGS then issues a service ticket to the client.

4. The client presents this service ticket to the requested network service. The service ticket proves both the user's identity to the service and the service's identity to the user.

Kerberos V5 and Domain Controllers

The Kerberos v5 services are installed on each domain controller, and a Kerberos client is installed on each Windows 2000 workstation and server. Every domain controller acts as a KDC. A Windows 2000 system uses a DNS lookup to locate the nearest available domain controller. That domain controller then functions as the preferred KDC for that user during the user's logon session. If the preferred KDC becomes unavailable, the Windows 2000 system locates an alternate KDC to provide authentication.

Delegation of Authentication

Delegation of authentication is a privilege that an administrator can grant to a user or computer account. By default, only domain administrators are assigned this privilege. This privilege must be assigned selectively to services that can be trusted.

In an N-tier application, the user authenticates to a middle-tier service. The middle-tier service authenticates to a back-end data server on behalf of the user.

Delegation depends on the middle-tier service being trusted for delegation. *Trusted for delegation* means that service can impersonate a user to use other network services.

Kerberos V5 Interoperability

Windows 2000 supports two types of Kerberos v5 interoperability. A trust relationship can be established between a domain and an MIT-based Kerberos *realm*. This means that a client in a Kerberos realm can authenticate to an Active Directory domain to access network resources in that domain. Within a domain, Unix clients and servers can have Active Directory accounts, and therefore obtain authentication from a domain controller.

Public Key Policies Overview

Using public key policy settings in Windows 2000 Group Policy you can:

➤ Have computers automatically submit a certificate request to an enterprise certification authority and install the issued certificate. This is useful for ensuring that computers have the certificates that they need for performing public key cryptographic operations in your organization (to use for IP security or client authentication, for example).

➤ Create and distribute a certificate trust list. A *certificate trust list* is a signed list of root certification authority certificates that an administrator considers reputable for designated purposes, such as client authentication or secure email. If you want to trust a certification authority's certificates for IP security but not client authentication, then a certificate trust list is the way you can implement that trust relationship.

➤ Establish common trusted root certification authorities. This policy setting is useful for making computers and users subject to common root certification authorities (in addition to the ones they already individually trust). It is not necessary to use this policy setting for certification authorities in a Windows 2000 domain because they are already trusted by all users and computers in the domain. This policy is primarily useful for establishing trust in a root certification authority that is not a part of your organization.

➤ Add encrypted data recovery agents and change the encrypted data recovery policy settings.

Using these public key policy settings in Group Policy is not necessary for deploying a public key infrastructure in your organization. However, these settings do give you additional flexibility and control when establishing trust in certification authorities, issuing certificates to computers, and deploying the EFS.

Setting Up Permissions and Auditing

You set up permissions and auditing by viewing the security properties of files, folders, shared folders, printers, and Active Directory objects.

When you set up permissions, you specify the level of access for groups and users. For example, you can let one user read the contents of a file, let another user make changes to the file, and prevent all other users from accessing the file. You can set similar permissions on printers, so that certain users can configure the printer and other users can only print from it.

You set up auditing to detect and record security-related events, such as when a user attempts to access a confidential file or folder. When you audit an object, an entry is written to the Windows 2000 security log whenever the object is accessed in a certain way. You determine which objects to audit, whose actions to audit, and exactly what types of actions are audited. Once you set up auditing, you can keep track of users who access certain objects and analyze security breaches. The audit trail can show who performed the actions and who tried to perform actions that are not permitted.

Permissions

Permissions define the type of access granted to a user or group for an object or object property. For example, the Finance group can be granted Read, Write, and Delete permissions for the file payroll.dat.

The permissions attached to an object depend on the type of object. For example, the permissions that can be attached to a file are different from those that can be attached to a Registry key.

Some permissions, however, are common to all types of objects. Common permissions are:

➤ Read permissions

➤ Modify permissions

➤ Change owner

➤ Delete

Objects and Object Managers

Each type of object is controlled by an object manager. There is a different object manager for each type of object. The object types, their object managers, and the tools you use to manage these objects are listed in Table 11.1.

File Permissions

File permissions include Full Control, Modify, Read & Execute, Read, and Write. Each of these permissions consists of a logical group of special permissions. Table 11.2 lists each file permission and specifies which special permissions are associated with that permission.

Folder Permissions

Folder permissions include Full Control, Modify, Read & Execute, List Folder Contents, Read, and Write. Each of these permissions consists of a logical group of special permissions. Table 11.3 lists each folder permission and specifies which special permissions are associated with that permission.

Table 11.1   Object types and managers.

Object Type	Object Manager	Management Tool
Files and folders	NTFS	Windows Explorer
Shares	Server service	Windows Explorer
Active Directory objects	Active Directory	Active Directory Users and Computers
Registry keys	The Registry	regedit32 command
Services	Service controllers	Security Templates, Security Configuration and Analysis
Printer	Print spooler	Start menu

Table 11.2   File permissions.

Special Permissions	Full Control	Modify	Read & Execute	Read	Write
Traverse Folder/Execute File	x	x	x		
List Folder/Read Data	x	x	x	x	
Read Attributes	x	x	x	x	
Read Extended Attributes	x	x	x	x	
Create Files/Write Data	x	x			x
Create Folders/Append Data	x	x			x
Write Attributes	x	x			x
Write Extended Attributes	x	x			x
Delete Subfolders and Files	x				
Delete	x	x			
Read Permissions	x	x	x	x	x
Change Permissions	x				
Take Ownership	x				
Synchronize	x	x	x	x	x

Table 11.3   Folder permissions.

Special Permissions	Full Control	Modify	Read & Execute	List Folder Contents	Read	Write
Traverse Folder/Execute File	X	X	X	X		
List Folder/Read Data	X	X	X	X	X	
Read Attributes	X	X	X	X	X	
Read Extended Attributes	X	X	X	X	X	
Create Files/Write Data	X	X				X
Create Folders/Append Data	X	X				X
Write Attributes	X	X				X
Write Extended Attributes	X	X				X
Delete Subfolders and Files	X					
Delete	X	X				
Read Permissions	X	X	X	X	X	X
Change Permissions	X					
Take Ownership	X					
Synchronize	X	X	X	X	X	X

Services Permissions

Unlike other programs, which are executed by a security principal (user or computer), services run in their own security context. In order to establish a security context, a service needs to log on to the system, just as security principals do. By default, a service logs on to the system using the System account.

You can choose to have a service use a different account. This may be useful when you need to provide a service with specific permissions. Services may often *impersonate* security principals, carrying out processes on their behalf. This occurs through the use of a service by a client program.

Files and folders can have the following permissions attached to them:

➤ Query Configuration

➤ Change Configuration

➤ Query Status

➤ Enumerate dependent services

➤ Start Service

➤ Stop Service

➤ Pause and Continue Service

➤ Interrogate Service

➤ Issue user defined control

Active Directory Object Permissions

When controlling access to Active Directory objects, there are two details to consider: the permissions that you are allowed to attach to the object and the ways in which you can attach these permissions in order to delegate administrative responsibility for Active Directory objects.

Active Directory objects can have the following permissions attached to them:

➤ Create Child—Can be specific to the type of object or general for any object under the container

➤ Delete Child—Can be specific to the type of object or general for any object under the container

➤ Read Property—Can be specific to an individual property of the object or general for all attributes of the object

➤ Write Property—Can be specific to an individual property of the object or general for all attributes of the object

➤ List Contents

➤ Write Self

➤ Delete Tree

➤ List Object

➤ Control Access—Can be specific to an individual control operation or general for all control operations on the object

Chapter Summary

IP security and PPTP encryption can protect data on your network as well as data transmitted over the Internet, and is controlled using a policy configuration that you create using the IP Security Policy Management snap-in.

Groups of computers on different physical segments prevent security violations. Kerberos-related exchanges between the clients and the domain controller are already encrypted, and the IPSec policy transmission from Active Directory to the member computers is protected by Windows LDAP security. IPSec should be combined with access control security. IPSec secures the network level traffic, so that attackers cannot interpret or modify the data.

L2TP/IPSec provides encapsulation and tunnel management for any type of network traffic, and IPSec in transport mode provides the security for the L2TP tunnel packets.

The encapsulated packets travel through the network inside the tunnel. IPSec and L2TP are combined to provide both tunneling and security for IP, IPX, and other protocol packets across any IP network. Because the UDP packet format is an IP packet, L2TP automatically uses IPSec to secure the tunnel based on the security settings in the user configuration of the L2TP tunnel. The IPSec IKE protocol negotiates security for the L2TP tunnel using certificate-based authentication by default. This authentication uses computer certificates to verify both the source and destination computers trust each other. If IPSec transport security is successfully established, then L2TP negotiates the tunnel including compression and user authentication options and performs access control based on the user identity. Configuration for L2TP/IPSec VPN remote access clients is performed using Network and Dial-Up Connections. The L2TP header carries tunnel control information. IPSec tunnel mode is supported only in gateway-to-gateway tunneling scenarios as well as for certain server-to-server or server-to-gateway configurations as an advanced feature. IPSec tunnel mode is not supported for client remote access VPN scenarios. L2TP/IPSec or PPTP should be used for client remote access VPN.

The original IP header usually carries the ultimate source and destination addresses, whereas the outer IP header usually contains the source and destination address of security gateways. IPSec tunnels provide security for "IP only" traffic. IPSec does not support protocol-specific, port-specific, or application-specific tunnels. PPTP is a de facto industry standard tunneling protocol first supported in Windows NT 4. L2TP is a networking technology that supports multiprotocol VPNs, which enable remote users to access corporate networks securely across the Internet.

Kerberos v5 is the primary security protocol for authentication within a domain. The Kerberos v5 authentication mechanism issues tickets for accessing network services.

11

Review Questions

1. Which of the following is provided by IPSec?

   a. Authentication

   b. Data Integrity

   c. Confidentiality

   d. All of the above

2. What is used to create IPSec policy configurations?

   a. Microsoft Management Console

   b. IPSec Security Policy Management Snap-In

   c. Vitual Private Networking

   d. PPTP

3. Which of the following predefined IPSec policies is used for computers that should not secure communications most of the time?

   a. Client

   b. Server

   c. Secure Server

   d. None of the above

4. Which of the following is a rule defined for IPSec connection types?

   a. Remote Access

   b. All Network Connections

   c. Local Area Network

   d. All of the above

5. Which servers belong to the highest security servers organizational unit?

   a. Root Servers

   b. Servers that store and exchange highly sensitive information

   c. Domain Name Servers

   d. Forwarding only servers

6. Which of the following formats for IPSec packets can be used in tunnel mode?

   a. ESP Tunnel Mode

   b. EPS Tunnel Mode

   c. AH Tunnel Mode

   d. Both a and c

   e. Both b and c

7. What does PPTP stand for?

   a. Point-to-Point Transfer Protocol

   b. Point-to-Point Tunneling Protocol

   c. Point-To-Point Transmission Protocol

   d. Point-to-Point Transaction Protocol

8. The statement "Networking technology that supports multiprotocol virtual networks" defines which of the following protocols?

   a. PPTP

   b. L2TP

   c. DHCP

   d. HTTP

9. Which of the following protocols is the primary security protocol for authentication within a domain?

   a. PPTP

   b. Kerberos

   c. L2TP

   d. TCP/IP

10. Where are the Kerberos services installed?

   a. Domain controllers and client

   b. Domain controllers only

   c. Clients only

   d. None of the above

Real-World Projects

James and Lesha Camille have been hired by Red Family Law Firm to implement a new server. As part of the server implementation, they need to duplicate the IPSec security policies already used on the existing servers. The first step they need to perform is to export IPSec security policies from an existing server, and the second step is to import it on the new server.

Project 11.1

To export an IPSec policy, perform the following steps:

1. In IP Security Policy Management, click on the IP Security Policies folder.

2. Click on Action, point to All Tasks, and then click on Export Policies.

3. Type the path and the name of the file to which you want the policy information saved.

4. Click on Save.

This procedure exports current IPSec policies.

James and Lesha then perform the required second step.

Project 11.2

To import an IPSec policy, perform the following steps:

1. In IP Security Policy Management, click on IP Security Policies.

2. Click on Action, point to All Tasks, and then click on Import Policies.

11

3. Type the path and the name of the file from which you are importing the IPSec policy information.

4. If you want to override all existing policies with the imported information, select the Delete All Existing Policy Information checkbox.

5. Click on Open.

This procedure imports the previously exported IPSec policies.

CHAPTER TWELVE

Certificate Authority (CA)

After completing this chapter, you will be able to:

✓ Install Certificate Authority (CA)

✓ Determine appropriate CA type and policy module

✓ Set object and folder permissions

✓ Test for successful installation

✓ Create certificates

✓ Set up automatic certification requests

✓ Issue certificates

✓ Import and export a certificate

✓ Revoke certificates

✓ Understand Encrypting File System (EFS)

✓ Use EFS Recovery Keys

A Certificate Authority (CA) is a service that issues the certificates needed to run a public key infrastructure. Microsoft Windows 2000 Certificate Services lets you create a CA for managing the Windows 2000 public key infrastructure (PKI). A CA issues certificates that affirm the identity and other attributes of the certificate subject to other entities. PKI refers to a system of digital certificates (also called public key certificates) and CAs that verify and authenticate the validity of each party involved in an electronic transaction, allowing the secure exchange of information on open networks, such as the Internet, extranets, and intranets. An Enterprise CA provides certificate management for users and computers in Active Directory. The CA can issue and revoke certificates. A CA can be an external commercial CA, or it can be a CA run by your company. The certificates enable a user to log on using a smart card, send encrypted email, code-sign documents, and more. Because a CA is an important trust point in an organization, most organizations have their own CA. This chapter describes basic information including installation and the security settings necessary for the configuration of an Enterprise CA.

Installing CA

Before installing CA, you must first determine the appropriate CA type: Enterprise Root, Enterprise Subordinate, Stand-alone Root, and Stand-alone Subordinate. You then need to create an Enterprise Administrator account to be used to install and configure CA. After you install CA, you need to set appropriate object and file permissions. We begin installation with a discussion on CA types to help you determine the appropriate type for your network. We then examine the installation requirements for each of the types and proceed with the installation instructions.

Root and Subordinate CA Types

Microsoft Windows 2000 provides two classes of CAs—an enterprise CA or a stand-alone CA—determined by the policy modules selected during installation. Within these classes, there can be two types of CAs—a root or a subordinate. The policy modules define the actions that a CA can take when it receives a certificate request. Note that by changing the policy modules, it is possible to change the functionality of the system. A customer can write a policy module and customize the CA's behavior using the Microsoft Platform Software Development Kit (SDK).

Enterprise and Stand-Alone Policy Modules

CAs are organized into hierarchies with the fundamental trust point—or root CA—at the top. All other CAs in the hierarchy are subordinate CAs and are trusted only because the root is trusted. There can be more than one enterprise root CA in a Windows 2000-based domain, and thus more than one hierarchy. It is also possible to mix and match stand-alone and enterprise CAs.

An enterprise CA requires that all users requesting certificates have an entry in the Windows 2000 Server Active DirectoryTM services, whereas a stand-alone CA does not. Also, an enterprise CA can issue certificates that are used to log on to a Windows 2000-based domain, but a stand-alone CA cannot. Enterprise CAs have a special policy module that enforces how certificates are processed and issued in a CA object in Active Directory. To set up an enterprise CA, you must have a working Active Directory and Domain Name System (DNS) server.

Each new stand-alone root CA starts a new hierarchy. A stand-alone CA has a simple policy module and does not assume that Active Directory service is available. However, if Active Directory is available, the stand-alone CA will take advantage of it.

Enterprise Root CA

An enterprise CA is the root of a Windows 2000-based corporate CA hierarchy. You should set up an enterprise CA if the CA will be issuing certificates to users and computers within your Windows 2000 domain. For security reasons, the enterprise CA is typically configured to issue certificates only to subordinate CAs.

Enterprise Subordinate CA

An enterprise subordinate is a CA that issues certificates within a corporation, but is not the most trusted CA in that corporation. It is subordinate to another CA in the hierarchy.

Stand-Alone Root CA

A stand-alone CA is the root or top of a CA trust hierarchy. You should install a stand-alone root CA if you will be issuing certificates outside of your Windows 2000 domain. A root CA typically issues certificates to subordinate CAs only. For example, you'll want to issue certificates to your customers so they can access your Web site. It is not feasible to give each customer an account in your directory.

12

Stand-Alone Subordinate CA

A stand-alone subordinate CA is one that operates as a solitary certificate server or exists in a CA trust hierarchy. You should set up a stand-alone subordinate CA when you will be issuing certificates to entities outside a corporation.

Installation Requirements

There are different installation requirements for the various CA types and policy modules. Each of the requirements must be met before the installation of CA.

Enterprise Root CA

Both enterprise CA and enterprise subordinate CA require the following:

➤ Windows 2000 DNS Service installed (required by Active Directory).

➤ Windows 2000 Active Directory installed. Enterprise policy places information into the Active Directory.

➤ Enterprise administrator privileges on the DNS, Active Directory, and CA servers.

The enterprise CA also requires enterprise subordinate CA, whereas enterprise subordinate CA requires a parent CA. This could be an external commercial CA or a stand-alone CA.

Stand-Alone Root CA

The stand-alone root CA requires administrator privileges on the local server. The stand-alone root CA requires a stand-alone subordinate CA, whereas the stand-alone subordinate CA requires a Root CA.

Stand-Alone Subordinate CA

The stand-alone subordinate CA requires the following:

➤ An association with a CA that processes the subordinate CA's certificate requests. Again, this could be an external, commercial CA.

➤ Administrative privileges on the local server.

Enterprise Adminstrator

Before installing CA, you must add an existing user to the Enterprise Admins group to give the appropriate permission to install and set up CA in a Windows 2000-based network. The following seven steps show how to add the user to the Enterprise Admins group. This user is then referred to as an enterprise administrator. You need to log on as an enterprise administrator to set up CA as well as the enterprise intermediary and enterprise-issuing certificate servers.

Installing Certificate Services

To install Certificate Services, use the Windows Components Wizard:

1. Click Start|Settings, and then click on Control Panel.

2. Double-click on Add/Remove Programs.

3. Click on Add/Remove Windows Components to start the Windows Components Wizard.

4. Select the Certificate Services checkbox, and then click on Next.

5. If you intend to use the Web components of the Certificate Services, ensure that the Internet Information Services (IIS) checkbox is selected. The wizard prompts you to specify the type of CA you want to install.

   If you are issuing certificates to entities in your organization, or if you need to have seamless integration with the Active Directory or enable smart card logon, select one of the following enterprise CAs:

   ➤ *Enterprise root CA*—Select this CA if you do not have any CAs in your directory or if you need a second enterprise root CA. The root CA will be registered in the directory, and all computers in your enterprise using that directory will automatically trust the root CA. It is good security practice to limit the root CA to issuing certificates to subordinate CAs only or to a few special purpose certificates. You should install an enterprise subordinate after you finish installing the root.

   ➤ *Enterprise subordinate CA*—Select this CA if you have already installed an enterprise root CA. You will have multiple enterprise-subordinate CAs serving different communities of users or providing different types of certificates. If there is more than one subordinate, it is possible to revoke the subordinate's certificate in case of disaster and not have to reissue all certificates in the organization.

   If you will be issuing certificates to entities outside your enterprise and do not want to use Active Directory or other Windows 2000 PKI features, select one of the following stand-alone CAs:

   ➤ *Stand-alone CA*—Select this CA if you do not already have a stand-alone CA or if you need a second root for a purpose different than the first.

   ➤ *Stand-alone subordinate CA*—Select this CA if this it will be a member of an existing CA hierarchy. The parent CA in the hierarchy can be a stand-alone CA, an enterprise CA, or an external commercial CA.

6. To change the default cryptographic settings, select the Advanced Options checkbox. Click on Next. In Advanced Options, specify the Cryptographic Service Provider (CSP), hash algorithm, and key length. Microsoft recommends that you use a long key length, such as 1024 or 2048, for a root CA or an enterprise CA. A long key length is computationally more expensive and may not be accepted by all hardware devices. For example, some smart cards may not accept certificates issued by a CA that has a 4096 bit key due to space limitations on the card.

12

You should never reuse keys unless you are restoring a CA after a catastrophic failure. You should then import a set of existing keys and install a new CA that uses those keys. In addition, if you are restoring a CA after a failure, you must select the Use The Associated Certificate checkbox. The private key is always stored locally on the server except in the case where a cryptographic hardware device is used where it is stored in the device. The public key is placed in the certificate, and in the case of an enterprise CA, the certificate is published in Active Directory.

7. The wizard prompts you to supply identifying information appropriate for your site and organization. The CA name, or common name, identifies the CA object created in the directory. The root CA Valid Time value is a trade off between security and administrative overhead. Each time a root certificate expires, an administrator has to update all trust relationships, and administrative steps need to be taken to move the CA to a new certificate. The default value is two years. Click on Next.

8. A dialog box defines the locations of the certificate database, configuration information, and the location where the Certificate Revocation List (CRL) is stored. The Enterprise CA always stores its information, including the CRL, in the directory. It is recommended that you select the Shared Folder checkbox. This option specifies the location of a folder where configuration information for the CA will be stored. Have all your CAs point to this folder. Administration tools can use this folder for determining CA configuration if the Active Directory is not available. If you do not have an Active Directory, this folder is required. If you are installing a CA in the same location as a previously installed CA, the Preserve Existing Certificate Database option will be enabled. Click on Next.

9. If IIS is running, a message prompts you to stop the service. Click on OK to stop IIS. You must stop IIS to install the Web components. If you do not have IIS installed, you will not see this message.

10. If you are installing a subordinate CA, the wizard then prompts you for information about how you will request the certificate. Click on Browse to locate an online CA or select Save The Request To A File if you will be making a request destined for a commercial CA or a CA that is not accessible from the network. If you create a file, you must take the file to a CA for processing. The CA provides you with a certificate, which you install using the Microsoft Management Console (MMC) snap-in. Click on Next.

If you saved a certificate request to a file, a dialog box called Microsoft Certificate Services appears. Click on OK to finish the installation. Click on Finish to close the wizard. When the installation is complete, take the Certificate Request file you created to your CA for processing. If you are using a Microsoft Certificate Service to process this file, you can refer to the *Step-by-Step Guide to Certificate Service Web Pages* for details about processing the request. By default, these pages are located at **http://servername/certsrv**, where servername is the name of the Windows 2000 server hosting the CA. When you have your new certificate, you can use the CA MMC snap-in to install the certificate and enable your CA.

Installing a Subordinate CA Certificate from a File

This section should be used if you created a certificate request file during installation of a subordinate CA. Before you begin this section, take the certificate request file to your CA for processing. Your CA will provide you with a certificate for this file.

1. Open the Certificate Services snap-in.

2. Right-click on the CA you want to install.

3. Click on Install CA Certificate.

4. Select the file containing the certificate provided by your CA.

5. Click on Finish to complete the setup.

The CA installation process is complete. You should proceed with a test to verify successful and proper installation.

Testing Certificate Server Installation

Whether you created an enterprise CA or a stand-alone CA, you can quickly check to see if your installation was successful. The simplest way is to open a command window, and type "net start" to see if the Certificate Service is running. For an enterprise CA, open the Certificate snap-in. Select Start | Programs | Administrative Tools | Certificate Authority and request a certificate. For a stand-alone CA, you can request a new certificate using Microsoft Internet Explorer 5 by connecting to the URL **http://Localhost/CertSrv**. Replace localhost with the name of the server.

Setting Object and Folder Permissions

After installing an enterprise CA, it is important to set appropriate object and folder permissions for use by Certificate Services. The following steps are recommended to set permissions on the Active Directory objects and folder shares.

Set permissions on Certlog, which is located in the Winnt\System32 folder, as follows:

➤ *Domain Administrators*—Full Control for this folder, subfolders, and files.

➤ *Enterprise Administrators*—Full Control for this folder, subfolders, and files.

➤ *System*—Full Control for this folder, subfolders, and files.

12

Set permission on CertSrv, which is located in the Winnt\System32 folder, as follows:

➤ *Authenticated Users*—Read and Execute for this folder, subfolders, and files.

➤ *Server Operators*—Modify for this folder, subfolders, and files.

➤ *Domain Administrators*—Full Control for this folder, subfolders, and files.

➤ *System*—Full Control for this folder, subfolders, and files.

➤ *Creator/Owner*—Full Control for this folder, subfolders, and files.

➤ Allow inheritable permissions on all child objects and enable propagation of inheritable permissions.

Set permission on Shared Folder (CertConfig share), name and location is specified by the administrator, as follows:

➤ *Domain Administrators*—Full Control, Change, and Read for share permissions.

➤ *Everyone*—Read for share permissions.

➤ *Domain Administrators*—Full Control for this folder, subfolders, and files.

➤ *System*—Full Control for this folder, subfolders, and files.

➤ *Enterprise Administrators*—Full Control for this folder, subfolders, and files.

➤ *Everyone*—Read for this folder, subfolders, and files.

You can set permissions using the Security tab in adsiedit.msc or with the Active Directory Sites and Services snap-in under the Services container. To view the Services container, click on Show Services Node on the View menu within the Microsoft Management Console (MMC). Set permission for Certificate Templates Container, which is located in the DC=Domain, CN=Configuration, CN=Services, CN=Public Key Services, as follows:

➤ *Authenticated Users*—Special Permission (List Contents, Read All Properties, Read Permissions) for this object only.

➤ *Enterprise Administrators*—Special Permission (List Contents, Read All Properties, Write All Properties, Read Permissions, Modify Permissions, Modify Owner, All Validated Writes, All Extended Rights, Create All Child Objects, Create [for all objects]) for this object only.

➤ *System*—Full Control for this object only.

➤ *Enterprise Administrators*—Full Control for this object and all child objects.

➤ *Domain Administrators*—Special Permission (List Contents, Read All Properties, Read Permissions, Write All Properties, Delete, Read Permissions, Modify Permissions, Modify Owner, All Validated Writes, All Extended Rights, Create All Child Objects, Create [for all objects]) for this object and all child objects.

➤ Allow inheritable permission from the parent to propagate to this object.

Set permission for Certificate Templates in the Certificate Templates Folder as follows:

➤ *Authenticated Users*—Special Permission (List Contents, Read All Properties, Read Permissions).

➤ *Domain Administrators*—Full Control.

➤ *Domain Users*—Special Permission (Enroll). Depending on the certificate template to which the administrator wants the user to have access, the user must have Read permission to the template. The user must have Enroll permission on the template to make a request for the template.

Set permission on Certification Authority, which is located in DC=Domain, CN=Configuration, CN=Services, CN=Public Key Services, as follows:

➤ *Authenticated Users*—Special Permission (List Contents, Read All Properties, Read Permissions) for this object only.

➤ *Enterprise Administrators*—Special Permission (List Contents, Read All Properties, Write All Properties, Read Permissions, Modify Permissions, Modify Owner, All Validated Writes, All Extended Rights, Create All Child Objects, Create [for all objects]) for this object only.

➤ *System*—Full Control for this object only.

➤ *Enterprise Administrators*—Full Control for this object and all child objects.

➤ *Domain Administrators*—Special Permission (List Contents, Read All Properties, Read Permissions, Write All Properties, Delete, Read Permissions, Modify Permissions, Modify Owner, All Validated Writes, All Extended Rights, Create All Child Objects, Create [for all objects]) for this object and all child objects.

➤ Allow inheritable permission from the parent to propagate to this object.

Set permission on Objects in Certification Authority Container as follows:

➤ *Enterprise Administrators*—Full Control.

➤ *Domain Administrators*—Full Control.

➤ *Cert Publishers*—Full Control.

> ➤ *Administrators*—Full Control.

> ➤ *Everyone*—Special Permission (List Contents, Read All Properties, Read Permissions).

Set permission on Enrollment Services, which is located in DC=Domain, CN=Configuration, CN=Services, CN=Public Key Services, as follows:

> ➤ *Authenticated Users*—Special Permission (List Contents, Read All Properties, Read Permissions) for this object only.

> ➤ *Enterprise Administrators*—Special Permission (List Contents, Read All Properties, Write All Properties, Read Permissions, Modify Permissions, Modify Owner, All Validated Writes, All Extended Rights, Create All Child Objects, Create [for all objects]) for this object only.

> ➤ *System*—Full Control for this object only.

> ➤ *Enterprise Administrators*—Full Control for this object and all child objects.

> ➤ *Domain Administrators*—Special Permission (List Contents, Read All Properties, Read Permissions, Write All Properties, Delete, Read Permissions, Modify Permissions, Modify Owner, All Validated Writes, All Extended Rights, Create All Child Objects, Create [for all objects]) for this object and all child objects.

> ➤ Allow inheritable permission from the parent to propagate to this object.

Set permission on Objects in Enrollment Services Container, as follows:

> ➤ *Authenticated Users*—Special Permission (List Contents, Read All Properties, Write All Properties, Read Permissions) for this object and all child objects.

> ➤ *Domain Administrators*—Full Control.

> ➤ *Enterprise Administrators*—Full Control.

> ➤ *Administrators*—Full Control.

Configuring the Policy and Exit Modules for Use by the Service

The Certificate Services architecture provides for replaceable policy and exit modules and processing. Policy modules incorporate decision logic that determines whether a certificate request should be approved, denied, or queued (left pending) for a later decision. Exit modules provide an opportunity to perform post-processing, such as publication of an issued certificate.

In Windows 2000, Certificate Services comes with a single policy module that incorporates two policies: Enterprise and Stand-alone and also contains one exit module (Enterprise). Users can replace these with their own modules. This is important for users who want to implement their own policy modules using the Platform SDK or for those who acquire third-party policy modules. To perform this walk-through, you need access to a second policy module, such as the Visual Basic sample policy module (policyvb.dll) available with the Platform SDK.

To configure the policy and exit modules for use by the service, follow these steps:

1. Copy the new policy module to windir\system32.

2. Register the new policy module using the **regsvr32** command: "regsvr32 policyvb.dll"

3. From the Certificate Authority snap-in, right-click on the name of the certification authority in question, and click on Properties on the context menu. The CA Properties window appears.

4. Click on the Policy Module tab.

5. Click on Select. Click to select the new policy module to be installed, for example, Certificate Services VB Policy. Click on OK.

6. A message box tells you that you must restart the Certificate Services. Click on Apply.

7. Click on Yes, and then click on OK to close the Properties window. A progress bar is displayed as the service is stopped and restarted.

8. To verify that policy module replacement has been successful, look in the Application Event Log for records showing that the service (CertSvc) and Data Base Engine (ESENT) have been stopped and started. Also, look at the property page and Policy Module tab (as described previously). The named policy module should be the new policy module.

Stand-Alone Policy Behavior

Certificate Server stand-alone policy behavior has changed. In the past, the default policy module immediately processed requests and issued the certificate. The new stand-alone policy retains the request in a pending mode or state until an administrator manually approves the request. This new behavior only affects the stand-alone CAs. Enterprise policy still processes the request immediately.

Installing Web Pages on a Remote Server

If the CA is an enterprise CA, the Certificate Services Web pages must be installed on the same computer as the CA. The CA needs to authenticate the client to ensure that it can request only the certificates that the client has permission to request. If the Web pages are on a different computer from the Web server, the CA cannot authenticate the user.

Installing the CA and Web Server

The CA must be installed after the Web server to ensure that the Web pages are installed. If the CA is installed first, it still functions, but you may not be able to access the Web pages. You can enable the Web pages by running the command:

```
certutil -vroot
```

Upgrading Certificate Server 1.0

When you upgrade from Windows NT Server 4 to Windows 2000, the Certificate Services executable and dynamic link library (DLL) files must be updated. It is important to run the dbcnvt.exe utility to convert the old version 1.0 database to the new format before the CA processes any new requests. Upgrades are not supported for any configuration that uses a version 1.0 database that has been modified.

Creating Certificates

Certificates are issued to a computer for use with public key security system services and applications. For example, Internet Protocol Security (IPSec) can use certificates to authenticate and communicate securely with remote computers. Automatic certificate requests for computers allow the domain administrator to request certificates from Windows 2000 Certification Authorities running enterprise policy. This can be done for all computers in a domain or organizational unit (OU) from a single point.

Setting Up an Automatic Certificate Request

The following steps show how to create automatic certificate requests in the default Group Policy Object (GPO) using the Group Policy snap-in. You must first install the Active Directory Users and Computers MMC snap-in.

1. Select Start | Programs | Administrative Tools | Active Directory Users and Computers. The Active Directory Users and Computers Snap-In appears, as shown in Figure 12.1.

2. Right-click on the domain node, and click on Properties.

3. By default, Windows 2000 creates the Default Domain Policy GPO. Select it, and click on Edit. This starts the Group Policy management snap-in.

4. Expand Computer Configurations by clicking on the + character next to it. In the same manner, expand the Windows Settings folder, expand Security Settings, and then expand Public Key Policies.

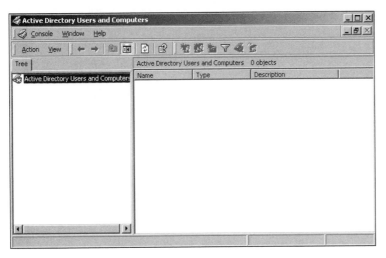

Figure 12.1 Active Directory User and Computers.

5. In the Public Key Policies folder, locate the Automatic Certificate Request Settings folder. Right-click on the Automatic Certificate Request Settings folder, point to New on the context menu, and then click on Automatic Certificate Request.

6. The Automatic Certificate Request setup wizard launches. Click on Next.

7. Select the certificate template to use in the request. In this example, you should select Computer. Click on Next.

8. Select the certification authorities on the Windows 2000 domain to send the certificate request. In this example, choose the enterprise root CA. An enterprise may have more than one CA. Note that CAs not running enterprise policy will not appear on this list. Click on Next.

9. Click on Finish to create the automatic certificate request. The request for the certificate will take place when the GPO is refreshed on the client.

Viewing a Certificate's Store

To verify that a certificate has been issued for the computers in the domain, you can use the Certificates snap-in to view a computer's certificate store.

Follow these steps to view a certificate's store:

1. Select Start|Run, type "mmc" in the Open box, and click on OK.

2. On the Console menu, click on Add/Remove Snap-In.

3. In the dialog box, click on Add.

4. In the Add Stand-Alone Snap-in dialog box, click on Certificates and click on Add.

12

5. In the next dialog box, select the Computer Account option to manage certificates for a computer. Click on Next.

6. Select either the Local Computer option or Another Computer. If you select Another Computer, type in the computer name or click on Browse to select a computer from the network. Click on Finish.

7. Click on Close. Click on OK. The Certificates management console for your computer is created.

8. Expand the Certificates node in the left pane. Expand the Personal folder, and then click on the Certificates folder. All certificates issued to your machine are listed in the right pane, as shown in Figure 12.2.

9. Double-click on any certificate in the store to view its details.

Issuing Certificates

Many types of PKI information must be widely published. In Windows 2000, this information is published in Active Directory. Published information includes the following:

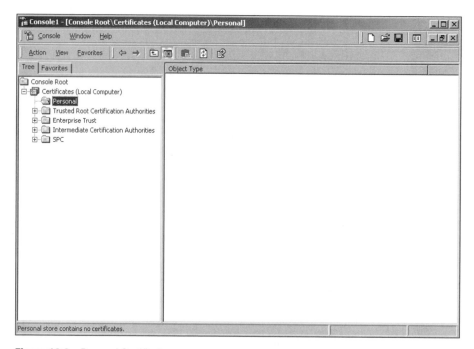

Figure 12.2   Personal Certificates.

➤ User certificates for asynchronous data exchange applications, such as Secure Multipurpose Internet Mail Extensions (S/MIME) and Encrypting File System (EFS).

➤ CA certificates for building certificate chains to trusted root authorities.

➤ CRLs to enable checking of status.

An enterprise CA can publish its own user certificates, CA certificates, and CRLs in Active Directory. Active Directory includes three directory partitions for specific types of data:

➤ *Domain data directory partition*—Contains all of the objects in the directory for this domain. Domain data in each domain is replicated to every domain controller in that domain, but not beyond its domain.

➤ *Configuration data directory partition*—Contains replication topology and related metadata. Active Directory-aware applications store information in the configuration data directory partition. This data is common to all domains in the domain tree or forest. Configuration data is replicated to all domain controllers in the forest.

➤ *Schema data directory partition*—Contains all object types that can be created in Active Directory. This data is common to all domains in the domain tree or forest. Schema data is replicated to all domain controllers in the forest.

The Windows 2000 operating system's global catalog, which plays a major role in logging on users (in a native-mode domain only) and in querying, is a database kept on one or more domain controllers. If a domain controller is also a global catalog, in addition to the domain data, configuration data, and schema data directory partitions, it also stores and replicates a fourth category of information: a partial replica of the domain data directory partition for all domains. This partial replica contains a subset of the properties for all objects of all domains in the forest, which is replicated to all domain controllers in the forest.

User certificates are published in the User object in the domain data directory partition. User certificates are also replicated to the Windows 2000 global catalog to provide access to the certificate across the forest.

CA certificates are published on a Certification Authority object and CRLs are published on a CRL Distribution Point (CDP) object in Active Directory. To ensure CA chain building and the availability of revocation status information, regardless of domain structure, these objects are published in the configuration data directory partition, and the objects' contents are replicated throughout the forest. The CDP pointers in the certificates are constructed in such a way that they work regardless of the domain to which the domain controller belongs in the forest.

12

Obtaining a Certificate

To obtain a certificate, the certification authority must be installed as either a root or subordinate enterprise CA.

To obtain a certificate, follow these steps:

1. Select Start | Programs | Administrative Tools | Certificates.

2. In the Certificates console, right-click on the Personal node.

3. Click on All Tasks on the context menu, and click on Request New Certificate as in Figure 12.3. The Certificate Request wizard launches. Click on Next.

4. Select the certificate template that you want the new certificate to be based on. In this scenario, select User. Click on Next.

5. Enter a friendly name or a description, if desired. Click on Next.

6. Click on Finish to send the certificate request to the CA.

7. Click on Install Certificate to install the certificate to the certificate store. You can also view the certificate before installation by clicking on View Certificate.

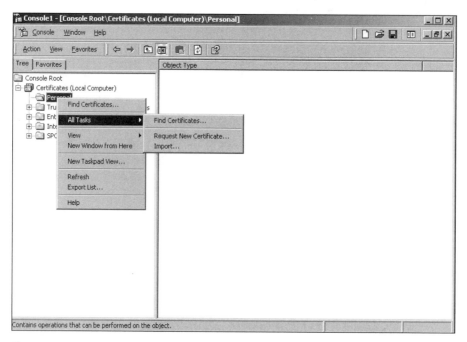

Figure 12.3 Request New Certificate.

Viewing a Certificate

You may need to look at your certificates in the certificate stores.

To view a certificate, follow these steps:

1. Open the Certificates management console. In the left pane, expand the certificate store that contains the certificate you want to view.

2. Click on the Certificates folder to see the list of certificates in that store.

3. Double-click on the certificate you want to view.

Exporting Certificates

You can back up important certificates and their corresponding private keys or move them to another computer. To enable exporting the private key with the certificate, that option must be chosen when a user requests a certificate using the Web enrollment form.

To export certificates follow these steps:

1. Right-click on the certificate(s) you want to export.

2. Point to All Tasks on the context menu, and click on Export to launch the Certificate Export Wizard. Click on Next.

3. If the certificate that you are exporting has a corresponding private key in the system, you can choose to export the private key with the certificate. You will only be able to export to a Personal Information Exchange—PKCS#12 file if you want to export the private key.

4. Select the export file format from the options as shown in Figure 12.4.

12

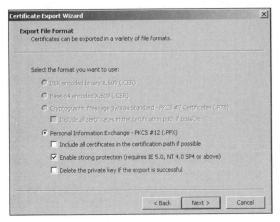

Figure 12.4   Certificate Export Wizard.

5. Click on Next. If the file specified is a Personal Information Exchange—PKCS #12 (*.pfx), you will be prompted for the password. Enter your password to export the file. Click on Next.

6. Enter the name of the file you want to export. Click on Next.

7. Click on Finish to export to the file.

Importing Certificates

You may restore certificates and the corresponding private keys from a file.

To import a certificate, follow these steps:

1. Right-click on the certificate store you want to import, and click on Install PFX on the context menu.

2. The Certificate Import Wizard launches. Click on Next.

3. In the File name text box, type the name of the certificate file that you want to import. Alternatively, you can find the file by clicking on Browse.

4. Click on Next. If the file specified is a Personal Information Exchange–PKCS #12 (*.pfx), you will be prompted for the password. Enter the password to import the file. Click on Next.

5. On the next page, select where you'd like to store the certificate. Click on Next.

6. This page contains summary information about the file that you are importing. Click on Finish to import the file. The certificate(s) are ready for use by the system.

Managing a Computer's Certificates

The Certificates MMC snap-in can be used to manage a computer's certificates.

To manage certificates, follow these steps:

1. Start the MMC by selecting Start | Run. Then type "mmc.exe" in the text box, and click on OK.

2. On the Console menu, click on Add/Remove Snap-In.

3. Click on Add to add a snap-in to the current console.

4. Select Certificates, and then click on Add.

5. Select the Computer Account option, and then click on Next.

6. Select the Another Computer option. Type the name of the computer you want to manage (or click on Browse to select from a list). Click on Finish.

7. Close the Add Stand-Alone Snap-in dialog box, and then click on OK to close the Add/Remove Snap-In dialog box. You have created the console with which to manage your computer's certificates.

8. On the Console menu, click on Save As. In the File name text box, type a name for this console, and then click on Save.

Revoking Certificates

In Certificate Services, to revoke a certificate means to mark an issued certificate in the database as being revoked. Revocation of certificates is a mechanism for invalidating a certificate prior to its natural expiration. Applications that check the revocation status of a certificate prior to use can then make a more informed decision about certificate validity and what process to perform. It is important to note that revoking a certificate is not sufficient to make this information available to applications. To make this information available to applications requires creation and publication of a Certificate Revocation List (CRL).

To revoke certificates, perform the following steps:

1. Click on the Issued Certificates folder to open it. In the results pane, click on the certificate you created earlier. Right-click on the selected certificate and point to All Tasks; then click on Revoke Certificate.

   If you'd like to revoke many certificates at once, you can use a filter. When you've set the filter, select the first certificate in the list, and then press Shift while selecting the last certificate: This selects the full list.

2. The Certificate Revocation dialog box appears. In the drop-down list, click on the reason for the revocation. For this example, select Key Compromise. Click on Yes after you select the correct reason code.

3. Verify that the revoked certificates are correctly marked in the database. Do this by viewing the contents of the Issued Certificates folder and the Revoked Certificates folder. The revoked certificates should appear in the latter, but not in the former.

Creating CRLs

Once certificates have been revoked, it is necessary to create a CRL and publish it, so that applications that perform revocation checking have something to check.

To create a CRL, perform the following steps:

1. Right-click on the Revoked Certificates folder. Point to All Tasks, and then click on Publish.

12

2. Select Publish.

3. Click on OK.

4. To verify that the CRL is published, right-click on the Revoked Certificates node, and click on Properties.

5. Click on the View Current CRL button. The CRL dialog box appears providing overall identification information for the CRL as shown in Figure 12.5.

6. To view the CRL contents, click on the Revocation List tab.

7. To view details on a particular revoked certificate, select it. The details are displayed in the Revocation Entry box, as shown in Figure 12.6. The Value box is provided in case the field values are too large for the Field/Value pair. Selecting one of the Field entries displays the full contents of the selected field.

EFS

The EFS is a feature of Windows 2000 that allows users to encrypt data directly on volumes that use the NTFS file system. It operates by using certificates based on the X.509 standard. If no CA is available from which to request certificates, the EFS subsystem automatically generates its own self-signed certificates for users and default recovery agents.

There are several circumstances in which an organization may want to implement CAs as opposed to allowing EFS to generate its own self-signed certificates. CA is more flexible at recovery management. With a CA infrastructure, it is possible for

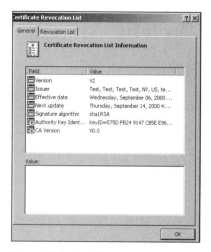

Figure 12.5 Certification Revocation List Properties.

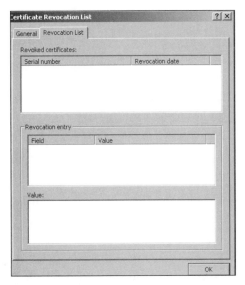

Figure 12.6 Certification Revocation List tab.

an organization to issue specific recovery certificates for dedicated recovery computers, rather than to domain controllers. Administrators can control the lifetime of issued EFS certificates and can publish certificate revocation lists to control how long recovery certificates are valid. CAs can be distributed throughout an organization, providing their own set of templates that define the types of certificates that can be issued at each level.

EFS Standards

Microsoft has identified some strong EFS guidelines. The following list contains the recommended standards in no particular order.

➤ Encrypt the My Documents folder for all users (%user profile%\My Documents). This ensures that the personal folder, where most Office documents are stored, is encrypted by default.

➤ Encrypt the Temp folder for all users (%temp%). This ensures that any temporary files created by various programs are encrypted, avoiding leaks.

➤ Users should never encrypt individual files, but should encrypt folders. Programs work on files in various ways. Encrypting files consistently at the folder level ensures that files do not get decrypted unexpectedly.

➤ The private keys should be generated on a computer that is physically secured or their certificates should be completely exported to a PFX file, protected under a strong password, and stored on a secure floppy disk.

➤ Recovery agent certificates should be assigned to special recovery agent accounts that are not used for any other purpose.

12

➤ Do not destroy recovery certificates or private keys when recovery agents are changed. Keep all of them until all files that may have been encrypted with them are updated.

➤ Designate two or more recovery agent accounts per OU. Designate two or more computers for recovery, one for each designated recovery agent account, and give permissions to appropriate administrators to use the recovery agent accounts.

➤ Implement a recovery agent archive program to ensure that encrypted files can be recovered using obsolete recover keys.

➤ Avoid using print spool files in your print server architecture, or ensure that print spool files get generated in an encrypted folder.

Using EFS Recovery Keys

The EFS supports data recovery by allowing recovery agents to recover file encryption keys (FEKs) and decrypt users' files. The Encrypted Data Recovery Policy (EDRP) is configurable for both a domain and a stand-alone server and must be configured by an administrator.

Once the EDRP is configured, it can be updated to specify an agent who can recover FEKs in the event that a user's private key becomes unavailable or unusable. This may occur when an individual user account becomes damaged, is deleted, or becomes otherwise unusable. Multiple recovery agents can be configured, and in no case is any user's private key revealed to a recovery agent. When a user's private key becomes unavailable, an agent can use his or her private key to decrypt the FEK that was originally used in the file encryption process. After the FEK is obtained, the recovery agent can then decrypt the user's file.

To assist in FEK recovery, each FEK is encrypted with all public keys in the EDRP. Each encrypted FEK is stored in the Data Recovery Field (DRF) containing the FEK created when a file is encrypted. If there is one recovery agent, there is one DRF for each encrypted file. When there are two recovery agents, there are two DRFs for each encrypted file, and so on.

The default on a stand-alone server includes only the local administrator in the EDRP. After the Dcpromo tool is used and a domain is realized, a default EDRP is created for the entire domain. At this point, all members of the domain participate in the EDRP. This policy uses a self-signed certificate to make the administrator account the recovery agent.

To make changes on a stand-alone server and add recovery agents:

1. Start the MMC.

2. Add the Group Policy snap-in for the local computer (this is the default GPO).

3. Open the following sections: Computer Configuration | Windows Settings | Security Settings | Public Key Policies | Encrypted Data Recovery Policy.

4. Right-click on Encrypted Data Recovery Policy, and then click on Add.

5. Follow the instructions in the wizard to add recovery agents.

To make changes to a domain structure and add recovery agents:

1. Start the MMC.

2. Add the Group Policy snap-in for the default domain policy. To do this, click on Browse when you are prompted to select a GPO. You can also add GPOs for other domain partitions (specifically, OUs).

3. Open the following sections: Computer Configuration | Windows Settings | Security Settings | Public Key Policies | Encrypted Data Recovery Policy.

4. Right-click on Encrypted Data Recovery Policy, and then click on Add.

5. Follow the instructions in the wizard to add recovery agents.

Chapter Summary

A CA is a service that issues the certificates needed to run a public key infrastructure. There are four types of CAs: Enterprise Root, Enterprise Subordinate, Stand-alone Root, and Stand-alone Subordinate.

The enterprise CA is typically configured to issue certificates only to subordinate CAs. Use a stand-alone root CA if you will be issuing certificates outside of a corporation's enterprise network. An enterprise CA requires that all users requesting certificates have an entry in the Windows 2000 Server Active DirectoryTM services, whereas a stand-alone CA does not.

Add an existing user to the Enterprise Admins group to give the appropriate permission to install and set up a CA in a Windows 2000-based network.

The Certificates MMC snap-in can be used to manage a computer's certificates. Using this snap-in you can create, issue, view, import, export, and revoke certificates.

Applications that check the revocation status of a certificate prior to use can then make a more informed decision about certificate validity and what process to perform. The creation and publication of a CRL is used to check for revocation status.

12

The EFS supports data recovery by allowing recovery agents to recover FEKs and decrypt users' files. The EDRP is configurable for both a domain and a stand-alone server.

Microsoft's established EFS guidelines state that users should encrypt only folders. Encrypting files consistently at the folder level ensures that files do not get decrypted unexpectedly.

Review Questions

1. Which CA types require that all users requesting certificates have an entry in the Windows 2000 Server Active DirectoryTM?

   a. Enterprise CA only

   b. Stand-Alone CA only

   c. Both Enterprise and Stand-Alone CAs

   d. Neither Enterprise or Stand-Alone CAs

2. User certificates should be required for which of the following asynchronous data exchange applications?

   a. S/MIME and EFS

   b. TCP/IP

   c. EFS only

   c. S/MIME only

3. The fundamental trust point in a CA's hierarchy is called what?

   a. Top CA

   b. Root CA

   c. Master CA

   d. Start CA

4. What should you do to implement security for print spool files?

   a. Nothing is required because print spool files are encrypted

   b. Check high security for all print spool files in the Certificate Services snap-in

   c. Make sure that print spool files are generated in an encrypted folder

   d. Allow only print operators to have access

5. An Enterprise Root CA requires everything that an Enterprise Subordinate CA requires except which of following?

    a. Enterprise administrator privileges on the DNS, Active Directory, and CA servers.

    b. Windows 2000 DNS service installed (required by Active Directory).

    c. Windows 2000 Active Directory installed. Enterprise policy places information into Active Directory.

    d. A parent CA. This could be an external commercial CA or a stand-alone CA.

6. What can be done when a user's private key becomes unavailable?

    a. Nothing; all data encrypted with the private key can no longer be decrypted.

    b. The user simply creates a new private key and uses it to decrypt data encrypted with the original user's private key.

    c. An agent can use his or her private key to decrypt the FEK that was originally used in the file encryption process.

    d. You must call Microsoft to hack the user's private key.

7. What is the simplest way to test if Certificate Services is running?

    a. Open a command window, and type "net start".

    b. Call the Enterprise Administrator

    c. Try to Issue a Certificate

    d. Try to Open a Web Page

8. In which of the following situations is the Encrypted Data Recovery Policy (EDRP) configurable?

    a. A domain only

    b. A stand-alone server only

    c. Both a domain and a stand-alone server

    d. Neither a domain or stand-alone server

9. Applications that check the revocation status of a certificate check which of the following?

    a. If the certificate has been issued

    b. If the certificate has be revoked

    c. If the certificate has been created

    d. If the certificate is part of the CRL

12

10. How should users encrypt individual files?

    a. Users should encrypt individual files, one at a time.

    b. Users should not encrypt individuals files, but put them in a folder and encrypt the folder instead.

    c. With their private encryption key only

    d. Encrypt with the individual file encryption key only

11. Where does Windows 2000 store computer certificates?

    a. In the user's profile

    b. In the requesting computer's certificate store

    c. In the Enterprise CA certificate store

    d. In the Subordinate CA certificate store

12. When does a client update a cached copy of a previously published CRL?

    a. As soon as a new CRL is published

    b. When the validity period expires, regardless if a new CRL is published sooner

    c. Either when the validity period expires, or as soon as a new CRL is published, whichever comes first

    d. Within 5 minutes of receiving notice of a new published CRL

13. What functions can PKI perform? [Select all that apply]

    a. Authentic message originator

    b. Authentic computer originator

    c. Confirm the physical location of a computer

    d. Ensure confidentiality of a message

    e. Confirm user security privileges

14. Which of the following statements correctly compares the Certificate Request Wizard and the Certificate Services Web pages?

    a. Use both to obtain certificates from an enterprise CA

    b. Use Certificate Request Wizard with enterprise CA but only use Certificate Services Web pages with stand-alone CA

    c. Use Certificate Services Web pages with enterprise CA or stand-alone CA

    d. Use Certificate Request Wizard with stand-alone CA

15. Which of the following formats can be used to import or export certificates? [Select all that apply]

    a. PKCS #12

    b. PKCS #7

    c. DER Encoded Binary X.509

    d. Base64 Encoded X.509

Real-World Projects

You are a network administrator at the Ebiz Web Company, and it is your responsibility to install Certificate Services. In order to do your job, you must be a member of the Enterprise Admins group. However, you quickly learn that you are not a member of this group. To correct this problem, you contact a current member of the group and advise him of this oversight. Surely the current member knows that you must be a member of the Enterprise Admins group to install Certificate Services. He agrees to add you to the group and asks for your username. You proudly respond "BigDeal", and the current member proceeds to add your name to the group.

Project 12.1

To add a user to the Enterprise Admins group, perform the following steps:

1. Select Start | Programs | Administrative Tools | Active Directory Users and Computers.

2. Create a user account with the name "BigDeal". Note that by default the user BigDeal is only a member of DomainUsers.

3. In the left pane, under Reskit.com, click on the Users folder.

4. Double-click on the Enterprise Admins group.

5. In the Enterprise Admins Properties dialog box, click on the Members tab, and then click on the Add button.

6. In the Select Users, Contacts, or Computers dialog, click on "BigDeal", and then click on the Add button. Click on OK.

7. Close the Active Directory Users and Computers window.

You decide to install Certificate Services immediately because the other member dropped everything to add you to the Enterprise Admins group. Fortunately, you remember that you need to start with the Windows Components Wizard. Because Microsoft wizards are so easy to use, you are confident the installation will be a success.

12

Project 12.2

To install Certificate Services, perform the following steps:

1. Select Start | Settings, and then click on Control Panel.

2. Double-click on Add/Remove Programs.

3. Click on Add/Remove Windows Components to start the Windows Components Wizard.

4. Select the Certificate Services checkbox, and then click on Next.

5. The wizard prompts you to specify the type of CA you want to install. Because you have Active Directory installed and there are no CAs registered with the Active Directory, setup defaults to Enterprise Root CA. Accept the default, and click on Next.

6. The wizard prompts you to supply identifying information appropriate for your site and organization. You set the CA name to "Ebiz Web Company" and Valid For Time to "two years". Click on Next.

7. A dialog box defines the locations of the certificate database, the configuration information, and the location where the CRL is stored. Because you are using Active Directory, the Shared folder must be set. You set the Universal Naming Convention (UNC) path to "eBizCA", and click on Next.

8. Click on OK to finish the installation. Click on Finish to close the wizard.

CHAPTER THIRTEEN

File, Web, and Print Services

After completing this chapter, you will be able to:

✓ Understand Internet Information Services 5.0

✓ Use Site Server ILS service

✓ Implement printer and protocol support

✓ Connect clients to a printer

✓ Use File and Printer Sharing for Microsoft Networks

✓ Use the different Windows file systems

✓ Implement Connection Point Services

✓ Administer PBS and PBA

✓ Monitor Phone Book Service activity

✓ Explain Unix and Windows network management

✓ Understand NIS server architecture

The features in Internet Information Services (IIS) make it easy to share documents and information across a company intranet or the Internet. IIS allows users to deploy scalable and reliable Web-based applications and bring existing data and applications to the Web. IIS includes Active Server Pages (ASP) .

Active Server Pages

ASP is a server-side scripting environment for creating dynamic, interactive Web server applications. With ASP, developers can combine HTML pages, script commands, and COM components as needed to create flexible and powerful Web-based applications. ASP pages are a combination of HTML tags, ASP script commands, and text. ASP files can be edited in any text editor as long as they are saved as text files with .asp extensions.

Windows Media Services

Windows Media Services can create, manage, and deliver Windows Media content over an intranet or the Internet. Windows Media Services provides Windows Media server components, including Windows Media Administrator and Windows Media Encoder. Windows Media Services is not installed by default during a Windows 2000 Setup.

Monitoring IIS

IIS provides Performance Monitor counters for monitoring server activity. The counters that are included are FTP Service object, Internet Information Services Global object, Web Service object, and Active Server Pages object.

FTP Service Object Counters

The File Transfer Protocol (FTP) service object counters show data about the anonymous and nonanonymous connections to the FTP server application. The counters can be reported on a per site basis.

FTP Commands

FTP transfers files to and from a computer running an FTP server service, sometimes called a *daemon* (a Unix program running in the background). FTP can be used interactively and is available only if the TCP/IP protocol has been installed. FTP is a service that, once started, can create a subenvironment where FTP commands can be used, and users can return to the Windows 2000 command prompt by typing the Quit subcommand. When the FTP subenvironment is running, it is indicated by the FTP command prompt.

Syntax and Parameters

The FTP syntax is as follows: FTP [-v] [-n] [-i] [-d] [-g] [-s:*filename*] [-a] [-w:*windowsize*] [*computer*]. The parameters are designated with [-*letter*], and some are considered optional in the command. Table 13.1 contains a list of the parameters and required elements in an FTP command.

In order for users to be able to access the FTP command, they must first have an account set up to allow them outside of the company's network. When FTP access is not restricted, all users have authorization to use the FTP command and no accounts need to be set up.

Internet Information Services Global Object

The IIS Global object contains counters that report on bandwidth throttling and on usage of the IIS Object Cache, a cache shared by the IIS services. *Bandwidth throttling* is a feature of IIS that limits the bandwidth used by the IIS services to a value set by an administrator. If the bandwidth used by the IIS services approaches or exceeds this limit, bandwidth throttling delays or rejects IIS service requests until more bandwidth becomes available. The IIS Object Cache stores frequently used objects and objects that would slow performance when retrieved repeatedly. The counters provided report on the size and content of the IIS Object Cache as well as its effectiveness, such as cache hits and misses.

Active Server Pages Object

The ASP object monitors applications running on a Web server that use ASP. To monitor requests processed by calls to Common Gateway Interface (CGI) applications or Internet Server Application Programming Interface (ISAPI) extensions, use counters on the Web Service object.

Table 13.1 FTP command parameters.

Parameter	Description
-v	Suppresses display of remote server responses.
-n	Suppresses autologin upon initial connection.
-i	Turns off interactive prompting during multiple file transfers.
-d	Enables debugging, displaying all FTP commands passed between the client and server.
-g	Disables file name globbing, which permits the use of wildcard characters (* and ?) in local file and path names. (See the glob command in the online Command Reference.)
-s:*filename*	Specifies a text file containing FTP commands; the commands automatically run after FTP starts. No spaces are allowed in this parameter. Use this switch instead of redirection (>).
-a	Use any local interface when binding data connection.
-w:*windowsize*	Overrides the default transfer buffer size of 4096bytes.
computer	Specifies the computer name or IP address of the remote computer to connect to. The computer, if specified, must be the last parameter on the line.

Each object in Active Directory has several different names. Active Directory creates a relative distinguished name and a canonical name for each object based on information provided when the object was created or modified. Each object can be referenced by its distinguished name, which is derived from the relative distinguished name of the object and all of its parent container objects.

LDAP

The Lightweight Directory Access Protocol (LDAP) relative distinguished name uniquely identifies the object within its parent container. For example, the LDAP relative distinguished name of a computer named *my computer* is CN=mycomputer. The LDAP distinguished name is globally unique. The canonical name is constructed in the same way as the distinguished name.

Security Principal Objects

Security principal objects are Active Directory objects assigned security identifiers and used to log on to the network. They can be granted access to domain resources. An administrator needs to provide unique names for security principal objects, such as user accounts, computer accounts, and groups. Security principal names must conform to the guidelines listed in Table 13.2.

From the information provided, Active Directory generates a security ID and a globally unique identifier (GUID) used to identify the security principal. Active Directory also creates an LDAP relative distinguished name based on the security principal name. An LDAP distinguished name and a canonical name are derived from the relative distinguished name and the names of the domain and container contexts in which the security principal object is created. If an organization has several domains, it is possible to use the same user name or computer name in different domains. The security ID, GUID, LDAP distinguished name, and canonical name generated by Active Directory will uniquely identify each user, computer, or

Table 13.2 Security principal name guidelines.

Type of Account Name	Maximum Size	Special Limitations
User account	20 characters or 20 bytes, depending upon the character set; individual characters may require more than one byte.	A user account cannot consist solely of periods (.), spaces, or the at (@) sign. Any leading periods or spaces are cropped.
Computer account	15 characters or 15 bytes, depending upon the character set; individual characters may require more than one byte.	A computer account cannot consist solely of numbers, periods (.), or spaces. Any leading periods or spaces are cropped.
Group account	63 characters or 63 bytes, depending upon the character set; individual characters may require more than one byte.	A group account cannot consist solely of numbers, periods (.), or spaces. Any leading periods or spaces are cropped.

group in the forest. If the security principal object is renamed or moved to a different domain, the security ID, LDAP relative distinguished name, LDAP distinguished name, and canonical name will change, but the globally unique ID generated by Active Directory will not change.

Site Server ILS Service

The Site Server ILS service is used to publish IP multicast conferences on the network. It can also be used to publish user IP address mappings for H.323 IP telephony. Site Server ILS service allows H.323 calls from NetMeeting to be made to the Phone Dialer provided in the Windows accessories. To support these functions, Site Server ILS service must be installed on at least one server on the network.

The Site Server ILS service offers a standards-based dynamic directory solution to the user location problem on the Internet. Site Server ILS service can be used to create dynamic network communities, enabling users to:

➤ Find people currently logged on to an Internet service or site.

➤ Use real-time communication software, such as Microsoft NetMeeting, to connect to other computers for Internet telephone calls.

Site Server ILS service runs as a service on Microsoft IIS. It handles multiple users and ILS queries simultaneously.

Printer and Protocol Support

For the administrator, Windows 2000 improved setup tools for common network configurations. In addition, improvement of the printers properties pages' user interface makes it easier for both end users and administrators to configure and support their printing needs. Windows 2000 provides improved remote administration by adding remote port administration. Now full remote administration and configuration for printers from any Windows 2000 computer can occur without the need to walk to any print server computer.

13

Internet Printing

The Windows 2000 printing architecture seamlessly integrates with the Internet. For the end user, Windows 2000 offers printing across the Internet. Some of these added benefits include:

➤ Print from Windows 2000 Server and Windows 2000 Professional clients to Windows 2000 print servers using a Uniform Resource Locator (URL).

➤ Use a browser to manage printers to pause, resume, or delete a print job, and view the printer and print job's status.

➤ Connect to printers on a network using Web point-and-print for single-click installation of a shared printer and install drivers from a Web site.

Monitoring

The new standard port monitor connects a Windows 2000 print server to network interface printers that use TCP/IP. It replaces LPRMON for TCP/IP printers connected directly to the network or through a network adapter. The new standard port is 50 percent faster than LPRMON. LPRMON is still required for a printer connected to a Unix, or VAX host.

The Print Queue can now monitor the performance of a local or a remote printer. Counters can be set up for a variety of performance criteria, such as bytes printed per second, job errors, and total pages printed.

Printers Published in Active Directory

Users can quickly search for and locate the most convenient printing resources through an improved user interface. By default, Windows 2000 Server makes all shared printers in the domain available as objects in Active Directory.

Connecting Clients to a Printer

After the printer is added on a Windows 2000 print server, set up clients to access it. The tasks provided to the client depend on the operating system used by the client's computers.

Windows 2000, Windows NT, Windows 95, and Windows 98 Clients

For Windows 2000, Windows NT 4, Windows 95, and Windows 98 clients no other software is needed to connect to a printer. The user only needs to connect to the shared printer using the Add Printer wizard, and select Network printer. The client can also search for the printer in My Network Places, right-click on it, and then select Connect. In both cases, the printer driver is automatically copied to the client computer. Windows 2000 and Windows NT 4 clients check the printer driver and printer configuration each time they connect. Windows NT 3.x clients check each time the spooler service on the client is started. If the driver is not current, a copy of the new driver is downloaded automatically. The printer driver for a client running Windows 95 or Windows 98 is not automatically kept current. If the driver on the printer server is updated, the driver on the client machine needs to be manually installed. Note that administrators should update the drivers on the print server, making it easier for these clients to update their drivers manu-ally from the print server instead of requiring floppy disks or CDs.

NetWare Clients

NetWare clients use IPX/SPX compatible transport to send print jobs over the network to the Windows 2000 print server. The server must have Microsoft File and Print Services installed for NetWare clients to be able to connect to Windows 2000 print servers and printers. File and Print Services for NetWare is a separate product. This tool enables a computer running Windows 2000 Server to provide file and print services directly to NetWare and compatible client computers. The server appears like any other NetWare server to the NetWare clients, and the clients can access volumes, files, and printers at the server. No changes or additions to the NetWare client software are necessary.

NetWare clients can install network client software on each client computer to provide direct access to NetWare servers and to Windows 2000 servers and printers. For example, on Windows 95 and Windows 98, clients that are connected only to the NetWare server need to add the Client for Microsoft Networks to add connectivity to Windows 2000 servers.

Unix Clients

Unix clients can connect to a Windows 2000 print server by using the line printer remote (LPR) monitor. This might be problematic because not all Unix systems support LPR specification, and different versions of Unix use different LPR command syntax.

Connect to the logical printer on a Windows 2000 print server from the client using the native LPR utility. Refer to the client operating system documentation for the correct command.

File and Printer Sharing for Microsoft Networks

The File and Printer Sharing for Microsoft Networks component allows other computers on a network to access resources using a Microsoft network. The component is installed and enabled by default. It is enabled per connection and is necessary to share local folders.

13

Windows File Systems

Before formatting a volume or partition, consider the file system with which to format it. Windows 2000 supports the NTFS file system and the File Allocation Table (FAT) as well as FAT32. NTFS is the recommended file system for Windows 2000 because it supports several features that the others do not. Because Windows 2000 is the only operating system that recognizes NTFS, format the volume or partition as FAT if files are located on a disk with another operating system. NTFS should be chosen if the machine is running only Windows 2000 and to take advantage of these NTFS features: compression, disk quotas, encryption, mount points, and remote storage.

NTFS, FAT, or FAT32?

There are three file systems for disk partitions to choose from: NTFS, FAT, and FAT32. NTFS is the recommended system. FAT and FAT32 are similar to each other except that FAT32 is designed for larger disks than FAT. The file system that works most easily with large disks is NTFS. NTFS has always been a more powerful file system than FAT and FAT32. Windows 2000 Server includes a new version of NTFS with support for a variety of features including Active Directory. The Setup program makes it easy to convert a partition to the new version of NTFS, even if it used FAT or FAT32 previously. This kind of conversion keeps files intact (unlike formatting a partition). If files do not need to be kept intact, it is recommended that the partition be formatted with NTFS rather than converting from FAT or FAT32. Formatting a partition erases all data on the partition, but a partition that is formatted with NTFS rather than converted from FAT or FAT32 will have less fragmentation and better performance. It is still advantageous to use NTFS, however, regardless of whether the partition was formatted with NTFS or converted. A partition can also be converted at a later time by using Convert.exe.

Choose FAT or FAT32 as the file system if you are creating a multiboot machine. For information on how to create a multiboot machine, see Chapter 1. The following information is a comparison of NTFS, FAT, and FAT32. Table 13.3 describes the compatibility of each file system with various operating systems.

Table 13.4 compares disk and file sizes possible with each file system.

Table 13.3   File system and operating system comparision.

NTFS	FAT	FAT32
A computer running Windows 2000 can access files on an NTFS partition. A computer running Windows NT 4 with Service Pack 4 or later might be able to access some files. Other operating systems allow no access.	Access is available through MS-DOS, all versions of Windows, Windows NT, Windows 2000, and OS/2.	Access is available only through Windows 95 OSR2, Windows 98, and Windows 2000.

Table 13.4   File system size limitations.

NTFS	FAT	FAT32
Recommended minimum volume size is approximately 10MB.		
Recommended practical maximum for volumes is 2TB (terabytes). Much larger sizes are possible.		
Cannot be used on floppy disks.	Volumes from floppy disk size up to 4GB.	
Does not support domains.	Volumes from 512MB to 2TB.	
In Windows 2000, a FAT32 volume only up to 32GB.		
Does not support domains.		
File size limited only by size of volume.	Maximum file size 2GB.	Maximum file size 4GB.

Connection Point Services

Connection Point Services (CPS) works with Microsoft Connection Manager to automate the updating of users' computers with new Points of Presence (POP). CPS consists of two major components: Phone Book Service (PBS) and Phone Book Administrator (PBA).

Phone Book Service

PBS is an IIS extension. When users query the phone book server, PBS automatically compares their phone book versions with the most recent files in the database, and then downloads the appropriate updates to the Connection Manager profiles residing on their computers. To run PBS, the server must be running IIS with both FTP and World Wide Web (WWW) services. The FTP service accepts updated phone book information posted from PBA, and the WWW service handles Connection Manager queries.

To install PBS on a server, complete the following steps:

1. Open the Windows Components wizard.

2. In Components, click on Management and Monitoring Tools (but do not select or clear the checkbox), and then click on Details.

3. In Subcomponents of Management and Monitoring Tools, select the Connection Manager Components checkbox.

4. Click on OK, and then click on Next.

Phone Book Administrator

PBA allows you to do the following:

➤ Create and edit multiple phone books. Each phone book is a collection of POPs, and each one is represented by a local access number for a specific region within a country or dependency.

➤ Choose service types (connection settings, such as ISDN access or multicast connection) for each POP. Service types, also called *POP settings*, help users to easily find POPs that suit their needs.

➤ Add and delete new regions and POPs.

➤ Associate POPs with network configurations defined in Connection Manager.

➤ Publish new phone book information to PBS.

➤ Using the command-line interface, import phone book information from other applications for distribution to end users.

➤ Export phone book and region information from a database to text files for use in other applications.

13

Before publishing, or *posting*, to the server, PBA uses a utility to compress the phone book files, increasing the speed at which you can download the new information to users.

Microsoft Connection Manager

Connection Manager is not an actual component of CPS, but rather a companion software package that you need to have in order to use CPS.

Microsoft Connection Manager is a client dialer and connection software tool that can be customized by using the Connection Manager Administration Kit (CMAK). CMAK is a wizard used to build a customized service profile.

How the Components Work Together

When PBA is provided with new phone book information, PBA updates the CPS database and posts the updates to the PBS. The next time a user connects to the service, the client copy of Connection Manager queries PBS for updated phone book information. PBS compares the phone book name and version sent from Connection Manager with the updated CPS database, and then downloads any new phone book information to the client computer.

PBS relies on WWW service, provided through IIS, to receive phone book queries from Connection Manager and download the appropriate updates. PBA relies on FTP service to post the CPS database files to PBS. PBA and PBS need a TCP/IP connection in order to post phone book information through FTP. FTP service must reside on the server.

Administering PBS and PBA

Connection Manager Components Setup configures the PBS folder to allow full access for all users. For added security, limit access to the PBS folder to administrative users. If only certain people need to post phone books to the server, make sure that the primary PBA computer is secure by protecting the PBA folder.

To secure a PBA folder (NTFS only), complete the following steps:

1. Open Windows Explorer.

2. Double-click on the Program Files folder, right-click on the PBA folder, and then click on Properties.

3. On the Security tab, clear the Allow Inheritable Permissions From Parent To Propagate To This Object checkbox.

4. Click on Remove.

5. Click on Add, click the account group, click on Add, and then click on OK.

6. In the Permission list, select the appropriate checkboxes, and then click on OK for Windows 2000 to register the changes.

To set the Write permission for the FTP virtual directory, complete the following steps:

1. Select Start | Programs | Administrative Tools, and then click on Internet Services Manager.

2. In the console tree, double-click on the server name.

3. Double-click on Default FTP Site, and then click on PBSData.

4. On the Action menu, click on Properties.

5. On the Virtual Directory tab, select the Write checkbox, and then click on OK for Windows 2000 to register the changes.

When removing PBS, not all data files are removed. The files must be deleted manually. Before deleting data, change Windows security settings in order to obtain access.

To remove PBS from a server, complete the following steps:

1. Open the Windows Components wizard.

2. In Components, click on Management and Monitoring Tools (but do not select or clear its checkbox), and then click on Details.

3. In Subcomponents of Management and Monitoring Tools, clear the Connection Manager Components checkbox.

4. Click on OK, and then click on Next.

Remote Administration of PBAs

There are two ways to administer a PBA: from a command line or from a remote computer. Characteristics to remember when administering a PBA are:

➤ A remote computer can be a portable or other computer that is used when administration cannot occur from the primary PBA computer.

➤ Deleting the PBA directory prevents an accidental start of PBA from the remote computer, but it leaves the necessary system files intact.

➤ Each server must have only one administration; however, one administration tool can post to multiple servers.

To administer from a remote computer by command line, complete the following steps:

13

1. Install PBA on the remote computer.

2. Delete *only* the PBA *directory* from the remote computer where PBA is installed.

3. Establish a network connection with the primary PBA computer.

4. Establish a network connection with the primary PBS computer.

5. On the remote computer, map a network drive to the PBA directory on the primary PBA computer.

6. Change the working directory to this new one.

Monitoring Phone Book Service Activity

Counters in System Monitor produce statistical information on the processor, memory, cache, network, and other object types. Table 13.5 lists PBS System Monitor counters. (Delta files contain only the current, incremental phone book updates, not the entire phone book file.)

To monitor the activity of PBS:

1. Open Performance.

2. In the console tree, click on System Monitor.

3. In the details pane, right-click on the empty graph, and then click on Add Counters.

4. Click on Select Counters From Computer, and enter a computer name.

5. In Performance object, click on PBServer Monitor.

Table 13.5   PBS counters.

Name	Description
Delta Upgrade Hits	The total number of delta phone book files (incremental phone book changes only) that have been successfully downloaded.
Delta Upgrade Hits/Sec	The number of delta phone book files that are successfully downloaded per second.
Error Hits	The total number of requests that could not be satisfied by PBS.
Error Hits/Sec	The number of requests per second that could not be satisfied by PBS.
Full Upgrade Hits	The total number of full phone book files that have been successfully downloaded.
Full Upgrade Hits/Sec	The number of full phone book files that are successfully downloaded per second.
No Upgrade Hits	The total number of requests for phone book files that did not require an update to the phone book file on the client computer.
No Upgrade Hits/Sec	The number of requests for phone book files per second that do not require an update to the phone book file on the client computer.
Total Hits	The total number of requests for phone book files.
Total Hits/Sec	The number of requests per second for phone book files.

6. Do one of the following:

   ➤ To select all counters, click on All Counters, and then click on Add.

   ➤ To select specific counters, click on Select Counters From List, click on the counter desired, and then click on Add. Repeat for each counter to be added.

7. Click on Close.

PBServer Monitor counters are not available unless PBS has been started. PBS starts automatically when a client computer requests a phone book.

Unix and Windows Network Management

Traditionally, Unix computers use files for storing directories and managing namespaces consisting of users, groups, networks, services, and so on. These files are maintained and updated on each computer, giving each administrator complete control over that computer.

However, this scheme is problematic in networks where network administrators need control over entire namespaces for overall access control and resource sharing. The /etc files of all computers have to be kept in sync, so that security and resource sharing can be achieved. For this reason, some ad hoc methods were developed to share these files among computers. One such method consists of distributing these files via remote distribution from one computer to all other computers. This requires that all updates to the namespace take place on the computer that distributes the changes to other computers.

Overview of NIS

In 1981, Sun introduced Network Information System (NIS), a simple network look-up service consisting of databases and processes. This protocol was formerly known as Yellow Pages (YP). NIS consists of a set of maps or databases consisting of data from /etc files and a set of computers among which these maps are shared. NIS is a protocol based on Open Network Computing (ONC) and Remote Procedure Call (RPC).

An NIS domain consists of clients and servers. Clients use NIS protocol to look up information, such as passwords, groups, and hosts stored in NIS databases on servers instead of local files. Databases are replicated among servers. There is one master server, which is used to update databases, whereas subordinate (slave) servers provide read-only access. Databases are kept consistent by copying them from master to server either periodically or when modified.

Clients use various functions or RPC calls to interface to this network look-up service. These include yp_match, yp_first, yp_next, yp_all, yp_order, and yp_master.

13

In addition, NIS on Unix includes some administrative tools to manage maps, namely: ypwhich, yppoll, ypset, ypcat, and domainname.

Overview of Windows Network Management

Windows NT 4 uses Windows NT Directory Service, which is a domain-based architecture for network management. Windows NT Directory Service is based on a secure directory database that contains user IDs, passwords, access rights, and organizational information. In the domain model, the domain controller holds the copy of the domain directory database. Clients talk to domain controllers to authenticate and authorize users.

With Windows 2000, Microsoft has introduced Active Directory, a flexible directory providing features, such as security and replication. It allows creation of a hierarchical structure of the organization consisting of domains, sites, Organizational Units (OUs), and trust relationships. Active Directory creates replicated, reliable storage for storing network objects, such as users or groups. It provides access to the directory database through protocols, such as LDAP, and a programmatic interface, such as Active Directory Services Interface (ADSI).

NIS Server Architecture

Server for NIS implements NIS server functionality by providing NIS protocol using the ONC-RPC mechanism. It implements NIS version 2 protocol necessary to serve NIS clients and subordinate NIS servers. Server for NIS is installed on Windows 2000-based domain controllers, whereas the Windows 2000-based domain structure remains unaffected. Windows clients continue to operate as before. The NIS domain uses one or more Windows domain controllers as NIS servers. One of the domain controllers acts as a NIS master for the NIS domain, and the other domain controllers with Server for NIS installed act as NIS subordinate (slave) servers. In addition, the NIS domain may continue to use existing Unix NIS servers as subordinate servers. Server for NIS provides NIS interfaces necessary to act as either a master or subordinate NIS server. Communication between a Server for NIS-based domain controller and Unix subordinate NIS servers is done using NIS protocols. On the other hand, communication between NIS servers based on Active Directory takes place through Active Directory replication. It does not use NIS protocol for this communication.

Use of Active Directory for Storing the NIS Map

The Unix NIS server stores NIS maps using the DBM format, which is supported natively on Unix. NIS is a simple directory wherein map data is flat. Server for NIS does not use the DBM format. It stores NIS maps using Active Directory. Active Directory provides a flexible and extensible mechanism to store directory information.

Server for NIS allows storing of NIS data in any container in Active Directory, although it stores maps for each NIS domain in a separate container. Administrators may specify any container that reflects the organizational structure in order to store that domain. Storing the objects in the default container for the NIS domain speeds up searches and improves the performance of NIS operations, including ypmatch and ypcat. Server for NIS can support multiple NIS domains at the same time. Each object includes an attribute listing the domain to which it belongs. Using this information, requests from each Unix client belonging to a particular domain receive maps associated with that domain only.

Storing NIS maps in Active Directory has a number of advantages, such as scalability and security. Access to Active Directory data is secure, which ensures that only authorized administrators may modify the data. With Active Directory replication, all domain controllers of the Windows domain have the copies of the NIS maps. This makes it possible for the remaining domain controllers to act as slave servers for the same NIS domain. Server for NIS does not use the NIS mechanism for keeping maps synchronized, but rather uses directory replication.

Extension of Active Directory Schema

While implementing NIS server functionality, Server for NIS does not store NIS maps as flat data or as plain text entries in Active Directory. It extends Active Directory schema to store Unix attributes. Each map is created as a separate Active Directory class. It stores NIS maps by associating each field of the map as a separate attribute. Entries in the NIS map are stored as objects of that class. Fields of NIS maps are stored as attributes of that object. The advantage of this approach is that it is possible to provide semantic meaning to fields of map entries. It is also possible to search entries using different fields. Because Active Directory allows searches on any attribute, maps can be searched (via ypmatch) on any of the attributes of the map.

As maps from each domain are migrated, Server for NIS creates objects corresponding to entries of each map. For nonstandard maps, it first defines the structure of the map, such as the key field and field separator, and then stores the map entries. During installation, Server for NIS creates a default NIS domain whose domain name is the same as the Windows 2000-based domain. NIS entries can be created or assigned to this domain.

Integration of NIS Maps with Active Directory

In addition to extending Active Directory for storing NIS maps, for certain classes, Server for NIS integrates NIS data with Windows objects stored in Active Directory. These NIS maps include password, group, and hosts. For these maps, NIS objects are not represented separately in Active Directory. If a corresponding Windows object is present in Active Directory, it adds Unix attributes to the same object, creating a unique object representing both Unix and Windows identities. If

13

no such Windows object exists, a new Windows object is created, Unix attributes are added to it, and Unix objects are made first-class entities of the Windows domain.

When Server for NIS creates an entry from the password map, it first checks if the user with user name is already present in Active Directory. If the user does not exist, it creates an object of class User with CN and samAccountName set to the Unix user name, thereby creating a Windows user with the same user name. It then adds Unix attributes to that user object. This allows Unix users to be created as Windows users in Active Directory and to be managed via Active Directory.

If a Windows user with the same user name as a Unix user being added already exists, it adds the Unix attributes of that existing object, allowing a Windows user to be made a user of an NIS domain as well. This allows the integration of Windows and Unix networks with each user represented uniquely. Those users that need only Windows access remain unchanged. Administrators can assign Unix attributes to existing Windows users and assign them to a particular NIS domain.

Entries from the group map are created in the same manner. If there is no Windows group with the same name as a group being migrated from NIS, a group with that NIS name is created. If a Windows group with the same name does exist, Unix attributes are assigned to that group. By assigning a GDI and a domain name, a Windows-based group also can be marked to be part of NIS.

Server for NIS maintains a reciprocal relationship between users and groups; meaning, if an NIS user is a member of some NIS group, the NIS group automatically acquires the user as a member. Server for NIS does not keep Unix user and Windows user memberships for a group synchronized. Each group maintains two sets of memberships: users who are members of the group in a Windows 2000-based domain and users who are members of that group in a Unix-based domain. This is due to differences in how Windows and Unix treat group memberships. Windows maintains a strict reciprocal relationship, whereas Unix maintains a lenient relationship between users and groups.

Entries from the host's map are treated similarly and integrated with the computer's class in Active Directory. They are created as members of the computer's class in Active Directory. This allows the entire network of Unix and Windows computers to belong to the same network. Server for NIS allows resolution of the host's map via Domain Name Server (DNS), providing a functionality that is available in NIS.

Migrating NIS Domains to Active Directory

Server for NIS provides migration tools to migrate NIS maps from a Unix NIS server to Active Directory. With migration, NIS map entries can be migrated and corresponding objects created in Active Directory. After the migration, Server for

NIS running on the domain controller takes the role of a NIS master. The NIS domain can be administered using Active Directory.

Migration tools make it easy to migrate all NIS maps, and hence the NIS domain, to a Windows 2000-based domain controller. Administrators do not have to re-create the NIS objects in Active Directory. These tools help ensure that the transition to Server for NIS is minimally disruptive and that all data is migrated. Migration tools flag migration errors and identify any conflicts. During the migration of an entry, if an entry with the same key value already exists in the Active Directory for the same NIS domain, conflict is identified. Administrators can forcefully overwrite existing entries, preserve existing entries, or manually resolve the conflict by merging the two entries.

Management of NIS Domains Using Active Directory Tools

Server for NIS allows administration of NIS maps using Active Directory-based tools. Entries from NIS maps, such as passwords, groups, and hosts, are migrated to their Active Directory objects, and therefore these objects may be managed using the Active Directory Users and Groups snap-in. In order to manage other standard and nonstandard maps, Server for NIS provides a command-line tool called nismap. Nismap allows administrators to add, delete, and edit entries from NIS maps. For example, consider a map called phones for domain physlab on Server for NIS. In this example, the administrator modifies the map entry for Linda by changing the phone numbers.

To deploy Server for NIS in a staged migration:

1. Identify the NIS domain that you want to migrate to Server for NIS. Choose the NIS domain that has a number of network objects, such as users or groups, in common with the Windows 2000-based domain you are migrating to.

2. Determine if you want to create an enterprise-wide NIS domain. This choice is influenced by the resource sharing that is desired between different domains. Determine the name of the intended global NIS domain.

3. Migrate the NIS maps from the master Unix-based NIS server to one of the domain controllers in the Windows domain.

4. Notify the subordinate NIS servers in the domain of the new Windows 2000-based master NIS server. Turn off the use of the old Unix-based master NIS server.

5. If the NIS domain is merged into a new domain, you need to set the NIS clients to use the new NIS domain using the domain name command.

6. Once migration of the master NIS server is completed, install Server for NIS on other Windows 2000-based domain controllers. Configure Unix clients to use the new master or subordinate Windows 2000-based server.

13

7. Turn off the use of the subordinate Unix-based NIS servers in a phased manner. You can then install Server for NIS on subsequent Windows domain controllers. Once Server for NIS is installed on a domain controller, it can take the role of another NIS server.

User Name Mapping

User Name Mapping provides a mechanism to map the dissimilar names that can exist between the Unix and Windows environments. User Name Mapping is used even when the names are the same in both environments, but its real strength is to allow mapping of users whose names are not the same in the two environments. Given that Unix user names are case sensitive, whereas Windows 2000 and Windows NT names are not, this can simplify maintaining and managing accounts in the two environments.

With User Name Mapping, you can create simple maps between Windows 2000 or Windows NT user accounts and the corresponding Unix accounts, and use the Advanced Map feature to map accounts with dissimilar names. Furthermore, User Name Mapping supports bi-directional one-to-many mapping, allowing a single Unix or Windows 2000 and Windows NT account be mapped to multiple accounts in the other environment. This enables a map to more than one administrative account in Windows 2000 and Windows NT to the Unix root account, for example. User Name Mapping uses either NIS to authenticate users or local passwd/group files that are maintained and authenticated using the Server for PCNFS. Install User Name Mapping on one or more servers if the user name conventions are different between Windows 2000 and Unix. This allows a map to the different user names in each environment in a way that is essentially transparent to the users. In a large enterprise environment where there is a well-established base of Unix users and administrators, it may be impossible to implement NIS as part of Active Directory.

The password synchronization will work with those accounts that have the same name in both environments to keep the passwords synchronized, regardless of whether the Unix environment is using NIS or /etc/passwd as its primary authentication mechanism.

In environments that are adopting Windows 2000 and Active Directory, Active Directory provides a major opportunity to simplify and consolidate all account maintenance into a single, easy-to-manage location. Use the NIS Migration Wizard to migrate an existing NIS domain to Active Directory, converting an existing NIS master server into an NIS subordinate server that points to the new Active Directory-based NIS master server. Where dissimilar accounts exist in the two environments, User Name Mapping provides a simple mechanism to map accounts between the two.

Chapter Summary

Windows Media Services provides Windows Media server components including Windows Media Administrator and Windows Media Encoder. Administrators should note that Windows Media Services is not installed by default during a Windows 2000 Setup.

Internet Information Server provides Performance Monitor counters to allow administrators to monitor server activity. The counters that are included are FTP Service object, Internet Information Services Global object, Web Service object, and Active Server Pages object. Site Server ILS service runs as a service on Microsoft IIS. Site Server ILS service can be used to create dynamic network communities, enabling users to find people currently logged on to an Internet service or site, and use real-time communication software, such as Microsoft NetMeeting, to connect to other computers for Internet telephone calls.

The new standard port monitor connects a Windows 2000 print server to network interface printers that use TCP/IP. By default, Windows 2000 Server makes all shared printers in the domain available as objects in Active Directory. For Windows 2000, Windows NT 4, Windows 95, and Windows 98 clients, no other software is needed to connect to a printer. Windows 2000 and Windows NT 4 clients check the printer driver and printer configuration each time they connect. The printer driver for a client running Windows 95 or Windows 98 is not automatically kept current. This tool enables a computer running Windows 2000 Server to provide file and print services directly to NetWare and compatible client computers. The server appears like any other NetWare server to the NetWare clients, and the clients can access volumes, files, and printers at the server. Unix clients can connect to a Windows 2000 print server by using the line printer remote (LPR) monitor. Windows 2000 supports the NTFS file system and the File Allocation Table (FAT) as well as FAT32. Windows 2000 Server includes a new version of NTFS with support for a variety of features including Active Directory.

13

CPS consists of two major components: Phone Book Service (PBS) and Phone Book Administrator (PBA). PBA relies on FTP service to post the CPS database files to PBS. FTP service must reside on the server. The FTP service accepts updated phone book information posted from PBA, and the WWW service handles Connection Manager queries. PBS starts automatically when a client computer requests a phone book.

An NIS domain consists of clients and servers. Server for NIS implements NIS server functionality by providing NIS protocol using the ONC-RPC mechanism. It implements NIS version 2.0 protocol necessary to serve NIS clients and subordinate NIS servers. Server for NIS is installed on Windows 2000-based domain controllers; however, the Windows 2000-based domain structure remains unaffected. The NIS domain uses one or more Windows domain controllers as NIS servers. One of the domain controllers acts as an NIS master for the NIS domain, whereas the other domain controllers with Server for NIS installed act as NIS subordinate (slave) servers. In addition, the NIS domain may continue to use existing Unix NIS servers as subordinate servers. Server for NIS provides NIS interfaces necessary to act as either a master or a subordinate NIS server. Communication between a Server for NIS-based domain controller and Unix subordinate NIS servers is done using NIS protocols. The Unix NIS server stores NIS maps using the DBM format, which is supported natively on Unix. NIS is a simple directory wherein map data is flat. It stores NIS maps using Active Directory, a flexible directory providing features, such as security and replication. Active Directory creates replicated, reliable storage for storing network objects, such as users or groups. Server for NIS stores maps for each NIS domain in a separate container. Server for NIS can support multiple NIS domains at the same time. With Active Directory replication, all domain controllers of the Windows domain have the copies of the NIS maps. Server for NIS does not use the NIS mechanism for keeping maps synchronized, but rather uses directory replication.

During installation, Server for NIS creates a default NIS domain whose domain name is the same as the Windows 2000-based domain. Server for NIS integrates NIS data with Windows objects stored in Active Directory.

Server for NIS provides migration tools to migrate NIS maps from a Unix NIS server to Active Directory. With migration, NIS map entries can be migrated and corresponding objects created in Active Directory. The NIS domain can then be administered using Active Directory. Migration tools make it easy to migrate all NIS maps, and hence the NIS domain, to a Windows 2000-based domain controller. Server for NIS allows administration of NIS maps using Active Directory-based tools.

With User Name Mapping, you can create simple maps between Windows 2000 or Windows NT user accounts and the corresponding Unix accounts, and use the Advanced Map feature to map accounts with dissimilar names. Install User Name Mapping on one or more servers if the user name conventions are different between Windows 2000 and Unix. Use the NIS Migration Wizard to migrate an existing NIS domain to Active Directory, converting an existing NIS master server into a NIS subordinate server that points to the new Active Directory-based NIS master server.

Review Questions

1. ASP files can be edited in any text editor as long as they are saved as text files with what extension?

    a. .txt

    b. .bmp

    c. .asp

    d. .jpg

2. With Windows Media Services, you can create, manage, and perform what other function with Windows Media content over an intranet or the Internet?

    a. Save

    b. Discuss

    c. Retrieve

    d. Deliver

3. Which counters show data about the anonymous and nonanonymous connections to the File Transfer Protocol Server application?

    a. FTP

    b. Internet Information Services Global object

    c. Web Service object

    d. Active Server Pages object

4. Which is the parameter and required element in an FTP command that suppresses display of remote server responses?

    a. -v

    b. -n

    c. -l

    d. -d

5. Which is the parameter and required element in an FTP command that turns off interactive prompting during multiple file transfers?

    a. -v

    b. -n

    c. -l

    d. -d

13

6. Which is the parameter and required element in an FTP command that enables debugging and displays all FTP commands passed between the client and server.

    a. -a

    b. -n

    c. -d

    d. -g

7. What monitors applications running on your Web server that use Active Server Pages?

    a. Internet Information Services Global object

    b. Web Service object

    c. Active Server Pages object

    d. FTP

8. Active Directory also creates what relative distinguished name, based on the security principal name?

    a. FTP

    b. LDAP

    c. ID

    d. RIP

9. The Site Server ILS service is used to publish what IP conferences on the network?

    a. Multicast

    b. Singular

    c. Combined

    d. Retrievable

10. How does the Windows 2000 printing architecture integrate with the Internet?

    a. Carefully

    b. Seamlessly

    c. Immutably

    d. Symmetrically

11. NetWare clients use what compatible transport to send print jobs over the network to the Windows 2000 print server?

    a. IPX/SPX

    b. TCP/IP

    c. NetBIOS

    d. AppleTalk

12. Which of the following file systems can you choose for disk partitions on a computer running Windows 2000?

    a. NTFS

    b. FAT

    c. FAT32

    d. All of the above

13. Which file system has always been a more powerful file system?

 a. NTFS

 b. FAT

 c. FAT32

 d. None of the above

14. Phone Book Administrator enables you to do all but one of the following:

 a. Add and delete new regions and POPs.

 b. Create and Edit multiple phone books.

 c. Associate POPs with network configurations defined in Subcomponents of Management and Monitoring Tools.

 d. Publish new phone book information to PBS.

15. Microsoft Connection Manager is an actual component of CPS.

 a. True

 b. False

Real-World Projects

Jester Computer Resources International has recently acquired a new company—Beethoven Technical Support Specialist. Because of this acquisition, Jester must integrate Beethoven's computer system into its own system. Beethoven's computers consist of Windows 2000 professional machines, Macintosh machines, and Unix machines. James, the IT administrator, has been informed that the field reps need to send their information in to the company but currently have to email this information to an individual who then stores it on the server, rather than FTPing the information in. Jester has assigned James the duty of coming up with and implementing a plan to integrate these computers.

After having met with the Unix using clients, James determines that the clients cannot be converted to Windows due to the proprietary nature of their software and job functions. James determines that users need to log onto a FTP server to send their information to the proper departments within the company.

13

Project 13.1

To set up FTP accounts for known users, complete the following steps:

1. Select Start|Programs|Administrative Tools, and then click on Internet Services Manager.

2. In the console tree, double-click on the server name, and then click on Default FTP Site.

3. On the Action menu, click on Properties.

4. On the Security Accounts tab, clear the Allow Anonymous Connections checkbox.

5. A warning appears indicating that unencrypted passwords can be transmitted over the network.

6. Click on Yes, and then click on Add.

7. In Name, click on one or more user names, and then click on Add.

8. When you finish adding users, click on OK.

By creating these FTP accounts, field personnel are able to send their information directly to the server.

Next, James wants to set up a plan to deploy an NIS server in a staged migration, so that users can have an easy transition to the new server.

Project 13.2

To deploy Server for NIS in a staged migration, complete the following steps:

1. Identify the NIS domain that you want to migrate to Server for NIS. Choose the NIS domain that has a number of network objects, such as users or groups, in common with the Windows 2000-based domain you are migrating to.

2. Determine if you want to create an enterprise-wide NIS domain. This choice is influenced by the resource sharing that is desired between different domains. Determine the name of the intended global NIS domain.

3. Migrate the NIS maps from the master Unix-based NIS server to one of the domain controllers in the Windows domain.

4. Notify the subordinate NIS servers in the domain of the new Windows 2000-based master NIS server. Turn off the use of the old Unix-based master NIS server.

5. If the NIS domain is merged into a new domain, you need to set the NIS clients to use the new NIS domain using the domain name command.

6. Once migration of the master NIS server is completed, install Server for NIS on other Windows 2000-based domain controllers. Configure Unix clients to use the new master or subordinate Windows 2000-based server.

7. Turn off the use of the subordinate Unix-based NIS servers in a phased manner. You can then install Server for NIS on subsequent Windows domain controllers. Once Server for NIS is installed on a domain controller, it can take the role of another NIS server.

By implementing NIS, Unix users can still have the same account on both the Unix system and on the Jester's Windows servers, thereby allowing them to keep their Unix access and still be able to communicate with the rest of the company.

CHAPTER FOURTEEN

Troubleshooting

After completing this chapter, you will be able to:

✓ Define troubleshooting

✓ Know where to start the troubleshooting process

✓ Use Windows 2000 utilities

✓ Use troubleshooters

✓ Use Administrative Tools

✓ Use **ipconfig**

✓ Use troubleshooting tools

There are two methods used to troubleshoot a problem: sequential and iterative. Sequential problem solving is a five-step process, which includes collecting information to clarify the problem, considering alternative explanations, formulating a hypothesis, testing the hypothesis, and analyzing the results. When using sequential problem solving, the process ends with step five. Iterative problem solving is the process most often used when troubleshooting computers. The iterative process uses the same five steps as the sequential process: however, when a technician reaches step five, he or she resumes the process, starting from step one. The reason for this is that computer problems are usually complex and require multiple corrections to fix them.

Where to Start

Not all computer problems are difficult to solve, so the first step is to look for a quick, obvious solution. A majority of problems can be fixed with a rebooting of the computer or with a check of all cable connections. However, not all problems are this easy to fix, so it is a good idea to keep a checklist of common problems and their solutions in an accessible location. Once a quick fix has been ruled out, there are a number of procedures that a technician can try:

➤ *Try to replicate the problem yourself.* See if the problem happens on another computer.

➤ *Examine the configuration.* If the problem occurs on another computer, compare the two computers and determine the differences between the two systems.

➤ *Go back to the basic configuration.* If a new piece of hardware or software was added, remove it, and see if the problem persists.

➤ *View the system as a group of subsystems.* Test the problem in small sections to see exactly where in the process the error is occurring.

➤ *Use a module replacement strategy.* Remove the troublesome hardware and either try it in another computer or try a new module in the same computer.

➤ *Try a hypothesis testing approach.* Run a small experiment to see if your solution works.

Generally, it takes more than one of these approaches to fix a PC problem.

Windows 2000 Utilities

There are several utilities included in Windows 2000. These utilities allow users to manage, maintain, and troubleshoot their servers.

Backup

The Backup utility helps you create a copy of the data on your hard disk. In the event that the original data on your hard disk is accidentally erased or overwritten, or it becomes inaccessible because of a hard disk malfunction, you can use the backup copy to restore your lost or damaged data. It is important to keep a backup copy of information in case of a system failure or natural disaster.

Many companies institute several layers to their backup plan. These layers include daily, weekly, and monthly backups. Each of these backups is stored on a different set of media and reused once every cycle. If there are errors that start to occur during the backup process do the following:

1. Keep a log of each backup.

2. Check to see if the error occurs in the same place each time.

3. If the error occurs in the same place, check to see if the file is corrupt or see if another application is trying to access the same file at the same time. If the error does not occur in the same place, most likely, your media is getting worn out and needs to be replaced.

It is a good idea to keep a log for all backup activity to help track errors and patterns before there is a problem with the system to help limit or prevent any downtime.

Administrators can use Windows 2000 to move or restore encrypted files or folders to a different computer from the one on which the encrypted files or folders are stored. If you have access to the second computer through a roaming user profile, you do not need to export and then import your file encryption certificate and private key because these are available on any computer that you log on to.

If you do not have access to the second computer, you can use the first computer to export your encryption certificate and private key in a .pfx file format to a floppy disk. To do this, use the Export command from Certificates in Microsoft Management Console (MMC). On the second computer, use the Import command from Certificates in MMC to import the .pfx file from the floppy disk into the Personal store.

When you move or restore encrypted files and folders to different computers, your file encryption certificate and private key must be available on those computers as well. Otherwise, you are not able to access those files or folders. If you first back up encrypted files and folders using Backup or another backup program designed for Windows 2000, you can copy or move encrypted files and folders to a volume that is not an NTFS file system volume. The backup version of the encrypted file or folder retains its encryption. You can then copy the backup version to backup tapes or to other file systems, such as FAT, or you can send it as an email attachment.

14

Restore the backup version to an NTFS volume to preserve the encryption. If your encrypted files and folders are on a computer using 128-bit encryption, restore the files and folders to a computer that is also using 128-bit encryption; otherwise, you will not be able to access your encrypted files. Files and folders encrypted on systems with 128-bit encryption are not accessible if restored to a system that is running standard (56-bit) encryption.

To schedule a backup:

1. Open Backup.

2. Click on the Backup tab, click on the Job menu, and then click on New.

3. Select the files and folders you want to back up by clicking on the box to the left of a file or folder. Select the checkbox for any drive, folder, or file you want to back up.

4. Select File or a tape device in Backup destination, and then save the file and folder selections by clicking on the Job menu, and then clicking on Save Selections.

5. In Backup Media Or File Name, type a path and file name for the backup file or select a tape.

6. Select any backup options you want, such as backup type and the log file type, by selecting the Tools menu and then clicking Options. When you have finished selecting backup options, click OK.

7. Click on Start Backup and make any changes you want to the Backup Job Information dialog box.

8. If you want to set advanced backup options, such as data verification or hardware compression, click on Advanced. When you have finished selecting advanced backup options, click on OK.

9. Click on Schedule in the Backup Job Information dialog box.

10. In the Set Account Information dialog box, enter the user name and password that you want the scheduled backup to run under.

11. In the Scheduled Job Options dialog box, in Job name, type a name for the scheduled backup job, and then click on Properties to set the date, time, and frequency parameters for the scheduled backup. When you have finished, click on OK, and then click on OK again.

Utility Manager

Utility Manager enables users to check an Accessibility program's status and start or stop an Accessibility program. Users with administrator level access can designate the program to start when Windows 2000 starts. The built-in programs accessible from the Utility Manager are Magnifier, Narrator, and On-Screen Keyboard. Narrator, a text-to-speech program, starts automatically when Utility Manager opens. This gives users who are blind or have low vision immediate access to Utility Manager.

As an example of the timesaving value of Utility Manager, if you use the visual aid Magnifier, you can specify that Magnifier start automatically the next time you turn on your computer. This eliminates the need for you to go through the steps of opening Magnifier each time you start Windows 2000.

Some items to keep in mind when using Utility Manager:

➤ To complete certain functions, you must be a member of the Administrators group.

➤ Most users with disabilities will need utility programs with higher functionality for daily use. The Accessibility tools that ship with Windows 2000 are intended to provide a minimum level of functionality for users with special needs.

To start and stop Accessibility programs:

1. Open Utility Manager.

2. To start or stop an Accessibility program:
    ➤ Select the program from the list, and then under Options click on Start.
    ➤ Select the program from the list, and then under Options click on Stop.

To start a program when Utility Manager starts, complete the following steps:

1. Open Utility Manager.

2. In the Name column, select the program.

3. Under Options, select the Start Automatically When Utility Manager Starts checkbox. To cancel the automatic start, clear the Start Automatically When Utility Manager Starts checkbox.

To start Accessibility programs when Windows starts, complete the following steps:

1. Open Utility Manager.

2. In the Name column, select the program.

3. Under Options select the Start Automatically When Windows Starts checkbox. To cancel the automatic start, clear the Start Automatically When Windows Starts checkbox.

14

Active Directory

Some of the operations master roles are crucial to the operation of your network, and others may be unavailable for quite some time before their absence becomes a problem. Generally, you will notice that the single master operations role holder is unavailable when you try to perform some function controlled by the particular operations master. If an operations master is not available due to computer failure or network problems, you can seize the operations master role. This is also referred to as forcing the transfer of the operations master role.

Before forcing the transfer, determine the cause and expected duration of the computer or network failure. If the cause is a networking problem or a server failure that can be resolved soon, wait for the role holder to become available again. If the domain controller that currently holds the role has failed, you must determine if it can be recovered and brought back online.

If you cannot add a domain, complete the following steps:

1. Select Start | Run, and then type "cmd".

2. At the command prompt, type "ntdsutil".

3. At the ntdsutil prompt, type "roles".

4. At the fsmo maintenance prompt, type "connections".

5. At the server connections prompt, type "connect to server", followed by the fully qualified domain name.

6. At the server connections prompt, type "quit".

7. At the fsmo maintenance prompt, type "seize domain naming master".

8. At the fsmo maintenance prompt, type "quit".

9. At the ntdsutil prompt, type "quit".

Note: A domain controller whose domain naming master role has been seized must never be brought back online.

If you cannot create objects in Active Directory, complete the following steps:

1. Select Start | Run, and then type "cmd".

2. At the command prompt, type "ntdsutil".

3. At the ntdsutil prompt, type "roles".

4. At the fsmo maintenance prompt, type "connections".

5. At the server connections prompt, type "connect to server", followed by the fully qualified domain name.

6. At the server connections prompt, type "quit".

7. At the fsmo maintenance prompt, type "seize RID master".

8. At the fsmo maintenance prompt, type "quit".

9. At the ntdsutil prompt, type "quit".

If the schema master is not available, either there is a network connectivity problem or it may also be due to a failure of the computer holding the schema master role. Temporary loss of the schema operations master is not visible to network users. And it is only visible to administrators when they are trying to modify the schema or install an application that modifies the schema during installation.

If you cannot modify the schema, complete the following steps:

1. Select Start|Run, and then type "cmd".

2. At the command prompt, type "ntdsutil".

3. At the ntdsutil prompt, type "roles".

4. At the fsmo maintenance prompt, type "connections".

5. At the server connections prompt, type "connect to server", followed by the fully qualified domain name.

6. At the server connections prompt, type "quit".

7. At the fsmo maintenance prompt, type "seize schema master".

8. At the fsmo maintenance prompt, type "quit".

9. At the ntdsutil prompt, type "quit".

Note: *Before seizing the schema master, remove the current operations master from the network and verify that the copy of the schema on the new operations master is up to date with the rest of the domain controllers in the forest.*

When changing group memberships and they do not take effect, the infrastructure master is not available. This may be caused by a network connectivity problem. It may also be due to a failure of the computer holding the infrastructure master role. Resolve the network connectivity problem or repair the computer holding the infrastructure master role before trying to seize the infrastructure master role. Some of the operations master roles are crucial to the operation of your network. Others can be unavailable for quite some time before their absence becomes a problem. Generally, you will notice that a single master operations role holder is unavailable when you try to perform some function controlled by the particular operations master.

14

If clients without Active Directory client software installed cannot log on, complete the following steps:

1. Select Start | Run, and then type "cmd".

2. At the command prompt, type "ntdsutil".

3. At the ntdsutil prompt, type "roles".

4. At the fsmo maintenance prompt, type "connections".

5. At the server connections prompt, type "connect to server", followed by the fully qualified domain name.

6. At the server connections prompt, type "quit".

7. At the fsmo maintenance prompt, type "seize PDC".

8. At the fsmo maintenance prompt, type "quit".

9. At the ntdsutil prompt, type "quit".

If clients are unable to access resources in another domain, complete the following steps:

1. Open Active Directory Domains and Trusts.

2. In the console tree, right-click on one of the domains involved in the trust you want to verify, and then click on Properties.

3. Click on the Trusts tab.

4. In either Domains trusted by this domain or Domains that trust this domain, click on the trust to be verified, and then click on Edit.

5. Click on Verify/Reset.

The ipconfig Command

The ipconfig diagnostic command displays all current TCP/IP network configuration values. This command allows users to determine which TCP/IP configuration values have been configured by Dynamic Host Configuration Protocol (DHCP).

ipconfig [/all | /renew [*adapter*] | /release [*adapter*]]

The following is a list of parameters for ipconfig:

➤ */all*—Produces a full display. Without this switch, ipconfig displays only the IP address, subnet mask, and default gateway values for each network card.

➤ /renew [*adapter*]—Renews DHCP configuration parameters. This option is available only on systems running the DHCP Client service. To specify an adapter name, type the adapter name that appears when you use ipconfig without parameters.

➤ /release [*adapter*]—Releases the current DHCP configuration. This option disables TCP/IP on the local system and is available only on DHCP clients. To specify an adapter name, type the adapter name that appears when you use ipconfig without parameters.

With no parameters, the ipconfig utility presents all of the current TCP/IP configuration values to the users including IP address and subnet mask. This utility is especially useful on systems running DHCP, allowing users to determine which values have been configured by DHCP.

To set DHCP class ID information at a client computer that is a DHCP-enabled client running Windows 2000, open the command prompt and use the ipconfig command-line utility to set the DHCP class ID the client will use when obtaining its lease from a DHCP server. Type the ipconfig "/setclassid" command at the command prompt, type "Local Area Connection" (be sure to include the quotes), and then type "MyNewClassId". Listing 14.1 shows how classid is set as an ASCII string for the DHCP class ID string for the local area network connection in use at the client computer. Listing 14.1 illustrates the use of the /setclassid switch.

Listing 14.1   The ipconfig command-line utility using the /setclassid switch.

```
C:\>ipconfig /setclassid "Local Area Connection" MyNewClassId

Windows 2000 IP Configuration

        DHCP ClassId successfully modified for adapter "Local
Area Connection"
```

In order for a DHCP options class to be in effect between a DHCP server and its clients, both have to be configured with identical class ID strings that identify the client as a member of a specific user or vendor options class when the client obtains its IP address lease.

To show DHCP class ID information at a DHCP-enabled client computer running Windows 2000, open the command prompt and use the ipconfig command-line utility. At the command prompt type "ipconfig /showclassid", and then type "Local Area Connection" (be sure to include the quotes). Listing 14.2 shows the ASCII string MyNewClassId that is currently set as the DHCP class ID for the local area network connection at the client computer. Listing 14.2 illustrates the use of the /showclasssid switch.

14

Listing 14.2   The ipconfig command-line utility using the /showclassid switch.

```
C:\>ipconfig /showclassid "Local Area Connection"

Windows 2000 IP Configuration

DHCP Class ID for Adapter "Local Area Connection":
        DHCP ClassID Name . . . . . . . . : Default BOOTP Class
        DHCP ClassID Description  . . . . : User class for BOOTP clients
        DHCP ClassID Name . . . . . . . . : Default Remote Access Class
        DHCP ClassID Description  . . . . : User class for remote access
                                            clients


        Host Name . . . . . . . . . . . . : HOSTA
        Primary DNS Suffix  . . . . . . . : example.microsoft.com
        Node Type . . . . . . . . . . . . : Hybrid
        IP Routing Enabled. . . . . . . . : No
        WINS Proxy Enabled. . . . . . . . : No

Ethernet adapter Local Area Connection:

        Connection-specific DNS Suffix  . :
        Description . . . . . . . . . . . : Combo PCMCIA EthernetCard
        Physical Address. . . . . . . . . : 00-00-00-00-7C-DC
        DHCP Enabled. . . . . . . . . . . : Yes
        Autoconfiguration Enabled . . . . : Yes
        IP Address. . . . . . . . . . . . : 10.0.0.51
        Subnet Mask . . . . . . . . . . . : 255.255.255.0
        Default Gateway . . . . . . . . . : 10.0.0.1
        DHCP Class ID . . . . . . . . . . : MyNewClassId
        DNS servers . . . . . . . . . . . : 10.0.0.3
        Primary WINS server . . . . . . . : 10.0.0.5
```

To optimize the command prompt for use with command-line tools, click on the upper-left corner of the command prompt window, click on Properties, and then click on the Options tab to modify the command prompt options. For command history, increase Buffer Size to 500 and Number of Buffers to 5. Under edit options, click on Quick Edit Mode and Insert Mode. Click on the Layout tab to increase the Screen Buffer Size to 2500, and then click on OK to apply the changes. When prompted, select the option "Modify shortcut that started this window".

Windows 2000 Troubleshooters

The Windows 2000 troubleshooters help you diagnose and solve technical problems that can occur with your computer. When you start a troubleshooter, you must answer a series of questions about the problem you are having. These answers help Windows 2000 find a solution to your problem.

There are several different troubleshooters, and each one is designed to solve a different type of problem. Table 14.1 lists the troubleshooters available and what they assist you with.

Table 14.1 Windows 2000 troubleshooters.

Troubleshooter	Description
Client Service for NetWare	Client Service for NetWare, including accessing NetWare servers and Novell Directory Services (NDS) objects, printing to NetWare printers, using NetWare login scripts, and logging onto an NDS tree.
DHCP	Configuring DHCP service on a server, related error messages, and events that appear in the event log.
Display	Video cards and display adapters, outdated or incompatible video drivers, and incorrect settings for your video hardware.
Group Policy and Active Directory	Group Policy and configuring Active Directory on a server, related error messages, and events that appear in the event log.
Domain Name System	Configuring Domain Name System (DNS) on a server, related error messages, and events that appear in the event log.
Hardware	Cameras, CD-ROM drives, game controllers, hard drives, keyboards, mouse devices, network adapters, and scanners. If problems are occurring with a sound card, modems, or a display or video adapter, there are individual troubleshooters for those devices.
Internet connections	Connecting and logging on to your Internet service provider (ISP).
Modem	Connections, setup configuration, and detection.
MS-DOS programs	Running MS-DOS programs on Windows 2000.
Multimedia and games	Installing and configuring Direct X drivers and games.
Networking (TCP/IP)	Internet and intranet connections (client-side only) that use Transmission Control Protocol/Internet Protocol (TCP/IP).
Print	Network or local printers and plotters, outdated or corrupted printer drivers, network and local printer connections, and printer configuration.
Routing and Remote Access	Dial-up networking connections.
Remote Installation Services	Installing Windows 2000 using Remote Installation Services.
Sound	Sound cards and speakers.
Startup and shutdown	Choosing an operating system at startup, corrupted Ntldr and Ntdetect files, and startup errors pertaining to floppy drives, SCSI host adapters, video, and hard drives.
Stop errors	System startup errors, including Stop errors that occur on Windows 2000 Server.
System setup	Installing and setting up Windows 2000.
Network Administration	Configuring and managing the Windows 2000 Server.
Windows 3.x programs	Running 16-bit Windows programs on Windows 2000
WINS	Configuring Windows Internet Naming Service (WINS) on a server, related error messages, and events that appear in the event log.

14

Note: If the error occurs with an MS-DOS program, you will need to use the MS-DOS troubleshooter.

To get the best results from the Windows 2000 troubleshooters, use these guidelines:

1. Resize the Help window and move it to the right half of your screen, so you can use the left half of your screen to follow the instructions.

2. Hide the navigation pane of the Help window by clicking on Hide on the Help toolbar.

3. Follow the troubleshooter steps exactly. (Note that if you do not, you may miss critical information and limit the effectiveness of the troubleshooter.)

4. Some troubleshooter steps require you to restart your computer or close the troubleshooter window. If this is required, and you only have access to one computer, you should either print out the troubleshooter steps before restarting or write the steps down.

Microsoft Management Console

You can use MMC to create, save, and open administrative tools (called *MMC consoles*) that manage the hardware, software, and network components of your Windows system. MMC is a feature of the Windows 2000 operating system, but can also run on Windows NT, Windows 95, and Windows 98 operating systems.

MMC does not perform administrative functions, but hosts tools that do. The primary type of tool you can add to a console is a snap-in. Other items that you can add include ActiveX controls, links to Web pages, folders, taskpad views, and tasks.

There are two general ways to use MMC: in *user mode*, working with existing MMC consoles to administer a system, or in *author mode*, creating new consoles or modifying existing MMC consoles.

Creating Consoles

Before you author a console, you should identify the tasks the console will perform, the components to be administered, and the snap-ins and controls that are needed to perform the tasks. You also need to consider whether you need to create a taskpad view and tasks. After you make these decisions, you can open a new console and start adding items to the console tree.

To create or edit a console, complete the following steps:

1. Open the console in author mode. (Use the command-line option /a.)

2. To view the complete command-line syntax, do one of the following:
   - ➤ Click Start, click Run, type "mmc", and then click OK.
   - ➤ At a command prompt, type "mmc", and then press Enter.

Snap-In Components

A snap-in is the basic component of an MMC console. Snap-ins always reside in a console; they do not run by themselves. When you install a component that has a snap-in associated with it on a computer running Windows, the snap-in is available to anyone creating a console on that computer, unless restricted by a user policy.

Stand-Alone and Extension Snap-Ins

MMC supports two types of snap-ins: stand-alone and extension. You can add a stand-alone snap-in, usually just called a *snap-in*, to a console tree without adding another item first. An extension snap-in, usually just called an *extension*, is always added to a stand-alone or extension snap-in that is already on the console tree. When you enable extensions for a snap-in, they operate on the objects controlled by the snap-in, including computers, printers, modems, or other devices.

When you add a snap-in or extension to a console, it may appear as a new item in the console tree. It may also add context menu items, additional toolbars, additional property pages, or wizards to a snap-in already installed in the console.

Adding Snap-Ins to a Console

You can add a single snap-in or multiple snap-ins and other items to a console. You can also add multiple instances of a particular snap-in to the same console to administer different computers or to repair a damaged console. Each time you add a new instance of a snap-in to a console, any variables for the snap-in are set at default values until you configure the snap-in. For instance, if you configure a particular snap-in to manage a remote computer, and then add a second instance of the snap-in, the second instance is not automatically configured to manage the remote computer.

In general, you can only add snap-ins that are installed on the computer that is authoring a console. However, in Windows 2000, if your computer is part of a domain, you can use MMC to download any snap-ins not locally installed but are available in the Active Directory service.

Adding Items to the Console Tree

You can help users locate the components they need in the console by arranging items hierarchically or in groups on the console tree. To add items to the console tree, use the Add/Remove Snap-in command on the Console menu of the main toolbar of MMC.

In the Add/Remove Snap-in dialog box, Snap-Ins Added determines the item on the console tree under which new items are added. The default value is Console Root. You can click an item in Snap-Ins Added to locate an object elsewhere on the console tree.

14

The Add Standalone Snap-in dialog box displays a list of available snap-ins. For computers running Windows 2000 that are members of a domain, this list includes both locally installed snap-ins and snap-ins published in the Active Directory service. For snap-ins that are available in Active Directory, Not Installed appears in the Vendor column.

To add snap-ins to MMC, complete the following steps:

1. Open MMC.

2. On the Console menu, click on Add/Remove Snap-in.

3. In the Add/Remove Snap-in dialog box, click on Add.

4. In the Add Standalone Snap-in dialog box, click on the snap-in you want to add to the console, and then click on Add.

5. You can add additional snap-ins by repeating steps 2 through 4.

If you have already installed a snap-in and you want to enable one of its extension snap-ins, you can use the Extensions tab in the Add/Remove Snap-in dialog box. On this tab, you can select any item in the console tree that can be extended and view the extension snap-ins that you can enable or disable. When you enable an extension snap-in, it is automatically inserted in the console tree under the selected item. If there is more than one instance of a snap-in on the console tree, all instances of the snap-in are extended.

After enabling an extension snap-in, you may notice that it appears in snap-ins that can be extended along with the stand-alone snap-ins. This means that the extension snap-in also has extensions that you can enable.

Like stand-alone snap-ins, an administrator can also publish extension snap-ins in the Windows 2000 Active Directory service. Extension snap-ins available to a user from Active Directory appear in the list of available extension snap-ins with any locally installed extension snap-ins, except that they are followed by the phrase "(not installed)". You must specifically download extension snap-ins from the directory service to make them available in a console. To download all extensions for a given item, clear the Add All Extensions checkbox on the Extensions tab of the Add/Remove Snap-In dialog box, and select the checkboxes next to each extension that you want to download.

You can add multiple instances of the same snap-in to a console either to manage multiple remote computers from the same console or to repair a damaged console. As an example of the latter situation, you may notice that a tool is behaving differently than expected, that its configuration is outdated, or that it is timing out because resources have been removed. To fix the console, try adding a new instance of the snap-in to the console, configure it as needed, and then remove the old instance of the snap-in from the console.

Adding Taskpad Views and Tasks

Before you add taskpad views and tasks to a console, determine how many taskpad views you need. If you need multiple taskpad views, you also need to determine how the tasks are divided among the taskpad views. You should also decide what kind of taskpad view you want to use—one that displays a list and tasks or one that displays tasks only.

To create a taskpad view for a console, the console must contain at least one snap-in. You can use the New Taskpad View wizard to configure the titles, headings, and lists that appear in the taskpad view and to define whether a taskpad view is associated with a single item or multiple items in the console tree.

After you complete the New Taskpad View wizard, you can use the New Task wizard to add tasks to the taskpad view. Tasks can include menu commands for the items in the console as well as commands that are run from a command prompt. You can create commands to act on part of the console tree or details pane, or to open another component on your computer. However, if you create a task from a menu command for an item in the console tree, and then you remove that item, the task is disabled.

To extend the functionality of Group Policy, complete the following steps:

1. Open Group Policy as a stand-alone MMC snap-in.

2. On the Console menu, click on Add/Remove snap-in.

3. Click the Extensions tab, select the snap-in extensions you want, and then click on OK.

4. To add an extension snap-in to an MMC console, open a saved console in author mode by doing the following:

   ➤ Right-click on the .msc file, and then click on Author.

   ➤ Select Start|Run, type "mmc *path**filename.msc* /a", and then click on OK.

5. On the Console menu, click on Add/Remove Snap-in, and then click on the item that you want to extend.

6. On the Extensions tab, in Available extensions, select the checkbox next to the extension you want to add, and then click on OK.

Viewing the Console Tree in a Console Window

When the console tree is visible, it appears in the left pane of a console window. What you view in a console window is determined by where the console window is rooted on the console tree. The initial window and any new windows that you create are rooted at Console Root. You can close console windows to hide the Console Root or entire portions of the console tree. You can then configure the console to prevent users from viewing hidden portions of the tree. However, the entire console tree is always saved when you save a console.

14

Rooting Console Windows on Items in the Console Tree

Although you can use MMC to make consoles that meet every administrative need for a group, you can also design simple consoles for less experienced users. For instance, after you add items to a console tree, you can open additional console windows rooted on any item in the console tree. You can use this method to create console windows that display specific administrative components of the console tree. You can then close windows that show portions of the console tree that users do not need.

To set MMC console options to limit user access, complete the following steps:

1. Open a saved console in author mode by doing one of the following:

   ➤ Right-click the .msc file, and then click on Author.

   ➤ Select Start | Run, type "mmc *path\filename.msc* /a", and then click on OK.

2. On the Console menu, click on Options.

3. To change the icon for the console, click on Change Icon; in File Name, type the path to a file containing icons; under Current icon click on an icon; and then click on OK.

4. To change the title for the console, type a new title in the box to the right of the icon.

5. To change the default mode for the console, in Console mode, click on the mode that you want the console to open in.

6. If the default console mode for the console is one of the user modes, do the following:

   ➤ To allow a menu to appear when users right-click on the contents of a taskpad view, select the Enable Context Menus On Taskpads In This Console checkbox.

   ➤ To prevent users from editing the console, select the Do Not Save Changes To This Console checkbox.

   ➤ To enable users to access the Customize View dialog box, select the Allow The User To Customize Views checkbox.

Configuring Console Options

There are several ways that you can customize the console window to fit your needs. You can use the Options dialog box, available from the Console menu, to choose an icon for, change the title of, and choose the default mode for a console. Icons are available from many sources including Shell32.dll, located on Windows 2000 and Windows NT in the systemroot\system32 folder.

You can change the title of the console; however, keep in mind that by default, as you click items in the console tree, the title bar displays the path to the selected item. Make note that if you change the title of a console, the title bar will not display this path. If you delete the title, the default behavior is restored.

When considering which mode to set as the default for a console, remember that if you use one of the user modes, you can open the console at any time using the Author or Run As commands. You will not need to use author mode for most management tasks.

Windows Management Instrumentation (WMI)

Windows Management Instrumentation (WMI) is an important tool for managing Windows 2000 security. It allows administrators to have universal management of information across an enterprise. WMI allows administrators to set and delete permissions for users and validation on IDs. For more information on all aspects of WMI, see Chapter 2.

WMI does not override or circumvent any existing security provided by the operating system. By default, all members of the Administrators group have full control of the WMI services on the managed computer. All others have read/ write/execute permissions on their local computer only. Permissions can be changed by adding a user to the Administrators group on the managed computer or by authorizing users or groups in WMI and setting their permission level. Access is based on WMI namespaces on computers running Windows 95 or Windows 98, and all users have full control locally. However, permissions can be set for users managing a Windows 95 or Windows 98 computer remotely. Security is checked only when a user connects to the Windows Management service; thus, any changes made to a user's permissions while the user is connected will not take effect until the next time the user starts a WMI service. For example, if a user's access is re-voked, the changes would not take effect until the user exits from WMI and attempts to connect to the service again.

To authorize WMI users and set permissions, complete the following steps:

1. Open WMI Control.

2. In the console tree, right-click on WMI Control, and then click on Properties.

3. Click on the Security tab.

4. Select the namespace for which you want to give a user or group access, and then click on Security.

5. In the Security dialog box, click on Add.

14

6. Perform one of the following steps:

➤ If you are setting permissions on a local computer, in the Select Users, Computers, or Groups dialog box, in Look in, select the domain containing the user or group you want to add. Then, in the Name list, double-click on the name of the user or group you want to add, or type the name in the lower box, and click on OK.

➤ If you are setting permissions on a remote computer, in the Add User dialog box, type the name of the user or group you want to add, and then click on OK.

7. In the Security dialog box, under Permissions, select the permissions to allow or deny the new user or group.

System Properties is a WMI tool you can use to view and change system properties on a remote computer or local computer. Using System Properties you can:

➤ *Change the size of the virtual memory paging file.* Change the settings for the virtual memory paging file on a computer that might run programs that require a lot of memory.

➤ *Restart a remote computer.* Restart a remote computer to apply settings changes or to detect new hardware.

➤ *View a computer's network identification.* View the computer name and domain information for other computers on your network.

Note: *To change certain system properties on a computer, you must be an administrator.*

Administrative Tools

A series of administrative tools is included in Windows 2000. These tools include Component Services, Computer Management, Data sources, Event Viewer, Event logging for IAS, and System Monitor.

Component Services

Component Services is used by system administrators to deploy and administer COM+ programs from a graphical user interface or to automate administrative tasks using a scripting or programming language. Software developers can use Component Services to visually configure routine component and program behavior, such as security and participation in transactions, and to integrate components into COM+ programs.

Log on as an administrator or a member of the Administrators group in order to complete this procedure. If your computer is connected to a network, network policy settings may also prevent you from configuring existing components.

1. Open the Control Panel.

2. Double-click on Add/Remove Windows Components.

3. Click on Configure, and then follow the instructions on the screen.

To add a new component, complete the following steps:

1. Open the Control Panel.

2. Double-click on Add/Remove Windows Components.

3. Click on Components, and follow the instructions in the Windows Components wizard.

Computer Management

Computer Management is used to manage local or remote computers from a single, consolidated desktop utility. It combines several Windows 2000 administrative tools into a single console tree, providing easy access to a specific computer's administrative properties, such as:

➤ Monitor system events, such as logon times and application errors.

➤ Create and manage shares.

➤ View a list of users connected to a local or remote computer.

➤ Start and stop system services, such as the Task Scheduler and the Spooler.

➤ Set properties for storage devices.

➤ View device configurations and add new device drivers.

➤ Manage server applications and services, such as the Domain Name System (DNS) service or the DHCP service.

Computer Management Interface

Computer Management uses a two-pane view similar to Windows Explorer. The console tree contains the administrative tools, storage devices, and server applications and services available on the local or remote computer. The three nodes in this tree are System Tools, Storage, and Services and Applications.

You perform administrative tasks by selecting a tool in the console tree and using menus and toolbars to act on that tool in the right, or results, pane that displays the tool's attributes, data, or available subtools. The results may be a list of what is contained by the object you select, or it may be another kind of management view, such as contents of the computer's application log.

You must be a member of the Administrators group to take full advantage of Computer Management. If you are not a member of the Administrators group, you

14

won't have access rights to view or modify administrative properties, and you won't have permission to perform administrative tasks.

You can also use Computer Management to control what the computer does in the event that it shuts down unexpectedly.

To specify what Windows 2000 does if the system stops unexpectedly, complete the following steps:

1. Open Computer Management (Local).

2. In the console tree, right-click on Computer Management (Local), and then select Properties.

3. On the Advanced tab, click on Startup and Recovery, and under Recovery, select the actions Windows 2000 should perform if a Stop error occurs.

Data Sources (ODBC)

You can use Data Sources Open Database Connectivity (ODBC) to access data from a variety of database management systems. For example, if you have a program that accesses data in a SQL database, Data Sources (ODBC) will let you use the same program to access data in a Visual FoxPro database. To do this, you must add software components called *drivers* to your system. Data Sources (ODBC) helps you add and configure these drivers.

To open Data Sources (ODBC), complete the following steps:

1. Open the Control Panel.

2. Double-click on Administrative Tools.

3. Double-click on Data Sources (ODBC).

Event Viewer

Event Viewer is used to view and manage logs of system, program, and security events on your computer. Event Viewer gathers information about hardware and software problems and monitors Windows 2000 security events. For more information on Event Viewer, see Chapter 2.

IPSec: Bad SPI Messages in Event Viewer

The IPSec: Bad SPI Messages in Event Viewer error may occur if a key lifetime value is set too low or if the SA has expired but the sender continues to transmit data to the receiver. To determine and correct the problem, use IPSec Monitor to examine the number of rekeys. For more information, see Using IPSec Monitor in Chapter 11.

If the number of rekeys is very large compared to the amount of time the connections have been active, increase the settings of the key lifetimes in the policy. Good values for high-traffic Ethernet connections are greater than 50MB and greater than five minutes.

Higher settings may not entirely eliminate bad SPIs, but should significantly reduce the occurrences.

Event Logging for Internet Authentication Service (IAS)

Internet Authentication Service (IAS) events, such as errors, are automatically recorded in event logs. You can also customize IAS properties to select other types of events to be logged in event logs.

If you select the Log rejected or discarded authentication requests option, rejected and ignored requests are logged. These messages are useful for understanding why a particular request was rejected or ignored. Requests can be rejected or ignored for several reasons. The following list contains some of the reasons why a request might be ignored:

➤ The request is not formatted according to RFC 2138 or 2139 for RADIUS.

➤ The RADIUS client, such as the network access server (NAS) or RADIUS proxy server, is unknown.

➤ The client has multiple IP addresses and sent the request on an address other than the one defined in IAS.

➤ The shared secret is invalid.

➤ The digital signature sent by the client is invalid.

➤ Support for the digital signature is not implemented on the client correctly (as specified in the RADIUS RFC).

➤ IAS could not find the user's domain.

➤ IAS could not connect to the user's domain.

➤ IAS cannot get permission to access the user's account in the domain.

➤ If you select Log successful authentication requests, this data is logged.

Local Security Policy

Local Security Policy is used to configure security settings for the local computer. These settings include the Password policy, Account Lockout policy, Audit policy, IP Security policy, user rights assignments, recovery agents for encrypted data, and other security options. Local Security Policy is only available on Windows 2000 computers that are not domain controllers. If the computer is a member of a domain, these settings may be overridden by policies received from the domain.

System Monitor

One of the main items that system monitor searches for is bottlenecks. Bottlenecks occur when there is an overwhelming demand on the system that causes a drastic decrease in performance. Analysis of your monitoring data may reveal problems, such as excessive demand on certain resources, resulting in bottlenecks. This section discusses common causes for bottlenecks and a recommended strategy for tuning and testing.

Causes of Bottlenecks

Demand may become extreme enough to cause resource bottlenecks for the following reasons:

➤ Resources are insufficient and additional or upgraded components are required.

➤ Resources are not sharing workloads evenly and need to be balanced.

➤ A resource is malfunctioning and needs to be replaced.

➤ A program is monopolizing a particular resource; this may require substituting another program, having a developer rewrite the program, adding or upgrading resources, or running the program during periods of low demand.

➤ A resource is incorrectly configured, and configuration settings should be changed.

Strategy for Tuning and Testing

Lack of memory is by far the most common cause of serious performance problems in computer systems. If you suspect other problems, check memory counters to rule out a memory shortage. Poor response time on a workstation is most likely to result from memory and processor problems; servers are more susceptible to disk and network problems.

Before you start tuning, consider the following recommendations:

➤ Make one change at a time; a problem that appears to relate to a single component may be the result of bottlenecks involving multiple components.

➤ Repeat monitoring after every change to understand the effect of the change and determine if additional changes are required. Note that it is important to keep records of the changes you make.

➤ Review event logs; some performance problems generate output you can display in Event Viewer.

➤ To see whether network components are playing a part in performance problems, compare the performance of programs that run over the network with locally run programs.

Tuning and Upgrading Tips by Component

This section lists tuning tips for resources that you are monitoring:

➤ Memory:

  ➤ Increase physical memory above the minimum required.

  ➤ Create multiple paging files.

  ➤ Determine the correct size for the paging file.

  ➤ Ensure that memory settings are properly configured.

  ➤ Run memory-intensive programs on your highest-performing computers or when system workload is light.

➤ Disk:

  ➤ Upgrade to a higher-speed disk, or add disks, including the disk controller and the bus.

  ➤ On servers, use Disk Management to create striped volumes on multiple physical disks. This increases throughput because I/O commands can be issued concurrently.

  ➤ Distribute programs among servers using Distributed File System to balance workload.

  ➤ Isolate tasks that heavily utilize disk I/O on separate physical disks or disk controllers.

  ➤ Use Disk Defragmenter to optimize disk space.

  ➤ If you want to improve the efficiency of disk access, install the latest driver software for your host adapters.

➤ Processor:

  ➤ Add a processor or upgrade to a faster processor.

  ➤ On multiprocessor computers, manage the processor affinity with respect to process threads and interrupts.

➤ Network:

  ➤ Configure your network so that systems shared by the same group of people are on the same subnet.

14

➤ Unbind infrequently used network adapters.

➤ If you are using more than one protocol, you can set the order in which the workstation and NetBIOS software bind to each protocol. Some reasons for changing the list order are:

  ➤ If the protocol you use most frequently is first in the binding list, average connection time decreases.

  ➤ Some protocols are faster than others for certain network topologies, so put the faster protocol first in the bindings list to improve performance. Because the server accepts incoming connections using the protocol chosen by the client computer, there is no reason to reorder server computer bindings.

  ➤ Install a high-performance network adapter in the server. If your server uses a 16-bit adapter, you can significantly increase performance by replacing it with a high-performance 32-bit adapter.

  ➤ Use multiple network adapters. Windows 2000 supports multiple adapters for a given protocol and multiple protocols for a given adapter. Although this configuration can create distinct networks that cannot communicate with one another, it is a way to increase file-sharing throughput.

Network Monitor

The biggest concern with computers today is security. As part of Network Monitor's built-in security, only those frames, including broadcast and multicast frames, sent to or from the local computer are displayed. Network Monitor also displays overall network segment statistics for broadcast frames, multicast frames, network utilization, total bytes received per second, and total frames received per second.

Detecting Other Installations of Network Monitor

To protect your network from unauthorized monitoring, Network Monitor can detect other installations of Network Monitor running on the local segment of your network. Network Monitor also detects all instances of the Network Monitor driver being used remotely (by either Network Monitor from Systems Management Server or System Monitor) to capture data on your network.

When Network Monitor detects other Network Monitor installations running on the network, it displays the following information about them:

➤ The name of the computer

➤ The name of the user logged on at the computer

➤ The state of Network Monitor on the remote computer (running, capturing, or transmitting)

➤ The adapter address of the remote computer

➤ The version number of Network Monitor on the remote computer

In some instances, your network architecture might prevent one installation of Network Monitor from detecting another. For example, if an installation is separated from yours by a router that does not forward multicasts, your installation cannot detect that installation.

The Network Data Stream

Network Monitor monitors the network data stream, which consists of all information transferred over a network at any given time. Before transmission, this information is divided by the network software into smaller pieces called *frames* or *packets*.

Frames, whether broadcast, multicast, or directed, are made up of several different pieces that can be analyzed separately. Some of these pieces contain data that Network Monitor can use to troubleshoot networking problems. For example, by examining the destination address, it can be determined whether the frame was a broadcast frame, indicating all hosts had to receive and process this frame, or a directed frame sent to a specific host. By analyzing frames, you can determine the exact cause of the frame, which helps determine whether the service generating these types of frames can be optimized.

For more information on Network Monitor, see Chapter 2.

Displaying Captured Data

Network Monitor simplifies data analysis by interpreting raw data collected during the capture and displaying it in the Frame Viewer window. To display captured information in the Frame Viewer window, on the Capture menu, click on Stop and View while the capture is running. Or, open a capture file (.cap).

14

The Frame Viewer window includes the following panes:

➤ *Summary*—General information about captured frames in the order in which they were captured.

➤ *Detail*—The frame's contents, including the protocols used to send it.

➤ *Hex*—A hexadecimal and ASCII representation of the captured data.

Troubleshooting Phone Book Service

Table 14.2 describes Phone Book Service (PBS) events and the actions you can take to correct errors. When an error has occurred, a message is posted to your Application Log.

Table 14.2   PBS error codes.

MessageID	Type	Message	Action to Perform
30000	Error	Unable to initialize the ODBC data source	Select Start|Programs|Administrative Tools, click on Data Sources (ODBC), and make sure that the Microsoft Access data source is set up properly.
30001	Error	Internal ODBC error	Select Start|Programs|Administrative Tools, click on Data Sources (ODBC), and make sure that the Microsoft Access data source is set up properly.
30002	Error	Unable to get query parameters	No action is required. If the problem persists, restart IIS Admin Service.
30003	Error	Error in sending HTML header	Make sure that IIS is running properly. If the problem persists, restart IIS Admin Service.
30004	Error	Error in sending HTML content	Make sure that IIS is running properly. If the problem persists, restart IIS Admin Service.
30005	Error	Cannot open file	Make sure the file exists and the file permissions are set properly.
30006	Information	New Phone Book detected!	No action is required.
30007	Error	Cannot disconnect!	Phone Book Service is unable to disconnect from the Microsoft Access ODBC data source. In the Control Panel, double-click on ODBC Data Sources, and make sure that the Microsoft Access data source is set up properly.
30008	Error	Cannot free resources	In the Control Panel, double-click on ODBC Data Sources, and make sure that the Microsoft Access data source is set up properly.
30010	Error	Internal Error	Free up the memory currently in use by closing any nonessential applications. You might also want to increase the physical or virtual memory of your system. Also, make sure that IIS is running properly.
30011	Information	ODBC Connection Established!	No action is required.
30012	Error	Cannot read registry key for ODBC.INI	The Phone Book Service registry is corrupted. Reinstall Phone Book Service.
30015	Error	Failure when waiting for child thread to terminate	Restart IIS Admin Service.
30016	Error	Failed to create a handle for monitored directory	Make sure the directory exists and file permissions are set correctly.
30017	Error	Cannot determine file system changes	Restart the computer.

(continued)

Table 14.2   PBS error codes (continued).

MessageID	Type	Message	Action to Perform
30018	Error	Unable to convert changed filename	Restart the computer.
30019	Error	Unable to initialize the ODBC data source: failed to allocate environment handle.	Free up the memory currently in use by closing any nonessential applications. You might also want to increase the physical or virtual memory of your system.
30020	Error	Unable to initialize the ODBC data source: failed to allocate connection handle.	Free up the memory currently in use by closing any nonessential applications. You might also want to increase the physical or virtual memory of your system.
30021	Error	Unable to connect to data source	Select Start|Programs|Administrative Tools, click on Data Sources (ODBC), and make sure that the Microsoft Access data source is set up properly.
30022	Error	Cannot get creation timestamp	Make sure that Newpb.mdb and Pbserver.mdb exist in the PBS Data database directory.
30023	Error	Cannot update phone book file	Make sure that the phone book is not write-protected.

To display the Application Log in Event Viewer, complete the following steps:

1. Select Start | Programs | Administrative Tools.

2. Click on Event Viewer.

3. Click on Application Log.

Chapter Summary

The five steps of troubleshooting are: collect information, consider alternative explanations, formulate a hypothesis, test the hypothesis, and analyze the results. Troubleshooters should remember that a majority of problems can be resolved with a simple reboot, and those that cannot generally take several steps to resolve.

Backup utility helps users create a copy of information in the event of a failure or data corruption. When performing backups, it is a good idea to keep a log of activities to monitor errors and patterns. When using Backup on files with 128-bit encryption, be sure to restore them on a computer with 128-bit encryption to be able to read them.

Active Directory allows users to manage operation master roles and to force the transfer of master roles. When working with a master, it is important to remember that:

➤ Domain master roles that have been seized must never be brought back online.

➤ Before seizing a schema master, remove the current operations master from the network.

14

Ipconfig is a diagnostic tool used to determine what all the current TCP/IP settings are on the server. Switches that can be used with this command include /all, /renew, and /release.

Windows 2000 comes with a series of built-in troubleshooters that are accessible through the Help system. These troubleshooters include DHCP, Display, Client Services for NetWare, Group Policy and Active Directory, Hardware, Internet connections, Modem, Networking, Print, Routing and Remote Access, Sound, Startup and Shutdown, Stop errors, System setup, Network Administration, and WINS.

MMC is a useful tool that groups administrative tools together in one convenient location. It allows administrators to create different views of the tools and add snap-ins. And it is compatible with other Windows OSs. There are two types of snap-ins: stand-alone and extension.

Administrative tools included in Windows 2000 that allow users to monitor the system include Component Services, Computer Management, Network Monitor, Data Sources, Event Logging, and Event Viewer. These tools combined allow users to manage security issues and access levels on the server. They also allow users to track information and network traffic on the system.

Memory shortage is the biggest problem encountered on systems today and often results in bottlenecks. There are several strategies for improving system memory usage, including increasing memory, making one change at a time to find the item(s) affecting the system, creating multiple paging files, reviewing event logs, and running memory intensive programs when system loads are light.

Review Questions

1. Which of the following is not a built-in program accessible from the Utility Manager?

   a. Magnifier

   b. Manager

   c. Narrator

   d. On-Screen Keyboard

2. The Ipconfig command displays all current network configuration values for what?

   a. TCP/IP

   b. IPX/SPX

   c. NetBIOS

   d. AppleTalk

3. What are the parameters for ipconfig/all?

    a. Renews DHCP configuration parameters

    b. Releases the current DHCP configuration

    c. Produces a full display

    d. None of the above

4. Which Windows 2000 Troubleshooter is for connections, setup configuration, and detection?

    a. Display

    b. Modem

    c. DHCP

    d. Internet Connections

5. Which Windows 2000 Troubleshooter is used if you have a problem with configuring Dynamic Host Configuration Protocol service on a server?

    a. Client Service for NetWare

    b. Display

    c. DHCP

    d. Hardware

6. What would you use Routing and Remote Access Troubleshooter for?

    a. Dial-up networking connections

    b. Sound cards and speakers

    c. Running MS-DOS programs on Windows 2000

    d. Connections, setup configuration, and detection

7. Which of the Windows 2000 Troubleshooters would you use for running 16-bit Windows programs on Windows 2000?

    a. Routing and Remote Access

    b. Remote Installation Services

    c. Sound

    d. System Setup

8. Microsoft Management Console is a feature of the Windows 2000 operating system, but can also run on all but one of the following:

    a. Windows NT

    b. Windows 3.1

    c. Windows 95

    d. Windows 98

14

9. MMC does not perform what kind of task?

   a. Configuration

   b. Administration

   c. Printing

   d. File management

10. To add snap-ins to MMC, complete all but one of the following steps:

    a. Open MMC.

    b. On the console menu, click on Add/Remove Snap-in.

    c. In the Add/Remove Snap-in dialog box, click on Remove.

    d. In the Add Standalone Snap-in dialog box, click on the snap-in you want to add to the console, and then click on Add.

11. Which of the following is not a step involved to extend the functionality of Group Policy?

    a. Open Group Policy as a stand-alone MMC snap-in.

    b. On the console menu, click on Add/Remove Snap-In.

    c. Click on the Extensions tab, select the snap-in extensions you want, and then click on OK.

    d. On the Extension tab, in the Snap-In dialog box, select the checkbox next to the extension you want to add, and then click on OK.

12. When the console tree is visible, where does it appear in a console window?

    a. Right side

    b. Left side

    c. Top

    d. Bottom

13. WMI is an important tool for managing which Windows 2000 program?

    a. Server

    b. Client

    c. Security

    d. Workstation

14. Which administrative tool do system administrators use to deploy and administer COM+ programs from a graphical user interface or to automate administrative tasks using a scripting or programming language?

    a. Component Services

    b. Computer Management

    c. Data Sources

    d. Event Viewer

15. Which administrative tool is used to view and manage logs of system, program, and security events on your computer?

    a. Data Sources

    b. Event Viewer

    c. Computer management

    d. Event logging for IAS

16. What can you use to control what the computer does in the event that it shuts down unexpectedly?

    a. Data Sources

    b. Even logging for IAS

    c. Computer Management

    d. Data Services

17. One of the main items that System Monitor searches for is what?

    a. Tuning

    b. Testing

    c. Passwords

    d. Bottlenecks

18. The biggest concern with computers today is what?

    a. Security

    b. Speed

    c. Reliability

    d. Broadcasting

19. Which of the following settings used to configure security settings for IAS events is only available on Windows 2000 computers that are not domain controllers?

    a. Account Lockout Policy

    b. Audit Policy

    c. Local Security Policy

    d. IP Security Policy

20. When Network Monitor detects other Network Monitor installations running on the network, it displays all of the following information about them except one. Which one does it not display?

    a. The name of the computer

    b. The name of the user logged on at the computer

    c. The adapter address of the remote computer

    d. The location of the user

14

Real-World Projects

Lesha and James are network administrators at Atlas World Communications, which is an international telecommunications company with 15,000 users worldwide. Lesha has just received a notice from the Help Desk technicians that customers are remarking that the network is very slow every Monday and Wednesday at 12:00 P.M. After reviewing logs, Lesha and James have found several problems:

➤ The Chicago office performs a file transfer to all other servers on the network at that time.

➤ The servers currently do not have any backups running on a regular basis.

➤ And, upon further investigation, they discovered that the server receives stop errors frequently and waits for an administrator.

To improve network performance, Lesha and James decide to start by reconfiguring the Chicago office file transfer.

Project 14.1

To reconfigure the file transfer to occur after normal business hours to prevent bottlenecking, complete the following steps:

1. Open Remote Storage

2. In the console tree, right-click Remote Storage. This displays the current schedule.

3. Click Change Schedule. This displays the File Copy Schedule dialog box.

4. In Schedule Task, click the arrow, and then select an interval.

5. In Start time, set the time by clicking the Up or Down Arrow.

6. Under Schedule Task Daily, in Every, change the value by clicking the Up or Down Arrow, if necessary.

7. To set multiple schedules, select the Show multiple schedules checkbox.

Project 14.2

To schedule a backup, complete the following steps:

1. Open Backup.

2. Click on the Backup tab, click on the Job menu, and then click on New.

3. Select the files and folders you want to back up by selecting the checkbox to the left of a file or folder under Click To Select The Checkbox For Any Drive, Folder, Or File That You Want To Back Up.

4. Select File or a tape device in Backup destination, and then save the file and folder selections by clicking on the Job menu, and then clicking on Save Selections.

5. In Backup media or file name, type a path and file name for the backup file or select a tape.

6. Select any backup options you want, such as the backup type and the log file type, by selecting Tools | Options. When you have finished selecting backup options, click on OK.

7. Click on Start Backup, and make any changes you want to the Backup Job Information dialog box.

8. If you want to set advanced backup options, such as data verification or hardware compression, click on Advanced. When you have finished selecting advanced backup options, click on OK.

9. Click on Schedule in the Backup Job Information dialog box.

10. In the Set Account Information dialog box, enter the user name and password that you want the scheduled backup to run under.

11. In the Scheduled Job Options dialog box, in Job name, type a name for the scheduled backup job, and then click on Properties to set the date, time, and frequency parameters for the scheduled backup. When you have finished, click on OK, and then click on OK again.

Project 14.3

To specify what Windows 2000 does if the system stops unexpectedly, complete the following steps:

1. Open Computer Management (Local).

2. In the console tree, right-click on Computer Management (Local), and then select Properties.

3. On the Advanced tab, click on Startup and Recovery; and under Recovery, select the actions Windows 2000 should perform if a Stop error occurs.

14

CHAPTER FIFTEEN

Practice Test

Question 1

Dan noticed the following Registry key setting: Busmaster:REG_SZ:NO in the HKEY_LOCAL_MACHINE\System\CurrentControlSet\Services\EL59X1\Parameters folder. This key probably exists to solve what problem?

○ a. PCI NIC bus contention

○ b. EIDE bus mastering contention

○ c. Scanner bus mastering contention

○ d. System-level bus mastering contention

Question 2

The NTFS file system contains, at its core, a file called the master file table (MFT). Which of the following statements is not true regarding MFT?

○ a. There is at least one entry in the MFT for every file on an NTFS volume.

○ b. There is one entry in the MFT for the MFT itself.

○ c. NTFS reserves space for the MFT.

○ d. When files are deleted from an NTFS volume, MFT shrinks.

Question 3

To determine the current size of the MFT on a Windows 2000-based computer, use:

○ a. dir /a $mft

○ b. Disk Defragmenter to analyze the NTFS drive, and then click on View Report

○ c. DiskDefrag, and then click on MFT

○ d. dir /s mft

Question 4

You seem to have a "fake system volume," but you are unable to delete it or reformat the partition using Disk Manager. How did you create this fake system volume?

○ a. You upgraded Windows NT 4 Service Pack 3 to Windows 2000 before applying Service Pack 6.

○ b. The original primary partition that you installed Windows 2000 on must have been corrupt.

○ c. You reinstalled Windows 2000 after a disk mirror failure without using an emergency repair procedure, a fault tolerant boot diskette, or the Recovery Console to make either half of the failed mirror bootable.

○ d. You installed Windows 2000 on a FAT32 partition.

Question 5

If your computer is a member of a Windows 2000-based domain and you encrypted the files by using a domain user account, your encrypted files can be recovered by the EFS Recovery Agent for your domain. Which of the following methods can be used for determining who the Recovery Agent is?

○ a. Use the Efsinfo utility to determine who the designated Recovery Agent is for a given file or set of files.

○ b. Use the ERD.

○ c. Logon as the Administrator, and use the Finger command.

○ d. Encrypted Files cannot be recovered.

Question 6

DHCP option inheritance follows a natural hierarchy. The correct order is:

○ a. Default or Server option, Scope option, Class option, Reservation option

○ b. Scope Option, Default or Server option, Class option, Reservation option

○ c. Reservation option, Class option, Scope option, Default or Server option

○ d. Default or Server option, Class Option, Scope option, Reservation option

Question 7

When you view the Scheduled Tasks log file, you see the following error message:

```
The attempt to log on to the account associated with the task failed,
     therefore, the task did not run.
0x80070057: The parameter is incorrect.
Verify that the task's Run-as name and password are valid and try again.
```

The most likely cause of this problem is:

○ a. You typed the user name incorrectly.

○ b. You entered an incorrect password.

○ c. You configured the task to use the System account.

○ d. You configured the task to use the Administrator account.

15

Question 8

When a domain user of a trusted down-level domain starts a Microsoft Management Console (MMC) snap-in, the following error message may be generated in a message box titled Active Directory:

```
Naming information cannot be located because: The specified domain either
    does not exist or could not be contacted. Contact your system adminis-
    trator or verify that your domain is properly configured and is cur-
    rently on-line.
```

The correct way to resolve this problem is:

○ a. Stop the Netlogon service on the domain controller.

○ b. Use Runas.exe.

○ c. Use Alias.exe.

○ d. Stop the Netlogon service on the down-level domain.

Question 9

When you start a Remote Install Service (RIS) client by using the Remote Install boot disk you created with the Remote Boot Floppy Generator (Rbfg.exe), you may receive the following error message:

```
Error: Can't resolve IP address address of the DHCP server
Press a key to reboot system.
```

If you do not have a router, how do you correct this problem?

○ a. Remove the router from the DHCP options #3.

○ b. You must install a router.

○ c. Set your gateway to be the same IP as the DHCP server.

○ d. You need to use an additional NIC card.

Question 10

You may use any of the following methods to change the number of IP hosts on any given subnet except:

○ a. Scope Extension

○ b. Resubnetting

○ c. Superscoping or Multinetting

○ d. Plusnetting

Question 11

To create dynamic updates of Pointer (PTR) records on a classless reverse lookup zone, set the following DNS configuration option:

○ a. DDNS

○ b. DPTR

○ c. CLDR

○ d. It is not possible to perform dynamic updates of DNS records on a classless reverse lookup zone.

Question 12

Which of the following file systems are supported by Windows 2000? [Check all correct answers.]

❑ a. NTFS

❑ b. FAT

❑ c. FAT16

❑ d. FAT32

❑ e. NFS

❑ f. HPFS

❑ g. CDFS

❑ h. NDS

15

Question 13

Carl is currently running Windows NT 4 Server and tries to install Windows 2000 Server, but is unsuccessful. Carl's most likely problem is:

○ a. You cannot install Windows 2000 Server while running NT. Carl should shutdown NT and boot from a bootable diskette before installing Windows 2000 Server.

○ b. The hard drive must be converted from the Windows NT proprietary file system NTFS to FAT before installing Windows 2000.

○ c. You must disable any virus protector before installing Windows 2000.

○ d. You must apply Service Pack 6 to Windows NT before upgrading to Windows 2000.

Question 14

Don creates a new Domain User using Windows 2000 on the Windows 2000 Server. He decides to test the account by trying to log on, but is unsuccessful. What error message did Don most likely encounter?

○ a. Wrong password

○ b. User cannot log on locally

○ c. No user profile

○ d. User must change password

Question 15

The Microsoft recommended RAM requirement for Windows 2000 is:

○ a. 32MB RAM

○ b. 53MB RAM

○ c. 128MB RAM

○ d. 256MB RAM

Question 16

The TCP/IP sliding window can be configured by which of the following methods?

○ a. By adding a Registry key

○ b. Through Control Panel

○ c. Through TCP/IP properties

○ d. Through RIP

Question 17

Which of the following represent a fully qualified domain name (FQDN)?

○ a. server/domain/host name

○ b. **www.microsoft.com**

○ c. **http://www.microsoft.com**

○ d. server/domain/host name

Question 18

The best way to configure a Windows 2000 Server to allow user access from either **www.mycompany.com** or **mycompany.com** is:

○ a. Multihome the server with two NICs to support the two host names **www.mycompany.com** and **mycompany.com**.

○ b. Configure two different IP addresses to one NIC, and then make two record entries in DNS mapping, one IP to **www.mycompany.com** and the other IP to mycompany.com.

○ c. Add a canonical record to the DNS database.

○ d. Purchase a second name from a Domain Name Service.

15

Question 19

You manage a network of 1,500 Microsoft clients all configured to use DHCP. You are asked to implement WINS for NetBIOS name resolution. What is the easiest way to configure these clients to use WINS?

○ a. Configure DHCP Server with options 44 WINS/NBNS and 46 WINS/NBT.

○ b. Configure DHCP Server with option 44 WINS/NBNS only.

○ c. Configure DHCP Server with option 46 WINS/NBT only.

○ d. Configure each client with the IP address of the WINS server.

Question 20

You try to upgrade your computer to Windows 2000 Server but receive an error. Which of the following operating systems will report an error when upgrading to Windows 2000 Server? [Select two.]

❏ a. Windows 95

❏ b. Windows 98

❏ c. Windows NT 4 Service Pack 5

❏ d. Windows NT 4 Service Pack 6

Question 21

How do you convert a Windows NT WINS database to Windows 2000 Server WINS database?

○ a. Copy the contents of the %systemroot%\system32\Wins folder from the Windows NT 4 server to the Windows 2000 server.

○ b. Use WINS Converter Utility.

○ c. You cannot convert a Windows NT WINS database to a Windows 2000 Server WINS database.

○ d. Use WINS database replication.

Question 22

You are the network administrator at a corporation that is upgrading to a Windows 2000 network. You are to install and configure all computers for Windows 2000. You should upgrade all current Windows NT 4 Workstation clients to Windows 2000 Professional. You should upgrade all current Windows NT 4 Server computers to Windows 2000 Server.

Required Requirement: Install a Windows 2000 network with all Windows 2000 Professional clients and Windows 2000 Servers.

Optional Requirements:

1. Choose the fastest way to install all computers, clients, and servers.

2. Use the Microsoft preferred way to install all computers, clients, and servers.

Proposed Solution:

Install Windows 2000 Server on one server, then use Remote Installation Service (RIS) included with Windows 2000 Server to install Windows 2000 Professional and all Windows NT Workstations and install Windows 2000 Server on all Windows NT Servers.

The proposed solution:

○ a. Meets the required and both optional requirements.

○ b. Meets the required but only one of the optional requirements.

○ c. Meets the required and none of the optional requirements.

○ d. Does not meet the required requirement.

Question 23

Which of the following statements is true regarding Silent RIP?

○ a. Silent RIP cannot be configured through the Windows 2000 Server Routing and Remote Access MMC snap-in.

○ b. Silent RIP is not supported in Windows 2000.

○ c. Silent RIP is no longer supported as a Registry enabled feature in Windows 2000 Server.

○ d. Silent RIP is quieter than RIP.

15

Question 24

When you connect your Windows 2000-based client computer to a Windows 2000-based server by using an alias name, you may receive the following error message:

```
System error 52 has occurred.
A duplicate name exists on the network.
```

To correct this problem you should:

○ a. Remove the duplicate name from DNS.

○ b. Use the primary computer name to connect instead of the alias.

○ c. Delete the alias name.

○ d. Change the IP address of the computer with the duplicate name.

Question 25

When attempting to create a Site Server Content Management store on a Windows 2000 Server, the following error may occur:

```
Failed to BeginTransaction on Content Index cache object — Error
      Number=80041820 (-2147215328) String=
```

The most likely problem is:

○ a. The String is blank, which means that you forgot to enter the password.

○ b. The Windows 2000 Server is running low on hard disk space.

○ c. The Indexing Service (formerly called Content Index) is not started.

○ d. The Windows 2000 Server is running low on virtual memory.

Question 26

On Windows 2000 Server, how many routes does RRAS components allow to the same destination?

○ a. 1

○ b. 4

○ c. 10

○ d. 20

Question 27

A domain-based Dfs root must be hosted on a:

○ a. Windows 2000 Domain Controller

○ b. Windows 2000 Server

○ c. Windows 2000 Advanced Server

○ d. Member Server in a Windows 2000 domain

Question 28

When you try to enable Active Desktop in Windows 2000 Server, the option is not available. If you right-click on the desktop, the Active Desktop option does not appear on the menu. In the Folder Options tool in Control Panel, the Enable Web content on my desktop option is unavailable on the General tab. To correct this problem you could:

○ a. Use Terminal Services Configuration to enable active desktop.

○ b. Reload Windows 2000 Server.

○ c. Apply the latest service pack.

○ d. Active Desktop is not available in Windows 2000 Server.

15

Question 29

In Microsoft Windows 2000 Professional, the Shutdown button is available in the Welcome screen after pressing Ctrl+Alt+Delete to log on. What is true about the Shutdown button in Windows 2000 Server?

○ a. In Windows 2000 Server, the Shutdown button is not available by default. To enable the Shutdown button use Group Policy (Local) Microsoft Management Console (MMC) snap-in.

○ b. In Windows 2000 Server, the Shutdown button is available in the Welcome screen after pressing Ctrl+Alt+Delete to log on.

○ c. There is no Shutdown button available in Windows 2000 Server.

○ d. In Windows 2000 Server, the Shutdown button is available by clicking on the Start button, and then selecting Shutdown from the popup menu.

Question 30

How do you enable both Remote Access Services (RAS) multilink connections and Bandwidth Allocation Protocol (BAP) on a RAS server?

○ a. Multilink connections must be manually enabled, but BAP is enabled by default.

○ b. Multilink connections is enabled by default, but you must manually enable BAP.

○ c. You must manually enable both multilink connections and/or BAP.

○ d. Remote Access Services (RAS) multilink connections and Bandwidth Allocation Protocol (BAP) are enabled by default in Windows 2000 Routing and Remote Access Services (RRAS).

Question 31

You have been asked to provide dynamic DNS for your entire network. How many WINS Proxy Agents are required, based on the scenario depicted in the figure below?

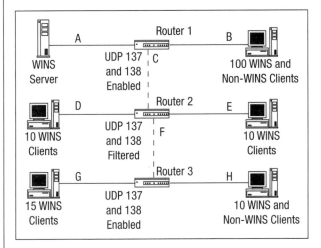

○ a. None

○ b. Two, one on segment H and one on Segment B

○ c. One on each segment

○ d. One for segment H only

Question 32

Which of the following are valid print services that can be installed on a Windows 2000 Server? [Check all correct answers.]

❏ a. Macintosh—Services for Macintosh

❏ b. NetWare—File and Print Services for NetWare

❏ c. Line Printer Daemon Service (LPD)—Services for Unix

❏ d. PostScript

15

Question 33

You currently have the following Microsoft Windows NT 4 file servers:

\\Research\Projects1

\\Research\Projects2

\\Research\Projects3

\\Research\Projects4

Required Requirement:

Add all four file servers to the Dfs tree on Windows 2000 Server

Optional Requirements:

1. Permit any user with the proper security credentials to obtain access to any file on any of the four file servers.

2. Provide for redundancy and load balancing by first trying to find the file server closest to the user requesting the information.

3. If the closest file server is either unavailable or busy, then access the next file server, and so on.

Proposed Solution: Add the Distributed File Systems snap-in to the Microsoft Management Console (MMC), and then add just one share called \\Research\Projects to the Dfs tree.

The proposed solution:

○ a. Meets the required and all optional requirements.

○ b. Meets the required but only one of the optional requirements.

○ c. Meets the required and none of the optional requirements.

○ d. Does not meet the required requirement.

Question 34

You are asked to enable a user or users to run programs that are not installed on the user's workstation computer.

Required requirement:

Allow all users to access the server and application running on the server.

Optional requirement:

1. Host a variety of programs and services, such as a Component Server, Terminal Service Server, Database Server, and E-mail Server.

2. Allow Remote Users access to all applications.

Proposed Solution: Implement a Windows 2000 Program Server to enable users to run programs that are not installed on the user's workstation computer. Install all necessary application and software on the Windows 2000 Server. Use Component Server to add services, such as Terminal Server, Application Load Balancing, Transaction Services, Application Management, and Message Queuing. Terminal Server is an environment that provides remote client access to Windows-based programs running on a Windows 2000 Terminal Server. The Database Server provides a stable platform for running and managing database software, such as Microsoft SQL Server

The proposed solution:

○ a. Meets the required and all optional requirements.

○ b. Meets the required but only one of the optional requirements.

○ c. Meets the required and none of the optional requirements.

○ d. Does not meet the required requirement.

15

Question 35

Often, administrators want to run software on only their Windows 98 clients or their Windows NT Workstation clients. They may not want to run some logon script commands on their Windows NT Server computers or domain controllers.

Required Requirement: Create a batch file that can be used to detect the operating system type.

Optional Requirements:

1. Make the batch file detect Windows 2000 Professional.

2. Make the batch file detect Windows 2000 Server.

3. Make the batch file detect Windows 95.

Proposed solution: You create a batch file as follows:

```
@echo offREM Batch file to detect OSREM --
if Windows_NT == %OS% goto WINNT
echo You are not running Windows NT (Windows 95/98 perhaps?)goto END:WINNT
gettype.exeif errorlevel=9 goto FILENOTFOUNDecho You are running Windows NT.
echo More Specifically:echo.if ERRORLEVEL=8 goto EIGHTif ERRORLEVEL=7 goto
     SEVEN
if ERRORLEVEL=6 goto SIXif ERRORLEVEL=5 goto FIVEif ERRORLEVEL=4 goto FOUR
if ERRORLEVEL=3 goto THREEif ERRORLEVEL=2 goto TWOif ERRORLEVEL=1 goto ONE
:FILENOTFOUNDecho.echo Gettype not found.echo.goto END:EIGHT
echo Windows NT Enterprise/Terminal Server Non-Domain Controllergoto
     END:SEVEN
echo Windows NT Enterprise/Terminal Server Domain Controllergoto END:SIX
echo Windows 2000 Server Domain Controllergoto END:FIVE
echo Windows NT Server Domain Controllergoto END:FOUR
echo Windows 2000 Server Non-Domain Controllergoto END:THREE
echo Windows NT Server Non-Domain Controllergoto END:TWO
echo Windows 2000 Professional installationgoto END:ONE
echo Windows NT Workstationgoto END:ENDpause
```

(continued)

Question 35 *(continued)*

The proposed solution:

○ a. Meets the required and all optional requirements.

○ b. Meets the required but only one of the optional requirements.

○ c. Meets the required and none of the optional requirements.

○ d. Does not meet the required requirement.

Question 36

When you connect a Microsoft Windows 2000 Server-based computer and a second computer to a manual switch that allows you to shift keyboard, monitor, and mouse input from one computer to the other, your Microsoft serial mouse works normally at first. However, after you switch the input from the Windows 2000 Server-based computer to the other computer and then back, the mouse stops working (hangs).

Required Requirement: Correct the problem as stated.

Optional Requirement: Use Windows 2000 Server support to utilize the manual switch boxes.

Proposed Solution: Open the file %WINDIR%\Inf\Msmouse.inf in Notepad. In the [Ser_Inst.HW.AddReg] section, remove the semicolon (;) from the following line:

```
; HKR,,''WaitEventMask'',0x00010001,0xFFFFFFFF
```

Save the file, and then quit Notepad. In Control Panel, double-click on System, and then click on the Hardware tab. Click on Device Manager, and then remove the serial mouse. On the Action menu, click on Scan For Hardware Changes to reinstall the mouse.

The proposed solution:

○ a. Meets the required and optional requirement.

○ b. Does not meet the required or optional requirement.

○ c. Meets the required but not the optional requirement.

○ d. Does not meet the required requirement but meets the optional requirement.

15

Question 37

How do default security settings in a clean installation of Windows 2000 compare to computers upgraded from Windows NT 4?

- ○ a. They are the same.
- ○ b. Computers upgraded from Windows NT 4 do not use the new default security settings. Instead, all existing security settings are maintained.
- ○ c. Clean installs default to highest security.
- ○ d. Upgrade installs default to lowest security.

Question 38

How do default groups compare between a Windows 2000 Server configured as a Member Server and a Windows 2000 Server configured as a Domain Controller?

- ○ a. Windows 2000 Server (configured as a Member Server) contains Users, Power Users, and Account Operators, but not Server Operators.
- ○ b. Windows 2000 Server (configured as a Domain Controller) contains Users, Server Operators, and Account Operators, but not Power Users.
- ○ c. They both contain the same groups.
- ○ d. Windows 2000 Server (configured as a Domain Controller) contains all the groups in Windows 2000 Server (configured as a Member Server) plus Server Operators and Account Operators.

Question 39

You have a network with Microsoft clients and NetWare servers.

Required Requirement: Allow Microsoft clients to access the NetWare servers.

Optional Requirement:

1. Minimize time and effort.

2. Do not require any additional software to be loaded on the client.

Proposed Solution: Use Windows Component wizard to install GSNW on the Windows 2000 Server, allowing the server to act as an NCP gateway to NetWare networks, allowing Microsoft (SMB) clients access to NetWare resources using the gateway.

The proposed solution:

○ a. Meets the required and all optional requirements.

○ b. Meets the required but only one of the optional requirements.

○ c. Meets the required and none of the optional requirements.

○ d. Does not meet the required requirement.

Question 40

The Microsoft Management Console (MMC) snap-ins for remote DNS, DHCP, or WINS administration are not listed on the Start menu of your Windows 2000 Server, but you want to administer these services running on another server. You should:

○ a. Install DNS, DHCP, and WINS on the server that you wish to use to administer these services.

○ b. Only administer these services from the server that currently has them installed.

○ c. Install these tools by double-clicking on the adminpak.msi file in the I386 folder on the Windows 2000 Server or Windows 2000 Advanced Server CD. Respond to the prompts as appropriate. The administration tools then appear on the Start menu in the Programs group as Administrative Tools.

○ d. Install these tools by double-clicking on the adminpak.msi file in the I386 folder on the Windows 2000 Server or Windows 2000 Professional CD. Respond to the prompts as appropriate. The administration tools then appear on the Start menu in the Programs group as Administrative Tools.

15

Note: Case studies are a new testing technique Microsoft uses in some of its tests. Although you probably won't encounter case studies in the Core Four exams, a case study is included in this practice test because it is a valuable way to reinforce the material you've learned.

Case Study 1

Problem Statement

Description: Your company has 30 users running Windows 2000 Professional, one Windows 2000 Server, Server1, configured as the PDC and a second Windows 2000 Server, Server2, configured as the File and Print server. Your company has purchased 10 internet addresses from the local Internet Service Provider (ISP). You need to provide Internet access to all 30 users and also provide external access to the file server for a couple of preferred customers.

Plan: Because your company has only 10 public Internet addresses but requires Internet access for 300 clients, the IT department recommends configuring all 30 client computers to access the Internet using NAT. The IT department will purchase, install, and configure a new Windows 2000 Server, Server3, as the NAT server that will provide all Internet access. The IT department states that NAT will provide the following benefits:

➤ Enable multiple users to use a single Internet connection

➤ Provide DHCP and DNS

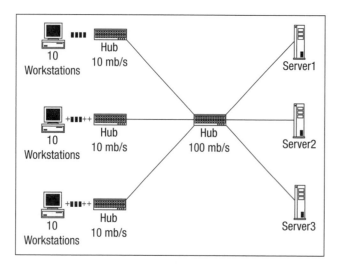

NAT Installation

Description: Use Routing and Remote Access to install NAT. Double-click on Server3, the name of the server to become the NAT server. Click on the plus sign next to IP Routing to show General. Right-click on General, click on New Routing Protocol, click on Network Address Translation (NAT), and then click on OK.

NAT Configuration

Description: Use Routing and Remote Access to install NAT. Double-click on Server3, the name of the NAT server that you wish to configure. Click on the plus sign next to IP Routing to show Network Address Translation (NAT). Right-click on Network Address Translation (NAT), and then click on Properties to set Configuration Options.

General

> Log errors only [default]
>
> Log errors and warnings
>
> Log the maximum amount of information
>
> Disable event logging
>
> Translation
>
> Remove TCP mappings after [default = 1,440 minutes (24 hours)]
>
> Remove UDP mappings after [default = 1 minute]
>
> Reset Defaults
>
> Applications
>
> Address Assignment
>
> Automatically assign IP addresses by using DHCP
>
>> IP Address
>>
>> Mask
>>
>> Exclude
>
> Name Resolution
>
> Resolve IP addresses for clients using Domain Name System (DNS)
>
> Connect to the public network when a name needs to be resolved
>
>> Demand-dial interface

15

Router Interface Installation

Description: Use Routing and Remote Access to add an interface to the NAT routing protocol. Double-click on Server3, the name of the NAT server that you wish to configure. Click on the plus sign next to IP Routing to show Network Address Translation (NAT). Right-click on Network Address Translation (NAT), and then click on New Interface. Set the interface type on the General tab, and then click on OK.

General

Public interface connected to the Internet

Translate TCP/UDP headers

Private interface connected to private network

Router Interface Configuration

Description: Use Routing and Remote Access to configure the interface. Double-click on Server3, the name of the NAT server that you wish to configure. Click on the plus sign next to IP Routing to show Network Address Translation (NAT). Click on Network Address Translation (NAT). In the details pane, right-click on the connection to configure, and then click on Properties.

General

Private interface connected to private network

Public interface connected to the Internet

Translate TCP/UDP headers

Address Pool

Add

Start address of address pool

End address of address pool

Subnet Mask

Reservation

Public IP address to reserve

Private IP address to receive

Allow incoming sessions to this address

Special Ports

Protocol

>TCP

>UDP

Add Special Port

>On this interface

>On this address pool entry

>Incoming Port

>Private Address

>Outgoing Port

Using NAT

Process: When a computer running NAT receives a packet from an internal client, it replaces the packet header and translates the client's port number and internal IP address to its own port number and external IP address. It then sends the packet to the destination host on the Internet and keeps track of the mapping information in a table, so it can route the reply to the client computer. When the NAT computer receives a reply from the Internet host, it replaces the packet header and sends it on to the client.

Advantages: NAT enabled the 10 users to share 30 Internet connections in this case. NAT provides both DNS and DHCP. NAT provides comprehensive protocol support, such as PPTP. NAT reduces IP address registration costs and conceals internal IP addresses from external networks, such as the Internet. NAT provides security that standard routers that do not support NAT cannot provide. Both NAT and Proxy Server allow Internet connections, restrict access to internal IP addresses, translate IP addresses and require client configuration but NAT does not require knowledge of the higher layer protocol.

Disadvantages: NAT and Internet Connection Sharing provide the same capabilities and both are supported by Windows 2000, but Internet Connection Sharing is much easier to configure. NAT is more processor intensive because of the translation process. NAT does not support all protocols. NAT translates the computer's IP address in the packet header, which prevents the use of Internet Protocol Security (IPSec).

15

Question 41.1

What must you do to configure NAT to allow an application to establish connections with a NAT client on port 27960?

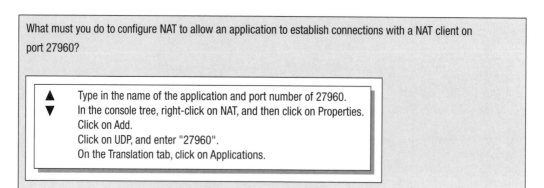

▲
▼
    Type in the name of the application and port number of 27960.
In the console tree, right-click on NAT, and then click on Properties.
Click on Add.
Click on UDP, and enter "27960".
On the Translation tab, click on Applications.

Question 41.2

Connect the option with the tab that it appears on.

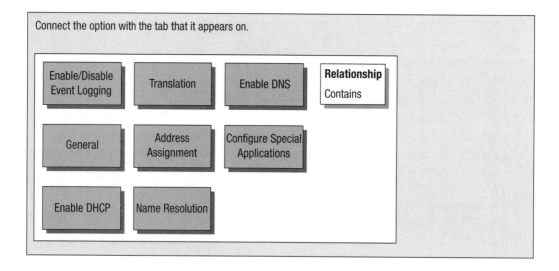

| Enable/Disable Event Logging | Translation | Enable DNS | **Relationship** Contains |

| General | Address Assignment | Configure Special Applications |

| Enable DHCP | Name Resolution |

Question 41.3

Connect the option with the tab that it appears on.

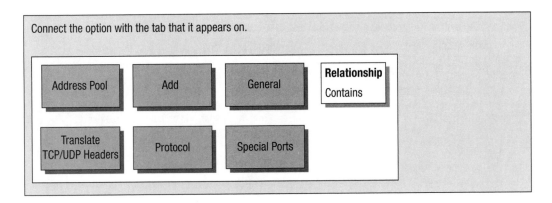

Question 41.4

Drag the correct computer label to each computer in the drawing. Some labels may be used more than once. Not all labels need to be used.

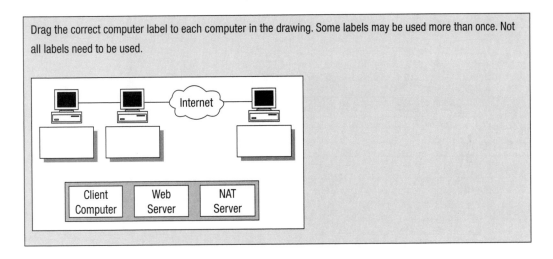

Question 41.5

When a server running NAT receives a packet from an internal client, it replaces the packet header and translates the client's port number and internal IP address to its own port number and external IP address. What does it do with the original header information?

○ a. Discards original information

○ b. Writes original information to a separate header, encrypts the header, and attaches it to the packet

○ c. Sends the original information back to the internal client

○ d. Keeps the original information in a local table

Question 41.6

Which of the following are features or benefits of using NAT? [Check all correct answers.]

❏ a. Provides DHCP

❏ b. Provides DNS

❏ c. Allows multiple users to share single connections to the Internet

❏ d. Provides comprehensive protocol support

Question 41.7

Which of the following are true of NAT? [Select two.]

❏ a. NAT costs slightly more to implement than non-NAT networks.

❏ b. NAT reduces IP address registration costs.

❏ c. NAT conceals internal IP addresses from external networks.

❏ d. NAT conceals external IP addresses from internal networks.

Question 41.8

Which of the following is true of NAT? [Check all correct answers.]

❏ a. NAT provides security that a standard router does not.

❏ b. NAT uses IPSec.

❏ c. NAT is more processor intensive than routing.

❏ d. NAT support all protocols.

Question 41.9

Which statement is true about NAT and Proxy Server?

○ a. Both NAT and Proxy Server provide connection to the Internet, but only NAT restricts access to internal IP addresses.

○ b. Both NAT and Proxy Server translate addresses.

○ c. Clients must be configured to use NAT, but not Proxy Server.

○ d. Both NAT and Proxy Server require knowledge of the higher layer protocol.

Question 41.10

Which statement is true when comparing NAT to Internet Connection Sharing?

○ a. Internet Connection Sharing and NAT do not provide the same capabilities.

○ b. NAT is much easier to configure than Internet Connection Sharing.

○ c. Internet Connection Sharing is much easier to configure than NAT.

○ d. Windows 2000 supports NAT, but not Internet Connection Sharing.

15

CHAPTER SIXTEEN

Answer Key

1. a	21. a	41.1 *
2. d	22. d	41.2 *
3. b	23. c	41.3 *
4. c	24. b	41.4 *
5. a	25. c	41.5 d
6. a	26. a	41.6 a, b, c, d
7. c	27. d	41.7 b,c
8. b	28. a	41.8 a,c
9. a	29. a	41.9 b
10. d	30. d	41.10 c
11. d	31. d	
12. a, b, c, d, g	32. a, b, c	
13. c	33. a	* For asterisked items, please
14. b	34. a	see graphical representation
15. d	35. a	of answer on the appropriate
16. a	36. c	page within this chapter.
17. b	37. b	
18. c	38. b	
19. a	39. d	
20. a,b	40. c	

Question 1

The correct answer is a. As a test procedure or if you are experiencing bus conten-tion with your 3Com 3C590 PCI or 3c595 (10/100 mb/sec) network cards, you can disable bus mastering to alleviate busmaster contention or to test whether busmaster contention is the cause of your problems. This procedure can also be used with other PCI bus Network Interface Cards.

Question 2

The correct answer is d. Because utilities that defragment NTFS volumes cannot move MFT entries and because excessive fragmentation of the MFT can impact performance, NTFS reserves space for the MFT in an effort to keep the MFT as contiguous as possible as it grows. As files are added to an NTFS volume, more entries are added to the MFT and so the MFT grows. When files are deleted from an NTFS volume, their MFT entries are marked as free and may be reused, but the MFT does not shrink. Thus, space used by these entries is not reclaimed from the disk.

Question 3

The correct answer is b. To determine the current size of the MFT on a Windows NT-based computer, type the following command on an NTFS volume: "**dir /a $mft**". To determine the current size of the MFT on a Windows 2000-based computer, use Disk Defragmenter to analyze the NTFS drive, and then click on View Report. This displays the drive statistics, including the current MFT size and number of fragments. Note that the results returned by the DIR command may not be current. The size reported by the DIR command may reflect cached data that reflects the size of the MFT at the time the system was started following an orderly shutdown.

Because of the importance of the MFT to NTFS and the possible impact on performance if this file becomes highly fragmented, NTFS makes a special effort to keep this file contiguous. NTFS reserves a percentage of the volume for exclusive use of the MFT until and unless the remainder of the volume is completely used up. Thus, space for files and directories will not be allocated from this MFT zone until all other space is allocated first.

Depending on the average file size and other variables, either the reserved MFT zone or the unreserved space on the disk may be used up before the other as the disk fills to capacity. Volumes with a small number of relatively large files will exhaust the unreserved space first, whereas volumes with a large number of rela-tively small files will exhaust the MFT zone space first. In either case, fragmentation of the MFT starts to take place when one region or the other becomes full. If the unreserved space becomes full, space for user files and directories will start to be allocated from the MFT zone competing with the MFT for allocation. If the MFT zone becomes full, space for new MFT entries will be allocated from the remainder of the disk, again competing with other files. With this hotfix, Windows NT can better accommodate volumes that must hold a large number of small files. A new Registry parameter is being introduced that can increase the percentage of a volume that NTFS will reserve for its master file table. NtfsMftZoneReservation is a REG_DWORD value in the HKEY_LOCAL_MACHINE\System\ CurrentControlSet\Control\FileSystem folder that can take on a value between 1 and 4, where 1 corresponds to the minimum MFT zone size and 4 corresponds to the maximum. If the parameter is not specified or an invalid value is supplied, NTFS will use a default value of 1 for this parameter. The exact ratios that correspond to each setting are undocumented because they are not standardized and may change in future releases.

Question 4

The correct answer is c. Any of the following three situations may create a fake system volume:

➤ After manually breaking a "system" partition mirror on a dynamic disk, the shadow drive erroneously remains flagged as a system partition in the LDM private region database.

➤ The system partition was originally located on a dynamic disk and was mirrored using Windows 2000 mirroring to another dynamic disk. If the mirror fails for any reason and both halves becomes unbootable, you may be forced to reinstall Windows 2000 from scratch. Doing so creates a new system volume, but the surviving dynamic disk database still has references to the original system volume partition. This creates a condition of having two different system partitions on separate drives.

➤ A dynamic disk set that contained a system partition was imported into the current system. The dynamic disk set imported still has the system partition flagged in the LDM private region database.

Before deciding to reinstall Windows 2000 after a disk mirror failure, try using emergency repair procedures, a fault tolerant boot diskette, or the Recovery Console to make either half of the failed mirror bootable. Once you have a bootable system partition, you can resync or reestablish the mirror. Note that this prevents the problem described in this question from occurring.

16

Question 5

The correct answer is a. If your computer is a member of a Windows 2000-based domain and you encrypted the files by using a domain user account, your encrypted files can be recovered by the EFS Recovery Agent for your domain. You can contact your system administrator or if you have access to the Microsoft Windows 2000 Resource Kit, you can use the Efsinfo utility to determine who the designated Recovery Agent is for a given file or set of files.

If your computer is not a member of a Windows 2000-based domain (it is a stand-alone server or a member of a Microsoft Windows NT 4-based domain), your local, built-in Administrator account may be the designated Recovery Agent for any users of your computer. To be able to recover encrypted information on a computer in this case, you must have backed up the Recovery Agent's private key before the loss of the key.

Question 6

The correct answer is a. DHCP option inheritance follows a natural hierarchy: default or server option, scope option, class option, reservation option. The option types are listed from least specific to most specific. A more specific option always takes precedence over a less specific option. Therefore, a scope option takes precedence over a server option. Normally, you can set more specific options at each level, and then remove them when necessary. When you remove a more specific option (for example, Scope Option 044 - WINS Servers), any less specific option then takes effect (for example, Server Option 044 - WINS Servers).

Question 7

The correct answer is c. When you create or modify a task in the Scheduled Tasks tool to use the System account, the task does not run as scheduled. This issue occurs because you cannot configure a task to use the System account using the Scheduled Tasks tool. To resolve this issue, run the Jt.exe program contained in the Microsoft Windows 2000 Resource Kit Supplement 1; <path>jt.exe /SC "" NULL where <path> is the location of the Jt.exe file.

Question 8

The correct answer is b. This issue occurs because MMC snap-ins are designed to connect to a domain controller for the logged on user or if the Netlogon service is not started on the domain controller. To work around this issue, if the Netlogon service is not started on the domain controller, start it. Otherwise, use any of the following methods:

Use command-line options to specify the default domain controller with which to make a connection.

Use the Runas.exe tool to configure the MMC snap-in to change the context of the user.

After you click on OK following the error message, you may change the focus of the MMC snap-in to a Windows 2000-based domain controller.

Question 9

The correct answer is a. This problem can occur if your default gateway (router), defined in the DHCP lease (option 3), is unavailable. To work around this problem if your router is unavailable, return it to operable status before attempting to set up RIS clients. Note that if you do not have a router, remove the router from the DHCP options, option 3.

The RIS client disk always attempts to communicate through the default gateway (if the default gateway is configured) to connect to RIS. This occurs even if the RIS and DHCP server are on the same subnet that the computer is on.

However, this is not true for computers that support Preboot Execution Environment (PXE) in BIOS or Boot ROM. Only certain PCI-based network adapters are supported currently and they are listed in the Rbfg.exe utility that creates the boot disk. This utility is in the %systemroot%\system32\reminst folder. Click on Rbfg.exe, and then click on the adapter list button in the Remote Boot Disk Generator screen to see the supported adapters.

You cannot add additional network adapters to the RIS Boot disk. Microsoft adds additional network adapters over time and makes the updates in the Rbfg.exe tool available through normal distribution channels, such as the Internet, Windows Update, and future service pack or feature pack updates.

Question 10

The correct answer is d. If you already have a DHCP scope and the Start Address and End Address do not currently include all addresses for your given subnet, you can increase the number of addresses in the scope by extending the Start Address or End Address in the scope properties.

The following example shows a Class C network with the following settings:

Subnet Address: 192.168.1.0

Subnet Mask: 255.255.255.0

This example yields a network of 254 hosts that occupy the range of addresses from 192.168.1.1 to 1921.68.1.254.

16

The scope you created has the following properties:

Start Address: 192.168.1.50

End Address: 192.168.1.150

Subnet Mask: 255.255.255.0

To increase the number of addresses available to clients, you can change either the Start Address or End Address as far as 1 and 254, respectively.

If your scope already covers the entire range and is fully used, you only have two other options: superscoping or resubnetting. Both of these options require you to make architectural changes to your network. Simply changing the DHCP scope parameters does not give you more leases. DHCP runs on top of your network subnet architecture and can hand out addresses however you want. Always treat the need to expand address ranges as a subnet architecture exercise first and foremost. After you decide which architecture to use, you can configure DHCP to conform to your network design.

Resubnetting is the recommended procedure for increasing a DHCP scope when the current scope has entirely consumed the current subnet mask. However, this method requires you to change all subnet hosts and gateways. If you have an address range that has run out of available host addresses, you may be able to change the subnet mask to include a larger share of host addresses. But simply changing the subnet mask requires that all routers and other statically assigned computers be reconfigured and all DHCP clients have renewed their lease obtaining the new parameters.

Additionally, the entire DHCP scope or scopes must first be deleted and then re-created using the new subnet mask. The potential for duplicate addresses exists during this period if you do not take steps to prevent leasing addresses that other clients may use. Despite all of the aforementioned caveats, resubnetting is still the recommended procedure. The resubnetting configuration creates no additional overhead on the subnet routers or gateways, and keeps all hosts on the same broadcast address.

The following example shows a depleted subnet with the following settings:

Subnet Address: 192.168.1.0

Subnet Mask: 255.255.255.0

This yields a network of 254 hosts with addresses from 192.168.1.1 to 1921.68.1.254.

The following example shows the result if you use the resubnetting option:

Subnet Address: 192.168.1.0

Subnet Mask: 255.255.254.0

You now have a network of 510 hosts with addresses from 192.168.1.1 to 1921.68.2.254, or 256 newly available DHCP addresses.

Before: ————192.168.1.0/24————R————192.168.5.0/24————

After: ————192.168.1.0/23————R————192.168.5.0/24————

Superscoping (also referred to as *multinetting*) may meet your requirements. If you do not want to change the subnetting of an existing network, you can add additional logical networks to the same physical wire. This puts an additional burden on the router or gateway configured with multiple logical subnets running on a single physical port. The additional burden may result in reduced network performance. Hosts on one logical subnet must be routed through the gateway to communicate with hosts on the other logical subnet, despite sharing the same physical wire.

The following example shows a depleted subnet with the following settings:

Subnet Address: 192.168.1.0

Subnet Mask: 255.255.255.0

The following example shows the results if you use the superscoping option:

Subnet Address: 192.168.1.0 and 192.168.2.0

Subnet Mask: 255.255.255.0

You now have two networks of 254 hosts (508 hosts total) with addresses from 192.168.1.1 to 192.168.1.254 and 192.168.2.1 to 192.168.2.254, or 254 newly available DHCP addresses.

Before: ——192.168.1.0/24————R——192.168.5.0/24————

After: ——192.168.1.0/24 and 192.168.2.0/24——R——192.168.5.0/24————

After you decide which option you want to use, you can choose the corresponding DHCP configuration.

If you use the resubnetting option, you need to delete and re-create the DHCP scope with the new subnet mask (it is not possible to change only the mask for a particular scope). If you are servicing existing clients within a portion of this range, you should turn on conflict detection until all your clients are migrated into the new scope. This action requires you to perform the following steps:

16

1. Configure the interface of each connected router and change the IP address for the connected interface, its subnet address, and its subnet mask.

2. Delete your current DHCP scope.

3. Create a new DHCP scope with the new subnet mask.

4. Enable the Conflict Retries option on the DHCP server (set to 1 or 2).

5. Force your DHCP clients to renew their DHCP leases.

6. Change the IP address, subnet mask, and/or default gateway on each statically-configured host.

When you use the superscoping option, you need to superscope a number of scopes together. Create each scope individually, and then create a superscope to incorporate the individual scopes. This action requires you to perform the following steps:

1. Add secondary IP addresses to the current router interfaces.

2. Create a new DHCP scope for the new logical subnet.

3. Create a superscope and add the old and new DHCP scopes as children.

Question 11

The correct answer is d. Domain Name System (DNS) dynamic updates of Pointer (PTR) records cannot be performed on a classless reverse lookup zone. To create PTR records in a reverse lookup zone, follow these steps on the parent and child DNS servers:

1. On the Parent DNS Server, Create a nonsubnetted reverse lookup zone. For example, if you have subnetted your 192.168.1.0 network into two subnets, 192.168.1.0-127 and 192.168.1.128-255, and you want to create reverse lookup zones for the first subnet, create a reverse lookup zone for 192.168.1.0. The zone name is 1.168.192.in-addr.arpa.

2. Right-click on the new zone, and then click on New Delegation.

3. Click on Next. In the Delegated Domain box, type 0/25, where 0 is the subnet address and 25 is the number of bits used for subnetting.

4. Click on Next. Add the child DNS server's name and address when you are prompted, click on OK, and then click on Finish.

5. Right-click on the parent zone (not the delegated zone), and then click on New Alias.

6. Type the alias (the last octet of the IP address). For example, type "1" for a host with an IP address of 192.168.1.1.

7. In the Fully Qualified Domain Name box, type the cname value. For example, type "1.0/25.1.168.192.in-addr.arpa", and then click on OK.

8. Repeat steps 6 through 8 for every host that needs to be added.

9. On the child DNS server, create a subnetted reverse lookup zone. For example, 0/25.1.168.192.in-addr.arpa.

10. Create PTR records for every host under the new zone. In the Host IP Number box, type the last octet of the IP address. In the Host Name box, type the fully qualified domain name of the host.

Question 12

The correct answers are a, b, c, d, and g. Windows 2000 supports FAT16, FAT32, and NTFS. FAT is assumed to be FAT16 unless otherwise stated; therefore both FAT and FAT16 refer to the same file system for this question. CDFS is the file system used for CD-ROMs and is supported by Windows 2000. NFS is a Unix proprietary file system. NDS is a Novell NetWare proprietary file system. Gateway services and third-party software allows Windows 2000 to access NDS and NFS, but native Windows 2000 does not support these file systems. Support for creating high-performance file system (HPFS) partitions is not available in Windows 2000. HPFS partitions must be removed before running Setup. IBM's OS/2 supports HPFS.

Question 13

The correct answer is c. You may receive errors if you try to install Windows 2000 while virus software is running. Microsoft recommends disabling any and all virus software before installing Windows 2000, and then enabling the virus software after installation.

Question 14

The correct answer is b. By default, domain users are not allowed to log on locally to a server. To test the new domain user account, log in to the domain from a Windows 2000 Professional machine. You can add the right to log on locally to server by editing user rights.

Question 15

The correct answer is d. Microsoft recommends 256MB RAM for Windows 2000 Server and 128MB RAM for Windows 2000 Professional. Assume that the question refers to Server for the exam, unless it specifically states Professional.

16

Question 16

The correct answer is a. You must add the TCP/IP Sliding Window key to the Registry before you can configure TCP/IP sliding window parameters. ForwardBufferMemory defines how much data can be stored; the default is 72,240. If the IPEnableRouter setting is 0, this parameter is ignored. NumForwardPackets defines the number of packets in the queue. TcpWindowSize defines the amount of data that can be outstanding on the network before acknowledgment; the default is 8,760 (six Ethernet packets). DefaultTTL is the default time to live of a packet in number of seconds. The Registry settings used to tune TCP/IP are located in the HKEY_LOCAL_MACHINE\SYSTEM\CurrentControlSet\Services\Tcpip\Parameters subkey. They are all DWORD entries.

Question 17

The correct answer is b. The unique name of the host, representing its position in the hierarchy, is called its *fully qualified domain name* (FQDN). An FQDN has the format server name.domain or subdomain.top-level domain. FQDN always uses periods to separate server name, domains, subdomain, and top-level domain.

Question 18

The correct answer is c. A cname, or canonical name, allows for an alias to a host. For instance, you can type "www.msn.com" or "msn.com" in your Web browser to reach the same Web page. In this case, the first answer record indicates that the name **msn.com** is actually a cname, or canonical name (alias) for the host name **www.msn.com**. The second answer record lists the IP address for that host, for example, 207.46.176.152.

Question 19

The correct answer is a. If you are using DHCP to configure WINS clients, be sure to set both options #44 WINS Servers and #46 Node Type. These options allow DHCP-configured computers to find and use the WINS server automatically. Although answer d would also work, it is not the easiest or best way to implement WINS for NetBIOS name resolution because you must configure each client computer. Making one configuration change to the DHCP server is preferred.

Question 20

The correct answers are a and b. When you run Winnt32.exe to upgrade a Microsoft Windows 95-based or Microsoft Windows 98-based computer to Windows 2000, you may receive the following message:

Windows 2000 Setup does not support upgrading from Windows 98 (or Windows 95) to Microsoft Windows 2000 Server.

You receive this message if you are trying to upgrade Windows 95 or Windows 98 to Windows 2000 Server, Advanced Server, or Datacenter server. Only Windows 2000 Professional supports upgrading from Windows 95 or Windows 98.

Question 21

The correct answer is a. The conversion may occur automatically for Windows NT 4 WINS databases. To attempt this, follow these three steps:

1. Type "net stop wins" on the Windows 2000 and Windows NT 4 servers.

2. Copy the contents of the %systemroot%\system32\Wins folder from the Windows NT 4 server to the Windows 2000 server.

3. Type "net start wins" on both servers. A message appears stating that the conversion process is taking place.

During the conversion process, you may be prompted for an additional file from the Windows 2000 Server CD. If this occurs, follow these three steps:

1. Copy the Edb500.dl_ file from the I386 folder on the CD to the %systemroot%\system32 folder on the server.

2. Expand the Edb500.dl_ file on the server by typing "expand edb500.dl_ edb500.dll".

3. Type "net start wins" to finish the conversion process.

Question 22

The correct answer is d. The Remote Installation Service (RIS) included with Windows 2000 Server is designed to install Microsoft Windows 2000 Professional clients. This service does not allow Windows 2000 Server to be installed using RIS. Because the proposed solution does not install the Servers, the required requirement is not met.

Question 23

The correct answer is c. Silent RIP is no longer supported as a Registry enabled feature in Windows 2000 Server. You can configure all RIP functionality in Windows 2000 Server in the Routing and Remote Access MMC snap-in. TCP/IP hosts have the capability to listen to the routing protocol traffic used by routers. This is known as *eavesdropping* or *wiretapping*. Eavesdropping hosts have the same routing information as the routers. An example of eavesdropping is Silent RIP. Silent RIP is the capability of a TCP/IP host to listen to RIP for IP routing traffic exchanged by RIP routers and update its routing table.

Question 24

The correct answer is b. This problem can occur when you try to connect to the server by using a cname alias created in the DNS zone. For example, with a command similar to this: net view *alias.domain name*.com (where *alias* is a cname record created for the server in the *domain name*.com zone), the server is not "listening" on the alias, and because of this, it is not accepting connections to that name. Use the primary computer name to connect instead of the alias.

Question 25

The correct answer is c. The cause of this problem is the Indexing Service (formerly called *Content Index*) is not started. In Windows NT 4, the Content Index Service installed with the Windows NT Option Pack (Internet Information Server 4.0) was set to start automatically. By default with Windows 2000 Server, the Indexing Service is set to start manually. To correct this problem in Windows 2000 Server, perform the following steps:

1. Log on as an Administrator.

2. Select Start | Programs | Administrative Tools, and then click on Services.

3. Scroll through the list of services, and right-click on Indexing Service. Select Properties.

4. Locate the Startup type section near the center of the window, and change it to Automatic.

5. Click on Start to start the service.

6. Click on OK to exit.

7. Rerun the makecm.vbs to create your Content store.

Question 26

The correct answer is a. When you configure a Microsoft Windows 2000 Server-based computer to accept incoming calls, you cannot configure the following redundancy features of Transmission Control Protocol/Internet Protocol (TCP/IP): Dead Gateway Detection and Accepting ICMP Redirects from Routers. This behavior occurs because, when you configure an incoming connection in Windows

2000 Server, the operating system enables Routing and Remote Access service (RRAS) components. RRAS components on Windows 2000 Server allow only one route to the same destination. To resolve this issue, install the RIP Listener (Silent RIP) component if the network uses Routing Information Protocol (RIP) routing protocols to provide the server with knowledge of redundant network paths. You can also use a router-based redundancy solution, such as the Virtual Router Redundancy Protocol (VRRP), to provide these features. If Microsoft Windows CE synchronization is the reason you need the incoming connection, use ActiveSync 3.0. This version does not use incoming connections and does not exhibit this behavior.

Question 27

The correct answer is d. Note there was an error on this information in the Server Distributed Systems Guide. On page 1007, the first bulleted item incorrectly states that a domain-based Dfs root has to be hosted on a Windows 2000 domain controller. Microsoft issued this change: "It must be hosted on a Member Server in a Windows 2000 domain."

Question 28

The correct answer is a. When you try to enable Active Desktop in Windows 2000 Server, the option is not available. If you right-click on the desktop, the Active Desktop option does not appear on the menu. In the Folder Options tool in Control Panel, the Enable Web content on my desktop option is unavailable on the General tab. This behavior can occur if Terminal Services is installed on the Windows 2000-based server and the Disable Active Desktop option is enabled for Terminal Services clients in the Terminal Services Configuration tool. When this option is enabled, the Active Desktop settings are also disabled on the local computer. To be able to view Active Desktop content on the Windows 2000-based server with Terminal Services installed, enable the Active Desktop for the Terminal Server clients. To enable this feature, follow these three steps:

1. Select Start | Programs | Administrative Tools, and then click on Terminal Services Configuration.

2. In the Terminal Services Configuration tool, click on Server Settings in the left pane. Client configuration options appear in the right pane. Right-click on Active Desktop, and then click on Enable, or double-click on Active Desktop, and then clear the Disable Active Desktop checkbox. Click on OK.

3. Log the current user off the Windows 2000-based server, and then log back on for the change to take effect.

16

Question 29

The correct answer is a. In Microsoft Windows 2000 Professional, the Shutdown button is available in the Welcome screen after pressing Ctrl+Alt+Delete to log on. However, in Windows 2000 Server, the Shutdown button is not available by default. To enable the Shutdown button, follow these steps:

1. Start the Group Policy (Local) Microsoft Management Console (MMC) snap-in.

2. Double-click on the following items to open them: Local Computer Policy, Computer Configuration, Windows Settings, Security Settings, Local Policies, and Security Options.

3. Double-click on Allow System To Be Shutdown Without Having To Logon, and then change the local policy to Enabled.

4. Click on OK.

The change takes effect when you restart the computer.

Question 30

The correct answer is d.

Remote Access Services (RAS) multilink connections and Bandwidth Allocation Protocol (BAP) are enabled by default in Windows 2000 Routing and Remote Access Services (RRAS). You can view or modify general server settings and specific policy profile settings from the RAS server. Specific policy profile settings are configured to use server settings by default. To view or edit server settings:

1. Start RRAS.

2. In the console tree, double-click on Routing and Remote Access.

3. Right-click on the server for which you want to enable multilink connections and BAP/Bandwidth Allocation Control Protocol (BACP), and then click on Properties.

4. Click on PPP to view or edit the server settings.

To view or edit specific remote access policies:

1. Start RRAS.

2. In the console tree, double-click on Routing and Remote Access.

3. Double-click on Remote Access Policies, and then click on a policy in the right pane.

4. Right-click on the policy, and then click on Properties.

5. Click on Edit Profile, and then click on Multilink.

Question 31

The correct answer is d. Only segment H requires WINS proxy agent. Router 2 filters broadcasts from non-WINS clients on segment H before they reach WINS server on A. Segment B does not require a WINS proxy agent because Router 1 will forward broadcast to segment A. Only subnet B and H contain non-WINS clients. Subnet A, C, D, E, and F do not contain non-WINS clients and should not be considered candidates for proxies.

Question 32

The correct answers are a, b, and c. Client computers that are not running Microsoft operating systems have additional requirements in order to print to network printers. The network administrator must install additional services on print servers and install the appropriate printer drivers on the client computers. Some of these client computers and the services needed for them to connect to the print server are:

1. Macintosh—Services for Macintosh

2. NetWare—File and Print Services for NetWare

3. Unix TCP/IP Printing, which is also known as Line Printer Daemon Service (LPD)—Services for Unix

Question 33

The correct answer is a. Shares on a Windows 2000 file server can be distributed across a site or domain by using the Windows 2000 Distributed file system (Dfs). With the Dfs infrastructure, a group of file servers are "seen" by the user as one entity. For example, suppose you have the following Microsoft Windows NT 4 file servers:

```
\\Research\Projects1
\\Research\Projects2
\\Research\Projects3
\\Research\Projects4
```

Using Windows 2000 Dfs, you have the ability to add all four file servers to the Dfs tree and use just one share called \\Research\Projects. This permits any user with the proper security credentials to obtain access to any file on any of the four file servers. Active Directory provides for redundancy and load balancing by first trying to find the file server closest to the user requesting the information. If the closest file server is either unavailable or busy, Active Directory uses Dfs to access the next file server and so on. To obtain this functionality, add the Distributed File Systems snap-in to the Microsoft Management Console (MMC).

16

Question 34

The correct answer is a. A program server enables a user or users to run programs that are not installed on the user's workstation computer. Windows 2000 Server provides high-level interfaces for commonly used services, such as database access and Active Directory services. These interfaces can be used from virtually any programming or scripting language, making for easy, rapid development. A program member server can host a variety of programs and services, such as a Component Server, Terminal Service Server, Database Server, and E-mail Server.

With Component Server, services such as Terminal Server, Application Load Balancing, Transaction Services, Application Management, and Message Queuing can be utilized. Terminal Server is an environment that provides remote client access to Windows-based programs running on a Windows 2000 Terminal Server. The Database Server provides a stable platform for running and managing database software, such as Microsoft SQL Server. If you are installing Windows 2000 Server, no further configuration of the operating system is needed to run the database software. Also, if you are using a database other than Microsoft SQL Server, that database must be compatible with Windows 2000.

Question 35

The correct answer is a. Using a simple batch file and a small executable file, you can tell if the client is a:

➤ Windows 95 or Windows 98 client

➤ Windows NT workstation

➤ Windows 2000 Professional installation

➤ Windows NT Server non-domain controller

➤ Windows 2000 Server non-domain controller

➤ Windows NT Server domain controller

➤ Windows 2000 Server domain controller

➤ Windows NT Enterprise/Terminal Server domain controller

➤ Windows NT Enterprise/Terminal Server non-domain controller

Copy the following text to a batch file:

```
@echo off
REM Batch file to detect OS
REM -----------------------------------
if Windows_NT == %OS% goto WINNT
echo You are not running Windows NT (Windows 95/98 perhaps?)
goto END

:WINNT
gettype.exe

if errorlevel=9 goto FILENOTFOUND

echo You are running Windows NT.
echo More Specifically:
echo.


if ERRORLEVEL=8 goto EIGHT
if ERRORLEVEL=7 goto SEVEN
if ERRORLEVEL=6 goto SIX
if ERRORLEVEL=5 goto FIVE
if ERRORLEVEL=4 goto FOUR
if ERRORLEVEL=3 goto THREE
if ERRORLEVEL=2 goto TWO
if ERRORLEVEL=1 goto ONE

:FILENOTFOUND
echo.
echo Gettype not found.
echo.
goto END

:EIGHT
echo Windows NT Enterprise/Terminal Server Non-Domain Controller
goto END

:SEVEN
echo Windows NT Enterprise/Terminal Server Domain Controller
goto END

:SIX
echo Windows 2000 Server Domain Controller
goto END

:FIVE
echo Windows NT Server Domain Controller
goto END
```

16

```
:FOUR
echo Windows 2000 Server Non-Domain Controller
goto END

:THREE
echo Windows NT Server Non-Domain Controller
goto END

:TWO
echo Windows 2000 Professional installation
goto END

:ONE
echo Windows NT Workstation
goto END

:END
pause
```

Copy the gettype.exe file and the batch file to the target workstations, and run the batch file.

You can obtain gettype.exe version 4.0 from Microsoft Product Support Services. Gettype.exe works by querying the Registry for the installation type and setting the DOS ERRORLEVEL appropriately:

Returns 1 for Windows NT Workstation.

Returns 2 for Windows 2000 Professional.

Returns 3 for Windows NT Server non-domain controller.

Returns 4 for Windows 2000 Server non-domain controller.

Returns 5 for Windows NT Server domain controller.

Returns 6 for Windows 2000 Server domain controller.

Returns 7 for Windows NT Enterprise/Terminal Server domain controller.

Returns 8 for Windows NT Enterprise/Terminal Server non-domain controller.

Silent mode can be set with the /s parameter. This tool can also be run against remote computers.

Question 36

The correct answer is c. When you connect a Microsoft Windows 2000 Server-based computer and a second computer to a manual switch that allows you to shift keyboard, monitor, and mouse input from one computer to the other, your Microsoft serial mouse works normally at first. However, after you switch the input from the Windows 2000 Server-based computer to the other computer and then back, the mouse stops working (hangs). Windows 2000 Server does not find the mouse when you scan for hardware changes in Device Manager. This behavior occurs because Windows 2000 Server and Windows 2000 Professional do not support manual switch boxes. To work around this behavior, change a value in the msmouse.inf file to turn off removal detection, as shown in the following six steps:

1. Open the file %WINDIR%\Inf\Msmouse.inf in Notepad.

2. In the [Ser_Inst.HW.AddReg] section, remove the semicolon (;) from the following line:

   ```
   ; HKR,,''WaitEventMask'',0x00010001,0xFFFFFFFF
   ```

3. Save the file, and then quit Notepad.

4. In Control Panel, double-click on System, and then click on the Hardware tab.

5. Click on Device Manager, and then remove the serial mouse.

6. On the Action menu, click on Scan For Hardware Changes to reinstall the mouse.

Question 37

The correct answer is b. Computers upgraded from Windows NT 4 do not use the new default security settings. Instead, all existing security settings are maintained. For backwards compatibility of programs in Windows 2000 Professional, access granted to the Power Users group provides the best avenue of compatibility with programs. New users are added to the Power Users group by default, so security conscious administrators may want to examine the option of removing users from this group. By default, the "Authenticated Users" special identity is also added to the Power Users group to ensure that domain users have the same level of access as they have had in the past. Users created by programmatic means are not added to the Power Users group by default.

16

Question 38

The correct answer is b. Some of the default security settings in Windows 2000 include a clean installation of Windows 2000 Professional and Windows 2000 Server (configured as a Member Server) provided Users (members of the Everyone and Users groups) do not have broad Write access to the system as in Microsoft Windows NT 4 and earlier. Such users have Read access to most parts of the system and Write access only under their own profile folders. Power Users (members of the Power Users group) have all the access that normal users and power users have in Windows NT 4 and earlier. Such users have Write access to parts of the system besides their own profile folders. This enables them to install programs and more. Administrators have all the access they have always had.

With a clean installation of Windows 2000 Server (configured as a Domain Controller) provided Users do not have broad Write access to the system: Such users have Read access to most parts of the system and Write access only under their own profile folders. Such users can only access domain controllers over the network. Local logon to domain controllers is denied. Server Operators, Account Operators, and other built-in groups have the same access as in Windows NT 4 and earlier. Administrators have all the access they have always had.

Question 39

The correct answer is d. You cannot install Gateway Services for NetWare (GSNW) and Client Services for NetWare (CSNW) in the same way as you do other optional networking components by using the Windows Component wizard. GSNW (in Windows 2000 Server) and CSNW (in Windows 2000 Professional) provide connectivity to NetWare networks. When GSNW is installed on a Windows 2000 server, the server can act as an NCP gateway to NetWare networks, allowing Microsoft (SMB) clients access to NetWare resources using the gateway. When CSNW is installed on a Windows 2000 Professional-based computer, the computer can function as an NCP client and can directly access resources on NetWare networks. Both GSNW and CSNW use NWLink IPX/SPX as the underlying protocol stack for connectivity to NetWare networks. Installing either GSNW or CSNW automatically installs the NWLink IPX/SPX/NetBIOS Compatible Transport protocol. Because it is necessary to control whether GSNW or CSNW is installed and bound or unbound on a particular connection interface, these components cannot be installed using the Windows Component wizard. Instead, they are installed using the Local Area Connection tool. After installation, these components are configured using the GWNW or CSNW tool in the Control Panel. Configuration information for GSNW or CSNW in the Control Panel is retained in the user's profile (saved on a per-user basis). The installation of GSNW or CSNW is not user specific, but is global for the computer. Note that GSNW or CSNW can also be installed during Windows 2000 Setup.

Question 40

The correct answer is c. The Microsoft Management Console (MMC) snap-ins for remote DNS, DHCP, or WINS administration may not be listed on the Start menu if the services are not installed. By default, the remote administration snap-ins are not installed on computers that are not hosting these services. For this reason, the snap-ins are not listed on the Add snap-in option. These tools are available in the adminpak.msi file in the I386 folder on the Windows 2000 Server or Windows 2000 Advanced Server CD. You can install these tools on servers that are not hosting these services. To install these tools, double-click on the adminpak.msi file in the I386 folder on the Windows 2000 Server or Windows 2000 Advanced Server CD. Respond to the prompts as appropriate. The administration tools then appear on the Start menu in the Programs group as Administrative Tools. Note that the adminpak.msi file is not available on the Windows 2000 Professional CD, but you can install it from the Server CD.

Question 41.1

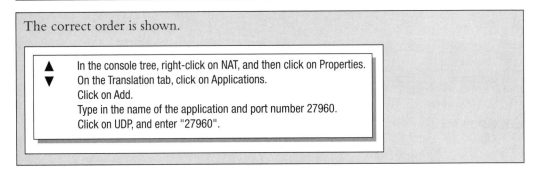

The correct order is shown.

▲
▼   In the console tree, right-click on NAT, and then click on Properties.
    On the Translation tab, click on Applications.
    Click on Add.
    Type in the name of the application and port number 27960.
    Click on UDP, and enter "27960".

Question 41.2

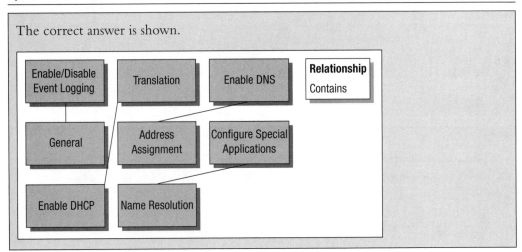

The correct answer is shown.

| Enable/Disable Event Logging | Translation | Enable DNS | **Relationship** Contains |

| General | Address Assignment | Configure Special Applications |

| Enable DHCP | Name Resolution |

16

Question 41.3

The correct answer is shown.

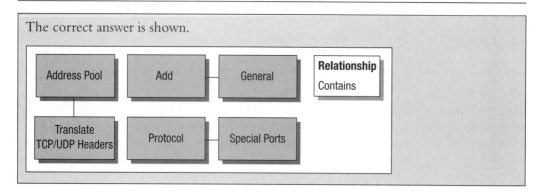

Question 41.4

The correct answer is shown.

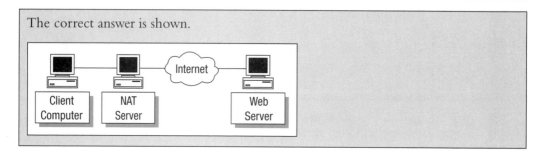

Question 41.5

The correct answer is d. When a computer running NAT receives a packet from an internal client, it replaces the packet header and translates the client's port number and internal IP address to its own port number and external IP address. It then sends the packet to the destination host on the Internet and keeps track of the mapping information in a table, so it can route the reply to the client computer. When the NAT computer receives a reply from the Internet host, it replaces the packet header and sends it on to the client.

Question 41.6

The correct answers are a, b, c, and d. NAT enabled the 10 users to share 30 Internet connections in this case. NAT provides both DNS and DHCP. NAT provides comprehensive protocol support, such as PPTP.

Question 41.7

The correct answers are b and c. NAT reduces IP address registration costs and conceals internal IP addresses from external networks, such as the Internet.

Question 41.8

The correct answers are a and c. NAT provides security that standard routers that do not support NAT cannot provide. NAT is more processor intensive because of the translation process. NAT does not support all protocols. NAT translates the computer's IP address in the packet header, which prevents the use of Internet Protocol Security (IPSec).

Question 41.9

The correct answer is b. Both NAT and Proxy Server allow Internet connections and restrict access to internal IP addresses. Both NAT and Proxy Server translate IP addresses. Both NAT and Proxy Server require client configuration. NAT does not require knowledge of the higher layer protocol.

Question 41.10

The correct answer is c. Both NAT and Internet Connection Sharing provide the same capabilities, but Internet Connection Sharing is much easier to configure. Using the Network Connection Wizard, you can enable Internet Connection Sharing by selecting one checkbox. Windows 2000 supports both NAT and Internet Connection Sharing.

Appendix A
Answers to Review Questions

Chapter 1 Solutions

1. **c.** Windows 2000 builds on the strengths of Windows NT 4.

2. **d.** XML Parser was specifically designed for Web documents.

3. **c.** Windows 2000 Terminal Services offer 20 percent more scalability.

4. **b.** Windows Media Services is used to configure and manage high-quality media content across the Internet and intranets.

5. **d.** Windows 2000 Server supports up to 1GB networks.

6. **a.** Routing and Remote Access allows the connection of remote workers, telecommuters, and branch offices to the corporate network through dial-up, leased line, and Internet links.

7. **d.** Kill Process Tree allows administrators to stop all processes related to a failed process or application without rebooting the system.

8. **a.** The System Preparation Tool saves deployment time by using SysPrep to create an image of a computer's hard drive that can be used to duplicate onto other computers.

9. **c.** Dynamic DNS Service simplifies object naming and location through Internet protocols and improves scalability, performance, and interoperability.

10. **a.** Group Policy provides server administration and task automation via the command line.

11. **c.** Network load balancing clusters provide high scalability and availability for TCP/IP-based services and applications by combining up to 32 servers running Windows Advanced Server into a single cluster.

12. **d.** Routing and Remote Access Service allows your Windows 2000 Server to operate as a remote access server, VPN server, or gateway.

13. **d.** Removable Storage makes it easier to track your removable storage media and manages the hardware libraries that contain them.

14. **a.** IntelliMirror provides the highest levels of control over portable desktop systems on systems running Windows 2000 Professional.

15. **c.** Volume Mount Points is used to connect, or mount, a local drive at any empty folder on an NTFS-formatted volume.

16. **b.** Using Distributed Authoring and Versioning, remote authors can manipulate files, file properties, directories, and directory properties on a server over an HTTP connection.

17. **a.** CIM is an extensive object-oriented schema for administering systems, networks, applications, databases, and devices.

18. **a.** ATM is a high-speed connection-oriented protocol designed to transport multiple types of traffic across a network.

19. **c.** NTFS is an advanced file system designed for use specifically within the Windows 2000 operating system.

20. **d**. Unix, Novell NetWare, and Windows NT Server can be used to integrate Windows 2000 Advanced Server into a preexisting environment.

Chapter 2 Solutions

1. **a.** Most small businesses use peer-to-peer networks to share Internet connections.

2. **b.** Protocols do not differentiate one LAN from another.

3. **b.** Each Internet computer that is independent of the other servers on the network is called a host.

4. **a.** TCP/IP is commonly used on an intranet belonging to an organization, usually a corporation, accessible only by the organization's authorized members, employees, or customers and vendors.

5. **d.** The proxy server intercepts all messages entering and leaving the network.

6. **d.** Square is not a principal topology used for LANs.

7. **a.** Ring gets its name from the setup of the cables attaching computers together, in which each computer is attached to the computer closest to it, and that one to the next one closest, and so on.

8. **d.** Monthly service charge, LAN connectivity equipment, and user training and support are all cost-related elements that should be considered when you examine WAN costs.

9. **c.** Members of the Users group can perform most common tasks, such as running applications, using local and network printers, and shutting down and locking the workstation.

10. **a.** The Replicator group supports directory replication functions.

11. **c.** Task Manager provides information about programs and processes running on your computer.

12. **b.** Performance Logs and Alerts is used to collect performance data automatically from local or remote computers.

13. **d.** You should start logging activity for routine monitoring on a 15-minute interval.

14. **a.** WMI is WBEM-compliant and provides integrated support for the CIM, which is the data model that describes the objects that exist in a management environment.

15. **c.** Logical Drives lets you manage mapped drives and local drives on a remote computer or local computer.

16. **b.** Network Load Balancing assembles several computers running server programs using TCP/IP.

17. **a.** Client affinity is used to associate client requests with cluster hosts.

18. **c.** A firewall is considered a first line of defense in protecting information.

19. **a.** Networks based on the bus topology are inexpensive, but do not scale well, are hard to troubleshoot, and are not fault tolerant.

20. **d.** Star-wired ring, star-wired bus, and daisy chains are hybrid topologies.

Chapter 3 Solutions

1. **c.** The third layer of the OSI model is the Session layer.

2. **a.** Address Resolution Protocol (ARP) is a required TCP/IP standard that resolves IP addresses used by TCP/IP-based software to MAC addresses used by LAN hardware.

3. **b.** The User Datagram Protocol (UDP) is used by some programs instead of TCP for fast, lightweight, unreliable transportation of data between TCP/IP hosts.

4. **d.** Transmission Control Protocol (TCP) is a required TCP/IP standard that provides a reliable, connection-oriented packet delivery service.

5. **a.** The network ID portion is indicated by the first two numbers of the IP address.

6. **c.** The host ID portion is indicated by the last two numbers of the IP address.

7. **b.** Class A is 1-126, Class B is 128-191, and Class C is 192-223. These addresses are used for assignment to TCP/IP nodes.

8. **a.** Routing is the primary function of the IP. IP datagrams are exchanged and processed on each host at the Internet layer.

9. **d.** All IP routing relies on the use of a routing table to communicate between network segments. TCP/IP hosts use a routing table for information about other IP networks and IP hosts.

10. **b.** The actual instruction is to click on Properties, not Add.

11. **a.** Internetwork Packet Exchange and Sequenced Packet Exchange (IPX/SPX) are transport protocols used in Novell NetWare networks. Together, they correspond to the Internet Protocol and Transport Control Protocol that are used in the TCP/IP suite.

12. **c.** A NetBIOS name is a 16-byte address (15 bit character and a service identifier) that is used to identify a resource on the network.

13. **d.** Computers running Windows 2000 are B-node (Broadcast) by default and become H-node (Hybrid) when they are configured as a WINS server.

14. **c.** NetBEUI is not routable, and the only configuration required for the protocol is a computer name.

15. **a.** Administrators can use the Network Monitor tool to capture protocol packets and monitor network activity.

Chapter 4 Solutions

1. **a.** DHCP is a TCP/IP standard.

2. **d.** DHCP servers use reservations to create permanent address lease assignments.

3. **c.** An exclusion range is a limited sequence of IP addresses within a scope.

4. **d.** A DHCP server should be limited to having no more than 1,000 scopes, a Microsoft recommendation.

5. **a.** User class IDs can be set and viewed at a Windows 2000 DHCP client using the **ipconfig** command.

6. **c.** You can manage DHCP servers remotely using Windows 2000 administration tools.

7. **b.** DHCP client support is provided for computers running under certain Microsoft operating systems only.

8. **d.** Five—the number of client addresses that are requested in advance is equal to the number of routing and remote access ports set to receive, plus one additional address.

9. **c.** When using DHCP and WINS together on a network, consider using additional DHCP scope options.

10. **d.** By default, the maximum number of log files the server permits to be stored is seven—one for each day of the week.

11. **c.** Class options are applied only to clients that are identified as members of a specifies user or vendor group.

12. **d.** Doamin controller, Member server, and Stand-alone server are all authorizing DHCP server types.

13. **a.** If you deploy Active Directory the computers operating as DHCP servers must be either domain controllers or domain member server.

14. **c.** Bridge is not a standard DHCO option for Microsoft clients.

15. **a.** DNS server is not an internal option type for Microsoft clients.

Chapter 5 Solutions

1. **b.** The largest top-level domain in use is .com for commercial organizations.

2. **c.** Top-level domain names cannot exceed 22 characters and fully qualified domain names can not exceed 155 characters.

3. **b.** The NetBIOS parameter was introduced to ensure interoperability with DNS naming in Windows 2000.

4. **a.** DNS is required for locating Windows 2000 DCs. The Netlogon service uses new DNS server support to provide registration of DCs in a DNS domain namespace.

   c. Windows 2000 servers can use Active Directory for storing and replicating zones. By directory-integrating zones, you can use additional Windows 2000 features, such as dynamic updates and record aging/scavenging.

5. **a.** The answer is true.

6. **b.** The DNS name

   c. The NetBIOS name

7. **a.** The answer is true.

8. **c.** Apply for and register a second-level domain name

9. **b.** To provide a name-to-address mapping service for computers on the Internet

10. **a.** The NetBIOS computer name

    c. The full computer name, the FQDN

11. **b, c.** A static ip address and a DNS name are required for a DNS server.

12. **b.** An iterative query is a best-efforts from a single DNS server.

13. **a.** A recursive query is the best answer using multiple DNS servers.

14. **b.** The primary zone contains the master copy of the zone database.

15. **d.** The secondary zone contains a copy of the zone database.

Chapter 6 Solutions

1. **c.** Name servers take name requests from clients and resolve computer (or domain) names to IP addresses.

2. **b.** DNS is a static service, meaning that someone has to enter the names and IP addresses manually before the DNS server can resolve them.

3. **a.** NetBEUI is usually used on small workgroups and is not routable.

4. **b.** Dynamic DNS is fully integrated with DNS to get all the benefits of TCP/IP and Internet-standards-based name resolution without having to maintain name resolution manually, as was the case previously.

5. **c.** Integration with DNS and DHCP enables clients using DDNS for name resolution to access hosts that are not registered in DDNS but are registered in WINS.

6. **d.** Dynamic update enables DNS client computers to register and dynamically update their RRs with a DNS server whenever changes occur.

7. **c.** Windows 2000 gives you the option of choosing to use standard primary zones or primary zones integrated with Active Directory.

8. **a.** One server can host and load the master copy of the zone when using a standard primary zone.

9. **b.** It is recommended that at least two DNS servers be used to host each zone.

10. **b.** Caching-only DNS servers do not host any zones and are not authoritative for a particular domain.

11. **e.** When planning for your DNS servers, it is important to perform capacity planning, review server hardware requirements, determine how many DNS servers are needed, and determine their roles in the network.

12. **c.** In many cases, adding more RAM to a DNS server can provide the most noticeable improvements in performance.

13. **d.** Approximately 4MB of RAM is used when the DNS server is started without any zones.

14. **b.** A secondary name server is used to offload DNS query traffic in areas of the network where a zone is heavily queried.

15. **d.** BIND boot configuration file, cache.dns, and root.dns are all files that relate to using and configuring DNS servers and clients for use under Windows 2000, but config.dns is not.

16. **c.** Zone_name.dns is used when a standard zone (either primary or secondary) is added and configured for the server.

17. **c.** A CNAME record is a canonical record used to create an alias.

18. **b.** The SOA resource record is always the first record in any standard zone.

19. **c.** The Host Information (HINFO) resource record specifies the type of CPU and operating system in the cpu_type and os-type fields, respectively, for the host DNS domain name in the owner.

20. **b.** Windows 2000 DNS servers use information stored in the System Registry to initialize services and load any zone data for use at the server.

Chapter 7 Solutions

1. **a.** 00h appended to a NetBIOS name indicates a workstation.

2. **b.** 20h appended to a NetBIOS name indicates a file server.

3. **b.** C-node is not a NetBIOS node type.

4. **b.** P-node does not use broadcasts.

5. **c.** M-node is a combination of B-node and P-node.

6. **d.** Windows for Workgroups, LAN Manager, and LAN Manager for Unix hosts are NetBIOS-based computers that use NetBIOS names..

7. **d.** WINS replication partners must run a server operating system.

8. **c.** Two WINS servers are recommended to provide a fault-tolerant WINS installation.

9. **b.** When using multihomed WINS servers, it is best to configure all server IP addresses as replication partners with other WINS servers.

10. **d.** For Windows 2000 client, you can configure WINS clients to use up to 12 servers.

11. **d.** The answer is none of the above, because NBTSTAT –RR is used to register and troubleshoot client connectivity and it is not listed. Note that in answer a the command is spelled incorrectly.

12. **a.** A WINS proxy is a client computer configured to act on behalf of other host computers that cannot directly use WINS.

13. **a.** Networks with Unix hosts and other non-WINS clients require WINS proxy agents to help resolve NetBIOS name queries for computers.

14. **d.** WINS proxy checks the B-node name registration against the WINS server database, deletes the released client names from its remote names cache, and attempts to resolve the name queries using information either locally contained in its cache of remote names or through the use of information it obtains from the WINS server.

15. **c.** Unique and group are NetBIOS name types.

16. **a.** NetBIOS names are registered with WINS and are normally released when the computer is properly shut down.

17. **b.** WACK stands for Wait for Acknowledgement.

18. **b.** The default burst-queue size is 500.

19. **a.** NetBIOS group names are registered by master browsers.

20. **a.** You manually configure WINS replication for a WAN environment.

Chapter 8 Solutions

1. **b.** False. Routing is the process of transferring data from a source host to a destination host.

2. **b.** In indirect delivery the destination internetwork address and the destination physical address are not for the same end system.

3. **c.** The Interface field indicates the network interface that is used when forwarding packets to the network ID.

4. **a.** The Lifetime field indicates the lifetime that the route is considered valid.

5. **d.** The hop count is a common metric.

6. **b.** Routing is the primary function of IP.

7. **c.** The maximum hop count used by RIP routers is 15.

8. **a.** A small internetwork is defined as having 2 to 10 networks.

9. **d.** The ping command can be used to test connectivity to a destination IP address.

10. **b.** Use Routing and RAS Admin to administer Windows NT 4 with RRAS.

11. **a.** Use Routing and Remote Access to administer Windows 2000 router.

12. **c.** You should set the default cost from one to two for satellite links.

13. **c.** The destination address is set to the MAC address of the default gateway for a message sent to a remote host.

14. **a.** Use the **netsh** command to configure Windows 2000 router from the command line.

15. **b, c, d.** Devices with two network cards or ports that have ip addresses with different network IDs are considered multihomed. Routers are always multihomed. Gateway servers are not necessarily multihomed and follow the same rule as other network devices.

Chapter 9 Solutions

1. **d.** "Send the information in multiple packets by using multicast addresses" is incorrect.

2. **b.** False. Multicast IP traffic is sent to a single address and processed by multiple hosts.

3. **d.** IP multicast addresses are reserved and assigned within the Class D IP address range.

4. **a.** The WINS server group address is 224.0.1.24 (a Class D reserved address).

5. **d.** On the Multicast Heartbeat tab, clear the Enable Multicast Heartbeat Detection checkbox.

6. **b.** The multicast address range is from 224.0.0.0 to 239.255.255.255.

7. **a.** The bulk of Internet traffic is multicast traffic.

8. **b.** There is no client/server component for NAT.

9. **c.** The default network ID is 192.168.0.0.

10. **a.** NAT doesn't configure them with an ISP.

11. **b.** IGMP is used to send and receive multicast traffic to and from the Internet.

12. **a.** Overlapping may occur if you use private ip address on the internet.

13. **c.** 224.0.0.9 is used by RIP.

14. **c.** A multicast router sends a host membership query to registered group members.

15. **a, b, c, d.** Windows 2000 includes built-in NAT editors for FTP, ICMP, PPTP, and NetBIOS over TCP/IP.

Chapter 10 Solutions

1. **c.** Account lockout is a security feature that denies access after a configured number of foiled attempts.

2. **b.** Remote Access policies are a set of conditions and connection settings that allow network administrators more flexibility in setting permissions and connection attributes.

3. **d.** PPP, SLIP and MS-RAS are all protocols supported by the Windows 2000 Routing and Remote Access service.

4. **a.** Microsoft clients do not support the use of the AppleTalk protocol.

5. **b.** A remote access server running Windows 2000 does not support SLIP clients.

6. **c.** PPTP by default is configured for 5 ports.

7. **b.** The DHCP server initially obtains 10 IP addresses for use with the Remote Access server.

8. **a.** PPP frames can be sent in plain text with a non-encrypted PPTP connection.

9. **b.** L2TP and IPSec must be supported by both the VPN client and the VPN server.

10. **a.** Conditions are one or more attributes that are compared to the settings of the connection attempt.

11. **c.** Using VPN, you will receive an automatic IP address when the DHCP server is down.

12. **a.** Use RAS IP tab to configure client IP addresses.

13. **c.** Use RAS PPP tab to configure software compression.

14. **d.** The User Accounts Dial-In tab is used to set individual user access rights.

15. **b.** Clear the No Encryption checkbox to enable encryption.

Chapter 11 Solutions

1. **d.** All of the items are provided by IPSec.

2. **b.** IPSec Security Policy Management Snap-in is used to create IPSec policy configurations.

3. **a.** Client is the predefined policy used for computers that should not secure communication most of the time.

4. **d.** All three answers are rules for IPSec types.

5. **b.** Servers that store and exchange highly sensitive information belong the highest security servers organizational unit.

6. **d.** Both ESP Tunnel Mode and AH Tunnel Mode are the formats for IPSec packets used in tunnel mode.

7. **b.** PPTP stands for Point-to-Point Tunneling Protocol.

8. **b.** L2TP is a networking technology that supports multiprotocol virtual private networks.

9. **b.** Kerberos is the primary security protocol for authentication within a domain.

10. **b.** Kerberos V5 services are installed on each domain controller, and Kerberos client is installed on Windows 2000 workstation and server.

Chapter 12 Solutions

1. **a.** An enterprise CA requires that all users requesting certificates have an entry in the Windows 2000 Server Active Directory™ services, whereas a stand-alone CA does not.

2. **a.** User certificates should be required for asynchronous data exchange applications, such as S/MIME and EFS.

3. **b.** CAs are organized into hierarchies with a fundamental trust point— or root CA.

4. **c.** Avoid using print spool files in your print server architecture, or ensure that print spool files get generated in an encrypted folder.

5. **d.** An Enterprise Root CA requires everything that an Enterprise Subordinate CA requires except a parent CA.

6. **c.** An agent can use his or her private key to decrypt the FEK that was originally used in the file encryption process.

7. **a.** The simplest way is to open a command window, and type "net start" to see if the Certificate Service is running.

8. **c.** The Encrypted Data Recovery Policy (EDRP) is configurable for both a domain and a stand-alone server.

9. **d.** Applications that check the revocation status of a certificate prior to use check the Certificate Revocation List (CRL).

10. **b.** Users should never encrypt individual files, only folders. Encrypting files consistently at the folder level ensures that files do not get decrypted unexpectedly.

11. **b.** Computer certificates are stored locally in the requesting computer's certificate store.

12. **b.** The client cache is not updated until the validity period expires, even when a new CRL is published.

13. **a, b, d.** PKI can authentic either the computer or messenger originator and ensures the confidentiality of a message.

14. **c.** Certificate Services Web pages can be used with enterprise CA or stand-alone CA but Certificate Request Wizard can only be used with enterprise CA not stand-alone CA.

15. **a, b, c, d.** All of these file formats can be used when importing or exporting certificates. PKCS#12 is Personal Information Exchange. PKCS#7 is Cryptographic Message Syntax Standard.

Chapter 13 Solutions

1. **c.** ASP files must have an .asp extension.

2. **d.** With Windows Media Services you can create, manage, and deliver Windows Media content over an intranet or the Internet.

3. **a.** The FTP counters show data about the anonymous and nonanonymous connections to the File Transport Protocol Server application.

4. **a.** –v is the parameter and required element in an FTP command that suppresses display of remote server responses.

5. **c.** –l is the parameter and required element in an FTP command that turns off interactive prompting during multiple file transfers.

6. **c.** –d is the parameter and required element in an FTP command that enables debugging and displays all FTP commands passed between the client and server.

7. **c.** The Active Server Pages object monitors applications running on the Web server that use Active Server Pages.

8. **b.** Active Directory also creates an LDAP relative distinguished name, based on the security principal name.

9. **a.** The site Server ILS service is used to publish IP Multicast conferences on the network.

10. **b.** The Windows 2000 printing architecture seamlessly integrates with the Internet.

11. **a.** NetWare clients use IPX/SPX compatible transport to send print jobs over the network to the print server.

12. **d.** NTFS, FAT, and FAT32 are all file systems for Windows 2000 computers.

13. **a.** NTFS has always been the more powerful file system.

14. **c.** Phone Book Administrator enables you to associate POPs with network configurations defined in Subcomponents of Management and Monitoring Tools.

15. **b.** Microsoft Connection Manager is not a component of CPS.

Chapter 14 Solutions

1. **b.** Manager is not a built-in program accessible from the Utility Manager.

2. **a.** ipconfig is a TCP/IP utility that displays all current network configuration values for TCP/IP.

3. **c.** ipconfig /all produces a full display of all configuration parameters.

4. **b.** Windows 2000 Modem Troubleshooter is for connections, setup configuration, and detection troubleshooting.

5. **c.** Windows 2000 DHCP Troubleshooter is used if you're having a problem with configuring Dynamic Host Configuration Protocol service on a server.

6. **a.** Windows 2000 Routing and Remote Access Troubleshooter is used for dial-up networking connection troubleshooting.

7. **d.** Windows 2000 System Setup Troubleshooter is used for troubleshooting running 16-bit Windows programs on Windows 2000.

8. **b.** Microsoft Management Console is a feature of the Windows 2000 operating system and can run on Windows NT, Window 95, and Windows 98, but not Windows 3.1.

9. **a.** MMC does not perform configuration.

10. **c.** To add snap-ins to MMC, you do not use click on Remove in the Add/Remove Snap-in dialog box.

11. **d.** To extend the functionality of Group Policy you do not select checkboxes next to the extensions that you want to add.

12. **a.** When the console tree is visible, it appears on the right side of the console window.

13. **c.** WMI is an important tool for managing Windows 2000 Security.

14. **a.** Component Services is an administrative tool used to deploy and administer COM+ programs from a graphical user interface and is used to automate administrative tasks using a scripting or programming language.

15. **b.** Event Viewer is an administrative tool used to view and manage logs of system, program, and security events on your computer.

16. **c.** Computer Management is used to control what the computer does in the event that it shuts down unexpectedly.

17. **d.** One of the main items that System Monitor searches for is bottlenecks.

18. **a.** The biggest concern with computers today is security.

19. **c.** Local Security Policy is used to configure security settings for IAS events and is available only on Windows 2000 computers that are not domain controllers.

20. **d.** When Network Monitor detects other Network Monitor installations running on the network, it displays the name of the computer, the name of the user logged on at the computer, and the adapter address of the remote computer, but does not display the location of the user.

Appendix B
Exam Objectives

Candidates for this exam operate in medium to very large computing environments that use the Windows 2000 network operating system. They have a minimum of one year's experience implementing and administering network operating systems in environments that have the following characteristics:

➤ Supported users range from 200 to 26,000+

➤ Physical locations range from 5 to 150+

Typical network services and applications include file and print, database, messaging, proxy server or firewall, dial-in server, desktop management, and Web hosting.

Connectivity needs include connecting individual offices and users at remote locations to the corporate network and connecting corporate networks to the Internet. This certification exam measures your ability to install, manage, monitor, configure, and troubleshoot DNS, DHCP, Remote Access, Network Protocols, IP Routing, and WINS in a Windows 2000 network infrastructure. In addition, this test measures the skills required to manage, monitor, and troubleshoot Network Address Translation and Certificate Services.

Installing, Configuring, Managing, Monitoring, and Troubleshooting DNS in a Windows 2000 Network Infrastructure	Chapter:
Install, configure, and troubleshoot DNS.	6
Install the DNS Server service.	6
Configure a root name server.	7
Configure zones.	7
Configure a caching-only server.	7
Configure a DNS client.	6
Configure zones for dynamic updates.	7
Test the DNS Server service.	6
Implement a delegated zone for DNS.	7
Manually create DNS resource records.	7
Manage and monitor DNS.	6

Installing, Configuring, Managing, Monitoring, and Troubleshooting DHCP in a Windows 2000 Network Infrastructure	Chapter:
Install, configure, and troubleshoot DHCP.	5
Install the DHCP Server service.	5
Create and manage DHCP scopes, superscopes, and multicast scopes.	5
Configure DHCP for DNS integration.	5
Authorize a DHCP server in Active Directory.	5
Manage and monitor DHCP.	5

Configuring, Managing, Monitoring, and Troubleshooting Remote Access in a Windows 2000 Network Infrastructure	Chapter:
Configure and troubleshoot remote access.	11
Configure inbound connections.	11
Create a remote access policy.	11
Configure a remote access profile.	11
Configure a virtual private network (VPN).	11
Configure multilink connections.	11
Configure Routing and Remote Access for DHCP Integration.	11
Manage and monitor remote access.	11
Configure remote access security.	11
Configure authentication protocols.	11
Configure encryption protocols.	11
Create a remote access policy.	11

Installing, Configuring, Managing, Monitoring, and Troubleshooting Network Protocols in a Windows 2000 Network Infrastructure	Chapter:
Install, configure, and troubleshoot network protocols.	4
Install and configure TCP/IP.	4
Install the NWLink protocol.	4
Configure network bindings.	4
Configure TCP/IP packet filters.	4
Configure and troubleshoot network protocol security.	4
Manage and monitor network traffic.	4
Configure and troubleshoot IPSec.	4
Enable IPSec.	5
Configure IPSec for transport mode.	4
Configure IPSec for tunnel mode.	4
Customize IPSec policies and rules.	4
Manage and monitor IPSec.	4

Installing, Configuring, Managing, Monitoring, and Troubleshooting WINS in a Windows 2000 Network Infrastructure	Chapter:
Install, configure, and troubleshoot WINS.	8
Configure WINS replication.	8
Configure NetBIOS name resolution.	8
Manage and monitor WINS.	8

Installing, Configuring, Managing, Monitoring, and Troubleshooting IP Routing in a Windows 2000 Network Infrastructure	Chapter:
Install, configure, and troubleshoot IP routing protocols.	9
Update a Windows 2000-based routing table by means of static routes.	9
Implement Demand-Dial Routing.	9
Manage and monitor IP routing.	9
Manage and monitor border routing.	9
Manage and monitor internal routing.	9
Manage and monitor IP routing protocols.	9
Installing, Configuring, and Troubleshooting Network Address Translation (NAT)	10
Install Internet Connection Sharing.	10
Install NAT.	10
Configure NAT properties.	10
Configure NAT interfaces.	10

Installing, Configuring, Managing, Monitoring, and Troubleshooting Certificate Services	Chapter:
Install and configure Certificate Authority (CA).	13
Issue and revoke certificates.	13
Remove the Encrypting File System (EFS) recovery keys.	13

Appendix B

Appendix C
Study Resources

Books

Albitz, Paul, Cricket Liu, and Mike Loukides. *DNS and BIND.* 3rd ed. Sebastopol, California: O'Reilly & Associates, 1998. ISBN: 1565925122. The definitive book on Domain Name Server (DNS).

Balter, Dan, Dan Holme, Todd Hogan, and Laurie Salmon. *MCSE Windows 2000 Professional Exam Cram.* Scottsdale, AZ: The Coriolis Group, September 2000. ISBN: 1576107124.

Bruzzese, J. Peter and Wayne Dipchan. *MCSE Windows 2000 Directory Services Design Exam Prep.* Scottsdale, AZ: The Coriolis Group, August 2000. ISBN: 1576106683.

Coriolis Technology Press. *Windows 2000 Server Database Little Black Book.* Scottsdale, AZ: The Coriolis Group, May 1999. ISBN: 1576103927.

Craft, Melissa, Mark A. Poplar, David V. Watts, and Will Willis. *Network+ Exam Prep.* Scottsdale, AZ: The Coriolis Group, 1999. ISBN: 1576104125. Readers give this book the highest Amazon rating possible!

Hoag, Melanie and Joel Stegall. *Exam Cram for Advanced NetWare 5 Administration CNE.* Scottsdale, AZ: The Coriolis Group, 1999. ISBN: 1576103528. "Advanced" is the operative word in this entry. This well-written book is not for the reader who has never touched a NetWare server.

Honeyman, Jeffrey. *Scripting Windows 2000.* New York, NY: Osborne/McGraw-Hill, 2000. ISBN: 007212444X. Automate tedious tasks at the command line or from within the Windows GUI. Shows you how to avoid commonly overlooked Windows 2000 pitfalls and scripting errors.

Johnson, David and Libby Chovanec. *MCSE Windows 2000 Server Exam Prep.* Scottsdale, AZ: The Coriolis Group, July 2000. ISBN: 1576106969.

Knight, Natasha. *MCSE Windows 2000 Server Exam Cram.* Scottsdale, AZ: The Coriolis Group, September 2000. ISBN: 1576107132.

Mclean, Ian. *Windows 2000 Security Little Black Book.* Scottsdale, AZ: The Coriolis Group, February 2000. ISBN: 1576103870.

McMahon, Richard and Glen Bicking. *MCSE Windows 2000 Security Design Exam Prep.* Scottsdale, AZ: The Coriolis Group, October 2000. ISBN: 1576107078.

Minoli, Daniel and Emma Minoli. *Delivering Voice over IP Networks.* New York: John Wiley & Sons, 1998. ISBN: 0471254827. This very technical read is a must for anyone preparing for the Cisco Certified Internetwork Expert (CCIE) exams.

Nielsen, Morten Strunge. *Windows 2000 Server Architecture and Planning.* Scottsdale, AZ: The Coriolis Group, 2000. ISBN 1576104362. Based on RC-1 of Windows 2000 Server, this title has the highest reader satification rating as of press time. This book is not so much a how-to book as it is an easy to follow, yet information-filled volume on the complexities of Windows 2000.

——————*Windows 2000 Professional Advanced Configuration and Implementation.* Scottsdale, AZ: The Coriolis Group, 2000. ISBN: 1576106071. Unlike the multitude of Windows 2000 books that try to cover everything, this offering focuses on one thing: Windows 2000 Professional, the update to NT 4 Workstation. It provides a strong focus on the differences between the two versions.

Scheil, Dennis and Diana Bartley. *MCSE Windows 2000 Directory Services Design Exam Cram.* Scottsdale, AZ: The Coriolis Group, September 2000. ISBN: 1576107140.

Schein, Phillip. *MCSE Windows 2000 Security Design Exam Cram.* Scottsdale, AZ: The Coriolis Group, September 2000. ISBN: 1576107159.

Simanski, Robert E. *Windows 2000 Reducing TCO Little Black Book.* Scottsdale, AZ: The Coriolis Group, February 2000. ISBN: 1576103153.

Simanski, Robert. *Windows 2000 Active Directory Black Book.* Scottsdale, AZ: The Coriolis Group, August 2000. ISBN: 1576102564.

Simmons, Kimberly, Jarret Buse, and Todd Halpin. *MCSE Windows 2000 Network Design Exam Cram.* Scottsdale, AZ: The Coriolis Group, September 2000. ISBN: 1576107167.

Stefik, Mark J. *The Internet Edge: Social, Legal, and Technological Challenges for a Networked World.* Cambridge, Massachusetts: MIT Press, 1999. ISBN: 026219418X. Covers many aspects of the paradigm shift in society brought by the Internet. We consider the author an authority because he is the principal scientist and manager of the Human Document Interactions at Xerox Palo Alto Research Center (PARC).

Stewart, Michael D., James Bloomingdale, and Neall Alcott. *MCSE Windows 2000 Professional Exam Prep.* Scottsdale, AZ: The Coriolis Group, August 2000. ISBN: 1576107035.

Taylor, Ed. *The Network Troubleshooting Handbook*. New York, NY: McGraw-Hill, 1999. ISBN: 0071342281. More than 100 sample tracers to help you identify and analyze problems. Tips and techniques on how to baseline your network.

————. *Network Architecture Design Handbook*. New York, NY: McGraw Hill, 1999. ISBN: 007063339. Truly a must have design handbook for the Network Architecture.

Taylor, Richard, Hank Carbeck, Derek Melber. *MCSE Windows 2000 Network Exam Cram*. Scottsdale, AZ: The Coriolis Group, September 2000. ISBN: 1576107116.

Wallace, Nathan. *Windows 2000 Professional Upgrade Little Black Book: Hands-On Guide to Maximizing the New Features of Windows 2000 Professional*. Scottsdale, AZ: The Coriolis Group, July 2000. ISBN: 1576107485.

Wallace, Nathan. *Windows 2000 Registry Little Black Book*. Scottsdale, AZ: The Coriolis Group, February 2000. ISBN: 157610348X.

Willis, Will, David V. Watts, and J. Peter Bruzzese. *MSCE Windows 2000 Directory Services Exam Cram*. Scottsdale, AZ: The Coriolis Group, September 2000. ISBN: 1576106888.

Wood, Adam. *Windows 2000 Active Directory Black Book*. Scottsdale, AZ: The Coriolis Group, November 2000. ISBN: 1576102564.

Online Resources

www.examcram.com.

www.experts-exchange.com provides the opportunity to search or ask questions on many topics.

http://www.microsoft.com/windows2000/default.asp is the product home page for Windows 2000. Be sure to go to downloads to download Windows 2000 Server and Windows 2000 Advanced Server help files. You can download the help files to any Windows platform, i.e. Windows 98.

www.ntsecurity.net/ is a good site that has an active email discussion list with many experts.

www.searchwin2000.com/ is a Web portal for combining Windows 2000 resources.

www.securityportal.com/ is frequently updated and has a good email service to keep you up-to-date.

http://support.novell.com/forums/ has support forums for a variety of Novell products.

Appendix C

www.sysinternals.com/ is a good site for advanced technical information and some freeware utilities for Windows 9x, NT, and Windows 2000.

www.winmag.com/ has many good Windows 2000 articles and links.

Glossary

Access Control List
See ACL

Access Method
The way that network devices access the network medium.

ACL
List of the available services, each with a list of the hosts permitted to use the service.

ACMS
Application Control & Management System

Active Directory
See AD

Active Hub
Multiported device that boosts *local area network (LAN)* transmission signals.

Active Monitor
Device responsible for managing a token ring. The device makes sure that tokens are not lost or that frames do not circulate indefinitely. A network node is selected to be the active monitor if it has the highest *media access control (MAC)* address on the ring.

AD
Similar to NDS in NetWare, AD uses the tree concept for managing resources on a network. Everything is an object that can be moved or edited across servers and domains.

Adapter
Personal computer board that provides network communication capabilities to and from that computer system. Another term for adapter is *network interface card (NIC)*.

Address Resolution
Conversion of a network address to the corresponding physical address.

Administrative Domain
Collection of hosts and routers and the interconnecting networks, managed by a single administrative authority.

Advanced Data Communications Control Protocol
An American National Standards Institute (ANSI) standard bit-oriented data link control layer protocol.

Advanced Peer-to-Peer Internetworking
See APPI

Advanced Peer-to-Peer Networking
See APPN

Agent
The part of the system that performs information reparation and exchange on behalf of a client or server application.

Alarm
A system message that notifies operators or administrators of a network problem.

Algorithm
Rule or process for arriving at a solution.

Alias
Name for a device other than the official name.

American National Standards Institute
See ANSI

American Standard Code for Information Interchange
See ASCII

Anchor
Hyperlink.

ANSI
This organization is responsible for approving U.S. standards in computers and communications. Standards approved by this organization are called *ANSI standards*.

APPI
An open-standard Internet Protocol (IP)-architecture for *Systems Network Architecture (SNA)* peer-to-peer networking.

APPN
An IBM *Systems Network Architecture (SNA)* facility that provides distributed processing based on type 2.1 network nodes and Logical Unit (LU) 6.2.

Appletalk
Networking protocol developed by Apple Computer for communication between Apple Computer products and other computers.

Application Layer
Top-most layer in the *Open Systems Interconnection (OSI) reference model*. This layer provides communication services, including electronic mail and file transfer.

ARCnet
A 2.5Mbps token bus *local area network (LAN)* developed by Datapoint Corporation. Its primary characteristics are simplicity, ease of use, and relative lack of expense.

ARM
High-level Data Link Control (HDLC) communication mode involving one primary and at least one secondary server, where either the primary or one of the secondary servers can initiate transmissions.

ARQ
Communications feature that enables the receiver to ask the transmitter to resend a block or frame because errors were detected by the receiver.

ASCII
A standard character-to-7 bit number-encoding scheme used in the computer industry.

Asynchronous
Transmission by individual bytes not related to specific timing on the transmitting end.

Asynchronous Response Mode
See ARM

Attached Resource Computer Network
See ARCnet

Attenuation
The difference between transmitted and received power due to loss through equipment, lines, or other transmission devices.

Authentication
Verification of identity.

Automatic Retransmission Request
See ARQ

Backbone
Central high-speed line or series of connections that form a major pathway within a network, connecting independent subnetworks.

Balanced

A transmission line in which voltages on the two conductors are equal in magnitude, but opposite in polarity with respect to ground.

Bandwidth

How much information can be sent through a connection, usually measured in bits per second.

Bandwidth Allocation Protocol

See BAP

BAP

Remote Access Services (RAS) protocol with multilink capabilities that allows one assigned line to be dropped if a user doesn't use all of the bandwidth.

Baud

How many bits a modem can send or receive per second.

Beacon

Signal from an IBM token ring device that indicates a serious problem with the ring, such as a broken cable. Beacon frames contain the address of the down station.

Best-Effort Delivery

The process that is used when a network system does not use an acknowledgment procedure to guarantee reliable delivery of information.

Bit

Smallest unit of information in a binary system represented by a one or zero (1 or 0).

Bit Error Rate

Percentage of transmitted bits received in error.

Bit Interleaving/Multiplexing

A process used in time-division multiplexing where individual bits from different lower speed channel sources are combined into one continuous higher speed bit stream.

Bits Per Second

See bps

bps

Measurement of how fast data is moved from one place to another.

Bridge

Device that forwards traffic between network segments based on *data link control layer* information and a common *network layer* address.

Broadcast

Multicast packet that all nodes on the network are always willing to receive.

Buffer

Type of storage device commonly used to compensate for differences in data rates or event timing when transmitting from one device to another.

Bulletin Board System

Computer equipped with software and telecommunications links that allow it to act as an information host for remote computer systems where users can carry on discussions, upload and download files, and make announcements.

Bus Topology

Linear *local area network (LAN)* architecture in which transmissions from network stations propagate the length of the medium and are received by all other stations.

Cable

Transmission medium of wires or optical fibers wrapped in a protective cover.

Carrier Sense Multiple Access with Collision Detection

See CSMA/CD

CGI (Common Gateway Interface)

Set of rules that describe how a Web server communicates with another piece of software on the same machine and how the other piece of software communicates to the Web server.

Checksum

A computed value that is dependent on the contents of a packet and that is sent along with the packet when it is transmitted. The receiving system computes a new checksum based on the received data and compares this value with the one sent with the packet. If the two values are the same, the receiver has a high degree of confidence that the data was received correctly.

Circuit

Communication link between two or more points.

Client

Computer that has access to services over a computer network. The computer providing the services is a server.

Client/Server Computing

Distributed processing network system in which transaction responsibilities are divided into two parts: client (front end) and server (back end). Both terms (client and server) can be applied to software programs or actual computing devices.

Cluster

A configuration when two or more terminals are connected to a single line or single modem.

Common Gateway Interface

See CGI

Compression

Technique that reduces the number of required bits representing information in data transmission or storage.

Congestion

Occurs when the offered load exceeds the capacity of a data communication path.

Control Point

See CP

CP (Control Point)

Element in a *Systems Network Architecture (SNA)* device that manages device resources and provides services to other devices.

CSMA/CD

Access method used by local area networking technologies, such as Ethernet.

Data

Information that is represented in digital form, including voice, text, facsimile, and video.

Data Flow Control Layer

Layer 5 of the *Systems Network Architecture (SNA)* model. It processes requests and responses that are exchanged between session partners.

Data Link Control Layer

Layer 2 in the *Systems Network Architecture (SNA)* model. It is responsible for the transmission of data between two nodes over a physical link.

Data Link Layer

The *Open Systems Interconnection (OSI)* layer that is responsible for data transfer across a single physical connection or a series of bridged connections between two networks.

Data Stream

Data transmitted through a communications line in a single read or write operation.

DDNS (Dynamic DNS)

DDNS will replace WINS as Microsoft's name resolution system. Like WINS, DDNS is dynamic; however, it is fully compatible with Unix and other systems that are DNS based.

Deadlock

Unresolved conflict for the use of a resource.

Dedicated Line

A communications line that is used by others.

DFS (Distributed File System)

A significant improvement to the drive mapping process that allows multiple network locations to be mapped to a single drive.

Diagnostic

Procedures and systems that detect and isolate a malfunction in a communications device, network, or system.

Disk Quotas

Allows administrators the ability to designate a certain amount of disk space to a user or group for storage.

Distortion

Unwanted change in waveform.

Distributed File System

See DFS

DLL (Dynamic Link Library)

The ability in Windows and OS/2 of executable memory to call software libraries.

Domain Name

Unique name that identifies an Internet site using two or more parts separated by dots.

Drop

A point on a multipoint channel where a connection to a networked device is made.

Dynamic Domain Name System

See *DDNS*

Dynamic-Link Library

See *DLL*

Dynamic Routing

Routing that adjusts automatically to network changes.

EAP (Extensive Authentication Protocol)

RAS protocol used for smart cards, generic token cards, MD5, and CHAP that uses an alternate encryption methodology for usernames and passwords.

Encapsulation

Technique used by layered protocols in which a layer adds header information to the protocol data unit from the layer above.

Encapsulation Bridging

Carries Ethernet frames from one router to another across different media.

Encryption

The manipulation of a packet's data to prevent anyone but the intended recipient from reading that data.

Enterprise Network

A network that connects most major points in a company. It is typically private and contained within a single organization.

Ethernet

Common method of networking computers in a *local area network (LAN)* that is faster than telephone lines. It can handle approximately 10,000,000 bps and can be used with almost any kind of computer.

Extensive Authentication Protocol

See EAP

FAT (File Allocation Table)

Record maintained by an operating system that indicates the status of files and disk space on the hard drive.

Fault Management
Attempts to ensure that network faults are detected and controlled.

FDM (Frequency Division Multiplexing)
A technique that allows information from multiple channels to be allocated bandwidth on a single wire based on frequency.

FIFO
First in, first out.

File Server
Computer with the principal purpose of storing files and providing network access to those files.

File Transfer
The copying of a file from one computer to another over a computer network.

File Transfer Protocol
See FTP

Filter
Process or device that screens incoming information for certain characteristics and allows or disallows the information to pass through based on those characteristics.

Firewalls
Combination of hardware and software that separates a *local area network (LAN)* into two or more parts for security purposes, designed specifically to control unwarranted access to your network.

Flow Control
Technique for ensuring that a transmitting system does not overwhelm a receiving system.

Fragment
A piece of a packet that is created when a router is forwarding an Internet Protocol (IP) packet to a network that has a maximum packet size smaller than the packet size. The router is forced to break the packet into multiple fragments.

Frame
Data link layer packet that contains the header and trailer information required by the physical medium.

Frame Relay
Protocol used across the interface between user devices and network equipment.

Frequency Division Multiplexing
See FDM

FTP (File Transfer Protocol)
Process of logging in to another Internet site for the purposes of sending and/or retrieving files.

Gateway
Hardware or software that translates between two dissimilar protocols.

Gigabyte
1,000 or 1,024 Megabytes.

Header
The portion of a packet preceding the actual data that contains source and destination addresses, error checking, and other fields.

Heterogeneous Network
A network running multiple network layer protocols.

Host
Computer that allows users to communicate with other host computers on a network.

Hub
Used to connect several computers together; used for the transfer of messages across the network; an Ethernet multiport repeater or concentrator; a hardware/

software device that contains multiple independent but connected modules of network and equipment.

Hybrid Network
An internetwork made up of more than one type of network technology, including *local area networks (LANs)* and *wide area networks (WANs)*.

ICS (Internet Connection Sharing)
Like Windows 98SE, Windows 2000 allows a single dial-up connection to be shared across the network. This has great implications for SOHOs and home users with multiple machines that will no longer need to purchase an application to provide this feature for them.

Intellimirror
Management tool that allows an administrator to configure each user's desktop, environment profile, usable disk space, and the applications they are allowed to use.

Interface
Connection between two systems or devices.

Interference
Unwanted communication or channel noise.

Internet Connection Sharing
See ICS

Intranet
A private computer network inside a company or organization that uses the same kinds of software that you would find on the public Internet.

IP Number (Internet Protocol Number)
Unique address number consisting of four parts separated by dots, used to identify computers on any network.

IPSec (Internet Protocol Security)
Remote Access Services (RAS) protocol that is an Internet Protocol (IP) layer driver that encrypts very low in the protocol stack.

IRQ (Interrupt Request)
A peripheral's signal to the central processing unit (CPU) asking for service.

Kerberos Security
Security protocol used for distributed security within a domain tree/forest. It allows transitive trusts and a single logon to provide access to all domain resources.

Kernel
The level of an operating or networking system that contains the system-level commands and the functions hidden from the user, including device drivers, memory management routines, scheduler, and system calls. The program running while the system is operating.

L2TP (Layer Two Tunneling Protocol)
Remote Access Services (RAS) protocol that uses a tunnel through public networks like the Internet for data encryption. Authentication is present on both ends. Header compression and *Internet Protocol Security (IPSec)* are used. This protocol replaces the Point-to-Point Tunneling Protocol (PPTP).

LAN (Local Area Network)
A computer network limited to the immediate area, usually the same building or floor of a building.

LAPM (Link Access Procedure for Modems)
Protocol that controls the initial communication between two modems.

LIFO
Last in, first out

Glossary

Limited Resource Link

Resource defined by a device operator to remain active only when in use.

Links

These are the hypertext connections between Web pages.

Local Area Network

See LAN

Local Bridge

A bridge that directly interconnects networks in the same geographic area.

Local Host

Host on the network that you are currently using.

Locked

When the computer stops and has to be rebooted to continue being used.

Log in

To connect to a host system or public access site; the account name used to gain access to a computer system or the act of accessing a computer system.

Loopback

A type of diagnostic test where the transmitted signal is returned to the sending device after passing through all or part of a communications link or network.

MAC (Media Access Control)

Lower portion of the data link layer.

MAC Address

Hardware address of a device connected to a shared media.

MAN (Metropolitan Area Network)

A data network that serves a city.

Master-clock

The source of timing signals that all network stations use for synchronization.

Medium

The copper wire, coaxial cable, optical fiber, or microwave used to support the transmission of data.

Mirror

An arrangement where information is written to more than one hard disk simultaneously. If one disk fails, the computer continues to work without losing anything.

Multicast

Packet with a special destination address that multiple nodes on the network may be willing to receive.

Multidrop

Communications arrangement in which multiple devices share a common transmission channel, although only one may transmit at a time.

Multihomed Host

A host with more than one connection to a network. This host may send and receive data over any of the links, but will not route traffic for other nodes.

Multiple-monitor Support

Borrowed from Windows 98, this allows multiple video cards to be used in a single computer to expand viewing acreage.

Multiplexer

Device that allows two or more signals to pass over and share a common transmission path.

Multiplexing

Putting multiple signals on a single channel.

Multipoint Line

A single communications line or circuit interconnecting several stations.

Name Server

A server on the network that resolves network names into network addresses.

NetBEUI (NetBios Extended User Interface)

An enhanced version of the Netbios protocol used by network operating to formalize the transport frame that was never standardized in Netbios and adds additional functions.

Network

Group of computers that can transmit information to each other electronically.

Network Address

Unique electronic address for all devices in a network.

Network Administrator

Person who maintains a network.

Network Layer

Layer 3 of the *OSI reference model* where routing occurs.

NIC (Network Interface Card)

An adapter card that allows a computer to connect physically to a network via wire.

NNTP (Network News Transport Protocol)

Protocol used by client/server software to carry USENET postings back and forth over a *Transmission Control Protocol/Internet Protocol (TCP/IP)* network.

Node

An addressable device attached to a computer network.

Open Architecture

An architecture according to which third-party developers can legally develop products and for which public domain specifications exist.

Open Circuit

Broken path along a transmission medium.

OSI (Open Systems Interconnection)

Suite of protocols designed by ISO committees to be the international standard computer network architecture.

OSI reference model

Network architectural model developed by ISO and CCITT that consists of seven layers, each of which specifies particular network functions, such as addressing, flow control, error control, encapsulation, and reliable message transfer.

Packet

The unit of data sent across a network.

Packet Switching

All the data coming out of a machine is broken up into smaller pieces called *packets*, with each packet containing a source and a destination address, enabling packets from different sources to commingle on the same lines and be sorted and directed to different routes by computers along the way.

Path Control Layer

Layer 3 in the *Systems Network Architecture (SNA)* model. This is the SNA layer that routes packets through a network.

Peer-to-Peer Computing

Each network device runs both client and server portions of an application.

Physical Control Layer

Layer 1 in the *Systems Network Architecture (SNA)* model.

Physical Layer

Open Systems Interconnection (OSI) layer that provides the means to activate and use physical connections for bit transmission.

Point of Presence

See POP

Point-to-Point

Dedicated connection between two pieces of equipment.

POP (Point of Presence)

A city or location to which a network can be connected, usually with dial up phone lines.

Port

A place where information goes into or out of a computer.

PPP (Point to Point Protocol)

Allows a computer to use a regular telephone line and a modem to make *Transmission Control Protocol/Internet Protocol (TCP/IP)* connections and connect to the Internet.

Presentation Layer

Open Systems Interconnection (OSI) layer that determines how application information is represented while in transit between two end systems.

Presentation Services Layer

Layer 6 of the *Systems Network Architecture (SNA)* model.

Propagation Delay

The time required for data to travel over a network from source to destination.

RADIUS (Remote Authentication Dial-In User Service)

An *RAS* protocol that is an RFC-based standard, authentication with Radius Server Service (IAS) for clients connecting via an ISP.

RAID

Redundant Arrays of Inexpensive Disks.

RAS (Remote Access Service)

Protocol that enables file and program access from a remote location.

Real-Time Transport Protocol

End-to-end network transport functions suitable for applications transmitting real-time data, such as audio, video, or simulation data, over multicast or unicast network services, designed to be independent of the underlying transport and network layers and supports the use of RTP-level translators and mixers.

Redirect

Part of the Internet Control Message Protocol (ICMP) and ES-IS protocols that allows a router to tell a host that another router would be more effective.

Redirector

Software that intercepts requests for resources within a computer and analyzes them for remote-access requirements.

Relay

Open Systems Interconnection (OSI) terminology for a device that connects two or more networks.

Remote Access Services

See RAS

Remote Host

Any host on the network that you are not presently using.

Request to Send

A modem control signal sent from the DTE to the modem that is used to tell the modem the DTE has data to send.

Ring Topology

Topology in which the network consists of a series of repeaters connected to one another by unidirectional transmission links to form a single closed loop.

RIS (Remote Installation Service)

Allows remote automated installation of Windows 2000 Professional workstations.

RJ-11
Standard four-wire connectors for telephone lines.

RJ-45
Standard eight-wire connectors for an Institute of Electrical and Electronic Engineers (IEEE) 802.3 1Base5 StarLAN network.

Route
Path that network traffic takes from its source to its destination.

Router
Special-purpose computer or software package that handles the connection between two or more networks.

Routing
Process of selecting the correct interface and the next hop for a packet being forwarded.

Routing Domain
A set of routers exchanging routing information within an administrative domain.

Routing Protocol
Accomplishes routing through the implementation of a specific routing algorithm.

Routing Table
A table stored in a router that keeps track of routes to particular network destinations.

Routing Table Maintenance Protocol
Apple Computer's proprietary routing protocol.

Secure Sockets Layer
See SSL.

Security Certificate
Information about the owner and the issuer, a unique serial number or other unique identification, valid dates, and an encrypted fingerprint that can be used to verify the contents and validity of the certificate. For a *secure sockets layer (SSL)* connection to be created, both sides must have a valid Security Certificate.

Segment
Term used in the Transmission Control Protocol (TCP) specification to describe a single transport layer unit of information.

Server
A computer or software package that shares its resources, such as printers and files, with other computers on the network.

Service Access Point
The point where the services of an OSI layer are made available to the next higher layer.

Session
A related set of communications transactions between two or more network devices.

Shielded Twisted Pairs
Term for cabling systems that are designed for data transmission and where the cables are shielded.

Shielding
Protective enclosure surrounding a transmission medium designed to minimize electromagnetic interference.

Simplex Transmission
Data transmission in only one direction.

Slotted Ring
LAN architecture based on a ring topology where the ring is divided into slots that circulate continuously.

SMTP (Simple Mail Transport Protocol)
Main protocol used to send electronic mail on the Internet.

Glossary

SNA (Systems Network Architecture)

A proprietary networking architecture used by IBM and IBM-compatible mainframe computers.

SNMP (Simple Network Management Protocol)

A set of standards for communication with devices connected to a *Transmission Control Protocol/Internet Protocol (TCP/IP)* network, including routers, hubs, and switches.

Source Address

The address of a sending network device.

Spooler

Application that manages requests submitted to it for execution in an orderly fashion from a queue.

SQL (Structured Query Language)

A specialized programming language for sending queries to databases.

SSL (Secure Sockets Layer)

A protocol designed by Netscape Communications to enable encrypted, authenticated communications across the Internet and Privacy, Authentication, and Message Integrity.

Star Topology

Local area network (LAN) topology in which end points on a network are connected to a common central switch by point-to-point links.

Structured Query Language

See SQL.

Synchronization

Establishing common timing between sender and receiver.

Synchronous Transmission

Data bits are sent at a fixed rate with the transmitter and receiver synchronized, eliminating the need for start and stop bits.

System Administrator

Person responsible for managing the systems being used.

Systems Network Architecture

See SNA.

T-1

Leased-line connection capable of carrying data at 1,544,000 bps, allowing full-screen, full-motion video. Requires at least 10,000,000 bps.

T-3

Leased-line connection capable of carrying data at 44,736,000 bps, allowing full-screen, full-motion video.

TCP/IP (Transmission Control Protocol/Internet Protocol)

This is the suite of protocols that defines the Internet.

Telnet

The command and program used to log in from one Internet site to another.

Terminal

Device that allows commands to be sent to a computer, usually the components are a keyboard and a display screen.

Terminal Access Controller

A device that connects terminals to the Internet, usually through dialup modem connections.

Terminal Emulator

Program that allows a computer to imitate a terminal.

Terminal Server

Device that connects many terminals to a *local area network (LAN)* through one network connection or connects many network users to its asynchronous ports for dial-out capabilities and printer access.

Terminator

Electrical resistor at the end of a transmission line that adsorbs signals on the line, thereby preventing signal bounce.

Throughput

The rate at which information moves through a particular point in a network system.

Token

Control information frame that grants a network device the right to transmit.

Token Bus

Local area network (LAN) architecture that uses token-passing access over a bus topology.

Token Passing

Method by which network devices access the physical medium in an orderly fashion based on possession of a *token*.

Token Ring

Type of *local area network (LAN)* with nodes wired into a ring. The nodes constantly pass a control message token among themselves. The node that has the token can send a message.

Topology

How computers on a network are connected and communicate with each other.

Transaction Services Layer

Layer 7 in the *Systems Network Architecture (SNA)* model.

Transmission Control Layer

Layer 4 in the *Systems Network Architecture (SNA)* model, responsible for establishing, maintaining, and terminating SNA sessions.

Transmission Control Protocol/Internet Protocol

See TCP/IP.

Transport Layer

Layer 4 of the *Open Systems Interconnection (OSI)* reference model. Responsible for reliable network communication between end nodes. Implements flow and error control to ensure reliable data delivery.

Tree Topology

Local area network (LAN) topology similar to a bus topology in which transmissions from a station propagate the length of the medium and are received by all other stations.

Trojan Horse

Computer program that carries within itself the ability to allow the creator of the program access to the system using it.

Trunk

A single circuit between two points that are switching centers of individual distribution points. Can usually handle many channels simultaneously.

Twisted Pair

Cable made up of a pair of insulated copper wires wrapped around each other to cancel the effects of electric noise.

UART (Universal Asynchronous Receiver/Transmitter)

Integrated circuit incorporating a receiver/transmitter that can convert parallel signals to the serial transmissions needed for asynchronous communications.

UDP (User Datagram Protocol)

A protocol that makes no provision for acknowledgment of packets received.

Univorm Resource Locator

See URL.

Unix

Type of computer operating system designed to be used by many people at the same time. Has *Transmission Control Protocol/*

Glossary

Internet Protocol (TCP/IP) built in. The most common operating system for servers on the Internet.

Upper (Layer Protocol)

Often used to refer to the next-highest protocol in a particular protocol stack.

Unshielded Twisted Pair

General term for unshielded cabling that is used for the transmission of data.

URL (Uniform Resource Locator)

The standard way to give the address of any resource on the Internet that is part of the *World Wide Web (WWW)* and is used to specify the location of a document or object.

Username

A unique designation by which each user is known to the system.

Value-Added Network (VAN)

Communications network that provides supplementary services.

Vector

Data segment of a *Systems Network Architecture (SNA)* message that consists of a length field, a key that describes the vector type, and vector-specific data.

Virtual Community

When people with similar interests join together on the Internet to discuss their views.

Virtual Corporation

When people work together via the Internet and not necessarily in a central workplace.

Virus

Program that replicates itself on computer systems by incorporating itself into other programs that are shared among computer systems.

WAIS (Wide Area Information Server)

Commercial software package that allows the indexing of large amounts of information, and then allows searches across networks, including the Internet.

WAN (Wide Area Network)

Any Internet or network that covers an area larger than a single building or campus.

WWW (World Wide Web)

The whole constellation of computers that can be accessed using Gopher, *File Transfer Protocol (FTP)*, Hypertext Transfer Protocol (HTTP), *Telnet*, USENET, *Wide Area Information Server (WAIS)*, and other tools.

Index

X

Y

Z

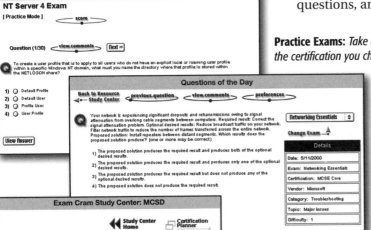

What's on the CD-ROM

The *MCSE Windows 2000 Network Exam Prep*'s companion CD-ROM contains the testing system for the book, which includes 50 questions. Additional questions are available for free download from **ExamCram.com**; simply click on the Update button in the testing engine. You can choose from numerous testing formats, including Fixed-Length, Random, Test All, and Review.

System Requirements

Software

To view the practice exams:

➤ Your operating system must be Windows 95, 98, NT 4, or higher.

➤ You need Internet Explorer 5.x.

Real world projects require Windows 2000 Server.

Hardware

To view the practice exams:

➤ An Intel Pentium, AMD, or comparable 100MHz processor or higher is recommended for best results.

➤ 32MB of RAM is the minimum memory requirement.

➤ Available disk storage space of at least 10MB is recommended.

For the real world projects, make sure that computers on which you will install Windows 2000 Server meet the following requirements:

➤ 133MHz Pentium or higher central processing unit (CPU).

➤ 256MB of RAM recommended with 128MB minimum.

➤ A hard disk partition with 1GB free space to accommodate the setup process.

Software developed by Dreamtech Software, India

Design and Performance of Earth Retaining Structures

Proceedings of a Conference

Sponsored by the
Geotechnical Engineering Division
of the
American Society of Civil Engineers

In cooperation with the
Ithaca Section, ASCE

Cornell University
Ithaca, New York
June 18-21, 1990

Geotechnical Special Publication No. 25

Edited by
Philip C. Lambe
and Lawrence A. Hansen

Published by the
American Society of Civil Engineers
345 East 47th Street
New York, New York 10017-2398

ABSTRACT

The proceedings of the 1990 Specialty Conference on Design and performance of Earth Retaining Structures presents a total of 50 papers addressing the general topics of historical perspectives, wall selection, contracting practices, waterfront structures, gravity walls, mechanically stabilized systems, cast-in-place walls, soil nailing, tied-back excavations and seismic design. The papers survey the current state of the practice of earth retention and support, detail the rapid and profound changes that design and construction practices have undergone in the last 20 years, and forecast technological developments which are likely to carry the practice into the next century. Invited papers by 16 internationally known experts address aspects of each of the general topics, including trends in ground movements, effects of material selection and construction practices, and advances in design analyses and procedures. The 34 other papers generally address specific case histories of various types of earth retaining structures, providing results of performance monitoring, comparing predicted to actual performance, and assessing the impacts of construction practice and design procedures on performance.

Library of Congress Cataloging-in-Publication Data

Design and performance of earth retaining structures: proceedings of a conference/sponsored by the Geotechnical Engineering Division of the American Society of Civil Engineers in cooperation with the Ithaca Section, ASCE, Cornell University, Ithaca, New York, June 18-21, 1990: edited by Philip C. Lambe and Lawrence A. Hansen.

    p.   cm.

"1990 Speciality Conference on Design and Performance of Earth Retaining Structures"—Pref.

Includes indexes.

ISBN 0-87262-761-6

1. Retaining walls—Design and construction—Congresses. 2. Earth pressure—Congresses. I. Lambe, Philip C. II. Hansen, Lawrence A. III. American Society of Civil Engineers. Geotechnical Engineering Division. IV. American Society of Civil Engineers. Ithaca Section. V. Specialty Conference on Design and Performance of Earth Retaining Structures (1990: Cornell University)

TA770.D47   1990

824.1'84—dc20   90-771

                                  CIP